INFRA-RED SPECTROSCOPY AND MOLECULAR STRUCTURE

INFRA-RED SPECTROSCOPY AND MOLECULAR STRUCTURE

AN OUTLINE OF THE PRINCIPLES

Edited by

MANSEL DAVIES

University Reader in Chemistry
The Edward Davies Chemical Laboratories
University College of Wales
Aberystwyth, Wales

ELSEVIER PUBLISHING COMPANY
AMSTERDAM - LONDON - NEW YORK
1963

SOLE DISTRIBUTORS FOR THE UNITED STATES AND CANADA

AMERICAN ELSEVIER PUBLISHING COMPANY, INC.

52 VANDERBILT AVENUE, NEW YORK 17, N.Y.

SOLE DISTRIBUTORS FOR GREAT BRITAIN

ELSEVIER PUBLISHING COMPANY LIMITED

12B, RIPPLESIDE COMMERCIAL ESTATE

RIPPLE ROAD, BARKING, ESSEX

LIBRARY OF CONGRESS CATALOG CARD NUMBER 63-14277

WITH 171 ILLUSTRATIONS AND 70 TABLES

Preface

This volume is intended to provide an introduction to the principles and practice of those aspects of infra-red spectroscopy which are of major interest in the study of molecular structure and molecular behaviour.

It is only since 1945 and the commercial production of recording spectro-meters that the infra-red field has become generally accessible for routine investigation and use. The result has been a great proliferation of research studies and applications, so that the region has acquired major status in the broad area of spectroscopy. The greatest number of participants have been in laboratories devoted to chemical studies, whilst inevitably many of the basic developments have been made by physicists. Recent advances in the use of interferometric spectrometers, far infra-red techniques, and dispersion and reflection methods will be permanent influences in future studies. The advent of the computer, too, has awakened a renewed interest in the problem of defining the force-field within polyatomic molecules. This problem, despite its difficulties, cannot be side-stepped in the elucidation of the bonding conditions within molecules. Whilst the recognition of such characteristic aspects as group frequencies has made infra-red spectra of outstanding value in the qualitative definition of molecular structures, it is to be hoped that their quantitative evaluation can equally help in the precise representation of valency conditions.

The present chapters, however, have not been written to provide a survey of recent advances. Their particular aim is to outline the basic principles, to illustrate such success as is possible with current methods, and to indicate their potential scope and present limitations. Accordingly, there is no attempt to provide anything in the nature of an encyclopaedic coverage, but rather, after a general survey of infra-red studies, each specialist has emphasized what he regards as the essential bases of his topic.

It will be no surprise to those familiar with infra-red studies to find the Herzberg volume *Infrared and Raman Spectra of Polyatomic Molecules* frequently referred to for further theoretical detail. Few physical topics developed in the last forty years have been as fortunate in having so masterly a presentation of fundamental aspects as Herzberg provides.

One particular problem in planning the present volume was that of deciding whether specific introductions should be included to the relevant aspects of group theory and wave mechanics. It will be seen that this has not been done. However, adequate references are provided for those who are not familiar with the symbolic languages of those mathematical methods. A further explanation is due in the general sense that the authors were restricted in the space available to them, and thus, to mention a specific instance, Dr. Martin originally illustrated many of his points by presentation of details from a variety of commercial infra-red spectrometers: most such variants have been omitted.

Finally, the editor wishes to record his thanks to the authors for their co-operation. Their contributions have cost them valuable time which they must have been loath to spare from their research and other activities. However – and despite some disadvantages in a multi-author work – the virtues of fundamental accounts by active leaders in each topic were successfully pressed upon them. In this respect it was a particular pleasure for the editor to be able to call upon three of his former research students as contributors. In addition, Dr. Norman Sheppard of Cambridge is gratefully thanked for his interest and help.

"If to do were as easy as to know what were good to do, chapels had been churches and poor men's cottages princes' palaces".

The Edward Davies Chemical Laboratories,   ·   MANSEL DAVIES
The University College of Wales,
Aberystwyth.
June, 1963

Contributors

Mansel Davies, University Reader in Chemistry, The Edward Davies Chemical Laboratories, University College of Wales, Aberystwyth, Wales.

E. A. V. Ebsworth, Inorganic Chemistry Laboratory, University of Cambridge.

J. C. Evans, The Dow Chemical Company, Midland, Michigan, U.S.A.

J. Fahrenfort, Spectroscopy Department, Koninklijke/Shell-Laboratorium, Amsterdam (Shell Internationale Research Maatschappij N.V.).

Dušan Hadži, Professor of Chemistry, University of Ljubljana, Jugoslavia.

H. E. Hallam, Department of Chemistry, University College of Wales, Swansea, Wales.

W. Jeremy Jones, Fellow of Trinity College, Cambridge.

S. Krimm, Professor of Physics, University of Michigan, Ann Arbor, Michigan, U.S.A.

A. E. Martin, Head of Infra-red Department, Sir Howard Grubb Parsons and Company Ltd., Newcastle upon Tyne.

Ian M. Mills, Chemistry Department, Reading University.

J. Overend, School of Chemistry, Institute of Technology, University of Minnesota, Minneapolis, Minnesota, U.S.A.

W. C. Price, F.R.S., Professor of Physics, King's College, London.

G. R. Wilkinson, Wheatstone Physics Laboratory, King's College, London.

Contents

Chapter I

Introductory Survey

MANSEL DAVIES

The Edward Davies Chemical Laboratories, Aberystwyth, Wales

(1) The Infra-red Region

The infra-red region of the spectrum extends from the visible (say 8000Å)
until it overlaps the micro-wave or very short radar range at wavelengths
of some millimetres. Perhaps its basic characteristic is that over this region
of approximately eleven octaves the principal source of radiation is thermal
emission from a hot source: this contrasts with the selective emission of
discharge tubes and similar sources in the visible and ultra-violet, and even
more so with the electronic generation of radiation by valves or klystron
sources in the radio and radar regions.

The physical optics of the infra-red is identical with that of the visible,
with minor modifications due to the increased wavelength. The operational
limit of the "visible" region is perhaps best taken as that set by photographic
sensitivity (*ca.* 13,000Å). Beyond that wavelength, the radiation must be
detected and measured by the response of a thermocouple, bolometer or
radiometer.

Wavelengths in the (non-photographic) infra-red have usually been
given in microns: $1\mu = 10{,}000Å = 10^{-4}$ cm. It has now been accepted that
the wavelength unit throughout the spectroscopic regions shall be the
nanometre (nm). $1\,\text{nm} = 10^{-9}\,\text{m} = 10Å = 10^{-3}\,\mu = 1\,m\mu$. Thus, $7.65\,\mu =$
7650 nm. Alternatively, and more significantly, the wavenumber, *i.e.* the
number of waves per cm, is used to characterize the radiation. The wavenumber unit is the reciprocal centimetre, cm^{-1}, and so has the convenient
values of 10,000 cm^{-1} to 10 cm^{-1} in the infra-red.

$$\tilde{\nu} \text{ (wavenumber in } \text{cm}^{-1}) = 1/(\text{wavelength in cm}) = 1/\lambda$$

As ν (frequency in $\text{sec}^{-1}) = c/\lambda$

where $c =$ velocity of electromagnetic radiation

$$= 2.9978 \cdot 10^{10} \text{ cm sec}^{-1}$$

$$\nu = c\tilde{\nu}$$

As the quantum of energy $(h\nu)$ is exchanged when a molecule absorbs or
emits the corresponding frequency, the wavenumber is proportional to this
energy. From the values of $h =$ Planck's constant, $J =$ mechanical equiv-

alent of heat; $N =$ Avogadro's number, it follows that a quantum of radiation of frequency c sec^{-1} or wavenumber 1 cm^{-1} has energy 1.9862×10^{-16} erg. Then 1 cm$^{-1} \equiv 1.9862 \times 10^{-16}$ erg/molecule $\equiv 2.8593$ cal/g mole $\equiv 11.962$ joule/g mole. Owing to this proportionality and to the further circumstance that the frequency of radiation is normally unchanged in passing from one medium to another whilst its wavelength varies with the refractive index, there is every reason for using the wavenumber as the unit in infra-red spectroscopic data. Although the frequency and wavenumber should be clearly distinguished, it is common practice in infra-red spectroscopy to use the same symbol (ν) for both, and thus to write "an absorption band at $\nu = 1673$ cm^{-1}". Little uncertainty can arise when the unit (cm^{-1}) is indicated, but this should not be spoken of "a frequency of 1673": it is "a wavenumber of 1673".

(2) Diatomic Molecules

Many of the basic aspects of molecular spectra are clearly seen in the case of diatomic molecules, and it will be helpful, here, briefly to review the behaviour of the diatomic molecule.

(2A) The vibrational frequency

The formation of a simple (X–Y) molecule (or, more generally, of any

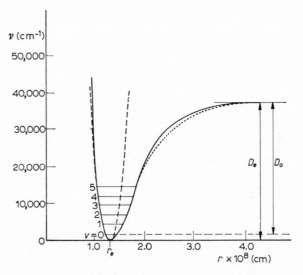

Fig. I, 1. Potential energy curve for a diatomic molecule, drawn approximately to scale for hydrogen chloride. The full curve is drawn for the ground state of HCl. The broken line and the dotted curve are, respectively, the potential curves for the harmonic oscillator and the Morse function. The vibrational levels are drawn up to the level $v = 5$; $r_e = 1.2744$Å.

chemical bond) can be envisaged energetically as arising from two forces: one of attraction which predominates at larger (X–Y) distances, and a second of repulsion which comes into play the more rapidly as the (X–Y) bond is compressed below its equilibrium length. These conditions give rise to the energy curve represented by the solid line in Fig. I, 1.

The minimum of the curve is taken as the arbitrary zero of energy. It is a reasonable first approximation (and the subsequent deductions confirm the adequacy of the assumption) to envisage the bonding force in the diatomic molecule as equivalent to the presence of an elastic spring. Quantitatively this means that any displacement, stretching or compressing, from the equilibrium bond length, will induce a restoring force proportional to the displacement and acting so as to reduce the displacement to zero: *i.e.* Hooke's Law is assumed to apply to the chemical bond near its equilibrium length. An immediate consequence is that slight displacement from equilibrium will lead to simple harmonic vibrations in the molecule. (See Fig. I,2).

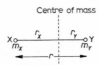

Fig. I, 2. A diatomic molecule XY.

The centre of mass (c.m.) is defined by $m_X r_X = m_Y r_Y$. Using $r = r_X + r_Y = r_X(1 + m_X/m_Y)$,

$$r_X = \left(\frac{m_Y}{m_X + m_Y}\right) r; \text{ and } r_Y = \left(\frac{m_X}{m_X + m_Y}\right) r.$$

If r_e is the equilibrium internuclear distance (see Fig. I, 1), stretching the bond will produce a displacement $(r - r_e)$ and a restoring force $-k(r - r_e)$: the negative sign expresses the condition that the force operates against the displacement, and k is the (assumed elastic) force-constant, or rigidity modulus for the bond. Being the force for unit displacement, it is given in dyne per cm (dyne cm^{-1}).

In the molecular vibrational mode of motion the centre of mass must not move – that would be introducing translational motion. Accordingly, the motion of the atoms is synchronized about the centre of mass and their equations of motion are

$$m_X \cdot \frac{d^2 r_X}{dt^2} = -k(r - r_e) = m_Y \cdot \frac{d^2 r_Y}{dt^2}$$

These are equivalent to

$$\frac{m_X m_Y}{m_X + m_Y} \frac{d^2 r}{dt^2} = -k(r - r_e)$$

or

$$\mu \frac{d^2(r-r_e)}{dt^2} = -k(r-r_e)$$

where μ = mass factor for the vibrator = $\dfrac{m_X m_Y}{m_X + m_Y}$ and r_e is, of course, a

constant. This is the equation for simple harmonic motion. Writing $(r-r_e) = x$, the solution is

$$x = x_0 \sin (2\pi v_e t + \phi)$$

x_0 is the amplitude of vibration, ϕ a phase angle constant and

$$v_e = \text{molecular vibrational frequency (sec}^{-1}) = \frac{1}{2\pi} \sqrt{\frac{k}{\mu}} \qquad (1)$$

As in circumstances where energy (V) is conserved

$$-k(r-r_e) = \text{force in the system} = -\frac{dV}{dr} = -\frac{dV}{d(r-r_e)}$$

$$V = \tfrac{1}{2}k(r-r_e)^2 + \text{constant}$$

The "constant" represents the arbitrary factor in fixing the energy scale for V. It is taken as zero in Fig. I, 1, and so fitting a parabolic function for that curve near its minimum.

This simple model predicts that the molecule would, classically, emit or absorb radiation of frequency v_e if it possessed a dipole. The latter is certainly a pre-requisite for infra-red absorption by a diatomic molecule: the homonuclear species (H_2, O_2, Cl_2, etc.) show virtually no infra-red spectra. The polar species (HCl, CO, etc.) not only show absorptions at a principal frequency v_e but also progressively weaker absorptions at their first, second, third, etc. overtones, i.e. at frequencies approximately $2v_e$, $3v_e$, $4v_e$, etc. For the interaction with radiation of a classically oscillating dipole this again is a consequence of the anharmonicity of the vibrations. The qualitative dissymmetry of the energy curve means that the function $V = \tfrac{1}{2}k(r-r_e)^2$ can at best fit only near the minimum.

(2B) The energy function

A simple empirical approximation for the energy function is to write the attractive and repulsive terms as inverse powers of the distance:

$$V = \frac{\alpha}{r^m} - \frac{\beta}{r^n} \qquad (2)$$

α and β are constants and $m > n$, to fit the predominance of repulsion at the shortest distances. In this expression the energy zero is taken for $r = \infty$.

Using the conditions

$$\left(\frac{dV}{dr}\right)_{r=r_e} = 0; \quad \left(\frac{d^2V}{dr^2}\right)_{r=r_e} = k;$$

it is readily found (Sutherland) that

$$k = \frac{m\alpha(m-n)}{r_e^{m+2}}; \quad \text{and} \quad D_e = kr_e^2/mn.$$

These expressions correspond to various empirical and approximate findings correlating k, r_e and D_e in diatomic molecules of similar character, where m and n do not vary markedly. Thus, using Raman spectra frequencies for O_2 and S_2, the following sequence can be constructed:

Molecule	O_2	S_2	SO	CN	NO
D_e/kr_e^2 in arbitrary units	0.098	0.111	0.093	0.096	0.080

A far more generally satisfactory expression for the energy is the empirical function put forward by Morse (in 1929):

$$V = D_e[1-e^{-a(r-r_e)}]^2 \tag{3}$$

Here a is a constant characteristic of the bond and the energy zero reverts to the $r = r_e$ value. D_e is the dissociation energy measured to the minimum in the curve. The simple Morse function can be seen to have the following appropriate properties:

(i) It has a single minimum at $r = r_e$; $V(r_e) = 0$.
(ii) At large separations the dissociation limit is approached and $V(r = \infty) = D_e$.
(iii) At small separations the energy rises steeply and for $r = 0$ becomes, as $e^{ar_e} \gg 1$, essentially $D_e(e^{2ar_e})$ which usually exceeds $10^3 D_e$. This is a reasonable approximation to the virtually infinite value it should attain.
(iv) For very small displacements, $(r-r_e)$, the exponential term is adequately expanded as

$$V = D_e[1-\{1-a(r-r_e)\}]^2 = D_e \cdot a^2(r-r_e)^2$$

Whence

$$k = d^2V/dr^2 = d^2V/d(r-r_e)^2 = 2D_e \cdot a^2$$

This relation gives the value of a from the vibrational frequency $(\nu_e = (1/2\pi)\sqrt{k/\mu})$,

$$a = \pi\nu_e \cdot \sqrt{\frac{2\mu}{D_e}}.$$

This is the only adjustable parameter if D_e and r_e are regarded as defined for the molecule.

References p. 21

(v) Inserted in the Schrödinger wave-equation the Morse function allows of a precise solution for the energy values of the permitted quantised vibrational states. The energy levels are given by

$$E_{\text{vib}} = h\nu_e(v + \tfrac{1}{2}) - \alpha h\nu_e(v + \tfrac{1}{2})^2 \tag{4}$$

Here v is the vibrational quantum number, h is Planck's constant, and α is the anharmonicity factor.

(2C) The vibrational levels

This expression is of the exact form found most generally suitable to represent the vibrational energy levels. The bands in the visible and ultraviolet spectra of diatomic molecules frequently allow a long sequence of such levels to be measured. Such expressions for the energy levels were established before the quantum theory clarified their origin. Occasionally terms in higher powers of $(v + \tfrac{1}{2})$ are added to equation (4).

As α is a small positive factor (*ca.* 10^{-2}), it is seen that with increasing v the vibrational energy levels come closer together. At the dissociation limit there will be no further increase of E_{vib} possible, *i.e.* the limiting value of v_L is given by $dE_{\text{vib}}/d(n + \tfrac{1}{2}) = 0$, or $(v_L + \tfrac{1}{2}) = 1/2\alpha$. Substituted in (4), this gives

$$E_{L(\text{vib})} = D_e = h\nu_e/4\alpha \tag{5}$$

This important relation allows an estimate of D_e to be made from ν_e and α, factors readily observed for the ground state of the diatomic molecule from its infra-red absorptions. The D_e value will be precise only insofar as the energy curve strictly follows the Morse function: a discrepancy of ten per cent from the correct value of D_e would not be uncommon. The applicability of this relation for determining bond energies in polyatomic molecules would be even further restricted, but it could lead to useful values in some cases of interest.

The dissociation energy D_e measured from the minimum in the energy relation, differs from D_0, the energy often directly assessable in band spectra. The latter has the ground vibrational state $v = 0$ as its reference level, and $(D_e - D_0) = (\tfrac{1}{2}h\nu_e - \tfrac{1}{4}\alpha h\nu_e)$. This is the zero point energy and measures the residual amount present in each vibrational mode even at the absolute zero of temperature.

Equation (4) embodies the result that the fundamental and the successively much weaker overtones are not found at wavenumber values $\omega_e (= \nu_e/c)$, $2\omega_e$, $3\omega_e$, etc., but rather at the values given by $\Delta E_{\text{vib}}/hc$.

ν (fundamental absorption) $= \nu \ (v = 0 \rightarrow v = 1) = \omega_e - 2\alpha\omega_e$;
ν (first overtone absorption) $= \nu \ (v = 0 \rightarrow v = 2) = 2\omega_e - 6\alpha\omega_e$;
ν ($\overline{v-1}$ th overtone absorption) $= \nu \ (v = 0 \rightarrow v = v) = v\omega_e[1 - \alpha(v+1)]$;
ν ("hot" band in absorption) $= \nu \ (v = 1 \rightarrow v = 2) = \omega_e - 4\alpha\omega_e$.

The marked influence of anharmonicity for a diatomic vibrator is readily seen from the observed wavenumber values of the fundamental and overtone absorptions of HCl;

$$\nu \ (v = 0 \to 1) = 2886 \ \text{cm}^{-1}; \quad \nu \ (v = 0 \to 2) = 5668 \ \text{cm}^{-1};$$
$$\nu \ (v = 0 \to 3) = 8347 \ \text{cm}^{-1}; \quad \omega_e = 2991 \ \text{cm}^{-1}; \ \alpha\omega_e = 52.3 \ \text{cm}^{-1}.$$

Only with exceptionally long path-lengths are absorptions beyond the third or fourth overtones measured in absorption: these can, however, be achieved experimentally or encountered terrestially (or even astronomically). Appropriate stimulation of infra-red emission (see Chapter XIII) provides greater intensity for these larger vibrational energy transitions within the electronic ground state. As already explained, ν is used as a general spectroscopic symbol for the observed frequency (sec^{-1}) or wavenumber (cm^{-1}), whilst ω_e is usually kept for zero-order (or harmonic) wavenumber values.

Before leaving the representations associated with the Morse function which provides a widely used approximation not only to the conditions within the diatomic molecule but also (less adequately) to the conditions in individual bonds in polyatomic molecules, some further comments can be made. The Morse function was an entirely empirical relation for whose considerable general success no quantitative interpretation was available for twenty-five years: qualitatively it represented the attractive and repulsive energy terms by related exponential and therefore judiciously variable factors. Other empirical exponential forms have been suggested: of these one due to Pöschl and Teller shows some slight improvement on the simple Morse function. However, in 1955 Lippincott provided a quantum mechanical argument justifying a related expression having the form:

$$V = D_e \ [1 - e^{-n(r-r_e)^2/2r}],$$

Here n replaces the Morse parameter a, and $k = D_e n/r_e$. This function has been shown to be, if anything, somewhat more precise than that of Morse but the latter has a long established position in the literature on bond energies.

Most diatomic molecules or chemical bonds stable at room temperatures have D_e values in excess of 10 kcal/g mol, $i.e. > 3500$ cm^{-1}. This is a consequence of the equipartition energy per degree of freedom, $\frac{1}{2}kT$, which is approximately $2.0 \cdot 10^{-14}$ erg/molecule or 100 cm^{-1} at 300° K. The corresponding Boltzmann factor, which roughly assesses the probability of decomposition per collision, is $e^{-D_e/kT} = e^{-35/2} = 2.5 \cdot 10^{-8}$. These factors ensure that bond stretching frequencies are usually above 200 cm^{-1}. Due largely to the exceptionally small mass-factor, the H$_2$ molecule has the highest ω_e value [4405 cm^{-1}, observable in the Raman spectrum]: the same factor helps to put HF ($\omega_e = 4141$ cm^{-1}) at the head of polar-bond frequencies. At the other extreme the Hg_2 molecule has ω_e *ca.* 36 cm^{-1}.

(2D) Rotational features

A rotating dipole is a classical model for the generation of electromagnetic waves determined by its own rotational frequency. The model is principally relevant to the molecular case in that a non-polar rotator neither emits nor absorbs rotational energy directly.

For the rotation, which must again take place about the centre of mass (Fig. I, 2), two axes can be chosen, each perpendicular to the inter-nuclear line and each perpendicular to the other. The energy of rotation about such orthogonal axes represents a total of two degrees of freedom as the motion about one has not even the smallest component about the other. The moment of inertia is

$$I = m_X r_X^2 + m_Y r_Y^2$$

$$= \text{(from } m_X r_X = m_Y r_Y) \ \frac{m_X m_Y}{m_X + m_Y} r^2 = \mu r^2.$$

The energy of rotation ($\frac{1}{2}I\dot\theta^2$, where $\dot\theta$ is the angular velocity) is limited by the quantum theory to the values $(h^2/8\pi^2 I)J(J+1)$ where J is the rotational quantum number. With the precondition of a polar molecule and $\Delta J = \pm 1$ for absorption or emission, the simple rotational spectrum becomes a series of lines separated by the frequency (sec^{-1}) interval $(h/4\pi I)$. As such rotational energy changes can occur in isolation to give a purely rotational energy spectrum or in conjunction with the ν value of a vibrational transition to give a sequence of similarly spaced lines above and below ν(vibrational), measurement of these spacings gives I and hence the value of r.

It is on this basis that the rotational features lead to the geometric parameters for simple molecules. Each moment of inertia can, in principle, be used to determine one bond length or one bond angle. The molecules must either be of few atoms (*e.g.* CH_3Cl, SF_2O) or of considerable symmetry (*e.g.* C_5H_5N) before significant results can be obtained by infra-red methods. Two limitations arise: as will be found in Chapter IV, unless two of the principal moments of inertia are nearly or actually equal, the rotational structure in the absorptions becomes very difficult to unravel; and if the moments of inertia are too high, the spectroscopic resolution of the lines is not possible in practice. In these respects microwave spectroscopy provides a far more powerful tool than infra-red: the resolution and sensitivity there are so high that many moments of inertia can often be obtained for the same structure from the different isotopes present in their natural abundance. In the infra-red, isotopically enriched molecules (*e.g.* with ^{2}H,

^{18}O, etc.) must be prepared if more than two structural factors are to be evaluated explicitly. However, gross features such as the order of magnitude of the moments of inertia and hence the essential (momental) shape of the molecule can often be determined from absorption band contours for the gaseous state. This may well suffice to establish the general symmetry of the molecule and hence, for instance, the particular isomeric form of the molecule

$$\left(e.g. \quad \begin{array}{c} CH_3 \\ \diagdown \end{array} N{=}N{=}N, \text{ and not } CH_3{-}N{\diagup\!\!\!\diagdown}\!\!\begin{array}{c} N \\ \| \\ N \end{array} \right).$$

Whilst it is usually a good approximation to assume the molecules are rigid structures (apart, that is, from internal vibrations) and that there is no coupling (or interaction) between rotational and vibrational energies, neither of these assumptions is strictly correct. The consequence of centrifugal expansion of the molecule on rotation is to give rotational energy levels

$$E_{rot}/h = BJ(J{+}1){-}DJ^2(J{+}1)^2$$

where $B = h/8\pi^2 I$ (in sec^{-1}); and $D \ll B$.

The dependence of D upon the stretching force constant (k) and moment of inertia (I) can be transposed into a dependence on the vibrational frequency (ν_e) and B. Using units of sec^{-1} throughout:

$$D = 4B^3/\nu_e^2.$$

This relation typifies the evaluation of k (or its equivalent) from a centrifugal stretching constant (D). In view of the great significance of such force constants in structural assessments, and the need to use all resources in evaluating them, the ready availability of D's from micro-wave spectra can provide important aid in calculating k's.

(3) Polyatomic Molecules

(3A) The vibrational modes and symmetry

Whilst the changes in going from the diatomic to the polyatomic molecule can be regarded as ones of degree only, the situation for the general molecule containing N atoms is sufficiently different to require a new approach and even new concepts. In the first place the N atoms before forming the molecule can each move in three perpendicular, and hence energy-independent, directions. Bonded together in the molecule, the translational motion of the unit represents three independent movements ($\dot{x}, \dot{y}, \dot{z}$), whilst rotation about three perpendicular axes accounts for another three. The residual ($3N{-}6$) "movements", or degrees of freedom, must involve neither translation nor rotation of the molecule: *i.e.* in general, they are the internal vibrations. More explicitly, the total vibrational energy can at any time be expressed as the sum of not more than $(3N-6)$ terms of the form $\frac{1}{2}kx^2$, where k is a force-constant and x an amplitude of vibration. These individual terms represent the "proper modes" of the frequently very complicated pattern of the resultant vibration within the molecule: they are the simplest and smallest number of independent vibrations by vector addition of which any possible vibrational oscillation within the structure can be compounded. For $N = 6$, *e.g.* CH_3OH, the number of such vibrations is already 12.

The complication of the spectrum when each such vibration may give an absorption at its own frequency is obvious. Two features help in resolving this situation. Firstly, only those vibrations during which a change in dipole moment occurs will be active (*i.e.* absorb or emit) in the infra-red: secondly, symmetry in the molecular structure may lead to pairs or even triplets of vibrations coinciding in frequency. Examples of the operation of these factors are methane, CH_4, $(3N-6 = 9)$, which shows only two fundamental absorption bands in the infra-red; and benzene, C_6H_6, $(3N-6 = 30)$, which has only four such fundamental infra-red absorptions. By "fundamental absorption" is meant one corresponding to an actual molecular frequency, say $\nu_1 = \nu$(molecular), and not an overtone $(2\nu_1$, etc.) or a combination tone, $(\overline{\nu_1+\nu_2}, \overline{\nu_1-\nu_2}$, etc.). The intensity of these subsidiary features is usually far less than (about one-tenth) that of the fundamentals: unfortunately, that is not an universal rule.

The two factors mentioned above (dipole moment change and molecular symmetry) are not unrelated, but we may, for qualitative discussion, consider them separately. The selection rule for infra-red activity, expressed in the form of requiring a finite dipole moment change during the vibration $(d\mu/dQ > 0$, where $\mu =$ dipole moment; $Q =$ vibrational coordinate or displacement) is not equivalent to requiring the molecule to have a permanent moment: that equivalence applies only for diatomic molecules. Methane and benzene each have zero dipole moments and equally certainly have vibrational modes during which a dipole moment appears. The closer deduction of the infra-red active frequencies involves a consideration of the symmetry of the dipole moment of the molecule and its change $(d\mu/dQ)$ in relation to the symmetry of the vibration. Similar considerations apply to the Raman activity but there the dipole moment factors are replaced by the molecular polarizability (α) and its change $(d\alpha/dQ)$.

The symmetry character of the molecule proves to be the principal determinant of its spectroscopic behaviour. So much is this so that it is impossible rationally to discuss polyatomic infra-red and Raman spectra other than on the basis of the symmetry features in the molecule — adding up as they do to its so-called point-group of symmetry elements. Examples of this procedure are outlined in Chapters IV and VI. Fortunately, the number of commonly occurring symmetry types of molecules is fairly restricted and a knowledge of their behaviour pattern covers the majority of compounds. Of course, the largest class of molecules is that lacking all symmetry elements. Even structures as simple as methylamine ($CH_3 \cdot NH_2$) and dichloroacetic acid ($Cl_2CH \cdot COOH$) are probably in this category. In such cases all ($3N-6$) vibrations are both infra-red and Raman active.

Another mode of classifying polyatomic molecules is based on the symmetry of their momental ellipsoids, *i.e.* by the relations between the three principal moments of inertia needed to give the total rotational energy of a three-dimensional body. For this, an axis passing through the centre of mass on being moved through all azimuths will define both a minimum (I_A) and a maximum (I_C) moment of inertia perpendicular to one another: the third principal axis (moment $= I_B$) is perpendicular to these two. Linear ($I_A = 0, I_B = I_C$), spherical tops ($I_A = I_B = I_C$), symmetric tops ($I_A = I_B \neq I_C$), and asymmetric tops ($I_A \neq I_B \neq I_C$) show different rotational structures associated with their vibrational absorptions. Even the contours of such absorptions, lacking the resolution of the rotational line structure, often suffice to suggest, if not to prove, the momental character of the molecule. The utility of such discrimination is usually to decide between two fairly different possible molecular configurations. Greater definition from infra-red spectra is only possible on the basis of precisely evaluated moments of inertia, and the limitations of that procedure have already been indicated.

(3B) Bonding and the molecular force field

To the chemist, one of the principal interests in molecular structural studies is an understanding of the bonding between the component atoms of the molecule. Classical chemical methods usually succeed in establishing the qualitative pattern with remarkable accuracy. But although the concepts of single, double and triple bonds are a hundred years old, chemical means scarcely suffice to produce any quantitative assessment of the bonding.

It is important to realize that there are alternative methods of measuring the degree of bonding. Numerical estimates, often of a semi-empirical character, can be made of the valence electron distribution in polyatomic molecules. These provide quantum-mechanical appraisals of the degree of bonding.

One much favoured estimate is the energy needed to break the individual bonds. In doing this, however, various rearrangements may occur in the molecular fragments, rearrangements which may be structural or of a minor electronic character: *i.e.* the dissociation energy will clearly vary with the nature of the fragments produced. Although sometimes difficult to evaluate, such changes are advisedly allowed for in estimating the actual bond energy.

The bond lengths, which can be determined by X-ray methods with reasonable accuracy in almost any molecular structure, provide a good criterion of bonding, and especially so their relative values in different bonds between the same pair of atoms. The basis of this is seen from curves such as Fig. I, 1. There the repulsive energy term, (*cf.* equation (2)), will be largely independent of the attractive forces and so the depth of the minimum (D_e) will increase with greater bonding and inevitably r_e will decrease. Thus the bond (X–Y) will usually give a smooth D_e—r_e curve from data in different molecules.

However, insofar as one is concerned with the normal state of the molecule, one of the best representations of its condition is provided by the potential energy field for the molecule: that is, a representation of the forces that arise when the atoms are displaced from their equilibrium positions. This becomes a determination of the various "force constants" for the bonds in the molecule and for the angular location of the atoms. When such forces alone are defined (*i.e.* bond stretching and angle bending) then we have the simple valence force field (S.V.F.F.) for the molecule. Experience shows that this is often too simple a representation: it is impossible to stretch one bond, or close one angle, without in some degree changing the other bonds and/or angles in the molecule. This means that cross-terms between the various bond-stretching (Δr) and angle-bending ($\Delta \theta$) displacements have to be introduced into the potential energy expression for the molecule. A general quadratic of the form (see Chapter V)

$$2V = \sum_i \sum_j F_{ij} R_i R_j \qquad (6)$$

must be written for the energy resulting from displacements R_i, R_j which are individual Δr or $\Delta \theta$ terms: the S.V.F.F. would restrict the expression to

$$2V = \sum_i F_{ii} R_i^2.$$

The F_{ij}'s are the generalized force-constant factors. Their deduction in the general case is a difficult problem: partly because the information available is restricted to a maximum of $(3N-6)$ vibrational frequencies. Sometimes even these are not all known. Reason dictates that one should not attempt to define more F's than there are frequencies available. This often means that all the terms in the general quadratic (equation (6)) cannot be evaluated and the problem must be approximated by writing at least some $F_{ij} = 0$. The *modus operandi* is presented in Chapter V.

Even in evaluating the terms of a complete quadratic the assumption is being made that the restoring forces are strictly harmonic, *i.e.* proportional to the displacements. To conform to this the ω_e's should be used in solving for the F's. Whilst this does not involve more than taking the observed fundamental frequencies and correcting them for the anharmonicities, only for a very limited number of polyatomic molecules can this be done as the overtones are very rarely measured in these cases. There is, in fact, a great dearth of information on anharmonicity in polyatomic molecules and its variation with vibrational type: the factor itself could be of much interest in many cases, and the correction for it will normally make only small changes of the order of one per cent in the F's.

The cross-term parameters, F_{ij}, are of especial significance; they measure the dependence of one feature, say a bond-length (i) on some other — perhaps an adjacent bond or angle (j). Their precise evaluation and interpretation in terms of electron-delocalization and other intra-molecular effects (Duchesne *et al.*) can reveal a great deal concerning the balance of forces within the structure. Despite the availability of computers which make such calculations far easier, no greater significance in the F's can be achieved without greater or more precise information on the vibrations being put in. This means that frequencies of isotopic molecules and anharmonicities should accompany such efforts: other data — such as centrifugal distortion constants, accurate bond-length force-constant relations, etc. — can also help.

Symmetry considerations, and therefore group theory, play a major role in any force-field calculations for polyatomic molecules. The potential function must have a symmetry conforming to that of the molecule: this means that it can be resolved into subdivisions, one for each symmetry class within the vibrations. This, at least, is so for a quadratic (harmonic) function. Whilst group-theory further indicates the form of the vibrations in a given force-field, there is no certainty that the actual vibrations will follow the predicted pattern: the assumed force-field may be incorrect and the real vibrations mixtures of (*i.e.* compounded from) those depicted. If the force-field is adequately defined then it also gives the correct vibrational forms.

A technique which may well help resolve difficulties in deciding the forms of vibrations is that of model-building. (Andrews, Badger, Wagner). The process is somewhat arbitrary in that the vibrations undergone by the model — which can be scaled to the correct mass and force system — are determined by the forces assumed in building it. However, a reasonable range of forces is fairly quickly explored. With appropriate controls and further development this procedure could be especially helpful for rather complicated structures.

(3C) Thermodynamic parameters

Chapters IV and VI adequately emphasize that a convincing assignment of the vibrational frequencies requires both a Raman and infra-red study of the molecule. Having decided what the values for the $(3N-6)$ frequencies are, a great deal of valuable information immediately follows on application of the partition function to calculate the principal molar thermodynamic factors (H, S, G, C_p). The moments of inertia can usually be deduced with sufficient accuracy by computing them for a model, *i.e.* if they are not available spectroscopically. As the lower frequency fundamentals contribute a preponderant share to the room-temperature values of these factors, the exploration of the low-frequency infra-red range and of the Raman spectrum is obligatory here. In most cases the uncertainties are no more than those inherent in calorimetric determinations.

Only indirectly do such calculations reveal structural information and then essentially by the differences arising between the calculated and calorimetrically determined (or otherwise anticipated) values. Two of the most commonly occurring discrepancies arise from non-rigidity within the molecule, and imperfect order (residual entropy) in the crystal state at the lowest temperatures. The crystalline forms of CO, N_2O, H_2O and some long-chain olefines are well-known examples of this latter condition. The spectroscopic entropies provide an estimate of the degree of disorder in the solid and that is necessarily correlated with the interactions and structure developed there.

Of even greater structural interest are the cases where internal group rotations or other non-rigid elements can either be detected by direct spectroscopic observation or produce discrepancies in thermodynamic factors. These systems have been the special concern of Mizushima and his school. Quantitative consideration of either spectroscopic or the thermo-dynamic data provides an estimate of the potential hindering such motion. These studies are now being extended by micro-wave and nuclear magnetic resonance methods. The presence of an internal rotator can have striking spectroscopic consequences: a vibrational mode, usually of a torsional or bending character, is replaced by a hindered rotation. A special instance is methyl alcohol, $CH_3-O\diagup^H$, in which the libratory motion (partly oscillatory, partly rotatory) of the hydroxyl group about the (C–O) axis produces a remarkable absorption resembling a series of rotational lines and extending from 200 cm^{-1} to 550 cm^{-1}. The detailed interpretation of these features (Dennison) is one of the most sophisticated achievements of molecular spectroscopy.

Another different aspect of rotation is the recently recognized ap-pearance of rotational features in the spectra of condensed phases (Sheppard). There seems to be no reason why this behaviour should not have been appreciated thirty years ago, but the general conviction that molecular rotation ceased on leaving the gaseous state, and the limitations and errors in some earlier observations, obscured the true state of affairs. Even now it is clear that only relatively very few molecules do rotate in condensed phases and that the infra-red spectra show this only in favourable small-molecule cases — perhaps most clearly, for the rotation of simple groups (such as –CH₃) anchored to longer or polar structures. The influence of solvent and other factors on this motion should provide interesting observations on inter-molecular interactions.

(3D) Condensed phase spectra

The vast majority of infra-red spectra have been recorded for the liquid, solution or solid states. The difference from the vapour state is primarily the disappearance in nearly all cases of any rotational structure from the spectra: this usually sharpens the vibrational absorption pattern for smaller molecules in liquids and solutions. Accordingly, insofar as deductions are based merely on the vibrational frequencies, no qualitative differences normally arise whether the gaseous or liquid phase spectra are studied. There are, of course, instances where the isomeric form of the molecule changes from one phase to the other: the *gauche-* and *anti*-isomers of ethane deriv-atives provide examples. However, very significant, if numerically minor changes in frequencies do occur on changing phase. These are instances of "medium" or "solvent" effects which are so prominent throughout much of chemistry. If only because of the ease with which such vibrational frequency shifts can be measured, and their simple quantitative assessment in terms of the displacement involved, much attention has been given to them. In the majority of cases where the shift is less than one per cent of the frequency concerned, it is clear that only minor influences are present. They, in turn, can arise from a variety of sources so that the quantitative interpretation of these effects is difficult. (Chapter XII).

Changes of intensity are often pronounced in going from one phase to another. This is not surprising when it is realized which second-order factors, in structural terms, determine intensities in infra-red spectra. Perhaps the over-all conformity of the gaseous, liquid and solid state spectra should rather be emphasized as a striking proof of the constancy in molecular structure. Basically this is an expression of the very much smaller inter-molecular interaction energies — which rarely exceed 5 kcal/mole for in-dividual covalent (X–Y) groups — compared with bond energies of the order of 100 kcal/mole.

In the crystalline state, however, pronounced differences from the isolated molecule spectrum can occur: not so much in the shift of previously observed absorptions, but in their splitting into a number of components and in the appearance of new absorptions. These new features arise from the coupling together of the molecules in the unit cell so that the vibrations in the crystalline state cannot be considered in terms of the individual molecules but rather of the total structure comprised within the unit cell. Clearly the symmetry of this structure will be different from that of the individual molecule: it will be compounded of that and the site symmetry in the crystalline lattice. This explains how frequencies not seen in the gaseous or liquid states can become prominent in the crystal: especially is this so for many combination tones $(\overline{\nu_1 + \nu_2}$, etc.) which can attain considerable intensity from the coupling together of individual molecular vibrations within the unit cell.

Group theory can be used to predict the permitted infra-red (or Raman) frequencies for molecular lattices. As in the case of the individual molecule, however, only the most general anticipations of their relative intensities is possible. Usually the isolated molecule frequencies remain easily the most prominent in the spectrum; any new features depend for their intensity upon the degree of coupling between the molecules in the unit cell. Non-polar saturated molecules show a minimum coupling: polar (or ionic) unsaturated species often show a great deal. Any distortion from its gas phase symmetry will normally result in a molecule showing more fundamental frequencies in absorption. A striking instance is provided by p-benzoquinone

$$O=C\underset{\displaystyle CH=CH}{\overset{\displaystyle CH=CH}{<}} >C=O$$

whose vapour spectrum shows relatively few absorptions, essentially because of the high molecular symmetry. In the solid state a rich vibrational spectrum appears with an exceptionally large number of combination bands, whose relatively great intensity indicates pronounced interactions within the crystal. The probability is, in this case, that some appreciable electron-delocalization occurs between individual molecules: these quinonoid molecules come into the class of organic semi-conductors. In this way infra-red spectra can reveal important aspects of crystal-state conditions. The emphasis on "crystal-state" is deliberate. A solid formed from a super-cooled liquid frequently shows no more absorptions than the liquid. Transformation to, or admixture with, the crystalline phase, can be followed from the absorptions characteristic of that condition. This is the basis of studies of the "degree of crystallinity" etc., especially in polymeric materials. Chapter VIII deals with these matters. Those larger (usually pseudo-spherical) molecules that rotate in the solid phase over various temperature ranges below the melting-point — the so-called "rotator phase" shown by camphor, methyl chloroform ($CH_3 \cdot CCl_3$), etc. — are of interest in this connection. Their infra-red spectra can often scarcely be distinguished from those of the liquids:

an observation which lends support to their being regarded as translationally-frozen liquids, a conclusion supported by X-ray, nuclear magnetic resonance and dielectric studies.

The unique feature of crystal phase absorptions is their anisotropy. Because the molecules are fixed in a limited number (sometimes only one) of definite orientations, the direction of the dipole moment changes in the oscillating groups (say ν(C=O) in long-chain ketones) is fixed with respect to the crystal axes. This means that the intensity of the absorption of polarized radiation will vary markedly with crystal orientation.

Most infra-red spectrometers (especially grating instruments) produce partial polarization of the radiation: as a consequence, intensity variations are often noticed in rotating a crystalline specimen, even if of uniform thickness, when measuring its absorption. Significant use can be made of this effect: (see Chapter VIII).

Inevitably, with the increased concentration of molecules per unit volume in the condensed phases, absorptions can appear far more intensely there. It is an interesting and valuable feature of classical optics that in these circumstances the frequencies of maximum absorption will suffer preferential reflection from crystals. The latter should advisedly scatter the minimum amount of radiation and a single polished crystal is the desirable specimen. From studies of this reflection process not only may absorptions and their intensities be determined but the general optical properties of the crystal can be evaluated (Chapter XI).

(3E) Intensities

The quantitative treatment of intensity is, notoriously, one of the most difficult aspects of spectroscopic work. In the infra-red it is certainly very much easier to determine absorption frequencies accurately than it is to measure intensities. This is a consequence of a number of factors including (a) the small and frequency-dependent amount of energy; (b) the limited resolving power (and radiation purity) in the spectrum, so that absorption contours are frequently a function of slit-width; and (c) the uncertainty provided by extended wings (or "tails") in the absorptions. Accordingly, very careful work is needed to achieve significance in absolute intensities but, (as Chapters X and XI show), a firm grip has now been taken on this problem and a number of procedures are available which ensure meaningful results. The practical unit of absolute intensity — cm^2 mmole^{-1} — is appropriately referred to as a "crawford".

The molecular interpretation of intensities is also recondite. The transition moment which quantum mechanical theory shows to be the determining factor for intensities is, in the infra-red, a function of the dipole moment change with the vibrational coordinate $(d\mu/dQ)$. This, in turn, is subtly dependent upon the polar character and electron mobility within the molecule. To this degree absorption intensities provide a delicate probe on bonding conditions and it can be anticipated that accumulating data will throw more light upon the factors and regularities involved, some of which are brought out in Chapter VII.

Despite the difficulties in absolute determinations and their inter-pretation, much progress has been possible in the simpler matter of relative intensities and, of course, standardized conditions on a particular instru-ment can be calibrated to measure concentrations of many species from their infra-red absorptions to say ± 1 per cent. Again, special interest attaches to intensity changes on change of phase: variations of more than a factor of five can occur from vapour to the solid state, but normally the changes are appreciably smaller.

(3F) Characteristic frequencies

One of the striking successes of the post-1945 years has been the increas-ingly subtle use to which characteristic frequencies have been put in correlating details of molecular structure (Bellamy, Norman Jones). In the hands of experienced and critical practitioners such methods have con-tributed greatly in the sophisticated field of organo-chemical structural studies. It is on a wider and perhaps more purely qualitative basis that few organic chemists are now happy if there is no infra-red spectrometer within easy reach of their preparative benches. The empirical correlation of changes in infra-red features with molecular structural details often appears to the outsider as a very arbitrary process: so many factors could be involved that a great deal of intuitive insight is needed to recognise what may be the controlling factor. Partly for this reason and partly for the excessive simplification imposed in some discussion, those familiar with the basic theory of molecular vibrations have often regarded many such developments of detail with a justifiably critical and sometimes with an unjustifiably jaundiced appraisal.

Accordingly, it is particularly helpful to find that, somewhat belatedly perhaps, theoretical analysis of the validity and limitations of the concept of group frequencies is now bearing fruit (Bernstein, King, Bratož). The outcome of these treatments reveals more explicitly the features and conditions which can plausibly be taken as quantitative measures of bond character. A typically significant assessment of the (C–H) bond has been made by Bernstein. He has shown how to evaluate the significant (mean) ν(C–H) frequency in standard hydrocarbon types: methane (2995 cm^{-1}), ethylene (3052 cm^{-1}), benzene (3055 cm^{-1}), acetylene (3334 cm^{-1}). Each of these frequencies is significant to *ca.* ± 5 cm^{-1} as a measure of the corresponding (C–H) bond: variations below this limit can arise from a variety of sources — changes in anharmonicity factors, in symmetry, in cross-terms in the potential function, in Fermi resonance, etc. It is on the basis of such controlled "group frequencies" that significantly reliable correlations with force-constants, bond lengths, bond orders, etc. are likely to be established.

It still seems a surprising fact that until about 1955 little was done towards the systematic application of infra-red methods in inorganic chemistry. Whatever the reasons for that, as Chapter IX illustrates, the lack has been rapidly remedied and further extensive proliferation in that field is certain to occur.

It must be remembered that even in the absence of adequate analysis, many infra-red features — and especially such simple features as ν(X–H), and ν(X=O) absorptions — have provided reliable indications of many processes of the greatest interest to the chemist. Qualitative, quantitative and kinetic aspects of often complex molecular systems have been elucidated from their infra-red absorptions. The present volume is confined to the basic physical aspects of such absorptions and with such strict correlation with molecular structure as current developments allow. It is with the confident anticipation that an appreciation of the fundamentals of the subject will contribute both to its proper understanding and even more rapid advancement that this volume has been compiled.

(4) Historical

Modern instrumental improvements and the multiplication of reliable recording spectrometers have meant that only rarely is it nowadays necessary for infra-red spectra predating 1945 to be consulted. It is relevant to recall, however, that many of the typical features most in use to-day had been established even many decades earlier. The major principles were established in the 'twenties and 'thirties with the application of the quantum theory to molecular systems.

Experimentally, and empirically, much pioneering work had been done in the nineteenth century. In 1882 Abney and Festing reported the absorptions of many organic compounds in the photographic infra-red out to 12,000 Å, or 8300 cm^{-1}. They wrote: "When we find a body having a band at (wavelength) 0.74 μ and another beginning at 0.907 μ and ending at 0.942 μ, we may be pretty sure that we have an ethyl radical present. In the aromatic group the critical line is at wavelength 0.867 μ. If that line be connected with a band we feel certain that some derivative of benzene is present." These observations foreshadow the use of infra-red absorption spectra in identifying characteristic molecular groups. Julius in 1892 plotted many absorption spectra of organic molecules from the visible to 1000 cm^{-1}

and in 1898 Rubens and Aschkinass used a sylvite (KCl) prism to find the absorption spectra of simple gases out to 500 cm^{-1}. These are some typical early studies. It could well be that features other than the recently re-introduced Ebert grating mounting (1889) will reappear from such pioneer work.

The systematic study of infra-red absorption spectra can be dated from Coblentz's work, on which the first volume was published by the Carnegie Institute in 1905*. Galvanometer deflections from a thermocouple response to the radiation, or a similar radiometer mirror deflection, formed the signal. A point-by-point traversal of his frequency range (5000 cm^{-1} to 670 cm^{-1}) meant that four hours or more were required to plot each spectrum — a situation essentially unchanged up to 1939 — and Coblentz's spectra remained the best single compilation up to that date. They established such features as the characteristic absorption bands of the *ortho-*, *meta-*, and *para-* substituted benzene nucleus which have been much used in the qualitative and quantitative analysis of mixtures of such isomers. It was largely on their basis that the critical early steps in analysing hydrocarbon (petroleum) mixtures were taken at Cambridge University in 1940 (Delia Agar). Lecomte and his students at Paris from the early 'twenties built up much of the systematics of characteristic frequencies and first observed many further features such as the influence of hydrogen-bonding on the spectra of hydroxylic and other compounds (Freymann, 1932).

The basic techniques of refined and particularly of grating molecular spectroscopy were largely developed at the Physics Department of the University of Michigan (Ann Arbor) by Randall and his co-workers, especially from 1919. Dennison, at the same school, laid the foundations of the theoretical interpretation of the vibrational spectra of polyatomic molecules and he has continued to make major contributions in that field for more than thirty-five years. It is interesting to recall that the first quantitative attempts to represent the constraining forces on atomic displacements within polyatomic molecules assumed that they were of a central character: that is, that restoring forces arose between each atom and all the others in the molecule. This, of course, was a physicist's aberration, derived by transposition from the gravitational field. It was Mecke who was principally responsible for the acceptance of the valence-force field, *i.e.* that the principal (but not necessarily the only) restoring forces arose from the relative displacements of atoms directly bonded or of the angles defined by the equilibrium bond positions. The consequences of this valence-force field were first derived for the simple molecular types (linear triatomic, pyramidal, tetrahedral, etc.) by Lechner (1932) using classical dynamical (Lagrangian) methods. It was Bright-Wilson Jr. who systematised the more general

* Coblentz died September 1962, aged 88.

group-theoretical treatment. Lechner's equations for the vibrational frequencies in terms of bond and angle force-constants were much used by Kohlrausch in his interpretation and deductions from Raman spectra, which, for a number of years, probably contributed more to the understanding of molecular structure and chemical-bonding than did the (then) more tedious infra-red studies.

The commercial production of recording infra-red spectrometers stimulated by developments in the 1939–45 war ushered in the great expansion in infra-red studies which has continued up to the present.

REFERENCES

The individual chapters carry literature references where further details of their topics can be found. The following texts include *introductory* accounts of group theory and wave mechanics as applied to molecular spectra:

G. M. Barrow, *Introduction to Molecular Spectroscopy*, McGraw Hill Inc., New York, 1962.

J. C. D. Brand and J. C. Speakman, *Molecular Structure*, Ed. Arnold, London, 1960.

K. S. Pitzer, *Quantum Chemistry*, Prentice–Hall, New York, 1953.

W. J. Eyring, J. Walter and G. E. Kimball, *Quantum Chemistry*, John Wiley, New York, 1944.

H. Margenau and G. M. Murphy, *The Mathematics of Physics and Chemistry*, van Nostrand Inc., New York, 1943.

F. Matossi, *Gruppentheorie der Eigenschwingungen von Punktsystemen*, Springer-Verlag, Göttingen, 1962.

Chapter II

Instrumentation and General Experimental Methods

A. E. MARTIN

Head of Infra-red Department, Sir Howard Grubb, Parsons & Co. Ltd.

(1) Historical

When it is remembered that infra-red prism spectrometers were well known in 1900 and echelette gratings were introduced by Wood and

TABLE II, 1

DEVELOPMENT OF THE INFRA-RED SPECTROMETER

1908	Coblentz[1]	Design and application of a sodium chloride prism spectrometer.
1910	Wood and Trowbridge[2]	Introduction of the echelette grating.
1918	Randall and Sleator[3]	Design and use of a high resolution grating spectrometer.
1927	Pfund[4]	Introduction of the on-axis paraboloid.
1931–1932	Randall[5]	Introduction of the off-axis paraboloid and ellipsoidal condensing mirror.
1932	Firestone[6]	First use of an a.c. detecting system.
1932–1938	Many workers[7]	Development of the sensitive evacuated thermocouple.
1942–1945	Several workers[8]	Development of a double-beam spectrometer (double-beam in space or double-beam in time).
1945	Roess[9]	First successful electronic a.c. amplifier for use with thermocouples.
1947	Wright and Herscher[10]	Description of the first thoroughly practical double-beam spectrometer (double-beam in time).
1955	Grubb Parsons[11]	Introduction of first wide-range prism/grating double-beam spectrometer.
1961	Perkin–Elmer	Introduction of first wide-range filter/grating double-beam spectrometer.

Trowbridge in 1910, it may seem surprising that the development of high performance double-beam spectrometers has been so slow. The reason is that the path of progress has been beset by a number of formidable obstacles, each one of which has had to be separately overcome. Some of the more important landmarks with approximate dates are given in Table II, 1.

As early as 1918 efficient grating spectrometers were in use and the higher resolution of these instruments quickly led to experimental results of the utmost importance to the theoretical worker. Fortunately, thermopiles in use during this period, though slow in operation, could detect very small amounts of energy when used in conjunction with sensitive d.c. galvanometers and a resolution of 1 cm^{-1} was attainable in favourable circumstances. These instruments did not come into wide use, however, because of the shortage of diffraction gratings and the difficulty of designing a monochromator to cover a wide wavelength range.

In the meantime, interest was concentrated on the prism spectrometer and the growth of large crystals of the more important prism materials[12] led to rapid improvement in performance of these instruments. On-axis and off-axis paraboloidal mirrors improved the optical performance, although, rather ironically, use of these expensive components could have been obviated by using spherical mirrors in the now popular Ebert system. Improved thermocouples were developed about 1938 but the advantage was in speed of response rather than sensitivity. However, an important gain was obtainable by reducing the size of the detecting element and using an ellipsoidal mirror to concentrate the radiation onto the small receiving area. This improved detecting system was in use as early as 1932 but was utilized with increasing effectiveness as detectors were gradually reduced in size to 2×0.2 mm, dimensions subsequently regarded as standard.

The next important advance was the use of interrupted radiation with a.c. amplification by Roess in 1945, although in 1932 Firestone had used a crude a.c. system in which radiation was chopped at a fixed frequency and the signal fed to a vibration galvanometer tuned to the same frequency. In 1946 the breaker-amplifier was developed and this enabled a.c. amplification to be used with even a sluggish detector. Unchopped radiation produced a d.c. signal from the thermocouple which was chopped mechanically at 75 c/s and then amplified at this frequency. The final output was synchronously rectified and recorded. The breaker-amplifier is occasionally used even to this day; its main disadvantage is the fact that the signal is subject to drift since any d.c. output from the thermocouple unrelated to the received radiation is amplified with the signal.

The a.c. system of Roess, despite some loss of sensitivity, rapidly became standard and was applied equally to the thermocouple and to the thermistor bolometer which was introduced in 1946. In the following year Wright and

Herscher described a double-beam system which made use of a.c. amplification and a properly designed servo system. Previous double-beam instruments had been described but no widescale use was possible until this new development, after which progress was rapid.

An interesting development devised by WALSH[13] in 1951 was the double-pass system by which the resolution of a prism spectrometer could be improved with reduction of stray light as a bonus. This helped the performance of small prism instruments considerably although, at first, it had the disadvantage that it could only be applied to single-beam spectrometers. Later, application to double-beam instruments became practicable[14] but it was not used extensively in this form.

As was inevitable when gratings became plentiful, the wide-range double-beam grating spectrometer ultimately appeared (1955) and since then competition with the prism instrument has been keen.

(2) **Modern Infra-red Spectrometers**

(2A) General description

All spectrometers use certain basic components, namely, source of radiation, condensing system for focussing energy onto the monochromator slit, monochromator to isolate a narrow spectral range, radiation detector, some form of amplifying system and output recorder. It is necessary to distinguish between single-beam and double-beam spectrometers, i.e. instruments which record energy vs. wavelength and those which measure the ratio between energy transmitted by sample and energy incident on the sample, and plot transmittance or a quantity related thereto as a function of wavelength (μ) or wavenumber (cm^{-1}). (One micron (μ) is equal to 0.001 mm and wavenumber is obtained by dividing 10,000 by the wavelength in microns).

Further, it is convenient to separate monochromators into those which use diffraction gratings and those employing prisms. Grating instruments may be further sub-divided into prism-grating and filter-grating types, depending on the means used for isolating a desired spectral order.

In single-beam spectrometers radiation is chopped at a constant frequency, the resulting signal from the detector is amplified and, after rectification and smoothing, is recorded. Double-beam instruments, on the other hand, employ some form of beam switching whereby radiation alternates between sample and reference paths many times per second, various means being available to determine the ratio of the two quantities of energy.

(i) Monochromator design

Two main varieties of prism and grating monochromator are widely used at the present time. In one system, Fig. II, 1, light from the entrance slit falls on an off-axis paraboloidal mirror and a parallel beam of radiation is directed onto the prism, whence it falls on the Littrow mirror[15] and after

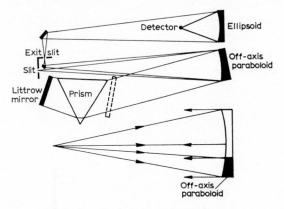

Fig. II, 1. Use of off-axis paraboloid in prism and grating monochromators.

reflection is returned through the prism almost along the original path. After a second reflection from the paraboloid the rays are brought to a focus in the plane of the exit slit to form a spectrum, and a narrow spectral region passes through the slit and is condensed by an ellipsoidal mirror onto the detector.

This system gives good service and provided that the slits are well made and a high quality paraboloid is employed, effective use is made of the prism. The wavelength is varied by rotating the Littrow mirror; and as the dispersion will vary rapidly with wavelength, a linear wavelength scale

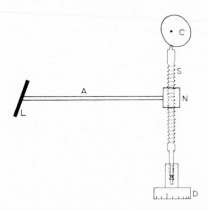

Fig. II, 2. Use of cam to obtain a linear wavelength scale.

necessitates a cam operated drive[16]. Thus, in Fig. II, 2, L is the Littrow mirror and A a rigid arm to rotate this mirror, a screw S being rotated by the wavelength drum D and causing the nut N attached to the lever arm to travel along the screw thread. The necessary correction is obtained by driving simultaneously cam C which moves the screw longitudinally as it rotates, so that the rate of movement of nut N is determined by adding or subtracting the motion imparted by the cam to that given by the screw. A comparatively small throw of the cam can compensate for large changes of dispersion (*ca.* 4:1). Drum D is uniformly divided to give a linear wavelength scale and a counting mechanism is provided to indicate complete turns.

To change from prism to grating, very little modification is required (Fig. II, 1). A plane grating is mounted in the position shown (dotted line) and is rotated steadily to provide a wavelength or frequency scan.

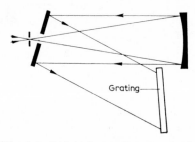

Fig. II, 3. Pfund optical system using an on-axis paraboloid.

Before off-axis paraboloids were available PFUND[4] used an on-axis paraboloid as shown in Fig. II, 3; the entrance and exit slits are in line one above the other.

More recently, the Ebert optical system, described originally in 1889[17], has been revived. Advantages are the replacement of an expensive paraboloid by less costly spherical mirrors, greater flexibility in optical arrangement and possibility of increasing the energy available. This system in which

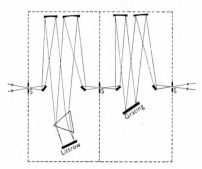

Fig. II, 4. Application of Ebert system to both prism and grating.

image distortion is kept low by using a symmetrical arrangement of off-axis mirrors, has been discussed by FASTIE[18] and its application to both prism and grating instruments is shown in Fig. II, 4. In the case of a grating, by having an appreciable angle between the incident and diffracted beams,

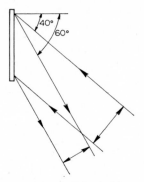

Fig. II, 5. Compression of diffracted beam from grating.

say 20° (Fig. II, 5), a useful compression of the beam is obtainable, the ratio being $\cos i_1/\cos i_2$, where i_1 and i_2 are the angles of incidence and diffraction; for example, if $i_1 = 40°$, the ratio is 1.53 to 1.

(2B) Radiation sources

Many infra-red sources have been suggested and tried, the most common being the Nernst filament, Globar, Welsbach mantle and, for longer wavelengths, the mercury lamp.

(i) Nernst filament

This source has been in use for a long period, since it was introduced in 1900. A typical composition is:

$$\left.\begin{array}{ll}\text{Zirconium oxide} & 90 \\ \text{Yttrium oxide} & 7 \\ \text{Erbium oxide} & 3\end{array}\right\} \text{parts by weight.}$$

The mixture, together with a small quantity of water and binding material, is extruded to form cylindrical rods from 20 to 50 mm in length and 1 to 2.5 mm in diameter. After air drying, the rods are progressively heated and finally fired at about 1800° C; platinum wire connections are put on the ends. The Nernst filament or Nernst is a relatively inexpensive and very useful source since it runs at about 1800° C and gives a continuous spectrum approximating to the emission from a black body at the same temperature (Fig. II, 6(a)). The true emission is obtained by multiplying the black body value at each wavelength by the Nernst emissivity factor (Fig. II, 6 (b)). The total energy dissipated is roughly 1.2 watts per square millimeter.

In order to 'light' the Nernst it must first be heated; when hot, the filament conducts electricity and is then self-maintaining. The Nernst can be run

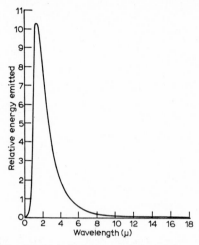

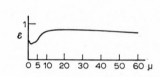

Fig. II, 6(a). Relative emission from black body at 2000° K.

Fig. II, 6(b). Variation with wavelength of Nernst emissivity, ε, relative to a black body.

from either a.c. or d.c., but the former is preferable since transport of material through the filament due to electrolysis is avoided.

A common difficulty with these sources is that most of the energy emitted is concentrated in the low wavelength region and, for example, the Nernst emits 200 times as much energy between 1 and 2μ as between 14 and 15μ. This difficulty is overcome in practice by programming the slits of the monochromator so that the energy is maintained reasonably constant over the working range.

The Nernst suffers from the disadvantage that its life is unpredictable – it may be six months or only six hours. Contact trouble leads to arcing near the ends and oxides of nitrogen are formed. When a Nernst is run for long periods, particularly when unattended, care should be taken to provide efficient ventilation so that corrosive products are rapidly removed from the instrument.

With solvents (CCl_4, CS_2, etc.), vapours inside the instrument can produce additional corrosive compounds (HCl and H_2SO_4) at the surface of the source in the presence of inevitable water vapour.

A Nernst must be protected from draughts. Its low thermal inertia leads to changes of surface temperature, with corresponding variations of energy emitted. Sources consuming more than, say 150 watts, require a water-cooled housing to prevent other parts of the instrument from being heated excessively.

(ii) Refractory filament

For process monitoring and similar applications, sudden failure of the source is undesirable, and alternatives have been devised even though some sacrifice in radiation output must usually be tolerated.

Perkin–Elmer manufactures a source similar in size to a large Nernst but considerably more robust. It consists of a refractory tube packed with a conducting mixture and consumes about 25 amps at 2 volts.

Grubb–Parsons also provides a long-lived source in which a platinum-rhodium wire is wound on a refractory former and coated with a refractory mixture (see also reference 19). Consumption is about 50 watts.

(iii) Globar

The Globar is a rod of carborundum which conducts readily at normal temperatures and so does not need to be heated on starting. It runs at about 1200° C and until recently suffered from the disadvantage that it could not be made in such small sizes as the Nernst filament and consequently dissipated embarrassing amounts of energy. Now Globars 3 mm in diameter have become available with a consumption of about 200 watts ($\sim$ 10 amps). As with the Nernst there are contact problems; silver or platinum wire can be wrapped round the ends and this is reasonably effective. One other form consists of a short length of high resistance carborundum joined to lower resistance (and therefore lower temperature) material at each end.

(iv) Welsbach mantle

The gas mantle or Welsbach mantle consists essentially of thorium oxide and it has been claimed that this material has a higher emissivity than the Nernst at wavelengths beyond 20μ. Owing to its low electrical conductance it is difficult to manufacture a practicable Nernst-type filament containing a high proportion of thoria and, probably, the energy gain would be small. If an unfired gas mantle is wrapped round a Nernst and the combustible material burned, the thoria in contact with the filament gives some slight improvement in energy beyond 20μ.

(v) Mercury lamp

A very suitable mercury lamp is Philips type MBL/U, 125 watts. The envelope is silica and attains a high temperature in use. Radiation emitted from the hot surface contributes a substantial proportion of the total available energy.

The starting voltage is 180 but when equilibrium has been attained the power consumption is 1.15 amps at 125 volts; a series ballast lamp may be used, but for a.c. operation a choke is more economical.

References pp. 82–84

This lamp is particularly suitable for wavelengths greater than 20μ since the proportion of shorter wavelengths which normally comprise stray radiation is considerably reduced.

(vi) Source stabilisation

A Nernst filament is usually run with a barretter lamp (or several in parallel) in series from the a.c. mains. The barretter consists of an iron or other wire in hydrogen and has the characteristic that over a large voltage range, *e.g.* 95 to 165, the current only changes by a few per cent. The Nernst requires about 100 volts so that the barretter also provides an inexpensive way of absorbing excess voltage.

For the Globar the barretter(s) may be placed in the primary of the step-down transformer from which it draws its low-voltage current.

When an a.c. stabiliser is available, it is a simple matter to arrange for a constant wattage to be dissipated in the source by employing the circuit

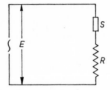

Fig. II, 7. Circuit for maintaining constant power dissipation in source.

shown in Fig. II, 7. E is the constant a.c. voltage, S the source resistance and R a constant series resistance. The power dissipated in S is $SE^2/(R+S)^2$ and if S changes to $(S+\Delta S)$, due to some change in the source, the wattage becomes:

$$\frac{(S+\Delta S)E^2}{(R+S+\Delta S)^2} = \frac{SE^2}{(R+S)^2}\left[1+\frac{\Delta S}{S}-\frac{2\Delta S}{(R+S)}\right]$$

when ΔS is small. If $R = S$ the power consumption remains unchanged.

(2C) Detectors

(i) Types of detector

The detector most commonly used in spectrometers is the thermocouple, followed at some distance by the Golay Cell. Metal bolometers (low resistance) and thermistor bolometers (high resistance) may also be used, and various photoconductive detectors as well as the indium antimonide photo-emissive (photoelectromagnetic) and photoconductive detectors are available. These latter detectors are, in the main, useful only for part or all of the region 1 to 7μ (10,000 to 1400 cm^{-1}) and are not therefore of great use in wide-range spectrometers. Further details are given by the authors mentioned below and by the manufacturers.

Wide range detectors generally can detect a radiation input of between 10^{-9} and 10^{-10} watt, *i.e.* at this level the signal output is equal to the noise voltage. Photoconductive detectors, suitable for restricted ranges, are considerably more sensitive, particularly when cooled. A general account of modern detectors is given by SMITH, JONES and CHASMAR[20], while a report on intrinsic and impurity activated detectors is given by BRATT *et al*[21].

(ii) Simple theory – thermocouple and bolometer

While a number of authoritative papers on these detectors have appeared[22], most of the important features relating to their design and operation can be made clear with a simple treatment.

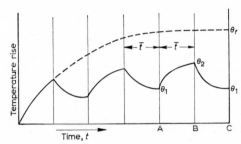

Fig. II, 8. Effect of intermittent radiation on detector.

Fig. II, 8 is intended to illustrate the variation of temperature of the receiving element of a thermocouple or bolometer when interrupted radiation is allowed to fall on its surface. Let E be the energy absorbed by the element in unit time, c the thermal capacity of the element and k a heat dissipation factor, the loss in unit time being $k\theta$, where θ is the temperature difference between the element and its surroundings. In the figure it is assumed that radiation is on for time l and off for an equal period. By the interval AB equilibrium has been reached, so that θ_1 and θ_2 are subsequently constant. θ_f is the temperature to which the element would rise if the radiation were not interrupted.

At any instant during the interval AB, $E = c(\mathrm{d}\theta/\mathrm{d}t)+k\theta$ and for any instant during the interval BC, $c(\mathrm{d}\theta/\mathrm{d}t)+k\theta = 0$. It follows that

$$\theta_2-\theta_1 = \frac{\theta_f\,(1-\mathrm{e}^{-kl/c})}{(1+\mathrm{e}^{-kl/c})} = r\theta_f \,,$$

where

$$r = \left(\frac{1-\mathrm{e}^{-kl/c}}{1+\mathrm{e}^{-kl/c}}\right), \text{ while } \theta_f = E/k.$$

Put $k/c = \alpha$, then

$$\mathrm{e}^{\alpha l} = (1+r)/(1-r) \text{ and } \alpha l = \ln[(1+r)/(1-r)] = 2r(1+r^2/3+r^4/5+ \ldots)$$

Now the frequency of interruption, $f = 1/2t$ and if, as is usually the case, $r < \frac{1}{2}$, $fr = \alpha/4 = $ constant, approximately. Further, $\theta_2 - \theta_1 = Er/k = E\alpha/4kf = E/4cf$. It follows that d.c. sensitivity is proportional to $1/k$, while a.c. sensitivity, for a frequency such that $r < \frac{1}{2}$, is proportional to $1/c$.

One assumption above is that the leads to the element contribute only to the heat loss factor. More refined treatments are possible.

Heat losses from the element to its surroundings are due to conduction by residual gas, conduction through leads, radiation loss and, in the case of a thermocouple, loss due to the Peltier effect. In order to obtain a high d.c. sensitivity these losses must be kept small, *i.e.* residual gas, lead diameter and element area must be minimized. A condensing system to give a much reduced image of the exit slit on the detector is essential; the common size of detector is 2×0.2 mm with a 5:1 or 6:1 reduction from the exit slit. A 10^{-4} mm vacuum (or better) is needed: a 30 to 1 increase in d.c. sensitivity on evacuation is common, but the effect on a.c. sensitivity is much less.

The element is blackened so that a substantial proportion of the incident energy is absorbed. The gain is, however, less than might be expected, since both c and the radiation loss are increased. For d.c. operation the element may be well blackened since c has no effect on the final temperature rise, θ_f, although equilibrium is attained more slowly when c is increased.

For high a.c. sensitivity different considerations apply. It is now imperative to minimize the thermal capacity c and efficient blackening with the minimal added material is vitally important. The method adopted is to evaporate gold onto the element in a controlled atmosphere at low pressure[23]. As the mass of the element is progressively reduced, with diminishing values for c and correspondingly higher sensitivity, a point is reached where r is greater than 0.5 and it is then necessary to reduce k to restore α to a satisfactory value. The reason for operating at low frequencies is obvious.

To produce a sensitive thermocouple it is necessary to keep the total resistance as low as possible and for this reason the leads must be kept short. Short leads however increase the conduction loss and so they must be thin. An approximate rule is that the conduction loss through the leads should equal the sum of the other heat losses. The effect of thermocouple resistance on detectivity will be considered later.

For metal bolometers similar considerations apply, but for thermistor bolometers conditions are somewhat different. This type of detector was developed at the Bell Telephone Laboratories during World War II[24]. A semiconducting material composed mainly of oxides of manganese, nickel and cobalt is used as a thin film of high resistance, with negative coefficient of resistance of about 4 per cent per °C. The thickness is *ca.*

0.01 mm, the standard area for spectrometer use being 2×0.2 mm, and the resistance *ca.* 2 megohms. Since the mass is much greater than for thermocouples, the heat loss may be increased in a similar ratio and evacuation of this type of detector is unnecessary. The high resistance helps as it permits direct coupling to the amplifier, so eliminating the expensive step-up transformer needed for low resistance detectors.

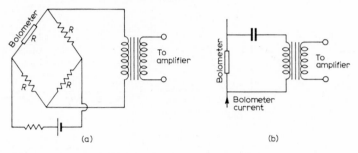

Fig. II, 9. Circuits for low resistance bolometers.

For all bolometers there is, however, the complication of providing a polarising voltage and some suitable circuits are shown in Figs. II, 9 and II, 10. The voltage supplied to the bridge must be exceptionally steady and adequate smoothing at the low frequencies normally used is troublesome.

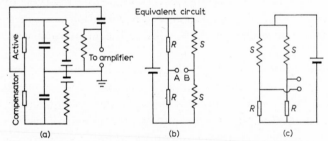

Fig. II, 10. Circuits for use with a thermistor bolometer.

The thermocouple benefits in that no polarising current is required, it is merely connected to the input terminals of a step-up transformer. Conversely, the thermistor bolometer needs no transformer since its usual resistance of about 2 megohms is ideal. The metal strip bolometer, however, suffers from needing a polarising current and a step-up transformer since its resistance is normally only a few ohms. Possible circuits are shown in Fig. II, 9; care must be taken that no appreciable d.c. flows through the transformer primary since its inductance is liable to be seriously reduced with impairment of performance. In Fig. II, 9(b), d.c. is prevented from flowing through the transformer primary by the capacitor, and this is probably the simplest arrangement.

(iii) Golay cell

A chamber containing a gas of low thermal conductivity (xenon) is sealed at one end with a window, A, of potassium bromide or other suitable material: radiation passing through the window reaches a thin absorbing film, B (Fig. II, 11), of low thermal capacity whose temperature rises

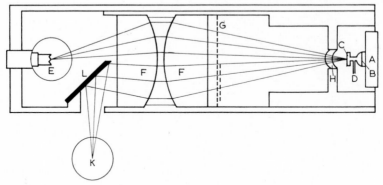

Fig. II, 11. The Golay cell.

appreciably. Gas in contact with the film is slightly heated and so the mirror membrane C sealing the other end of the gas chamber sufters some distortion. To obviate room temperature changes affecting the detector a fine leak, D, connects the detector chamber with a ballasting reservoir of gas on the other side of the membrane. When steady radiation falls on the detector, the pressure is the same on both sides of the membrane which therefore remains flat.

A special optical system is required to convert movements of the membrane, due to incident chopped radiation, into an electrical signal. Light from the exciter lamp E passes through a condenser F, F, then through a line grid G, and is concentrated on the mirror membrane. A lens H, between the line grid and the mirror membrane focuses the beam so that, in the absence of any deformation, an image of one part of the line grid is superimposed on another part of the same grid. If the image of a gap between lines coincides with a gap in the grid, light will be transmitted and may be detected by photocell K after reflection from mirror L.

Deformation of the mirror membrane causes a corresponding change in the relative position of line image and grid, and hence a change in the intensity of light reaching the photocell. This photoelectric amplification raises the signal well above the noise level of the subsequent amplifier. Synchronous rectification provides a d.c. signal with improved signal-to-noise ratio, the effective band-width of the system being only 0.1 c/s. The standard receiver element has a diameter of 3 mm; a chopping frequency of 10 c/s is normally used and the exciter lamp E is run from a specially stabilised source. Phasing pulses for the synchronous rectifier are obtained from a lamp and photocell attached to the chopper unit.

The Golay cell is a non-selective detector and the receiving membrane is of unblackened aluminium. It is so thin that it absorbs quite well from the visible to the far infra-red and microwave regions. At short wavelengths the sensitivity falls when the wavelength is comparable with the film thickness and at long wavelengths when the wavelength approaches the diameter of the receiving element.

In sensitivity the Golay equals the best thermocouples and has the important advantage from its larger area that a much less expensive condensing system usually suffices. In a spectrometer there is little difference between a good thermocouple and a Golay cell for wavelengths up to 50μ (200 cm^{-1}). At lower frequencies much larger infra-red sources are needed to compensate partially for the low energy output at long wavelengths. Using a $5:1$ condensing system with a Golay detector, most of the radiation passing through a slit 15 mm high $\times$ 15 mm wide can be made to enter the detector, whereas with a thermocouple the maximum slit dimensions would normally be 10×1 mm. Provided the larger slit has been filled the energy advantage over the thermocouple in this case is thus $18:1$.

(iv) Noise in detectors

Detectors which have a definite resistance R generate a noise voltage spontaneously across their terminals with r.m.s. value E, given by the equation

$$E^2 = 4kTR(f_2 - f_1),\tag{1}$$

where k is Boltzmann's constant, T the absolute temperature, and f_2 and f_1 in cycles per second are the upper and lower limits of the band of frequencies passed by the measuring system; it is assumed that all frequencies are amplified similarly over this range. At a temperature of 300° K, $E^2 = 1.66 \times 10^{-20} R(f_2 - f_1)$, where E is measured in volts and R in ohms. Voltage E is known as Johnson noise and is due to the random motion of electrons in the detector.

Amplifiers also produce noise, and when designing an a.c. amplifier for use with a low resistance thermocouple or bolometer, it is necessary to use a step-up transformer which will have the effect of increasing the detector noise to a value several times greater than that produced by the amplifier. It is sometimes thought that the main purpose of the transformer is to increase the signal voltage, but this is really incidental and once the detector noise has been raised well above that due to the amplifier, there is no further advantage to be gained in increasing the transformer ratio since signal voltage and noise are stepped up equally. Random noise

References pp. 82–84

voltages, *e.g.* E_1 from detector and E_2 from amplifier are added in such a way that the total noise, E, is given by $E^2 = (E_1^2 + E_2^2)$.

Since $E_1 \propto \sqrt{R}$, a transformer with ratio $1:n$ will increase the noise voltage to nE_1, which is proportional to $\sqrt{n^2 R}$, and the input resistance, as seen by the amplifier, is $n^2 R$. As an example, a thermocouple with a resistance of 20 ohms, connected across the primary of a $1:300$ transformer, will have an effective resistance of $20 \times 300^2 = 1.8$ megohms, which is a very suitable input value for an a.c. amplifier.

Eqn. (1) shows that it is advantageous to reduce the band width of the amplifier, and this is effected either by incorporating sharply tuned filter circuits or by employing synchronous rectification. In practice the chopping frequency is likely to be from 10 to 20 c/s with a band width of 1 c/s. The corresponding Johnson noise across a 2 megohm resistor is then 0.18 microvolt at normal temperature. $E \propto \sqrt{\Delta f}$, where Δf is the band width, so that any further improvement by reducing Δf below 1 c/s is not very great. With a narrow band width the chopping frequency must be correspondingly stable as the amplifier output is sensitive to signal frequency. The chopper motor must be run from a stable oscillator (not the mains) or synchronous rectification must be used. Synchronous rectification has the advantage of improved signal-to-noise in much the same way as with sharply tuned filters: the noise voltage is very nearly proportional to $1/\sqrt{T}$, where T is the time constant of the smoothing circuit. With a sharply tuned amplifier the response time is increased similarly as the signal-to-noise ratio is improved by reducing band width.

Only by careful manufacture is it possible to produce semiconductors with noise down to the Johnson value, *i.e.* to the value appropriate to metals (eqn. 1). Although noise may be near the Johnson level in the absence of current, some materials show a considerable increase of noise on passage of current. Thermistor bolometers require a steady current while in use and may show this effect. A screened compensating resistance similar to the detector can be housed with it; a typical bolometer circuit is shown in Fig. II, 10, (a) and (b). Initial balance ensures that there is no signal voltage between A and B, but if the resistance of the receiving element changes from R to $(R + \Delta R)$ when receiving radiation, the compensator being fixed at R, a voltage of $E(R + \Delta R)/(2R + \Delta R) - E/2$ will appear between A and B. This voltage is nearly $E\Delta R/4R$ and represents the peak to peak swing obtained with chopped radiation, provided the bolometer attains temperature equilibrium during each half period of the radiation cycle. The effective resistance in assessing noise is $(R + S)/2$ so it helps to keep S small, but in practice, to avoid current drain from the supply, S is made roughly equal to R. In the alternative circuit (Fig. II, 10(c)), the signal voltage may be doubled by making S large compared with R, but then noise corresponds to a resistance of $2R$ and the nett gain is only $\sqrt{2}$ times; moreover a higher polarising voltage is then needed.

The Golay cell does not suffer from Johnson noise but it has the mechanical equivalent — Brownian motion fluctuations due to random bombardment of the mirror membrane by gas molecules. This form of noise is proportional to $\sqrt{kT/K}$, where K is the restoring force on the membrane per unit displacement, and is similar both in form and amount to Johnson noise.

(v) Superconducting bolometer

Since $E \propto \sqrt{T}$, a low-temperature detector will favour low noise. Despite practical difficulties with the usual detectors, superconducting bolometers have been used successfully at a few °K. MARTIN and BLOOR[25] have described a superconducting tin bolometer which changes its resistance rapidly over a very small temperature interval near its transition temperature (3.7° K). As little as 10^{-12} watt of incident energy can be detected from ~ 5000 to 20 cm^{-1} (2 to 500μ) with a time constant of 1.25 seconds; a further improvement by a factor of at least 10 is claimed to be possible.

(vi) Condensing systems for use with detectors

(a) *Spherical mirror*   This is the simplest form of condenser but it is unable to form a sharp image on a very small detector, and much of the energy is wasted. As an example, if a spherical mirror 2″ diameter is placed 12″ from a slit 10×1 mm and the radius of the mirror is such that radiation from the centre of the slit falling on the centre of the mirror is focussed at a point 2.4″ from the mirror, 44 per cent of the radiation passing through the slit and falling on the mirror will fall within an area 2×0.2 mm in the focal plane. When using a spherical mirror it is important to use it on-axis since image quality deteriorates rapidly for even small angles off-axis. Off-axis operation may occasionally be tolerated with the Golay cell by reason of the large collecting area.

(b) *Ellipsoidal mirror*   To obtain a perfect image it is necessary to employ an ellipsoidal mirror as shown in Fig. II, 12. The image reduction is usually 5 or 6 to 1; for higher ratios the angle of incidence of extreme rays on the detector window and on the element itself becomes increasingly large, and reflection and other losses reduce the efficiency. Less expensive replica mirrors of quite good quality are becoming available.

(c) *Off-axis ellipsoid*   Perkin–Elmer has produced replica off-axis ellipsoids which make useful condensers for bulky detectors (*e.g.* Golay). The average reduction in image size is 6:1 but the ratio varies considerably for different rays (Fig. II, 13).

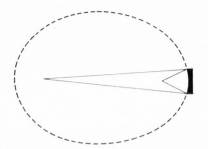

Fig. II, 12. Reduced image formed
by on-axis ellipsoid.

Fig. II, 13. Reduced image formed
by off-axis ellipsoid.

(d) Pair of spherical mirrors The microscope objective described on
page 73 may be used as a 5:1 condenser for use with a detector. This
condenser is about as expensive as an ellipsoid but has the advantage that
it may be used with bulky detectors such as the Golay cell.

(e) Spherical and plane mirrors This system is shown in Fig. II, 14 and
it is seen that the loss of energy due to the hole in the plane mirror can be
kept to a small proportion of the total.

(f) One plane and two concave mirrors In this system, illustrated in
Fig. II, 15, an ellipsoidal mirror M_1 forms a reduced image of the slit and

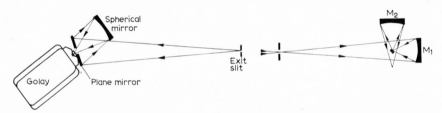

Fig. II, 14. Condensing system
for Golay detector.

Fig. II, 15. Condensing system
for use with bulky detector.

almost at the focus is placed a very small plane mirror, which reflects the
radiation onto a second spherical mirror M_2: this forms a final image of the
slit just outside the original beam of radiation, where the detector, *e.g.* a
Golay cell, is placed.

(g) Germanium immersion An ingenious condenser is a germanium hemisphere and some details are given by DE WAARD and WORMSER[26]. When
applied to a thermistor bolometer, the element is actually mounted centrally
on the plane surface of the hemisphere, separated only by a thin film which
must (i) be transparent to infra-red radiations, (ii) afford good optical
contact between the thermistor and the germanium, and (iii) have appropriate thermal conductivity and adequate dielectric strength. Such a
bolometer is said to be germanium immersed.

Such a condenser could form the window of a Golay cell, thus providing a detector and condenser in a single unit. The efficiency of the device is due to the high refractive index of germanium, about 4, and the linear reduction of image size is also close to this value, so that the reduction of image area is 16 times.

(2D) Dispersion by a prism

When a parallel beam of radiation passes through a prism of transparent material, rays of different wavelength are dispersed, *i.e.* deviated to varying degrees. In the interest of economy the beam emerging from the prism is usually returned through it so that the rays undergo further dispersion, but firstly consider a single passage as shown in Fig. II, 16. The angles of

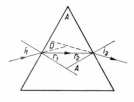

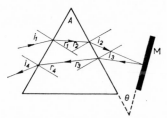

Fig. II, 16. Single passage of a ray through a prism.

Fig. II, 17. Prism with Littrow mirror.

incidence and refraction are i_1 and r_1 while the refracted ray makes an angle r_2 with the normal to the second face. On leaving the prism the angle of emergence is i_2.

From Snellius's law

$$\sin i_1 = \mu \sin r_1,$$

where μ is the refractive index of the prism material at a particular wavelength. For a fixed incident ray i_1 is constant, and on differentiating

$$0 = d\mu \sin r_1 + \mu \cos r_1 \cdot dr_1$$

and

$$dr_1 = -\frac{\sin r_1}{\cos r_1} \cdot \frac{d\mu}{\mu}$$

Similarly, $\sin i_2 = \mu \sin r_2$ and on differentiation

$$\cos i_2 \cdot di_2 = d\mu \sin r_2 + \mu \cos r_2 \cdot dr_2$$

But $r_1 + r_2 = A$, the prism angle, so that $dr_2 = -dr_1$ and

$$di_2 = \frac{d\mu \sin r_2}{\cos i_2} + \frac{d\mu \sin r_1 \cos r_2}{\cos r_1 \cos i_2} = \frac{\sin A \, d\mu}{\cos r_1 \cos i_2}$$

Naturally, in a monochromator it is desirable to have as large a change in

References pp. 82–84

i_2, Δi_2, as is practicable for a given variation in μ, $\Delta\mu$. Consequently $\sin A/(\cos r_1 \cos i_2)$ must be as large as is reasonable and therefore both A and i_2 must be large. It follows that i_1 and i_2 will both have the maximum permissible value, so that

$$r_1 = r_2 = A/2 \quad \text{and} \quad \frac{\sin A}{\cos r_1 \cos i_2} = \frac{2 \tan i_2}{\mu}.$$

Thus the maximum resolving power is set by the maximum value of i_2. Taking $\mu = 1.5$ as an average value and $i_1 = i_2 = 60°$, r_1 and r_2 are close to 35° and A is approximately 70°, $\sin A/(\cos r_1 \cos i_2) = 2.3$, whereas for the more usual angle of 60° and angle of incidence of 48.6° the corresponding value is 1.5. An increase in resolving power of roughly 50 per cent is thus obtainable for an increase in prism angle of 10°.

(i) Minimum deviation

From Fig. II, 16 it can be seen that the deviation of a ray caused by a single passage through a prism is

$$D = (i_1 - r_1) + (i_2 - r_2) = i_1 + i_2 - A,$$

and when D is a minimum

$$di_1 + di_2 = 0,$$

so that $di_1 = -di_2$ and it follows that $i_1 = i_2$.

In early prism spectrometers it was the custom to use the Wadsworth mounting[27] whereby the prism was used at minimum deviation throughout the range of the instrument. The extra complication of doing this, however, is not worth while and in latter-day spectrometers the prism is only strictly at minimum deviation at a single wavelength, about 10μ for a $2-15\mu$ instrument using a sodium chloride prism.

We have also to consider a second passage of the ray through the prism after reflection from the Littrow mirror M in Fig. II, 17. It can be shown that

$$\Delta i_4 = \frac{\Delta\mu \sin A}{\cos i_4 \cos r_3} \left[1 + \frac{\cos i_3 \cos r_4}{\cos r_1 \cos i_2} \right]$$

and since in most cases $i_2 \approx i_3$ and $r_1 \approx r_4$,

$$\Delta i_4 \approx \frac{2\Delta\mu \sin A}{\cos i_4 \cos r_3} \approx \frac{4 \tan i\Delta\mu}{\mu},$$

where i is the mean of i_1 and i_4.

In an actual spectrometer i_1 and i_4 are fixed, and in order to design a scanning mechanism to cover the desired spectral range, it is necessary to calculate θ (Fig. II, 17) for a number of wavelengths throughout the range.

(ii) Resolution when energy limited

In order to resolve adjacent images of the entrance slit formed by wavelengths λ and $\lambda + \Delta\lambda$, the limiting condition is seen to be $f\Delta i_4 = s$, where f is the focal length of the condensing mirror and s the width of the entrance slit (page 44). Thus

$$\frac{4f\Delta\mu}{\mu} \cdot \tan i = s \text{ and } \Delta\lambda = \frac{\mu s}{4f \tan i} \cdot \frac{d\lambda}{d\mu}, \tag{2}$$

very nearly. Table II, 2 gives approximate values of $\Delta\lambda$ and $\Delta\nu$ (wavenumber) for a typical sodium chloride monochromator for which $A = 60°$, $f = 50$ cm, $s = 0.1$ mm and $i = 48.4°$.

TABLE II, 2

SPECTRAL INTERVAL FOR A PRISM SPECTROMETER (LITTROW), CALCULATED FROM
EQUATION (2)

60° NaCl prism, $f = 50$ cm, $i = 48.4°$, 0.1 mm slits

λ (μ)	$d\mu/d\lambda$	$\Delta\lambda$ (μ)	$\Delta\nu$ (cm^{-1})	λ (μ)	$d\mu/d\lambda$	$\Delta\lambda$ (μ)	$\Delta\nu$ (cm^{-1})
2	0.0028	0.024	60	9	0.0060	0.011	1.4
3	0.0022	0.030	34	10	0.0068	0.010	1.0
4	0.0027	0.025	15	11	0.0076	0.009	0.7
5	0.0033	0.020	8	12	0.0085	0.008	0.5
6	0.0039	0.017	5	13	0.0095	0.007	0.4
7	0.0045	0.015	3	14	0.0105	0.006	0.3
8	0.0052	0.013	2	15	0.0115	0.006	0.25

Using a sodium chloride prism monochromator, the Nernst energy distribution is such that to maintain constant energy, the slits must be progressively opened as the wavelength increases. For example, the slit width may be 0.05 mm at 2μ (5000 cm^{-1}), 0.13 mm at 5μ (2000 cm^{-1}), 0.3 mm at 10μ (1000 cm^{-1}) and 1 mm at 15μ (667 cm^{-1}). The corresponding values of $\Delta\lambda$ vary between 0.03 and 0.05μ over this range, a certain amount of light scatter at the low wavelength end causing the measured $\Delta\lambda$ to be rather greater than the theoretical value. Since $\Delta\lambda$ is roughly constant throughout the spectrum it is reasonable to allow the same time interval Δt for any wavelength interval $\Delta\lambda$, so that $d\lambda/dt$ is constant and therefore a wavelength scan linear in time is required for most efficient operation of this type of spectrometer.

(iii) Prism materials

Only a few natural crystals were originally available for the manufacture of prisms, viz. rock salt, fluorite, quartz and sylvite (KCl). This range has now been considerably extended by the production of large crystals from the molten salts[12] and Table II, 3 contains details of the more important of them. Optical dispersion curves have the general characteristic that the

TABLE II, 3

PRISM MATERIALS

Material	Longwave limit λ_{max} (microns)	$d\mu/d\lambda$ at $\frac{2}{3}\lambda_{max}$
SiO$_2$	3.5	0.021
LiF	5.5	0.019
CaF$_2$	8.5	0.013
NaCl	15	0.007
KBr	25	0.004
CsBr	35	0.003
CsI	50	0.003

rate of change of refractive index with wavelength ($d\mu/d\lambda$) is high in the visible, low in the region of 2μ (5000 cm^{-1}) and then rises steadily until the limit of transmission is reached.

(iv) Temperature effects

Because of refractive index changes with temperature, an accurate wavelength calibration necessitates thermostatting the instrument (especially the prism), usually at a temperature of 25° C.

In many cases ($d\mu/dT$) is not accurately known, but a correction can be made using the coefficient of linear expansion of the prism material, α. Approximately, $d\mu/dT = -3\alpha(\mu-1)$.

(v) Curvature of spectral image

Images of a straight entrance slit at the exit slit of a prism monochromator are always curved, and this effect may lead to a significant impairment of resolving power. The general expression for a prism monochromator of the Littrow type is

$$\frac{1}{R} = \frac{2}{f}\left(1-\frac{1}{\mu^2}\right)\left[\tan i_1 + \frac{\sin i_2 \cdot \cos r_1}{\cos i_1 \cdot \cos r_2}\right]$$

where R is the radius of curvature of the image and all angles (measured from the mid-point of the slit) have the same significance as before. At minimum deviation this equation simplifies to $1/R = (4/f)(1-1/\mu^2)\tan i$, in accordance with the result given by ROEMER and OETJEN[28] and others.

Image curvature may be largely allowed for by curving either the entrance or exit slit jaws to compensate for the average curvature produced by the prism. It is the entrance slit jaws that are usually curved; a straight image is formed on the exit slit and this facilitates final adjustment of the instrument. For double-beam operation where two images of the source are alternately focussed on the entrance slit, it is easier to maintain correct optical alignment when a straight entrance slit is employed.

(2E) Dispersion by a grating

(i) Theory of the diffraction grating

The echelette grating was first produced in 1910 by WOOD and TROWBRIDGE[2] for use in the infra-red part of the spectrum. This grating is not essentially different from other types but the ruling interval is chosen to be suitable for the infra-red region and the groove form is controlled so that energy is concentrated in a desired part of the spectrum.

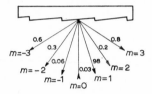

Fig. II, 18. Energy distribution (per cent) from grating: normal incidence, wavelength 4.78μ, grating space 16.933μ, groove angle 8° 12′.

Fig. II, 18 shows the groove shape in an ideal grating and illustrates how the energy is concentrated in certain orders. These results were calculated by STAMM and WHALEN[29]. The value of 98 per cent in the first order is for a perfect grating and in practice 70 per cent is regarded as quite good. A common expression is that a grating is blazed for a certain wavelength in a given order.

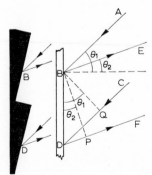

Fig. II, 19. Principle of the diffraction grating.

Fig. II, 19 shows the action of a grating. AB and CD represent two parallel rays incident at points B and D, and BD is assumed to be equal to the groove spacing, d. Since B and Q are on a common wave front there is no difference of phase between them. The ray CDF clearly travels an additional distance (QD+DP) compared with ray ABE, and for B and P to be on a common wave front

$$QD+DP = m\lambda,$$

where λ is the wavelength of the radiation and m is an integer defining the order of a spectrum. But $QD = d \sin \theta_1$ and $DP = d \sin \theta_2$, where θ_1 and θ_2 are the respective angles of incidence and diffraction and are given the same sign if on the same side of the normal to the grating surface and opposing signs if on opposite sides of the normal.

Thus

$$d (\sin \theta_1 + \sin \theta_2) = m\lambda \qquad (3)$$

and if $\theta_1-\theta_2$ is put equal to δ, we have $2d \sin (\theta_1-\delta/2) \cos \delta/2 = m\lambda$. In instruments of the Littrow type δ is small and we may write with little error $2 d \sin \theta = m\lambda$, where θ is the mean of the angles of incidence and diffraction. In the Ebert system (Fig. II, 4), however, δ may be quite appreciable and a value of $20°$ is not uncommon. From equation (3) it is seen that λ cannot exceed $2d$ for a given grating and since in practice θ is rarely as large as $60°$, λ does not normally exceed $\sqrt{3}d$.

(ii) Resolution when energy limited

By differentiating equation (3) with θ_1 constant, we obtain

$$d \cos \theta_2 d\theta_2 = m d\lambda \qquad (4)$$

and

$$d\lambda/d\theta_2 = d/m \cdot \cos \theta_2.$$

From Fig. II, 20 it can be seen that a change of $\Delta\theta_2$ in the angle of incidence on the condensing mirror M causes the image on the exit slit to shift by an

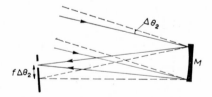

Fig. II, 20. Image shift due to change of angle of incidence on condensing mirror.

amount $f\Delta\theta_2$, where f is the focal length of the mirror. Two monochromatic images of wavelengths λ and $\lambda+\Delta\lambda$ traversing the exit slit, width s, can only be separated if $f\Delta\theta_2 > s$, so that the limiting condition is

$$\Delta\lambda = \frac{sd \cos \theta_2}{mf} \approx \frac{sd}{mf}$$

Thus the resolving power, which is inversely proportional to the spectral interval $\Delta\lambda$, is proportional to the spectral order and to the focal length, but varies inversely as the slit width and the groove width. As an example, in the Grubb Parsons GS2 monochromator the grating has 2,500 grooves per inch (d is nearly 10μ) and $f = 500$ mm, so that in the first order with s equal to 1 mm, $\Delta\lambda \approx 0.02\mu$.

(iii) Practical grating systems

In favourable conditions a single echelette grating can cover a 5 to 1 wavelength range in the first order. The efficiency falls off more rapidly at the low wavelength end than at long wavelengths and the useful range contracts rapidly on changing to higher orders. However, the energy loss at low wavelengths ($> 2\mu$) is compensated for by the increased radiation coming from the Nernst.

The Grubb Parsons Model GS2 uses a Merton-N.P.L. 2,500 l.p.i. grating replica (blazed for 10μ) in four orders to cover the range 2 to 15μ (5000 to 667 cm^{-1}) as follows:

2 to 2.5μ	fourth order	5000 to 4000 cm^{-1}
2.5 to 3.75μ	third order	4000 to 2670 cm^{-1}
3.5 to 5μ	second order	2860 to 2000 cm^{-1}
5 to 15μ	first order	2000 to 670 cm^{-1}

Subsequently, by using a 1,200 l.p.i. grating the wavelength coverage was extended to 23μ (435 cm^{-1}) with only a small loss of resolution. Breaking the spectrum into four parts is unfortunate but not serious since the first and third orders are of most importance to the organic chemist. In comparison, a spectrometer employing a sodium chloride prism has very poor resolution in the 3μ region and a change to another prism is necessary.

More recently, two interchangeable gratings in the first order have been used instead of a single grating. The chief advantages of doing this are: extension of wavelength range, particularly below 2μ; division of spectrum into fewer parts, e.g. two instead of four; and making the problem of order selection easier. Some examples of the choice of gratings in modern grating instruments are given in Table II, 4.

There is no special difficulty in extending the range of double-beam grating instruments from 25 to 50μ. Current practice is to provide a relatively inexpensive spectrometer to cover the ranges 15 to 45μ (670 to 220 cm^{-1}) or 23 to 50μ (435 to 200 cm^{-1}). Some details of Grubb Parsons longwave spectrometers are also given in Table II, 4.

(iv) Order selection

When a grating is set to wavelength λ in the first order it is equally well set

TABLE II, 4

CHARACTERISTICS OF GRATINGS USED IN SOME COMMERCIAL SPECTROMETERS

Instrument	Range (μ)	Lines/inch	Order	Blaze (μ)
PE 125	1—2.5	7620	2	1.5
,,	2—5	7620	1	3
,,	5—12.5	1524	2	7.5
,,	10—25	1524	1	15
PE 237	2.5—8	6096	1	3.75
,,	5—16	3048	1	7.5
Beckman IR7	2.5—3.6	1905	4	3
,,	3.3—5.0	,,	3	4
,,	4.9—9.1	,,	2	6
,,	8.7—15.4	,,	1	12
GS2	2—2.5	2500	4	2.5
,,	2.5—3.75	,,	3	3.33
,,	3.5—5	,,	2	5
,,	5—15	,,	1	10
GP Spectromaster	0.6—2.0	7500	2	1.75
	1—5	7500	1	3.5
	5—25	1500	1	11
Grubb Parsons	15—35	1200	1	20
,,	15—45	762	1	30
,,	23—50	508	1	45

for $\lambda/2$, $\lambda/3$, $\lambda/4$, etc., in the second, third, fourth and higher orders. The distribution of energy between the various orders mainly depends on two factors: whether the grating is set near the blaze angle, and the energy distribution from the infra-red source. In practice it is rare to require an order higher than the fourth to be isolated, and it becomes increasingly difficult to isolate higher orders. For example, when using wavelength λ the nearest interfering wavelength is at $\lambda/2$, i.e. $\lambda/2$ away. When operating at $\lambda/4$ however, it is necessary to exclude $\lambda/3$ on one side ($\lambda/12$ away) and $\lambda/5$ on the other side ($\lambda/20$ away). Moreover, when an auxiliary prism mono-chromator is used to reject the unwanted orders, the usual decrease of dispersion as the wavelength is reduced adds to the difficulty. For this reason in the Grubb Parsons Model GS2, two prisms are used, CaF_2 (high dispersion) from 2 to 5μ (5000 to 2000 cm^{-1}) and KBr (low dispersion) from 5 to 15μ (2000 to 670 cm^{-1}). In this monochromator the prism unit is very compact, 6″ from entrance to exit slit, and the prism size only $2'' \times 2'' \times 1\frac{1}{2}''$ high. In the Beckman Model IR7, which also uses a single grating in four orders, a single fore-prism is employed and the necessary resolution is obtained by making the prism unit considerably larger.

It is of course necessary to link the grating and prism units together so that the wavelengths remain in step throughout a complete order. A cam drive is employed to rotate the Littrow mirror at the speed required.

Between 25 and 50μ, prisms of CsBr (to 35μ, 285 cm^{-1}) and CsI (to 50μ, 200 cm^{-1}) are used. While these materials are expensive, prisms need only be $30°$ with $1\frac{1}{2}'' \times 1\frac{1}{2}''$ face, so that their cost is not unduly high.

As an alternative to using a prism, various filters have become available in the last few years and already they are being applied to wide range spectrometers. SMITH[30] has described the following range of semiconductors to cover the region 1 to 24μ:

Si	$1-1.95\mu$	$10000-5130$ cm^{-1}
Ge	$1.88- 3.1$	$5320-3230$
PbS	$3- 4.3$	$3330-2330$
InAs	$3.8- 5.6$	$2630-1790$
$n-$InSb	$5.5- 8.4$	$1820-1190$
InSb	$7.8-13.4$	$1280- 745$
InSb+MgO (reflection)	$12.4-24.2$	$805- 413$

In the Perkin–Elmer model 237 with two interchangeable gratings, four interference-type filters are used for the range 2.5 to 16μ.

Semiconductor filters have been found very useful for order-selection since they have sharp absorption edges, on the low wavelength side of which they absorb completely while transmitting well at longer wavelengths. These materials have a high refractive index, about 4, and consequently a large proportion of incident radiation is lost by reflection unless the filter is bloomed with a $\lambda/4$ layer of lower refractive index material. When suitably bloomed the transmittance may be increased from 40 to 90 per cent.

The usable wavelength range of a filter in the first order of a grating must be restricted since at wavelength λ, $\lambda/2$ must be rejected, while wavelengths a little longer than $\lambda/2$ must be transmitted. In practice the wavelength ratio of 2 is replaced by a value of 1.7 to 1.8. Thus in the Perkin–Elmer Model 237 four filters are used as follows:

Filter	Range (μ)
1	$2.5-4.5$
2	$4.5-8$
3	$5-9$
4	$9-16$

The filters are mounted in a turret and change automatically when the appropriate wavelength is reached. Interference filters with the necessary characteristics are being perfected, and F-centre filters, made by irradiating alkali halide in an atomic pile, have been employed to a limited extent.

Grating–prism monochromators for the region 20 to 50μ (500 to 200 cm^{-1})

tend to suffer from stray light when employed near the blaze angle, since the prism unit normally used has low resolution and some high order radiation approaching the energy maximum of the source may find its way to the exit slit. Such radiation may be reduced by replacing plane mirrors in the monochromator by roughened metal reflectors or fine gratings which diffract away radiation of low wavelengths while specularly reflecting the desired longer wavelengths. In some cases reststrahlen filters (crystal plates which reflect preferentially over a range of the order of 10 to 20 microns) or polythene sheet with suitable compounds incorporated in it may be used, and a useful paper giving details of such filters has been published by MITSUISHI, YAMADA and YOSHINAGA[31].

(v) Provision of linear wavelength scale

Since the general equation of the grating is

$$d\ (\sin\theta_1 + \sin\theta_2) = m\lambda,$$

we have

$$2d\sin\left(\frac{\theta_1 + \theta_2}{2}\right)\ \cos\ \left(\frac{\theta_1 - \theta_2}{2}\right) = m\lambda$$

and if $\theta_1 - \theta_2 = \delta$,

$$2d\sin\ (\theta_1 - \delta/2)\ \cos\ \delta/2 = m\lambda.$$

It is convenient to have a wavelength drive in which a uniformly divided drum is arranged to rotate the grating at the necessary rate for the drum to indicate accurate wavelengths directly. Incomplete solutions of this problem by BADGER et al.[32] and FASTIE[18] can be replaced by the accurate solution[33] shown in Fig. II, 21. AB is an arm attached rigidly to the grating

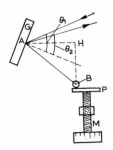

Fig. II, 21. Linear wavelength drive, micrometer type.

G at A and having a spherical end B which is held in contact with a flat plate P attached to a micrometer screw M, the axis of which is perpendicular to P. The axis of the micrometer screw is supposed to lie in the plane of the paper while the surface of the grating and of plate P are perpendicular to this plane. AH is drawn perpendicular to the axis of the micrometer. It follows that sin BAH = BH/AB and if BAH is made equal to $(\theta_1 - \delta/2)$, since AB is constant, BH $\propto \sin (\theta_1 - \delta/2) \propto \lambda$. Thus BH is accurately proportional to λ and the uniformly divided micrometer drum can be used to indicate wavelengths directly.

(vi) Provision of linear wavenumber scale

The corresponding arrangement to obtain an exact linear wavenumber scale[34] is shown in Fig. II, 22. As before, an arm AB is attached to grating G

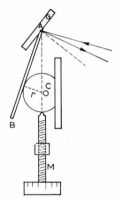

Fig. II, 22. Linear wavenumber drive, micrometer type.

and a micrometer screw M is provided, but now the screw is used to drive forward a circular member C which is constrained to move along the axis of the micrometer screw, this axis passing through O, the centre of C, and the centre of rotation of the grating, A. Since sin BAO = r/AO, where r is the radius of the circular member C, and if BAO is made equal to $(\theta_1 - \delta/2)$, AO $\propto 1/\lambda \propto \nu$, where ν is in wavenumbers. The uniformly divided micrometer drum can now indicate wavenumbers directly.

(vii) Curvature of spectral image

The reason for the curvature of the slit image can be seen from Fig. II, 23.

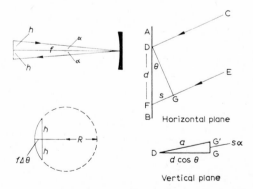

Fig. II, 23. Curvature of image formed by grating.

Assuming that rays from the centre of the slit after collimation travel horizontally, while the plane of the grating, represented by AB, is vertical, the usual grating equation holds good: $2\,FG = m\lambda = 2s$. Rays from the top or bottom of the slit, however, after being collimated make a small angle α with the horizontal, where $f\alpha = h$ (f is the focal length of the collimator and h the half-height of the slit). Accordingly, FG in the equation must be replaced by slightly different distances, s_1 for the incident ray and s_2 for the diffracted ray. Imagine ray EF to be rotated about F in a vertical plane, through angle α, then the point where a perpendicular from D strikes E'F is changed from G to G'. In the triangles DGF and DG'F

$$d^2 \cos^2 \theta + s^2 = a^2 + s_1^2 = d^2 \cos^2 \theta + s^2 \alpha^2 + s_1^2$$

from which

$$s_1^2 = s^2\,(1-\alpha^2)$$

and

$$s_1 = s(1-\alpha^2/2) = d \sin \theta(1-\alpha^2/2),$$

very nearly.

If θ' is the corresponding angle for the diffracted ray and s_2 the corresponding path difference,

$$s_1 + s_2 = m\lambda = 2d \sin \theta$$

Therefore

$$d(1-\alpha^2/2)\,(\sin \theta + \sin \theta') = 2d \sin \theta$$

and

$$(1-\alpha^2/2)\,(1+\sin \theta'/\sin \theta) = 2$$

Let

$$\theta' = \theta + \Delta\theta,$$

then

$$\sin \theta' = \sin \theta + \cos \theta\Delta\theta$$

and

$$(1-\alpha^2/2)\,(2 + \cot \theta\Delta\theta) = 2.$$

Thus $\cot \theta\Delta\theta = \alpha^2$, and assuming that the image is the same size as the entrance slit, it follows that in the figure, $2R/\Delta\theta = h^2 = f^2\alpha^2$, very nearly, where R is the radius of curvature.

Therefore $2R\alpha^2 \tan \theta = f\alpha^2$ and $R = f/2 \cdot \cot \theta$, a result first derived by MINKOWSKI[35]. Unlike the prism monochromator, the grating instrument gives an image whose curvature varies rapidly with wavelength. However, the mean curvature is generally less than for a prism monochromator of similar focal length and, for example, for a 2,500 l.p.i. grating in an instrument with a focal length of 50 cm, R is approximately 22 cm at 15μ and 100 cm at 5μ. Fortunately, least curvature occurs at short wavelengths where the slitwidth is small.

(viii) Spectrosorter*

A special form of simplified grating spectrometer, known as the Spectrosorter, is shown in Fig. II, 24. Radiations from two limbs of a U-shaped wire, S_1, S_2, heated electrically to about $900°$ C, fall on a spherical mirror

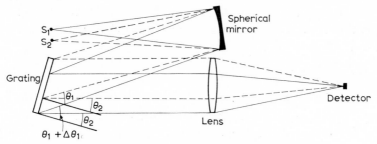

Fig. II, 24. Optical system of the Spectrosorter.

and parallel beams are directed onto a diffraction grating, in size little more than $1'' \times 1''$. The diffracted beam from the grating falls on a fluorite lens and is focussed onto a 3×1 mm indium antimonide detector. As is shown in the figure, rays from the two limbs of the filament correspond to two slightly different angles of incidence on the grating, θ_1 and $\theta_1 + \Delta\theta_1$, while only rays which leave the grating at angle θ_2 with the normal can reach the detecting element. Accordingly, we may write for the radiations corresponding to angles θ_1 and θ_2

$$d(\sin \theta_1 + \sin \theta_2) = m\lambda$$

and on differentiation obtain for the first order

$$d(\cos \theta_1 \, \Delta\theta_1) = \Delta\lambda$$

A circular disc rotating close to the infra-red source carries two rows of holes spaced around two concentric circles differing in radius by an amount equal to the spacing of the limbs of the source, so that radiation is transmitted alternately from the two limbs through the disc to reach the collimating mirror. The angle of incidence on the grating consequently alternates between θ_1 and $\theta_1 + \Delta\theta_1$ at a frequency of 1000 c/s, and finally the detector produces a signal at this frequency provided that there is some energy difference between the two beams of radiation. For a 7,500 l.p.i. grating and a source spacing of 4.5 mm, $\Delta\lambda = 0.15\mu$, approximately.

Trimmers provided make it possible, in the absence of sample or other absorption, to equalize the energy associated with the wavelengths λ and $\lambda + \Delta\lambda$ so that minimum output signal results. As soon, however, as a sample with appreciable absorption at one or other of these two wavelengths is introduced into the optical path, the energy falling on the detector is no

* Pat. Appn. No. 14453/58

longer constant and an increased output signal is obtained. In some circumstances the output is proportional to the slope of the absorption band and the instrument provides an inexpensive form of derivative spectroscopy (see page 83). This does not, however, exhaust the potentialities of the Spectrosorter and a more detailed account may be referred to[36].

If one of the two beams of radiation is blanked off, the instrument becomes a conventional spectrometer of somewhat limited performance over the range 1 to 7μ.

(ix) Grating vs. prism

In any monochromator, radiation passes through the entrance slit, width s, and falls on the collimating lens or mirror, area A, the energy passing through the optical system being proportional to sA/f^2, where f is the focal length of the collimator. After dispersion and formation of a spectrum by a lens or mirror having the same focal length f, a length of spectrum s will correspond to a wavelength interval $\Delta\lambda$ and angular variation $\Delta\theta$, and the energy E passing through an exit slit s is proportional to $sA\Delta\lambda/f^2$. But $f\Delta\theta = s$ and

$$f\Delta\theta/\Delta\lambda = s/\Delta\lambda = f d\theta/d\lambda$$

Therefore, for a fixed wavelength interval $\Delta\lambda$, $E \propto (A/f)d\theta/d\lambda$ and for instruments of similar aperture, E is proportional to the angular dispersion $d\theta/d\lambda$ and to the focal length f.

From equation (2), $\Delta\lambda$ for a prism monochromator is $(\mu s_1/4f \tan i)\, d\lambda/d\mu$, where s_1 is the slit width, and for a grating instrument of equal aperture and focal length, we have from eqn. (4): $\Delta\lambda = d \cos \theta_2 \Delta\theta_2$ when $m = 1$. Since $f\Delta\theta_2 = s_2$, where s_2 is the slitwidth, $\Delta\lambda = s_2 d \cos \theta_2/f$, and when $\Delta\lambda$ has the same value for the two instruments, $(\mu s_1/4f \tan i)\, d\lambda/d\mu = s_2 d \cos \theta_2/f$. The energy gain with the grating is s_2/s_1 and this is equal to

$$(\mu/4d \tan i \cos \theta_2)\, d\lambda/d\mu$$

If a 2,500 l.p.i. grating at 10μ is compared with a 60° NaCl prism at the same wavelength, the energy gain with the grating is six to one for the same resolving power.

With very fine slits a limit is set to resolution of both prisms and gratings by diffraction effects (see page 57). With the same 2,500 l.p.i. grating, 4 inches wide, at 10μ, the smallest resolvable interval is 0.1 cm^{-1} in comparison with 1.0 cm^{-1} for a sodium chloride prism (7.5 cm base). In practical cases it is customary to add $\Delta\nu$ (diffraction) to $\Delta\nu$ (slit width) and both values for a typical NaCl prism monochromator are given in Tables II, 2 and II, 8 (pp. 41, 48).

The superior resolving power of the grating compared with the prism can be made use of in various ways. As an example, consider a Grubb

Parsons GS2 monochromator with a 2,500 l.p.i. grating and 50 cm focal length. As already shown, the smallest wavelength interval for resolution of two adjacent bands is approximately 0.02μ for 1 mm slits, *i.e.* 2 cm^{-1} at 10μ, whereas with a sodium chloride prism with 7.5 cm base, the diffraction limit at 10μ is 1.0 cm^{-1}, *i.e.* to compete with the grating at 10μ the prism monochromator requires slits 0.1 mm wide. Apart from instrumental losses, the energy gain with the grating is therefore 10 times in this case. Alternatively, the focal length of the grating monochromator may be reduced from 50 to 12.5 cm, and with 0.5 mm slits the resolution obtained is 4 cm^{-1} at 10μ, *i.e.* equal to the prism monochromator ($f = 50$ cm) with 0.3 mm slits and still with an energy advantage of 5/3.

(2F) Points common to prism and grating monochromators

(i) Wavenumber vs. wavelength presentation

The majority of infra-red spectrometers have a linear wavelength scale and employ a wavelength scan linear in time. However, there are arguments in favour of a linear wavenumber scale and some modern instruments are provided with such a scale and employ a wavenumber scan linear in time.

Prism spectrometers when programmed to give constant energy over a wide wavelength range give an approximately constant wavelength interval, *i.e.* $\Delta\lambda = $ constant, leading to a constant rate of wavelength scan (see p. 41). The dispersion of NaCl increases approximately four times between 2 and 15μ so that some form of variable drive is needed whereby $d\theta/dt$ is increased in the ratio 1 to 4 between 2 and 15μ, θ measuring the angular rotation of the Littrow mirror. Since wavenumber $\nu = 10000/\lambda$, $\Delta\nu \propto \Delta\lambda/\lambda^2$ and $d\nu/dt \propto d\lambda/dt \cdot 1/\lambda^2$, so that to obtain a linear wavenumber scan $d\lambda/dt \cdot 1/\lambda^2$ is constant and $d\theta/dt \propto \lambda^2 d\theta/d\lambda$. Therefore $d\theta/dt$ must be varied in the ratio of 1 to 225 between 2 and 15μ. This is a difficult mechanical problem even when the total range is divided into two or more differently scaled regions.

In the case of a grating the problem is easier. Since the spectral interval in a single order is roughly constant for a given grating and fixed slitwidth s, $\Delta\lambda \propto s$ and it is reasonable to scan a spectral region at a rate proportional to s. For example, with a linear wavelength scale between 5 and 25μ, and a corresponding increase in slitwidth in the ratio 6 to 1, the speed of rotation of the wavelength drum, $d\theta/dt$, should be increased six-fold between 5 and 25μ.

Similarly, for a linear wavenumber scan, where θ represents the angular rotation of the wavenumber drum, $d\nu \propto s/\lambda^2$ and the speed of rotation of the drum, $d\theta/dt$, is proportional to s/λ^2 and should be reduced in the ratio 25 to 6 between 5 and 25μ.

References pp. 82–84

A practical difficulty arises with a linear wavenumber scale, namely the need to provide an acceptable presentation of spectra over a substantial wavelength range without several changes of scale. It is possible to present a reasonable spectrum between 1 and 15μ on a linear wavelength basis with only one change of scale, say at 5μ. With a linear wavenumber scale, on the other hand, the comparatively unimportant region 1 to 2μ (5000 cm^{-1}) occupies 67 per cent more chart length than the much more important region 2 to 5μ (3000 cm^{-1}). Again, assuming no change of scale between 5 and 15μ, the region 5 to 10μ (1000 cm^{-1}) occupies three times as much space as the valuable region 10 to 15μ (333 cm^{-1}). In Fig. II, 25 a com-

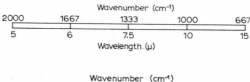

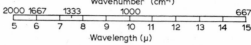

Fig. II, 25. Linear wavelength and linear wavenumber presentation.

parison between the two modes of presentation is made. It will be seen that a change to a linear wavenumber scale increases the chart length available for the region 6 to 10μ in the ratio 4:5 while the length occupied by the region 10 to 15μ is halved, if the overall length from 5 to 15μ is the same in both cases.

(ii) Wavenumber and wavelength calibration

An important point is that spectrometers are calibrated by the manufacturer under static conditions, *i.e.* zero recording speed; this is so for maximum

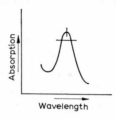

Fig. II, 26. Measurement of peak wavelength.

accuracy. When checking against a sharp absorption band the correct method is not to set to the peak, which is rounded and does not give a critical reading, but at two points having the same height on either side of the maximum, the mean of the two wavelengths being taken (Fig. II, 26).

Preferably, symmetrical bands should be selected but if a band is not symmetrical, discretion must be exercised and measurements made close to the peak.

The prism instrument is easily calibrated by making use of the data published by DOWNIE, MAGOON, PURCELL and CRAWFORD[37]. A very simple and rapid method is to make use of a number of bands of polystyrene and Table II, 5 gives the band positions. When many spectra are recorded

TABLE II, 5

BANDS OF POLYSTYRENE SUITABLE FOR WAVELENGTH CALIBRATION OF PRISM
SPECTROMETERS

Wavelength (in μ) corrected to vacuum	
3.423	9.358
5.145	9.731
6.245	11.035
6.697	11.886
6.893	13.244
8.668	14.298

fairly rapidly, the occasional use of polystyrene under similar operating conditions ensures a reasonably reliable calibration. Polystyrene has the advantage that it is equally suitable for the calibration of single and double-beam spectrometers, whereas water vapour and CO_2, which are widely used for single-beam calibration, are normally ruled out for double-beam measurements. A more reliable standard than polystyrene is indene, preferably with 0.8 weight per cent of camphor and cyclohexanone to provide (C=O) stretching frequencies. Full details are given by JONES et al.[38]

With modern grating spectrometers accurate calibration is very easily carried out. For greatest accuracy the data given in *Tables of Wavenumbers for the Calibration of Infra-red Spectrometers*, (Butterworths, 1961), should be used. A little less accuracy between 5 and 15μ is obtained by using the three calibration points given in Table II, 6. With an instrument employing one grating in different orders, no further calibration is required for the

TABLE II, 6

THREE CALIBRATION POINTS FOR THE ACCURATE CALIBRATION (SINGLE-BEAM)
OF A GS2, 2 TO 15μ, SPECTROMETER

Wavelengths corrected to vacuum and obtained from "Tables of Wavenumbers" mentioned
in the text

Substance	Chart No.	Line No.	Wavelength, μ
Water vapour	22	30	5.349
Ammonia	31	11	10.506
Carbon dioxide	34	19	14.861

second, third and fourth orders since one merely divides first order wavelengths by 2, 3 or 4. Also, any errors in the first order are reduced in the
same ratios.

Grating monochromators which make use of the patented drive described on p. 48 have the important property that wavelength error when
plotted against apparent wavelength, as indicated by the drum or dial
fitted, gives a straight line provided that the angle between grating and
actuating arm is correct. Thus the three check points mentioned above
suffice for quite an accurate calibration over a wide range.

(iii) Stray radiation

Some stray radiation appears in any spectrometer but prism–grating
instruments are usually satisfactory in this respect since the double monochromator employed makes it difficult for unwanted radiation to reach the
detector. Filter–grating spectrometers tend to suffer a little from stray
light since the filter is being used in difficult conditions.

Prism spectrometers are rather prone to this trouble, particularly at
wavelengths beyond, say, 10μ (1000 cm^{-1}). Excellent filters are available
for removing stray light, the only difficulty being that the filter must be
removed for part of the wavelength scan. For example, a bloomed indium
antimonide filter will remove all radiation below 7μ (> 1430 cm^{-1}) and
transmit above 60 per cent between 8 and 15μ (1250 to 670 cm^{-1}). Some
suitable filters for cutting off the long waves and transmitting the shorter
(stray) wavelengths are listed in Table II, 7.

TABLE II, 7

FILTERS FOR ESTIMATING STRAY LIGHT

Filter	Wavelength in μ, above which transmittance is less than 0.1 %
10 mm Silica	4.4
1 mm Silica	5
10 mm LiF	8
1 mm LiF	12
10 mm CaF$_2$	12
3 mm CaF$_2$	13

An alternative method is to use a liquid or solution with a conveniently
placed absorption band. If at some particular wavelength the transmission
is 10 per cent and the measurement is repeated with the same substance but
in a cell three times as long, the correct transmission cannot exceed 0.1 per
cent. Any radiation apparently transmitted by the cell must therefore be
stray light.

(iv) Theoretical resolving power of prisms and gratings

The theoretical resolving power of prisms and gratings is determined in exactly the same way. It is first necessary to calculate $\Delta\theta/\Delta\lambda$ in each case, where $\Delta\theta$ is the change in angle of a ray for a difference in wavelength $\Delta\lambda$. The minimum resolvable wavelength interval is determined by the smallest angle $\Delta\theta$ which can be resolved by the condensing lens or mirror. In Fig. II, 27 the monochromatic ray OP is perpendicular to the plane of lens L, the

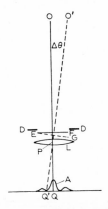

Fig. II, 27. Smallest angular difference which can be resolved.

effective aperture of which is determined by the rectangular diaphragm D,D. Let EF represent a wave front arriving at the lens from an infinitely distant point O, which after passage through the lens is brought to a focus at Q. The image is not an actual point but a diffraction pattern in the plane QQ'. EG represents a similar plane wave front incident from distant point O' which is brought to a focus at Q', *i.e.* a diffraction pattern similar to A but centred about Q' instead of Q. For separable images Q' must not be closer to Q than the first minimum of pattern A (Rayleigh). The minimum value of angle OPO', which will be called $\Delta\theta$, may be determined as follows.

Fig. II, 28. Determination of $\Delta\theta$.

In Fig. II, 28, D_1D_2 represents the diaphragm (mid-point E) and also the wave front of the incident parallel radiation, while D_1C represents the diffracted wave front which after passing through the condensing lens is brought to a focus at Q' (Fig. II, 27). Suppose that the path increment D_2C is equal to λ and that A and B are two points on the wave front D_1D_2 such that $D_1A = EB$. Now the path difference between AA' and BB' is $\lambda/2$, so that disturbances from A and B arriving together at the focus will annul each other. By pairing off points in a similar fashion throughout the left hand half and right hand half of the wave front, it is clear the two halves of the wave front will cancel out and that Q′ will represent a minimum provided that

$$w\Delta\theta = \lambda \tag{5}$$

where w is the width of the diaphragm.

(a) Prism In Fig. II, 29, AC and BD are parallel rays falling on one face of prism P and AB represents the wave front of the incident radiation. EG and EF represent, respectively, the wave fronts of two wavelengths λ and

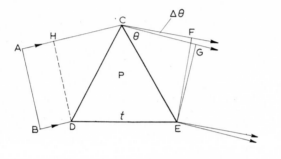

Fig. II, 29. Diffraction limit for a prism.   Fig. II, 30. Diffraction
                                                     limit for a grating.

$\lambda+\Delta\lambda$ after passage through the prism. The time for radiation of wavelength λ to travel from H to G must be the same as for D to E, so that HC+CG=μt, where t is the thickness of the prism at its base and μ the refractive index. Similarly, for radiation of wavelength $\lambda+\Delta\lambda$, HC+CF = $(\mu-\Delta\mu)t$, and CG−CF = $\Delta\mu t$.

TABLE II, 8

DIFFRACTION LIMIT FOR A SODIUM CHLORIDE PRISM SPECTROMETER (LITTROW), $(\lambda/2t)(\Delta\lambda/\Delta\mu)$, WHERE $t = 10$ CM.

λ (μ)	$\Delta\lambda$ (μ)	$\Delta\nu$ (cm^{-1})	λ (μ)	$\Delta\lambda$ (μ)	$\Delta\nu$ (cm^{-1})
2	0.004	9	9	0.008	0.9
3	0.007	8	10	0.007	0.7
4	0.007	5	11	0.007	0.6
5	0.008	3	12	0.007	0.5
6	0.008	2	13	0.007	0.4
7	0.008	1.6	14	0.007	0.3
8	0.008	1.2	15	0.007	0.3

But $CG-CF = CE\ [\cos\theta-\cos(\theta+\Delta\theta)] = CE\sin\theta\,\Delta\theta = w\Delta\theta$, where w is the width of the emergent beam. It follows from equation (5) that

$$\Delta\theta = \lambda/w = t\Delta\mu/w \text{ and } \Delta\lambda/\lambda = \Delta\lambda/t\Delta\mu.$$

When a Littrow arrangement is used the radiation traverses the prism twice and t is effectively doubled. The diffraction limit $\Delta\lambda$ is in consequence halved. Some values are given in Table II, 8.

(b) Grating For the grating we have equation (3)

$$d(\sin\theta_1+\sin\theta_2) = m\lambda$$

and differentiating with θ_1 constant, we have

$$d\cos\theta_2\Delta\theta_2 = m\Delta\lambda \qquad\qquad (4a)$$

In Fig. II, 30, CE represents a complete grating while EF and EG are wave fronts of diffracted radiation corresponding to wavelengths λ and $\lambda+\Delta\lambda$. CF and CG must each be equal to a large integral number of wavelengths and the minimum path difference between G and F is one wavelength when $\Delta\lambda$ is the minimum wavelength interval which can be resolved. Therefore

$$CG-CF = \lambda = nd\cos\theta_2\Delta\theta_2,$$

where n is the total number of lines in the grating surface. Making use of equation (4a) we have $nm\Delta\lambda = \lambda$ and $\lambda/\Delta\lambda = mn$, *i.e.* the total number of lines multiplied by the order of the spectrum.

(v) Effect of unequal slits

In most modern spectrometers slits are ganged together and programmed so that within the mechanical accuracy of the instrument equal slits are ensured. A grating–prism monochromator will, of course, have three slits but only the entrance and exit slits of the grating part need to be considered. The results apply equally well to prism monochromators. When one slit is opened with respect to the other, two things happen: firstly, energy is increased, which may be welcomed, and secondly, the resolution is impaired. These effects will be considered separately.

(a) Energy We assume a continuous source with uniform energy distribution over a small wavelength range. We can therefore imagine an infinite number of monochromatic images of the entrance slit spread across the exit slit. Limiting wavelengths for this slit are λ_1 and λ_4 (see Fig. II, 31(a)). Between λ_1 and λ_2 energy E will increase linearly with wavelength as shown in Fig. II, 31(c), remain constant between λ_2 and λ_3, and decrease linearly between λ_3 and λ_4. The wavelength spread is proportional to s_1+s_2 and the energy passing through the exit slit is proportional to the area of the curve,

i.e. $\propto s_1$. But E is also obviously proportional to s_2, so that we may write $E \propto s_1 s_2$.

When s_1 is smaller than s_2, the conditions are as shown in Fig. II, 31(b) and the energy distribution is indicated in Fig. II, 31(d). Again, the energy

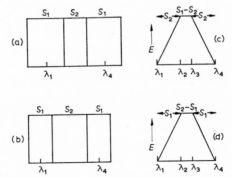

Fig. II, 31. Energy available when slits are unequal: (a), $s_1 > s_2$, and (b), $s_1 < s_2$.

passing through the exit slit is proportional to the area of the curve, *i.e.* to s_2, and since it must also be proportional to the entrance slit, $E \propto s_1 s_2$ as before.

Beyond the point where the condensed image of the exit slit is wide enough to fill the receiving element of the detector, there is no gain in opening the exit slit further, but energy continues to increase in proportion as the entrance slit is opened.

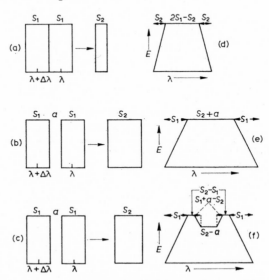

Fig. II, 32. Conditions for limiting resolution when: (a), $s_1 > s_2$, and (b) and (c), $s_1 < s_2$.

(b) Resolution   In order to determine the smallest resolvable interval, two cases may be considered as before:

(a) Entrance slit s_1 > exit slit s_2. In Fig. II, 32(a) two monochromatic images of s_1, corresponding to wavelengths λ and $\lambda+\Delta\lambda$, adjoin, and as these images traverse the exit slit the variation of energy will be as shown in Fig. II, 32(d). This is the limiting condition, since any separation of the two images will enable the wavelengths to be clearly resolved. Therefore $\Delta\lambda$ is proportional to s_1 and is independent of s_2.

(b) Entrance slit s_1 < exit slit s_2. Here we imagine the two monochromatic images of s_1 to be separated by a space a and in Fig. II, 32(b), $s_2 = (s_1+a)$. Fig. II, 32(e) shows that the wavelengths are not resolved, but as soon as s_2 is made less than (s_1+a), Fig. II, 32(c), the presence of two separate wavelengths is shown, Fig. II, 32(f). The limiting condition is $s_2 = s_1+a$ and since $\Delta\lambda \propto s_1+a$, it follows that $\Delta\lambda \propto s_2$.

The general rule is that when the slits are unequal, $\Delta\lambda$ is determined solely by the larger of the two.

(vi) Loss of resolution due to curvature of spectral image

When a curved image falls on an exit slit which is straight or incorrectly curved some loss of resolution is inevitable. It is not easy to evaluate the effect in general terms and a concrete example is helpful in assessing its magnitude. Suppose that the slits are 10×0.125 mm and that the radius of curvature of the image (R) is 10 cm. In the diagrammatic representation, Fig. II, 33, BC = AB and maximum energy (in this case 75 per cent of

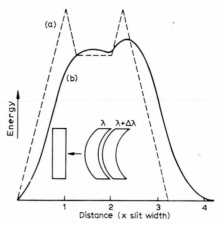

Fig. II, 33. Position for maximum energy when curved image
falls on straight exit slit.

Fig. II, 34. Impairment of resolution with curved images on
straight exit slit.

that obtained with a straight image) passes through the slit when DE is equal to half the slit height.

References pp. 82–84

The effect of curved images on resolution is illustrated in Fig. II, 34(b). Suppose that two monochromatic images of equal energy and differing slightly in wavelength, whose centres are spaced apart $0.125 \times 5/4$ mm, traverse the slit in succession, the transmitted energy being plotted as a function of distance. Comparison with the related curve for straight images similarly spaced is instructive. With straight images two wavelengths can just be resolved when their spacing slightly exceeds 0.125 mm, and with an additional separation of $(0.125/4)$ mm a well-defined doublet is obtained, Fig. II, 34(a). With the curved images, on the other hand, this same separation only just suffices to resolve the bands, and slits of $0.125 \times 5/4$ mm with straight images are about as effective, in this particular case, as slits of 0.125 mm with curved images. The unsymmetrical appearance of the energy curve in (b) may also be noted.

For any spectrometer having a prism or a grating, the situation outlined is reproduced when $s = 1/8\,R$, where s (slitwidth) and R are both given in cm (slit length $= 1$ cm).

(2G) Single-beam operation

(i) Single-beam radiation unit

The assembly of components needed by any monochromator for directing radiation into the entrance slit is conveniently called the Radiation Unit.

Essential components are the radiation source (draught free), a condensing system to form an image of the source on the entrance slit and, in order to produce an alternating signal from the detector, a synchronously driven rotating sector interrupting the radiation at a constant frequency, usually about 10 cycles per second. Some means for introducing gas, liquid or solid samples into the radiation path is required, and occasionally other items such as reflecting microscope, polarizer or reflectance attachment are accommodated.

A single spherical mirror forming an image of the Nernst on the slit brings the source uncomfortably close to the slit and is rarely used. Adding a plane mirror (see Fig. II, 35) overcomes this disadvantage and the region

Fig. II, 35. Simple optical system for use with single-beam spectrometer.

AS is available for the sample. A 10-cm gas cell may usually be employed; for considerably longer path lengths some form of multi-reflection cell (see page 76) may be used.

A primary focus can be provided (Fig. II, 36) and liquid and solid samples mounted at this point give minimum scatter. Fig. II, 36(a) reduces the focussed image to half size or less so that quite small samples may be examined, while the arrangement of Fig. II, 36(b) enables fairly long gas

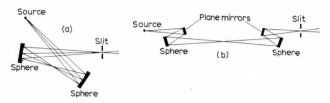

Fig. II, 36. Source and optics for single-beam operation.

cells, say 20 cm, to be accommodated. Two spherical mirrors can be so arranged that the second one partially neutralizes aberrations caused by the first (Fig. II, 37). The rule is that beams 1 and 2 reflected from mirrors M_1 and M_2 should be on the same side of the primary focus. For accurate

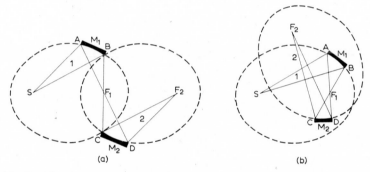

Fig. II, 37. Combinations of pairs of spherical mirrors giving more (a) or less (b) aberration.

images M_1 and M_2 should strictly be ellipsoidal (as illustrated) and S and F_1 are the foci of one ellipse while F_1 and F_2 are the foci of a second mirror of similar form. In (a) the radius of curvature at A is clearly greater than at B and greater at D than at C. Thus the ray SA first strikes a less strongly curved part of mirror M_1 and then a less strongly curved part of mirror M_2. Consequently two spherical mirrors will be a poor substitute for the two ellipsoids. Conversely in (b), ray SA after striking a less strongly curved part of mirror M_1 strikes a more strongly curved part of mirror M_2 at D. In consequence, spherical mirrors with a curvature halfway between the values for M_1 at A and M_2 at D will give an acceptable final image at F_2.

Some manufactures, notably Perkin–Elmer, use toroidal mirrors in their optical systems in place of sphericals. These mirrors have different radii of curvature in the horizontal and vertical planes and so give some lateral condensation when forming an image on a spectrometer slit. This property is particularly useful when the wider refractory sources (see page 29) are employed.

(ii) Optical arrangement for maximum signal

In any condensing system there is some choice regarding the size of image formed at the monochromator slit and it is of interest to determine the condition for passing maximum energy through the slit. It is supposed that there is no restriction on size of source but that the surface brightness is constant whatever the size. Two situations arise: (a) collimator more than filled and (b) collimator partly filled. Assuming that the entrance slit has constant dimensions, $a \times b$, and that the Nernst image is always larger than the slit, it follows that the energy collected by the collimator is proportional to A_2/f^2 in the first case and A_1/v^2 in the second (Fig. II, 38(a), (b)). As v is re-

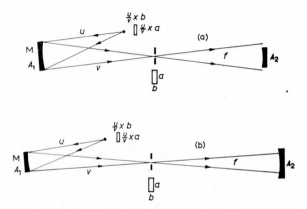

Fig. II, 38. Energy for different condensing arrangements.

duced the energy increases, until the collimator is filled when $A_2/f^2 = A_1/v^2$.

It does not matter how many mirrors are interposed between the source and the slit, provided that each mirror in turn is large enough to intercept the whole of the incident beam.

(2H) Double-beam operation

(i) Some double-beam systems

Fig. II, 39 shows the optical arrangements employed in three commonly used systems. In each case radiation is taken from the source and split into two paths, sample and reference, and some form of beam switching is employed to focus alternately radiation from the two paths onto the entrance slit of the monochromator. A switching frequency between 10 and 20 c/s is usual. If the sample absorbs, say 50 per cent of incident radiation at a given wavelength, then the radiation falling on the detector may be

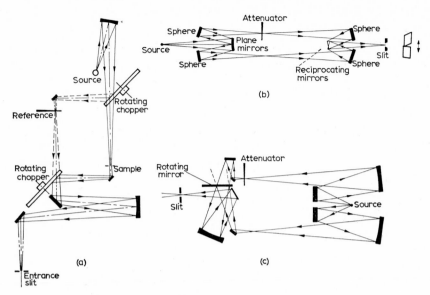

Fig. II, 39. Double-beam optical systems:
(a) Beckman IR7
(b) Grubb Parsons DB1
(c) Perkin-Elmer 421.

represented diagrammatically as shown in Fig. II, 40. The steady component of the output signal from the detector is ignored by the a.c. amplifier, while the alternating component is amplified and fed to a servomotor which varies the position of a comb or other attenuator in the reference path. The intensity of the comparison beam is steadily reduced until the two beams

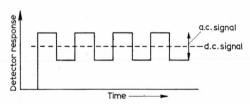

Fig. II, 40. Idealized response from detector of double-beam spectrometer.

are made equal, at which point the alternating output from the detector becomes zero and the servomotor comes to rest. The attenuator at this point reduces the beam energy to 50 per cent to balance the energy in the sample path. It is of course essential to have a linear relation between energy transmitted and attenuator position, and to obtain a complete spectrum it is only necessary to record attenuator position as the wavelength or frequency is varied.

While the comb provides a simple means of balancing the two beams there are objections to it. If the comb is imaged sharply on the detector, discontinuities will occur as images of individual teeth pass on or off the ends of the detector. This effect can be minimized by avoiding a sharp image of the comb on the detector and by increasing the number of teeth, although some compromise on both counts is necessary in practice.

In the Unicam Model SP100 a rotating starwheel moves in and out of the beam and this avoids the difficulties associated with a comb. In the Hilger Model H800 and the Perkin–Elmer Model 125 an aperture diaphragm is used: while this method is extremely simple it assumes uniform intensity over the area of the beam of radiation.

Fig. II, 39(b) shows a pair of oscillating plane mirrors employed for beam switching, and radiation is taken from closely adjacent areas of the radiation source. In Fig. II, 39(c) different areas of the source are also used but in Fig. II, 39(a) the same area is employed for both beams — a desirable feature.

In future a completely electronic method of determining the energy ratio of the two beams will probably become standard: in fact the Cary–White Model 90 does this. Sample and reference beams are chopped at two different frequencies, 13.1/3 and 26.2/3 c/s, respectively, and tuned circuits give separate signals proportional to energy in the sample beam, I, and in the reference beam, I_0. After rectification and smoothing the ratio of the two voltages may be obtained by using a potentiometric recorder.

Another possibility is to interrupt both beams at the same frequency but in such a manner that energy is received from the two paths alternately with complete obscuration between consecutive exposures. The resulting signal is shown diagrammatically in Fig. II, 41: the signal waveform is the

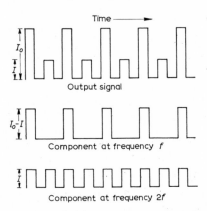

Fig. II, 41. Waveform with obscuration between consecutive exposures.

sum of two components, (I_0-I) at the repetition frequency f and I at frequency $2f$. For a square-wave the signal of frequency f has amplitude

$(I_0-I)\sqrt{2}/\pi$ while that of frequency $2f$ has amplitude $(I_0+I)/\pi$, including the second harmonic of (I_0-I). After amplification and electronic processing, d.c. signals proportional to (I_0-I) and (I_0+I) are obtained. Appropriate circuitry then gives a voltage proportional to the ratio I/I_0. This result applies not only to a square wave but to other more realistic waveforms.

(ii) Operation of servo system

When using a double-beam spectrometer some understanding of the characteristics of a typical servo system is desirable. A simplified analysis of such a system leads to the equation $f = (K_1 V/J)^{\frac{1}{2}}$, where f is its natural frequency, V the so-called loop-gain, which measures the amount of drive per unit error in position of the comb attenuator in the reference beam, J the moment of inertia of the moving parts and K_1 a constant. V is proportional to the product of slit width and amplifier gain and when it is greater than a critical value, given by the relation $V = K_2 K_3^2/J$ (K_3 is the tachometer constant in volt seconds and K_2 is another constant), the servo system oscillates at frequency f. It is then necessary to reduce the slit width and/or the gain until V falls to the critical value, while if reduced still further the response becomes increasingly sluggish and a low recording speed must be used with ample time for the true spectrum to be obtained. (The tachometer generates a damping voltage proportional to the servo-motor speed).

(3) Accessories

Useful information on spectrometer accessories is obtainable from two recent textbooks, by Brügel and by Willis and Miller, while an earlier text by Norman Jones and Sandorfy will be found of considerable value. These works[39] may be consulted when necessary to augment the brief details which follow.

(3A) Absorption cells

(i) Gas cells

The standard type of gas cell is made from glass tubing of suitable diameter and wall thickness about 2 mm, with its ends ground and polished accurately square to the axis of the tube. Threaded brass rings are cemented onto the ends of the tube, windows of NaCl or other material, 5 mm thick, are placed in position and metal caps internally threaded are screwed on the metal rings to hold the windows firmly in position. A cork washer is interposed between the metal cap and the window to prevent breakage, and a minute trace of grease is applied to the polished ends of the tube prior to assembly to ensure gas tightness. A glass tap is provided for filling, the normal

procedure being to evacuate the cell, test for leaks, and admit the desired
gas to the pressure required. If windows are not accurately square to the
axis of the tube, the image on the monochromator slit may be displaced
and the results seriously impaired. This effect is particularly noticeable
with the thick windows commonly used for gas cells.

Germanium and silicon windows are now available for gas cells. These
materials transmit beyond 1.7 and 1μ, respectively, and may be bloomed
for high transmission in any desired spectral region to at least 20μ.

An inexpensive cell is shown in Fig. II, 42. Thin polythene sheet is used

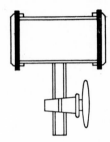

Fig. II, 42. Inexpensive gas cell.

as a window material and is held in position by rubber O rings. Such cells[40]
are useful for containing gases used for checking wavelength calibration.

(ii) Heated gas cell

When a heated cell is required this is conveniently obtained by winding a
heating tape round the body of a standard gas cell. If necessary, a metal
tube somewhat longer than the cell and slightly larger in diameter may
be cut longitudinally into halves which are placed round the cell body and
held in position by the heating tape. The most reliable method for attaching
windows is to clamp them in position using P.T.F.E. or lead gaskets.

(iii) Liquid cells

(a) Simple type Liquid cells may be made from rectangular or circular
plates, but the latter have the important advantage that it is easier to
ensure dimensional accuracy and circular spacing washers are more readily
made than rectangular ones. The standard diameter is one inch.

The simplest cell consists of two circular plates of NaCl or other material
spaced apart by means of a metal washer. Its main disadvantage is that
the thickness is not accurately known. It can be roughly determined by
measuring the thickness of the material from which the spacer is made, or,
rather better, by measuring with a micrometer the thickness of the two
windows separately before assembly and then the overall thickness after
completion.

It is sometimes possible to estimate the cell thickness by weighing the components before filling and then weighing the completed cell.

With samples which absorb intensely it may be difficult to obtain sufficiently thin washers to give an appropriately short path length. In such cases it is possible to dispense with a spacer and use a capillary film between the plates.

(b) Semi-permanent cells (demountable type) This type also consists of 1 inch windows but in one of them two small holes are drilled and tapped, and brass filling tubes are screwed into the holes, small gaskets of P.T.F.E. being used to make a liquid-tight seal. Filling and cleaning with suitable solvent are effected with a hypodermic syringe fitted with a large needle, 1 mm diameter and ground at the tip to a cone.

While it is possible to dismantle these cells and change the spacer, it is better practice to have several made up with spacers of different thickness.

(c) Spacing washers The cell thickness may commonly vary from 0.01 to several mm. Lead washers are useful for thicknesses between 0.05 and 0.8 mm; aluminium foil may be employed for thicknesses below 0.05 mm while P.T.F.E. is suitable for spacers 1 mm and over. Pure gold is sometimes used when an inert material is required. An excellent seal is made by using a ridged lead washer of the form shown in Fig. II, 43. It is not advis-

Fig. II, 43. Cross section of ridged lead washer (exaggerated).

able to use the washer a second time since its sealing propertiers are largely lost after the ridges have been compressed.

Long cells for liquids can be of a pattern similar to those used for gases.

(d) Variable path cells The modern cell of this type has been developed from that described by GORDON and POWELL[41]. It consists of two main parts, an internally threaded cylindrical portion carrying a window at one end, and a similar slightly smaller part also provided with a window and threaded externally so as to screw into the first member. The distance apart of the windows is indicated on a scale engraved on the outer surface of the cell. A very popular cell of this type is manufactured by Research and Industrial Instruments Company Ltd.[46].

(e) Cell for volatile liquids The usual type of cell is unsuitable for liquids of low boiling point and a modification described by WILLIS and MILLER[39] may be used. The cell is provided with two small bore filling tubes, one above the other, and these communicate with a glass reservoir charged with the liquid to be investigated. The top of the reservoir terminates in a tap which is finally closed to prevent evaporation.

(f) Measurement of cell thickness   When the windows of a cell are sufficiently flat and parallel to one another, interference fringes may be observed when the transmittance of the empty cell is measured in a spectrometer as a function of wavelength. These interference bands may be used[42] to measure the cell thickness t, the relation being $t = n\lambda_1\lambda_2/2(\lambda_2-\lambda_1)$, where n is the number of maxima (or minima) between the wavelengths λ_1 and λ_2.

(iv) Heated cell

In one design a rectangular shape is adopted and a small heater provided on each side of the cell. A thermocouple determines the temperature, and thermostatic control may be applied if desired. Thermal radiations from the heated cell must be allowed for. In a double-beam instrument the energy received from the sample is the sum of that radiated from its surface and that transmitted from the Nernst. This total energy is balanced against the Nernst radiation transmitted by the comb attenuator. At a particular wavelength we have

$$\alpha E_\lambda + f(T, \lambda) = \alpha' E_\lambda$$

where E_λ is the radiation of wavelength between λ and $\lambda+\Delta\lambda$ received from the Nernst, α the transmittance of the sample, α' the transmittance of the comb and $f(T, \lambda)$ the energy radiated from the sample and cell at temperature T. It follows that $\alpha = \alpha' - f(T, \lambda)/E_\lambda$ and if a black body at the same temperature is placed in the reference beam in a position corresponding to that of the sample, so that the radiation from it is transmitted by the comb, radiation from the Nernst being cut off, $f(T, \lambda)$ for the sample may be determined. The emission from the Nernst must also be measured for accurate results.

Single-beam measurements are more straightforward since E_λ, $\alpha E_\lambda + f(T, \lambda)$ and $f(T, \lambda)$ may be measured in succession at a given wavelength, *i.e.* with sample out of the beam, heated sample in the beam, and Nernst energy cut off, respectively.

(v) Low temperature cell

Details of a useful cell are given by WILLIS and MILLER[39], the construction being based on a demountable Dewar with the cell inside the evacuated space at the lower part of the vessel, windows being provided in the outer wall to permit passage of radiation.

Radiation errors occur with cooled cells just as with heated ones since now the detector radiates more energy to the cold sample than it receives. Corrections may be applied in similar ways to those suggested for the heated cell.

(vi) Microcells

The design of most microcells follows obvious lines. If to be placed at a focus, two plates of NaCl or other material separated by a washer of amalgamated lead or gold foil may form the cell, a rectangle, say, 10×1 mm, having been removed from the foil to accommodate the sample. Capillaries drilled through one plate and communicating with the two ends of the sample area are used for filling, a hypodermic syringe needle being used for the purpose. Sealing plugs of stainless steel may be employed.

Research and Industrial Instruments Company markets several different varieties of this type of cell with spacing washers varying from 0.007 to 2 mm. The minimum volume of such a cell is 0.07 mm³, equivalent to $70\mu g$ of sample approximately. By sacrificing some energy the cell area can be reduced to 5×1 mm and $35\mu g$ of sample will then suffice.

Another type of cell, marketed by Connecticut Instrument Corporation, depends on cavities formed in infra-red transparent materials. These cells have been described by JONES and NADEAU[43].

· The sample area can be reduced very considerably if one employs a beam condenser (see page 74). With a 5 to 1 linear reduction, a cell may be made by drilling a 1 mm hole in a flat piece of stainless steel 1 mm thick, and cementing on either side a thin window, fine capillaries being drilled through the metal spacer from either side into the sample region to provide a means of filling. With a one per cent solution, $10\mu g$ of sample can be made to yield a spectrum with such a cell.

The use of tiny capillary tubes as microcells has been advocated, and silver chloride[44] and polythene[45] have been suggested as suitable materials. With a capillary 0.075 mm bore filled with sample over a length of 1 mm, only $5\mu g$ of sample is required, and with some dilution 1 μg can be made to give an acceptable spectrum. While optical conditions appear favourable

Fig. II, 44. Passage of rays through capillary cell when in correct position.

in Fig. II, 44, they are not so fortunate in the vertical plane and a considerable loss of energy must be accepted when using capillary tubes.

(3B) Window materials

A fair range of transparent materials is available for infra-red windows and a good criterion for the limit of usefulness is to take the wavelength at which the transmittance of a 5 mm layer drops to 50 per cent. Details of suitable materials are summarized in Table II, 9.

TABLE II, 9

LONGWAVE LIMIT FOR VARIOUS WINDOW MATERIALS

(~ 50 % transmittance for 5 mm Layer)

Material	Wavelength, μ
Glass	$\sim$ 2.5
Silica	3.6
LiF	6.7
CaF$_2$	10
BaF$_2$	13
NaCl	18
KBr	30
CsBr	40
CsI	$\sim$ 50

Germanium and silicon are useful to at least 20μ but need to be bloomed (see page 47) to reduce the high reflection loss. While a $\lambda/4$ layer is easily applied at low wavelengths, at 20μ much greater difficulty is experienced.

(3C) Miscellaneous items

(i) Device for checking linearity of transmittance scale

A satisfactory device for checking linearity is a rotating sector of known transmittance placed in the sample beam. A fairly high speed of rotation is desirable, 2000 to 3000 r.p.m., and a d.c. motor must be used to avoid any possibility of the chopper running in synchronism with the beam switcher. Two equal symmetrical openings in the rotating disc help by giving better balance and a higher chopping frequency.

(ii) Reflectance attachment

Fig. II, 45 shows the optical arrangement employed for use with Grubb Parsons instruments when reflectance measurements are to be made.

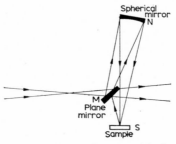

Fig. II, 45. Reflectance attachment for use with double-beam spectrometer.

Radiation which normally would focus in the sample area is diverted by one surface of plane mirror M to the spherical mirror N and forms an image on the surface S to be investigated; from the second surface of M it continues along its original path. The specimen must be reasonably flat to avoid undue loss of energy and is located by being held against two stops.

(iii) Reflecting microscope

A correctly designed combination of two spherical mirrors makes a very effective microscope objective for use in infra-red spectroscopy. An exactly similar mirror pair condenses radiation from the Nernst onto the sample at S (Fig. II, 46) and a 1 : 1 image of the source is finally thrown on the slit of the

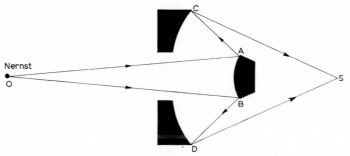

Fig. II, 46. Microscope objective or condenser employing spherical mirrors.

monochromator. The image reduction at S is determined approximately by the ratio of the angles CSD and AOB. The former rarely exceeds 60° in practice but the latter can be made as small as desired, although it must be realised that energy entering the monochromator will be greatly reduced since it is proportional to the square of angle AOB. Objectives of this type lose much energy, particularly by obscuration of the beam by the small mirror. A further loss is caused by the sample, for rays at high incident angles are appreciably reflected. An overall transmission of 50 per cent is regarded as quite satisfactory.

An average monochromator may have an aperture of about $f/5$, and then a reduction of sample size of 5 to 1 (25 to 1 in area) makes full use of the aperture of the instrument; a 10 to 1 ratio would reduce the energy available to one quarter. If w is the width of sample which when magnified m times by the objective just fills a slit of width s, then available energy is proportional to s^2/m^2 for $m > 5$, and since $w \times m = s$, the energy is proportional to w^2. Since a certain minimum energy is required for efficient operation, w ultimately reaches a constant minimum value which is independent of the magnification m.

Fig. II, 47 shows a reflecting microscope incorporated in a double-beam system. The sample beam usually passes through a focus at S and by using four plane mirrors M_1, M_2, M_3 and M_4 and the microscope unit O, O', the focus is transferred to S' and the micro sample may be mounted at this point. There is an enlarged sample image on the entrance slit and a white screen at the slit will allow any desired portion of the sample area to be selected for spectroscopic examination. Focussing is conveniently carried out by mounting the units on two parallel rods of circular section and sliding them backwards and forwards.

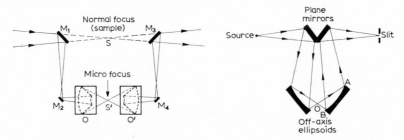

Fig. II, 47. Application of reflecting microscope to double-beam spectrometer.

Fig. II, 48. Reflecting microscope using two off-axis ellipsoids.

An alternative design of microscope by Perkin–Elmer uses two off-axis ellipsoidal mirrors, Fig. II, 48: they are replicas moulded from a convex master. A disadvantage of this system is that the magnification changes considerably as the ray path changes from AO to BO.

Yet another beam condenser employs two potassium bromide lenses in place of mirror optics. A condensation of 3.5 to 4 times is obtained and a transmission of 60 to 70 per cent between 2.5 and 15μ is claimed[46].

(iv) Absorbance presentation

Most double-beam spectrometers record transmittance, T, or absorption $(1-T)$ as ordinate, but the spectrum changes shape with the quantity of absorbing material. This difficulty is eliminated by plotting absorbance or optical density, $\log_{10} 1/T$, as ordinate, and since the absorbance, A, is equal to $a\,b\,c$ (Beer's law), where a is the absorptivity of the sample, b the length of absorbing path and c the concentration of absorbing material, A is directly proportional to the amount of sample; all spectra of a given compound will therefore differ only by an ordinate scale factor. For analytical purposes the total absorbance A_n is the sum of separate contributions from different molecular species, so that $A_n = A_1 + A_2 + \ldots$

Where a servo system maintains an optical null, a specially wound potentiometer giving a d.c. voltage proportional to $\log_{10} 1/T$ as T varies from 1 to 0, can be attached to the balancing mechanism. Usually the absorbance range 0 to 1 (transmittance range 1 to 0.1) corresponds to full scale on the output recorder.

(v) Ordinate scale expansion

The photometric accuracy of a well-designed double-beam spectrometer when there is no energy limitation can be 1 part in 4000. This makes scale expansion practicable in favourable circumstances. Scale expansion may be usefully employed to increase the size of small — 2 or 3 per cent — absorption bands to at least half scale on the recorder. With an expansion of 20:1 the accuracy is only reduced to 1 part in 200. The uncertainty of reading with scale expansion applied, *i.e.* the difference between two readings obtained by balancing first from an up-scale position of the pen and then from a down-scale position, divided by the scale expansion factor, serves to check the original estimate of 1 in 4000.

Ordinate expansion is now available on a number of instruments, the usual factors being $\times 2$, $\times 5$, $\times 10$ and $\times 20$. The servo-balancing system is coupled to a potentiometer and a voltage picked off proportional to the transmittance or absorbance of the sample. The former voltage, for example, may be separately recorded to produce a duplicate spectrum or, after backing off if necessary, applied at a suitable level to the recorder so that any part of the transmittance scale, say 100 to 95 or 50 to 45 per cent, may correspond to full scale on the recorder.

Another method of expansion is to use a comb attenuator with nearly parallel teeth so that its full transmittance range is 100 to 90 or 100 to 80 per cent. Such combs are rather troublesome to make and the change they cause in servo-system characteristics must be allowed for.

(vi) Integrator

The main advantages of integrated spectra ('staircase' presentation) are that the area of an absorption band becomes the height of a step, *i.e.* the difference between ordinates at two chosen wavelengths, and the reduction in noise which is automatically obtained[47]. The ordinate scale should of course be in absorbance and not transmittance. The area of a band is also independent, to some extent, of the resolution of the spectrometer used.

Two main types of integrator are available, a velocity-servo computing arrangement described by Perkin–Elmer[48], and a simpler electronic device manufactured by W. G. Pye & Co. Ltd. and known as an integrating amplifier. Further information may be obtained from these manufacturers.

(vii) Polarizer

Crystals or any specimens with an appreciable degree of internal orientation exhibit dichroism in the infra-red region, and spectra obtained with polarized light can confirm the assignment of absorption bands to particular group vibrations, etc. [See Chapter VIII].

The most commonly used polarizer consists of several thin silver chloride plates mounted at the polarizing angle (Brewster angle) and placed at a convenient point in the optical path, usually in front of the monochromator slit or near a focus.

One of the best transmission polarizers is probably that described by ELLIOTT *et al.*[49], which employs a pile of selenium films each of 4μ thickness. Five films produce between 94 and 100 per cent polarization between 2 and 14μ. Unfortunately, this polarizer is too fragile for general use.

To obtain good efficiency the polarizing material must have a high refractive index (silver chloride 2.0 and selenium 2.54) but this requires a large angle of incidence, 60 to 70°, and leads to a rather bulky unit.

But for polarization effects in the spectrometer, the dichroic ratio could be measured by placing the sample in the spectrometer with its axis of orientation vertical and recording the spectrum twice, once with the plane of polarization vertical and again with the plane horizontal. Unfortunately, with grating spectrometers in particular, the optical system already produces marked polarization, especially over one fairly narrow wavelength region for each grating[50].

In the ideal case the dichroic ratio R_D is given as A_π/A_σ, *i.e.* the absorbance with electric vector parallel to axis of orientation divided by the absorbance with electric vector perpendicular to axis of orientation. Instrumental effects can be minimized by taking certain precautions[39] but measurement of the true dichroic ratio is quite difficult.

(viii) Long-path cell and small volume gas cell

Thanks to the work of WHITE[51] attractive forms of multi-reflection gas cell are now available. A compact form suitable for use with standard double-

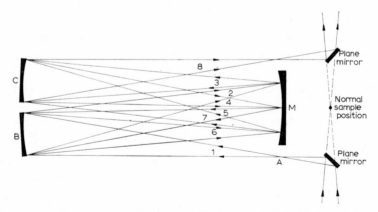

Fig. II, 49. Multi-reflection cell (8 traversals) for use with double-beam spectrometer.

beam spectrometers is shown in Fig. II, 49 and consists essentially of three spherical mirrors, having the same radius of curvature and spaced apart a distance equal to the radius. Starting with an image of the Nernst at A, a

succession of images is formed across mirror M which need only be sufficiently large to accept an image length to match the monochromator slit.
The apertures of the other mirrors should be comparable with the aperture
of the monochromator. By symmetrically tilting mirrors B and C the
number of traversals can be changed.

Multi-reflection cells have at least two valuable applications:

(a) Determination of contaminants in air and other gases (less than one
part per million in volume). The sensitivity can be increased when required
by pressurizing the cell and a ten-fold gain presents no difficulty.

(b) Recording vapour spectra of many organic compounds at a moderate
temperature (up to 100° C). A pressure of 10 mm or less in a 1 m path is
sufficient in most cases.

A good account of multi-reflection cells is given by STEPHENS[52] who
describes 3 m cells with path lengths up to 216 m. The optimum path for
maximum gas sensitivity is reached when reflection losses reduce the
energy to $1/e$ of its initial value. Uncoated aluminium reflectors gave the
best results, the reflection coefficient being 0.975 between 2 and 10μ.

(4) Experimental Methods and Techniques

(4A) Sample preparation

In analytical work a fair amount of time goes in processing samples so that
good spectra may be obtained. Gases and most organic liquids present
little difficulty, but solids and aqueous solutions, for example, require
special handling which will be described in this section. WILLIS and MILLER[39]
give useful information on intractable solids, *e.g.* rubbery materials and
insoluble resins.

(i) Solutions in organic solvents

Examining a substance in solution is a very important method in infra-red
work and, in principle, it is almost of universal application since most
compounds are soluble in some solvent. Drawbacks arise since all solvents
have some absorption bands in the infra-red region and frequently non-
absorbing solvents will not dissolve the material to be examined. Details of
many solvents are given in the textbooks mentioned[39]. CCl_4 and CS_2 between
them cover the whole range 2 to 15 μ but unfortunately are poor solvents
for many compounds. Chloroform and bromoform are useful since they are
transparent from 4 to 8μ where it is otherwise difficult to find a satisfactory
solvent. Some solvents, *e.g.* CCl_4, may be rapidly dried by bubbling dry air
(P_2O_5 or from liquid air) through the liquid. Heated cells (see page 70) are
useful when the solubility is too small at room temperature.

Since many organic compounds absorb intensely in the infra-red, a very small pathlength is needed when dealing with pure substances. This reduces the accuracy of quantitative measurements since not only must the pathlength be carefully measured but any variation over the cell area must be avoided. A solution allows the path to be increased to 1 mm or more and quantitative accuracy is much improved. Solvent effects must of course be looked for and both frequency and intensity changes of bands are common (see Chapter XII).

The difference technique (see page 81) is applicable to solutions, solvent absorption being eliminated to a large extent by placing a cell filled with pure solvent in the reference path. A variable path cell is best used for the solvent and a semi-permanent cell for the solution. Interactions will sometimes prevent complete cancellation for the whole spectrum. However, this technique is very useful and is even applicable to a limited extent to aqueous solutions. It is vitally important to ensure that sufficient energy is transmitted throughout the wavelength range recorded. It is possible to operate even when solvent absorption is more than 90 per cent provided adequate servo drive is available. Steps to be taken are: open up slits if the energy is too low; increase amplifier gain; check balance of servo system with radiation cut off; scan slowly, if necessary, to allow more time for recording bands where the energy is low. Compensation by having solvent in the reference beam allows the solution pathlength to be much increased, with consequent improved sensitivity at low concentrations.

(ii) Aqueous solutions

The intense absorption by water throughout much of the infra-red region seriously restricts the use of aqueous solutions and, in addition, many of the usual window materials are ruled out because of their solubility. Calcium fluoride is usable to 9μ while the rather fragile barium fluoride extends the range to 12μ. However, silicon and germanium windows, bloomed to reduce the reflection loss, are now becoming available and the window situation has become much easier. Various grades of Irtran manufactured by Kodak are also obtainable.

To obtain useful spectra, use of a double-beam spectrometer is essential, so that water absorption can be carefully cancelled out. From the visible to 2.5μ, relatively long pathlength glass cells can be used but elsewhere it is impracticable to exceed 0.075 mm. Usable regions are 3.5 to 5.8μ (2860 to 1720 cm^{-1}) and 6.5 to 10.5μ (1540 to 950 cm^{-1}) for H_2O and 4.7 to 8μ (2130 to 1250 cm^{-1}) and 8.8μ onwards (below 1140 cm^{-1}) for the rather more transparent D_2O. At 9μ, 0.075 mm of H_2O transmits only 2 per cent of the incident radiation and it is therefore necessary to employ a spectrometer with negligible stray light. A low resolution grating instrument is best for this type of work since the low transmittance can be off-set by opening the slits wide.

The solute concentration must exceed one per cent in water; pH variation may assist.

Small quantities of water in other liquids can often be determined by using the 1.4 and 1.9μ water absorption bands; bands near 2.7μ are also useful.

Useful reviews of the spectroscopy of aqueous solutions have been given by STERNGLANZ[53] and by GOULDEN[54].

(iii) Alkali halide discs

In this method about 1 mg of finely ground sample is mixed thoroughly into 200 mg of a suitable alkali halide of high purity, say KBr. The mixture is further ground and a transparent disc is made by placing a suitable quantity in a 15 mm diameter die (Fig. II, 50) provided with a highly polished flat

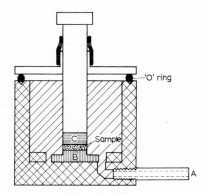

Fig. II, 50. Die for alkali halide discs.

anvil, B, inserting a similar platen, C, and finally applying a force of about ten tons on the platen. Either a hand operated screw or a hydraulic press may be used, and after about a minute the die can be taken apart and the KBr disc removed. Points to be noted are the evacuation of the die through A to remove water vapour, which if trapped in the disc causes it to break up, and fine grinding of the sample material. The KBr powder must be dried in an oven at 110° C. This technique, introduced by SCHIEDT and REINWEIN[55] and by STIMSON and O'DONNELL[56], is extremely useful, but spectra are not always consistent and sometimes marked peculiarities are encountered. FARMER[57] has instanced peculiar spectra obtained under stated conditions and demonstrated that grinding, in excess of five minutes, can lead to abnormal spectra.

Dies making alkali halide discs of much smaller diameter, down to 0.5 mm, can be obtained. These minute discs are, of course, used with a microscope (see p. 74).

(iv) Liquid mulls — internal standard

A spectrum of a solid material can be obtained by adding a drop of medicinal paraffin to a little finely ground sample, and placing some of the slurry between transparent plates with or without a thin spacing washer. Paraffin has a few absorption bands due to ($>$ CH_2) and ($-CH_3$) groups but much of the range 2 to 15μ is relatively free from absorption. The paraffin greatly reduces the scatter of radiation which the powder would give. The closer the refractive indices of paraffin and solid the smaller the scatter. As the wavelength increases the scatter also diminishes rapidly. As bands of interest may be obliterated by those of paraffin, a fully fluorinated hydrocarbon, 'Fluorolube', or other hydrogen-free liquid can replace it. To avoid anomalous scattering effects the sample material should be ground to a fineness such that the wavelength exceeds the average particle size.

Quantitative accuracy with liquid mulls is poor but may be improved by mixing with the solid a known proportion of a suitable material, *e.g.* lead thiocyanate. This is a useful internal standard since its sharp, intense band at 4.9μ (2040 cm^{-1}) will estimate the amount of solid in the optical path.

(v) Preparation from melt

Thin layers of low melting point solids may be prepared by melting a small quantity between transparent windows on a hot plate. Synthetic polymers will in many cases flow into thin layers if pressed at a sufficiently high temperature.

(vi) Casting from solution

A solution of the sample may be poured over a horizontal plate of glass or infra-red transparent material in an oven. After solvent evaporation a thin film remains and, if it is a polymeric substance, may usually be stripped off the glass plate. Alternatively, the film may be examined on the transparent supporting plate.

(vii) Films on reflecting surfaces

A variant of this last technique is to cast the film on a polished piece of flat metal and use the reflection attachment described on page 72. Radiation enters the film, is reflected from the polished plate and the effective thickness is thus doubled.

(viii) Attenuated total reflection

In this method, the sample material is pressed in optical contact with one face of a transparent prism or half-cylinder of suitably high refractive index, so that internal reflection of radiation can take place at the faces in contact.

The reflected radiation is modified by the absorption properties of the sample material and the resulting spectrum resembles that obtained by conventional means. The method was described by FAHRENFORT[58] and ATR units are manufactured by the Connecticut Instrument Corporation and others.

An analogous effect is observed in the microwave region, where it can be studied with comparative ease, and a paper by BRADY, BRICK and PEARSON[59] describes some interesting experiments performed with 3-cm waves.

(ix) Difference spectra

When a small absorption band is used for the determination of a minor component and considerable background absorption also occurs, the obvious step of increasing the pathlength (or concentration of solute in the case of a solution) cannot be carried very far since absorption will approach 100 per cent and spectral details will tend to be lost. If incident radiation I_0 is reduced to I after passage through a length l of absorbing sample,

$$I = I_0\, e^{-kl},$$

where k is proportional to the absorptivity of the sample. We require to find the condition giving the maximum variation in I, ΔI, for a given variation Δk in k, and since

$$dI/dk = -I_0 l\, e^{-kl},$$

sensitivity is a maximum when $kl = 1$ and $I = I_0/e$. It then follows that $\Delta I/I = -\Delta k/k$ and a 1 per cent change in k gives a 1 per cent change in I or a 0.368 per cent change in I_0.

When it is practicable to obtain a material with similar absorption to the sample but without the minor absorption, it is possible to increase the sensitivity of the determination still further by placing an equal pathlength of this substance in the reference beam. $\Delta I/I$ will be directly measured as one per cent on the double-beam chart and is equal to $-l\Delta k$ as before; if l is made twice its former value, the energy will be reduced by a further factor of $1/e$, but *provided that sufficient energy remains*, sensitivity will be doubled.

Closely similar compounds usually have a small frequency difference in

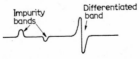

Fig. II, 51. A difference spectrum showing non-identity of two samples.

their absorption bands. If exactly the same amounts of two such compounds are placed in the separate light paths of a double-beam spectrometer, owing to this small frequency difference, differentiation occurs as an absorption band is traversed and the usual differentiated band appears (Fig. II, 51).

If, however, the substances are truly identical, a straight line is recorded. Thus a method is available for proving the absolute identity of two compounds. Even if one of them is not quite pure or dissimilar amounts are used, only small, normally shaped bands will result, but if the differentiated band is found, proof of some constitutional difference is provided.

(x) Derivative spectroscopy

In this form of presentation, instead of plotting absorbance A (or transmittance) against frequency ν (or wavelength), $dA/d\nu$ or $d^2A/d\nu^2$ is plotted against ν. The advantages claimed are that strong, slowly changing background absorption is eliminated while bands are made appreciably sharper. The first derivative of a spectrum is not readily recognisable but the second derivative is similar to the parent spectrum, peaks occurring at the same frequency in the two cases.

If a small band $A_1 = f(\nu)$ is superimposed on a background represented by $A_2 = a+b\nu+c\nu^2$, a, b and c being constants, the total absorbance $A = A_1+A_2$ and $d^2A/d\nu^2 = 2c+f''(\nu)$, so that the effect of the background disappears except for a constant displacement.

A disadvantage of this mode of operation is that any noise present in the signal tends to be amplified with respect to $dA/d\nu$ or $d^2A/d\nu^2$. The technique has been described by several authors [60].

(xi) Reference spectra collections

Most spectroscopists need reference spectra and a number of collections are now available. The more important are listed below:

Sadtler Standard Spectra, ($\sim$20,000), K. G. Heyden, London.

Documentation of Molecular Spectroscopy, ($\sim$7,000), Butterworths Scientific Publications, London.

American Petroleum Institute (Research Project 44), (2,250 hydrocarbons), H. K. Lewis & Co. Ltd., London.

ASTM - Wyandotte Infra-red Cards, (IBM punched cards), American Society for Testing Materials, Philadelphia.

Index of Published Infra-red Spectra, (2 Vols., 10,000 references), Ministry of Aviation, H.M.S.O., London.

REFERENCES

[1] W. W. COBLENTZ, *Investigation of Infra-red Spectra*, Carnegie Inst. Pub., Washington, 1908.
[2] R. W. WOOD AND A. TROWBRIDGE, *Phil. Mag.*, 20 (1910) 770.
[3] W. W. SLEATOR, *Astrophys. J.*, 48 (1918) 125.
[4] A. H. PFUND, *J. Opt. Soc. Am.*, 14 (1927) 337.
[5] H. M. RANDALL, *Rev. Sci. Instr.*, 3 (1932) 196.
[6] F. A. FIRESTONE, *Rev. Sci. Instr.*, 3 (1932) 163.

[7] C. H. CARTWRIGHT, *Z. Physik*, 92 (1934) 153.
   A. H. PFUND, *Rev. Sci. Instr.* 8 (1937) 417.
[8] E. LEHRER AND K. F. LUFT, *Z. tech. Physik*, 23 (1942) 169.
   E. B. BAKER AND C. D. ROBB, *Rev. Sci. Instr.*, 14 (1943) 362.
   G. B. B. M. SUTHERLAND AND H. W. THOMPSON, *Trans. Faraday Soc.*, 41 (1945) 174.
[9] L. C. ROESS, *Rev. Sci. Instr.*, 16 (1945) 172.
[10] N. WRIGHT AND L. W. HERSCHER, *J. Opt. Soc. Am.*, 37 (1947) 211.
[11] A. E. MARTIN, *Ind. Chemist*, 32 (1956) 379.
[12] D. C. STOCKBARGER, *J. Opt. Soc. Am.*, 14 (1927) 488; *Rev. Sci. Instr.*, 7 (1936) 133; *J. Opt. Soc. Am.*, 39 (1949) 731.
[13] A. WALSH, *Nature*, 167 (1951) 810; *J. Opt. Soc. Am.*, 42 (1952) 94.
[14] J. C. O. ROCHESTER, *Brit. Pat.* 732, 719, appn. date Sept., 1952; *Perkin-Elmer Instrument News*, 7 (1956) 7.
[15] O. LITTROW, *Am. J. Sci.*, 35 (1862) 413.
[16] G. M. SISSON, *Brit. Pat.* 713, 288 (1954).
[17] H. EBERT, *Wied. Ann.*, 38 (1889) 489.
[18] W. G. FASTIE, *J. Opt. Soc. Am.*, 42 (1952) 641.
[19] L. W. HERSCHER, *Rev. Sci. Instr.*, 20 (1949) 833.
   L. GENZEL AND N. NEUROTH, *Z. Physik*, 134 (1953) 127.
[20] R. A. SMITH, F. E. JONES AND R. P. CHASMAR, *Detection and Measurement of Infra-red Radiation*, Oxford University Press, Oxford, 1957.
   T. S. MOSS, in *Advances in Spectroscopy, Vol. I*, ed. H. W. THOMPSON, Interscience Publishers, New York, 1959.
[21] P. BRATT, W. ENGELER, H. LEVINSTEIN, A. MACRAE AND J. PEHEK, *Infrared Phys.*, 1 (1961) 27.
[22] D. F. HORNIG AND B. J. O'KEEFE, *Rev. Sci. Instr.*, 18 (1947) 474.
   R. CLARK JONES, *J. Opt. Soc. Am.*, 43 (1953) 1.
[23] L. HARRIS AND J. K. BEASLEY, *J. Opt. Soc. Am.*, 42 (1952) 134.
[24] W. H. BRATTAIN AND J. A. BECKER, *J. Opt. Soc. Am.*, 36 (1946) 354.
[25] D. H. MARTIN AND D. BLOOR, *Cryogenics*, 1 (1961) 159.
[26] R. DE WAARD AND E. M. WORMSER, *Proc. Inst. Radio Engrs.*, 47 (1959) paper 3.3.3.
[27] F. L. O. WADSWORTH, *Phil. Mag.*, 38 (1894) 137.
[28] H. ROEMER AND R. A. OETJEN, *J. Opt. Soc. Am.*, 36 (1946) 47.
[29] R. F. STAMM AND J. J. WHALEN, *J. Opt. Soc. Am.*, 36 (1946) 2.
[30] S. D. SMITH, communicated I. R. D. G. Meeting, Reading, Sept., 1961.
[31] A. MITSUISHI, Y. YAMADA AND H. YOSHINAGA, *J. Opt. Soc. Am.*, 52 (1962) 14.
[32] R. M. BADGER, L. R. ZUMWALT AND P. A. GIGUÈRE, *Rev. Sci. Instr.*, 19 (1948) 861.
[33] A. E. MARTIN, *Brit. Pat.* 779, 199, appn. date July, 1954.
[34] A. E. MARTIN, *Brit. Pat.* 790, 928, appn. date June, 1955.
[35] R. MINKOWSKI, *Astrophys. J.*, 96 (1942) 306.
[36] A. E. MARTIN, *Ind. Chemist*, 38 (1962) 569.
[37] A. R. DOWNIE, M. C. MAGOON, T. PURCELL AND B. CRAWFORD, *J. Opt. Soc. Am.*, 43 (1953) 941.
[38] R. N. JONES, N. B. W. JONATHAN, MARJORY A. MACKENZIE AND A. NADEAU, *Spectrochim. Acta*, 17 (1961), 77.
[39] W. BRÜGEL, *An Introduction to Infra-red Spectroscopy*, (English translation), Methuen, London, 1962.
   H. A. WILLIS AND R. G. J. MILLER, *Molecular Spectroscopy (Part II)*, Heywood, London, 1961.
   R. N. JONES AND C. SANDORFY, *The Application of Infra-red and Raman Spectrometry to the Elucidation of Molecular Structure*, in *Chemical Applications of Spectroscopy*, Interscience Publishers, New York, 1956.
[40] *Brit. Pat.*, Appn. No. 43450/61.
[41] R. R. GORDON AND H. POWELL, *J. Sci. Instr.*, 22 (1945) 12.
[42] D. C. SMITH AND E. C. MILLER, *J. Opt. Soc. Am.*, 34 (1944) 130.
   G. B. B. M. SUTHERLAND AND H. A. WILLIS, *Trans. Faraday Soc.*, 41 (1945) 181.

[43] R. N. JONES AND A. NADEAU, *Spectrochim. Acta*, 12 (1958) 183.
[44] E. R. BLOUT, M. PARRISH, G. R. BIRD AND M. J. ABBATE, *J. Opt. Soc. Am.*, 42 (1952) 966.
[45] W. S. MOLNAR AND V. A. YARBOROUGH, *Appl. Spectroscopy*, 12 (1958) 143.
[46] Research and Industrial Instruments Company, Lordship Lane, London S.E. 22.
[47] A. E. MARTIN, *Nature*, 181 (1958) 1195.
[48] *Perkin-Elmer Instrument News*, 9 (1958) 1.
[49] A. ELLIOTT, E. J. AMBROSE AND R. TEMPLE, *J. Opt. Soc. Am.*, 38 (1948) 212.
[50] A. YAMAGUCHI, I. ICHISHIMA AND S. MIZUSHIMA, *Spectrochim. Acta*, 12 (1958) 294.
A. JACKSON, communicated I. R. D. G. Meeting, Teddington, March, 1962.
[51] J. U. WHITE, *J. Opt. Soc. Am.*, 32 (1942) 285.
[52] E. R. STEPHENS, *Infrared Phys.*, 1 (1961) 187.
[53] H. STERNGLANZ, *Appl. Spectroscopy*, 10 (1956) 77.
[54] J. D. S. GOULDEN, *Spectrochim. Acta*, 15 (1959) 657.
[55] U. SCHIEDT AND H. REINWEIN, *Z. Naturforsch.*, 7b (1952) 270.
[56] M. M. STIMSON AND M. J. O'DONNELL, *J. Am. Chem. Soc.*, 74 (1952) 1805.
[57] V. C. FARMER, *Chem. and Ind. (London)*, (1955) 586.
[58] J. FAHRENFORT, *Spectrochim. Acta*, 17 (1961) 698; J. FAHRENFORT AND W. M. VISSER, *Spectrochim. Acta*, 18 (1962) 1103.
See especially, PERKIN-ELMER, *Instrument News*, 14 (1963).
[59] J. J. BRADY, R. O. BRICK AND M. D. PEARSON, *J. Opt. Soc. Am.*, 50 (1960) 1080.
[60] G. L. COLLIER AND F. SINGLETON, *J. Appl. Chem. (London)*, 6 (1956) 495.
C. S. FRENCH, *Symposium on Instrumentation and Control*, Berkeley, California, May, 1957.
A. E. MARTIN, *Nature*, 180 (1957) 231.
A. E. MARTIN, *Proceedings of the Conference on Molecular Spectroscopy*, Pergamon, London, 1958, p. 107.

Acknowledgements

Thanks are due to the following firms who generously contributed information relating to their products:

Applied Physics Corporation
Barnes Engineering Company
Beckman Instruments, Inc.
Connecticut Instrument Corporation
Hilger & Watts Ltd.
The Perkin-Elmer Corporation
Research and Industrial Instruments Company
Unicam Instrument Ltd.

It is a pleasure also to thank a number of my colleagues who have made important contributions to the development of some of the spectrometers and accessories mentioned; particularly valuable assistance has been given by R. HASWELL, E. HENDERSON, W. A. SCOTT and J. SHIELDS.

Chapter III

Low Frequency Infra-red Spectroscopy

G. R. WILKINSON

Wheatstone Physics Laboratory, King's College, London

The far infra-red region has only recently been extensively investigated by spectroscopists[1]. It is to a certain extent a matter of choice where the limits of this region of the electromagnetic spectrum are selected and here we will define it as the region between 1 cm^{-1} and 200 cm^{-1}. The region is one in which the concepts and principles of optical and microwave spectroscopy overlap. The delayed progress in developing the far infra-red region stems principally from the difficulty of generating radiation in this frequency range and from the intense atmospheric water vapour absorption.

In this far infra-red region occur the pure rotational transitions for molecules with permanent dipole moments and the lattice modes of crystals. The former provide information on the geometry of molecules in their ground states whilst the latter permit the calculation of interatomic forces and the prediction of thermodynamic data.

It will be convenient to consider first problems and progress in instrumentation and then to survey spectroscopic achievements and possibilities in the study of gases, solids and liquids.

(1) Instrumentation

Infra-red instrumentation is dealt with fully in Chapter II; hence here only some of the special features of importance in the far infra-red will be considered.

(i) Sources

The absorption spectra of substances can be measured either using a source which emits over a wide frequency range such as a black body emitter or by using a variable frequency which can be scanned over a narrow frequency range. The former is clearly valuable for the study of absorption bands extending over a wide range, whilst the high intensity variable frequency source is highly desirable for the investigation of line spectra such as those associated with pure rotation.

The continuous source against which others are compared is the black body source whose energy spectrum is given by the Planck radiation formula, (Chapter XIII, p. 442):

$$E_\nu \, d\nu = \frac{2\pi h \nu^3}{c^2(e^{h\nu/kT}-1)} d\nu$$

This expression gives the radiation emitted from unit area of surface in unit time in the frequency range ν to $\nu+d\nu$. In the far infra-red region $h\nu$ is usually very much less than kT hence the term $e^{h\nu/kT}$ may be approximated by $(1+h\nu/kT)$; hence the black body radiation equation reduces to

$$E_\nu \, d\nu = \frac{2\pi k \, \nu^2}{c^2} T d\nu$$

It may be noted the emission is proportional to the square of the frequency and to the absolute temperature. As the total radiation of all frequencies is proportional to T^4, most of the radiation lies in the near infra-red. Hence increasing the temperature of the source considerably increases the unwanted radiation and more efficient filtering is required. It is clear that a black body is a most unsuitable source for the far infra-red region.

The most effective source which is readily available and reliable is the quartz-enveloped mercury arc of the type used for street lighting. As the envelopes are made of fused quartz, which does not have a very good transmission when hot, most of the emission in the high frequency region of the far infra-red is from the hot quartz surface. In the low frequency region, the emission is mainly from the discharge. If the lamp is run from an alternating voltage source the former is not modulated whilst the latter is modulated at twice the a.c. excitation frequency. Much further research is required on the emission from discharge tubes in the far infra-red in order to select more efficient sources.

If one approaches the problem of producing far infra-red radiation from the microwave end of the spectrum it is natural to enquire into the feasibility of extending the frequency range of devices in which oscillations are produced in cavities by electron beams.

These sources have an extremely narrow bandwidth but may be scanned over a small frequency range. Such a source of high intensity is ideal for spectroscopic applications involving the absorption spectra containing hyperfine structure. A further advantage lies in the extremely high precision that can be obtained in frequency measurement by frequency division. It is, however, very difficult to decrease the size of microwave cavity resonators beyond a few millimetres and hence it is necessary to generate high harmonics from a klystron. In 1962 the upper limit was little above 20 cm^{-1}. As yet, comparatively little effort has been expended on the problem of improvement of harmonic generation. FROOME[2, 3] has recently devised a scheme to obtain high harmonics from a klystron using a high pressure discharge in argon as the harmonic generator. It is hoped ultimately to achieve frequencies up to 30 cm^{-1} by this method. Several methods by which it may be possible to generate far infra-red radiation by means which depend upon the acceleration and deceleration of electron beams have been described in the literature[4].

Masers or lasers (p. 456 ff.) should be capable of producing mono-chromatic radiation in this region of the spectrum. However, few of the possible schemes are likely to result in a variable frequency source, which is required for most spectroscopic applications.

(ii) Detectors

In view of the lack of energy from far infra-red sources it is extremely important that the detectors should have a high sensitivity. With the comparatively long wavelengths it is essential that a careful selection of the detector surface is made to ensure maximum absorption. The most useful detector at present for the far infra-red region is the Golay pneumatic cell (p. 34), for which the minimum detectable power is of the order of 5×10^{-11} watts for a 1 c.p.s. bandwidth, and the time constant is about 15 milli-seconds. The detector may be used in vacuum, and as it does not require cooling, few problems arise with condensing the beam onto the window. Several types of beam condenser for use with spectrometers having long slits have been developed.

If a detector of higher sensitivity is required, then it is necessary to use a type requiring liquid helium coolant. In the superconducting bolometer, the temperature is maintained so that the sensitive element is just over the threshold of superconductivity and hence the absorption of radiation leads to a large change in current which may be amplified. A simple bolometer may be constructed from a carbon resistor; it has a high sensitivity at 1.5° K. Other detectors include the antimony-doped germanium photo-conductive cell[5] which has its highest sensitivity in the 70—125 cm^{-1} region and a time constant of 10^{-5} sec. Another photoconductive detector which is useful below 100 cm^{-1} uses an element of high purity n-type indium antimonide. It requires for its operation a magnetic field of about 6000 oersted and a temperature of the order of 1.5° K. The magnetic field may be obtained from a superconducting niobium solenoid.

(iii) Dispersion

Gratings of the echelette type form convenient dispersion elements for the far infra-red region. Many of the problems associated with the production of these gratings have now been overcome and good replica gratings for the higher frequency region are available (p. 45). For spectroscopic consideration it is preferable to express the grating equation, which is normally written as $n\lambda = 2d \sin \theta$, in terms of wavenumbers,

$$v = \frac{n}{2d} \operatorname{cosec} \theta.$$

In general, it is advisable to use a grating in the first order *i.e.*, $n = 1$. Gratings are usually blazed at about 30° and hence $\operatorname{cosec} \theta = 2$. If $1/d$ is the number of lines/cm, then frequency in wavenumbers corresponding to the blaze angle is

$$v = \frac{1}{d} = \text{the number of lines/cm.}$$

Useful working limits of a grating are approximately between $\frac{2}{3}v_0$ and $\frac{3}{2}v_0$. Thus a grating with 60 lines/cm is blazed at $v_0 = 60$ cm^{-1} and may be used over the range 40—90 cm^{-1}. The limit of resolution of a grating is determined by the extreme path difference of the diffracted radiation. This is $2L \sin \theta$ and hence the resolution in cm^{-1}, if L is measured in centimetres, is $v = 1/2L \sin \theta$. When $\theta \sim 30°$ this reduces to $v = 1/L$. If L is 15 cm then $\Delta v \sim 0.07$ cm^{-1}. At present, sources and detectors are the limiting factor controlling resolution, rather than diffraction. One of the disadvantages of a diffraction grating is the necessity to have several gratings to cover the whole of the far infra-red region, *e.g.* to cover the region from 10—500 cm^{-1} a selection of five gratings with, say, 20, 40, 80, 150 and 300 lines/cm are required. Another is the fact that a grating produces a dispersed spectrum of which only a very small fraction of the whole falls in the detector at any one instant; the rest is effectively wasted. An interferometer does not necessarily suffer from these defects and its development for use in the far infra-red

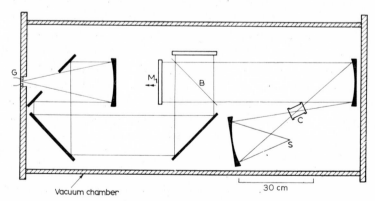

Fig. III, 1(a). The National Physical Laboratory far infra-red interferometer. S, mercury lamp. B, beam divider. M_1, movable mirror. G, Golay detector. C, sample gas cell.

region has been one of the most important advances in this field in recent years. The type of interferometer devised by Michelson, advocated by Strong and turned into a practical device by GEBBIE[6] is shown in Fig. III, 1(a), and the pure rotational spectrum of gaseous HCl recorded using this instrument is depicted in Fig. III, 1(b). Radiation of all

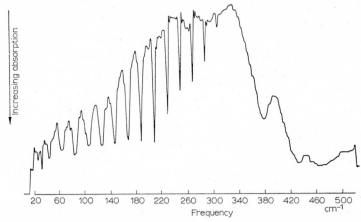

Fig. III, 1(b). The pure rotational spectrum of gaseous hydrogen chloride recorded using the interferometer.

frequencies passed by the filter falls simultaneously on the detector. On scanning the movable reflector an interferogram $I(x)$ is produced, from which it is possible to obtain the spectral intensity G by means of the Fourier transformation

$$G(\nu) = \int I(x) \cos (2\pi\nu x)\mathrm{d}x.$$

The actual computation is carried out using a digital computer. In the N.P.L. programme the output is plotted directly as the percentage transmission versus the frequency, by a pen recorder. If the distance moved by the scanning plate is l then the resolution is given by the expression $\Delta\nu = 1/2l$. Thus if $l = 5$ cm, $\Delta\nu = 0.1$ cm^{-1}. The interferometer is particularly valuable for the study of infra-red emission spectra, and should do much to develop an interest in experimental observations in this region.

(iv) Filters

As mentioned previously, most sources which are used in the far infra-red emit a large amount of radiation at frequencies other than those required, hence efficient filtering is essential.

The scatter filter has long been used in the far infra-red[7]. This consists simply of a metallic plate which has been roughened so as to reflect radiation whose wavelengths are long compared with the surface imperfections, and scatters unwanted shorter wavelength radiation. A more effective and controllable filter is produced by using a grating for this purpose. A useful approximation for the frequency below which the radiation is reflected is ν(reflected) $< 0.6/d$, where $1/d$ is the number of lines/cm. Hence for a scatter grating with 100 lines/cm, radiation with frequencies greater than 60 cm^{-1} are diffracted and these with lower frequency are reflected. The actual form of the reflection curve depends upon the groove shape and on the angle of incidence.

On account of the strong interaction between far infra-red radiation and ionic crystals the latter may be used to isolate definite frequency bands. Reststrahlen plates of this type are available to cover most of the far infra-red region. A suitable selection of crystals in order of increasing frequency are KRS–5, CsI, CsBr, KI, KBr, KCl, NaCl, BaF$_2$, NaF, LiF and MgO.

Selective beam choppers are very effective as filters. A material is used which is opaque in the required frequency range but is transparent at higher frequencies. Hence only the wanted radiation is modulated and detected by the tuned amplifier. Suitable filter chopper materials include all the materials that are mentioned for use as reststrahlen plates. It is advisable to include a beam limiting device to compensate for reflection losses. Interference filters may be constructed of layers of different dielectric constant.

Black polyethylene, which is carbon black embedded in polyethylene, has good transmission beyond about 400 cm^{-1} and is invaluable for the removal of near infra-red radiation. Crystalline quartz is useful on account of its high absorption extending over most of the range from 240 cm^{-1} to 2400 cm^{-1}.

There are a number of suitable window materials for use in the far infra-red. These include quartz and diamond for detector windows. Polyethylene, polystyrene and polyethylene terephthalate are excellent for gas cell windows in the form of thin films and as thicker plates for liquid cells. They have very good transmission due to their comparatively low refractive indices. CsI pressed discs are useful for solid state sampling at frequencies higher than 120 cm^{-1} if cooled to 100° K. Polarizers may be constructed from a pile of films set at the Brewster angle, that is the angle for which $\tan \theta = n$ where n is now the refractive index. For polyethylene n is 1.46 in the far infra-red. In the very far region a transmission polarizer consisting of horizontal strips of spacing d can be used. Waves of frequencies less than $\nu = 1/3d$ are highly polarized, e.g. if there are 30 lines/cm, frequencies below 10 cm^{-1} are highly polarized.

In view of the long wavelengths, the accuracy required in reflecting surfaces is not high; condenser grade polishing only is required — in fact shaped pressed metal sheets are frequently quite adequate. Light pipes are especially valuable in the far infra-red.

The vacuum necessary for work in this region rarely exceeds 100μ Hg.

However, if the sample is cooled in the vacuum enclosure, then it is necessary to remove water vapour either by a diffusion pump or by a cold trap so as to prevent condensation on the specimen.

(v) Instruments

Many instruments have been described in the literature, only a few of which will be considered here. Fig. III, 2 shows the optical layout of a typical

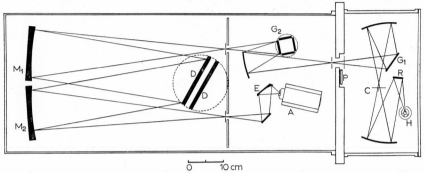

Fig. III, 2. A far infra-red spectrometer for use in the region 10—200 cm^{-1}. (King's College, London).

far infra-red spectrometer. The source is an 80 volt fused-quartz-envelope mercury discharge lamp. A reststrahlen plate is mounted immediately after the source so as to prevent considerable amounts of ultra-violet and visible radiation falling on the sample. The radiation is chopped at 10 c.p.s. by a radiating beam interrupter C. Samples are placed in the beam at the focus near C. The first scatter grating G_1 reflects the radiation on to the fore slit which is covered by black polythene approximately 0.025 mm thick. This is quite opaque to visible and near infra-red radiation. All the slits are coupled together. The second scatter grating is placed between the first slit and the monochromator entrance slit. It is mounted on a table with two other scatter gratings and a mirror. This table can be rotated through a right angle from the outside by means of a flexible drive. The radiation is collimated by the first spherical mirror M_1 and after diffraction by the grating is focussed by M_2 onto the exit slit. The focal length of the spherical mirrors is 75 cm. Two gratings D are mounted back to back on the grating table which can be rotated through 180°. The Golay detector A receives radiation from the ellipsoidal mirror E. The whole optical path is evacuated. Provision is made to permit specimens to be changed without allowing the pressure to rise in the main monochromator compartment.

A commercially available grating instrument for the far infra-red region is the Perkin–Elmer 301 (Fig. III, 3) which covers the range 60—600 cm^{-1}. This is the first double-beam instrument in this range. The water vapour is

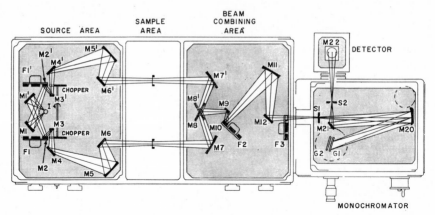

Fig. III, 3. The Perkin–Elmer 301 far infra-red double beam spectrophotometer.

largely removed by flushing with dry air. The source in the higher frequency range is a Globar and in the lower frequency range a mercury lamp. Selective choppers, reststrahlen plates and toroidal mirrors are duplicated to produce both sample and reference beams which are alternately passed to the monochromator by means of a rocking mirror. The grating mounting is of the Littrow type. A Golay detector is employed.

An entirely different principle is used in an instrument built by H. A. GEBBIE[6] at the National Physical Laboratory, Teddington, England. The optical layout is essentially that of the Michelson interferometer. The beam splitter consists of a very thin sheet of polyethylene terephthalate. A mercury lamp is used as a source and a Golay cell as detector. The interferogram is obtained by moving one mirror. The output is recorded directly by a digitilizer onto punched tape ready for insertion into a digital computer. An instrument based on this design is marketed by Grubb Parsons, Newcastle-upon-Tyne, England.

(2) General Features

In view of the very large number of units used in physics and chemistry to characterise electromagnetic radiation and to measure energy, it may be valuable to consider their relation to one another and their orders of magnitude in the far infra-red region. Fig. III, 4 shows some of the units used. In view of the fact that the energy of a photon is directly proportional to frequency, there is little point in referring to wavelengths in spectroscopy. The concept of wavelength is only valuable for the discussion of such phenomena as the diffraction, interference and scattering of electromagnetic radiation. Frequency in cycles per second is the quantity that is directly measured in the microwave region but this is rarely used in the far infra-red;

however, it may be noticed that 10^{12} c.p.s. is a convenient unit and with suitable designation may be more used in the future. The most widely used unit in infra-red spectroscopy — the wavenumber (cm^{-1}) — is especially convenient for the far infra-red region. The millielectron-volt is also a

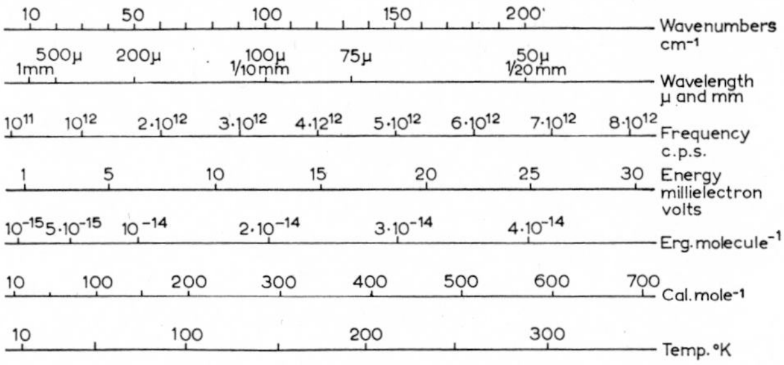

Fig. III, 4. Energies, frequencies, wavenumbers and wavelengths in the far infra-red region

convenient unit and deserves wider use in view of the suitability of the electron-volt for the discussion of electronic energies. The electron-volt is now more widely used in nuclear, atomic, molecular and solid state physics than the erg. The calorie is a unit which is gradually becoming obsolete. Absolute temperature is of course a measure of energy: Boltzmann's constant is the factor which gives it the dimensions of energy.

From Fig. III, 4 it may be seen that corresponding to $\nu = 200$ cm^{-1} the equivalent energy is 25 millielectron-volts or 572 cal. mole^{-1} or 4×10^{-14} erg molecule^{-1}, whilst the equivalent temperature is 287° K. The frequency is 6×10^{12} c.p.s. and the wavelength 50μ, or $\frac{1}{20}$th of a millimetre. At the low frequency end the corresponding figures are 10 cm^{-1} = 1.25 milli-electron-volts = 28.6 cal. mole^{-1} = 2×10^{-15} erg molecule^{-1} = 14.4° K = 3×10^{11} c.p.s. = 1 mm.

The population of any level with energy E_i is proportional to

$$\frac{g_i \, e^{-E_i/kT}}{Z}$$

where g_i is the degeneracy of the level, and Z is the partition function, or, if the energy is expressed in terms of wavenumbers (cm^{-1}),

$$g_i \, e^{-1.43\nu/T}$$

Thus, if the temperature is say, 300° K the factor for a singly degenerate level is approximately $e^{-\nu/200}$. Hence for a value of $\nu = 200$ cm^{-1}, the factor is now 0.27, whilst for 100 cm^{-1} and 10 cm^{-1} this then becomes 0.37 and 0.49 respectively. At 90° K the value becomes approximately $e^{-\nu/60}$ and the proportions for 200 cm^{-1}, 100 cm^{-1} and 10 cm^{-1} are 0.034 and 0.16 and 0.46. Thus the low lying energy levels in which we are interested in far infra-red studies are appreciably populated at room temperature. It also demonstrates the desirability of reducing the temperature below $90°\,\mathrm{K}$ if the region of investigation lies beyond 50 cm^{-1}. In nearly all cases investigated, a sharpening of absorption spectra results from cooling the specimen.

The thermodynamic properties of a system may be calculated from the partition function: $Z = \sum g_i\, e^{-E_i/kT}$. It is clear that it is the terms containing low-lying energy levels which are of the greatest importance in the expression for Z. Many of these can be obtained from low frequency infra-red studies, and the results combined with Raman data.

(3) Spectroscopy

In this chapter it is not possible to give an account of all the spectroscopic studies that can be made in the far infra-red but rather the aim is, by considering some of the fundamental principles of low frequency infra-red spectroscopy, to draw attention to possibilities and to illustrate them by reference to recent work in this field. For purposes of discussion gases, solids, and liquids are treated separately.

(3A) Gases

Pure rotational spectra of molecules occur in the microwave and far infra-red regions. It is necessary first to consider in some detail the rotational energies of molecules[8]. The moment of inertia I of a rigid body about an axis is defined by the relation

$$I = \sum m_i\, r_i^2$$

where r_i is the perpendicular distance of the ith atom of mass m_i from the axis. If $1/\sqrt{I}$ is plotted radially, the surface is in general an ellipsoid, termed the momental ellipsoid, the axes of which are the principal axes of inertia. It is conventional to designate the principal axes A, B and C such that $I_A < I_B < I_C$.

Molecules may be classified by reference to the relative values for the three moments of inertia: those possessing three different moments of inertia are termed asymmetric tops, while if all three principal moments of inertia are equal the molecule is called a spherical top. Where two of the moments of inertia are equal but different from the third, the molecule is called a symmetric top. Symmetric tops may depart from the convention $I_A < I_B < I_C$ for in these cases it is customary to choose the unique or highest-fold axis as the A axis; as a result, these molecules may be further subdivided into prolate and oblate symmetric tops, for which the moments of inertia are governed by the expressions $I_A < I_B = I_C$ and $I_A > I_B = I_C$

respectively. Typical examples of such structures are CH_3Cl and C_6H_6. A linear molecule is a special case of a prolate symmetric top in which $I_A = 0$, the momental ellipsoid being a circular disc.

(i) Linear molecules

Here it is necessary to distinguish between those molecules which have a centre of inversion and those that do not. The former belong to point group $D_{\infty h}$ and the latter to $C_{\infty v}$. Molecules having a centre of inversion do not possess a permanent dipole moment and hence do not have a pure rotational spectrum. The intensity of the pure rotational infra-red spectrum depends upon the dipole moment of the molecule. However, all molecules exhibit a pure rotational Raman spectrum. The allowed energy levels of a linear rigid rotor are given by

$$E = \frac{h^2 J(J+1)}{8\pi^2 I_B}$$

Hence the rotational term value is

$$F(J) = \frac{E}{hc} = BJ(J+1)$$

where B, the rotational constant, is equal to $h/8\pi^2 cI_B$ and J is the rotational quantum number. Transitions between the different rotational levels in the microwave and infra-red regions are governed by the selection rule

$$\Delta J = \pm 1$$

For absorption of radiation, $\Delta J = +1$ and transitions occur from the lower rotational level J'' to the upper level J' *i.e.* $J' = J''+1$. The frequencies in wavenumbers are then given by the expression

$$\nu = F(J')-F(J'') = 2B(J+1)$$

where J now refers to the lower state and is given by $J = 0, 1, 2\ldots$ Thus the spectrum of the rigid rotator consists of a series of equidistant lines of spacing $2B$. If centrifugal distortion is taken into consideration the term value becomes

$$F(J) = BJ(J+1)-DJ^2(J+1)^2$$

D being much smaller than B. For a diatomic molecule, $D = 4B^3/\omega^2$ where ω is the vibrational frequency. The rotational transition frequencies are

$$\nu = F(J')-F(J'') = 2B(J+1)-4D(J+1)^3$$

and hence we have a series of lines whose spacing decreases as J increases. The degeneracy of a rotational level of a linear molecule is $(2J+1)$. The thermal population N_J of the level may be shown to be

$$N_J \propto (2J+1) \exp\left(\frac{-hcBJ(J+1)}{kT}\right)$$

Because the statistical weight term increases with J while the Boltzmann factor decreases, the population of the levels reaches a maximum at a J value given by

$$(J_{max}+\tfrac{1}{2}) = \left(\frac{kT}{2Bhc}\right)^{\frac{1}{2}}$$

For a diatomic molecule the moment of inertia $I = \mu r^2$ where r is the internuclear distance and $\mu = m_1 m_2/(m_1+m_2)$
Numerically

$$I = \frac{h}{8\pi^2 cB} = \frac{27.994 \times 10^{-40}}{B}$$

Hence

$$r^2 = \frac{168.6259\,(m_1+m_2)}{m_1 m_2 B}$$

where B is measured in cm^{-1} and m_1, m_2 in atomic mass units; thus the internuclear distance r can be calculated. The moment of inertia of a linear polyatomic molecule is given by

$$I = \sum_i m_i z_i^2 - \frac{1}{M}\left(\sum m_i z_i\right)^2$$

where z_i is the distance of the ith mass from any chosen origin and M the total mass of the molecule. As there are now several internuclear distances, it is necessary to obtain the rotational constants of one or more isotopically substituted species. A problem immediately arises as, whilst the equilibrium bond distances probably change by a negligible amount on isotopic substitution, this is not so for the different ground states of the isotopic species.

In view of the fact that the $J = 0$ and often higher J levels can frequently be measured using microwave spectroscopy, and as high precision vibration-rotation data are available, the frequencies of these rotational lines can usually be calculated with higher precision than they can be measured in the far infra-red region. Consequently, the lines are of considerable value as frequency standards in this region. CO is especially suitable for the $4-150$ cm^{-1} region. Others whose spectra have been recorded include NO, HCl, HBr and HI. Of the linear polyatomic molecules HCN is a particularly useful calibrant in the $4-100$ cm^{-1} region (Fig. III, 5). The rotational lines of DCN and N_2O[9] have also been resolved.

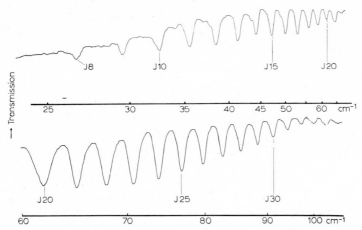

Fig. III, 5. Part of the pure rotational spectrum of hydrogen cyanide recorded with the spectrometer shown in Fig. III, 2.

(ii) Symmetric top molecules

Symmetric top molecules have two equal principal moments of inertia. The prolate type has $I_A > I_B = I_C$ and the oblate $I_A = I_B > I_C$. The energy levels of a symmetric top molecule are given by

$$E_{JK} = \frac{h^2 J(J+1)}{8\pi^2 I_B} + \frac{h^2 K^2}{8\pi^2}\left(\frac{1}{I_A} - \frac{1}{I_B}\right)$$

which is usually written

$$\frac{E_{JK}}{h} = [BJ(J+1)+(A-B)K^2]$$

$$A = \frac{h}{8\pi^2 c I_A} \qquad B = \frac{h}{8\pi^2 c I_B}$$

The selection rules for pure absorption are $J \to J+1$ and $\Delta K = 0$. Here K is a measure of the angular momentum about the symmetry axis. Hence the absorption frequencies are given by

$$\nu = 2B(J+1)$$

the same expression as was obtained for linear molecules. If the effects of centrifugal distortion are included

$$\nu = 2B(J+1)-4D_J(J+1)^3-2D_{JK}(J+1)K^2$$

The last term leads to the splitting of each line into $(J+1)$ components $(K \ge J)$. However, the splitting is small and can rarely be resolved in the far infra-red. Only one principal moment of inertia of a symmetric top molecule can be measured directly from the pure rotational spectrum.

Hence it is essential to use isotopic substitution. As yet, the pure rotation spectra of few symmetric top molecules have been obtained in the far infra-red region. NH_3 has probably been the example most frequently studied.

(iii) Spherical top molecules

A molecule for which all the moments of inertia about an axis through the centre of mass are equal is termed a spherical top, and the rotational term value is

$$F(J) = BJ(J+1) - DJ^2(J+1)^2$$

This expression is the same as that for a linear molecule but in place of $(2J+1)$ degeneracy of the latter we now have a degeneracy of $(2J+1)^2$. This arises because in addition to the $(2J+1)$ special degeneracy of J there is a $(2J+1)$ degeneracy with respect to a fixed direction in the molecule. Only in the case of accidental equality of I_A, I_B and I_C will the molecule have a permanent dipole moment, and hence the true spherical top invariably has no pure rotational spectrum in the infra-red.

(iv) Asymmetric top molecules

If a molecule does not possess a three- or higher-fold symmetry axis it is called an asymmetric top, for in general all three moments of inertia are different. The problem of finding the allowed energy levels is complicated and no complete or general solutions are available.

It is advantageous to consider the asymmetric rotor by examining the two extreme cases — the prolate and oblate symmetric tops. Several different parameters have been used for the degree of asymmetry. Ray's parameter is defined by

$$\kappa = \frac{2B - A - C}{A - C}$$

when $B = C$ (*i.e.* a prolate symmetric top) the expression equals -1, and when $B = A$ (*i.e.* an oblate symmetric top) it becomes equal to $+1$. Wang's parameter is especially appropriate for slightly asymmetric tops

$$b_p = \frac{C - B}{2A - B - C}$$

$$b_0 = \frac{A - B}{2C - B - A}$$

and in the case of the approximately prolate top, the total rotational energy may be expressed in the form

$$\frac{E}{h} = \frac{B+C}{2} J(J+1) + \left(A - \frac{B+C}{2}\right)\omega$$

ω may be expanded in the form

$$\omega = K^2 + c_1 b_p + c_2 b_p^2 + c_3 b_p^3 + \cdots .$$

The numerical values of these coefficients are given in *Microwave Spectroscopy*[8]. For the case which approximates to the oblate top the expression to use is

$$\frac{E}{h} = \frac{A+B}{2} J(J+1) + \left(C - \frac{A+B}{2} \right) \omega$$

$$\omega = K^2 + c_1 b_0 + c_2 b_0^2 + c_3 b_0^3$$

For the more asymmetric cases it is better to express the energy in the form

$$\frac{E}{h} = \frac{A+C}{2} J(J+1) + \tfrac{1}{2}(A-C) E_\tau$$

where E_τ is a function of the asymmetry parameter $\kappa = (2B-A-C)/(A-C)$. King, Hainer and Cross have used a power series expression for E_τ

$$E_\tau = a_0 + a_1 \kappa + a_2 \kappa^2$$

The total angular momentum J is, as usual, a constant in direction and magnitude. Whereas for a symmetric top there are $(J+1)$ sub-levels of different energy for each J value corresponding to $K = 0, 1, 2$ etc., in the case of an asymmetric top there are $(2J+1)$ different energy levels for each J.

The pure rotational spectrum of H_2O has been very widely studied and is now largely understood. As the absorption lines of H_2O occur throughout the region between 1 cm^{-1} and 500 cm^{-1}, they form useful secondary standards for spectrometer calibration (Fig. III, 6). Other asymmetric

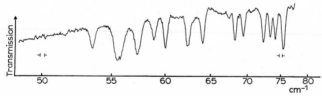

Fig. III, 6. The absorption spectrum of water vapour between 50 and 80 cm^{-1}.

tops whose pure rotational spectra have been studied in the far infra-red include O_3, NO_2 and SO_2.

Probably the most fruitful studies of gases that can be carried out in the far infra-red region are those in the torsional modes of molecules[10]. The main object of such observations is the calculation of potential barrier heights restricting rotation. Examples that have been investigated so far include: CH_3OH, N_2H_4, $CF_3 \cdot CHF_2$, $(CH_3)_3O$, and $(CH_3)_3Si-O-Si(CH_3)_3$.

(3B) Solids

In order to discuss the molecular vibrations of solids it is necessary to recall the main types of bonding that occur in solids[11]. The prototypes may be diagrammatically represented as shown:

Molecular

Ionic —|— Covalent

Metallic

In most solids the bonding is not of one single type. However, for discussion it is easier to deal first with those that have the bonding of one type only. In evaluating theoretically the possible modes of vibration of a solid it is necessary to have a knowledge of the force constants between the atoms. The net charges on the atoms are of the greatest importance in considering the interaction of electromagnetic radiation with a solid. The vibrational spectra have been worked out for quite simple lattices such as those possessed by the alkali halides and some metals. In view of the difficulty in finding exact solutions for real crystals it is necessary to make approximations — these lead to a more immediate appreciation of the physics involved. Thus in molecular crystals it is frequently useful to distinguish between:

(a) The internal modes of molecules which lead to infra-red absorption mainly in the region above 200 cm^{-1}.

(b) Lattice modes which involve the relative motion of the molecules as a whole; these can be further subdivided into translational modes and librational modes.

The question whether particular modes of vibration are active in the infra-red must be settled by reference to the symmetry of the unit cell.

Results of measurements in the infra-red and ultra-violet on solid materials are usually quoted in terms of the refractive index n and the absorbance k, whilst in the microwave and radio frequency regions it is the complex dielectric constant ε^* that is usually measured. The relationship between the functions are given in the equations below.

The real part of the dielectric constant ε' is given by

$$\varepsilon' = n^2 - k^2$$

and for the imaginary part

$$\varepsilon'' = 2nk \qquad \text{and} \qquad \varepsilon'' = \frac{2\sigma}{f}$$

where σ is the conductivity and f the frequency in cycles/sec. The absorbance $\alpha = 4\pi k/\lambda = 4\pi\nu k$. For the power factor, tan δ, the relationship is tan $\delta = \varepsilon''/\varepsilon'$. When the absorption is weak we have the familiar result that the dielectric constant is equal to the square of the refractive index. The functions ε', ε'', n and k are in general anisotropic, and are frequency dependent.

The damping constant may be obtained from the width of the dielectric constant curve at half maximum,

$$\gamma = v^+_{\frac{1}{2}} - v^-_{\frac{1}{2}}$$

where $v^+_{\frac{1}{2}}$ and $v^-_{\frac{1}{2}}$ are the frequencies at half maximum on the high and low frequency sides of v_0.

It is not possible to calculate complete data on the optical constants or dielectric constants of solids from absorption spectra alone, and it is desirable to measure the reflection spectrum also as a function of frequency: n and k can then be obtained from the reflectivity R. The reflection at normal incidence is the square of the modulus $|r|$ which is obtained from the relationship $r = |r| e^{i\theta}$. The phase change on reflection, θ, can be computed from the reflection spectrum using the Kramers-Kronig relationship (see Chapter XI, p. 382) in the form

$$\theta_{v_0} = \frac{1}{\pi} \int_0^\infty \frac{d \log |r|}{dv} \cdot \log \left| \frac{v + v_0}{v - v_0} \right| dv$$

which may be converted into a form suitable for digital computation. The complex number r is then related to the optical constants n and k by use of the Fresnel equations

$$n = \frac{1 - |r|^2}{1 + |r|^2 - 2|r| \cos \theta}$$

$$k = \frac{2|r| \sin \theta}{1 + |r|^2 - 2|r| \cos \theta}$$

Owing to the considerable difficulty in measuring the percentage reflection when the reflection is small, considerable care must be exercised in the computation of n and k.

The refractive index n may be obtained, in the spectral regions in which the solid has a sufficiently high transmission, from the measurement of interference fringes. The equation from which the refractive index is obtained is

$$N\lambda = 2nd$$

where N is the order of the fringe and d the thickness of the solid. It is essential to use this equation and to determine the fringe order if the refractive index n is not constant. Completely wrong results are obtained in such cases if the expression

$$n = \frac{1}{2d \cdot \Delta v},$$

where Δv is the fringe separation in wavenumbers, is used.

References pp. 109–110

(i) Molecular crystals

The energy levels of a solid are of course essentially a property of the whole system. However, in view of the fact that the forces between the covalently bonded atoms are much greater than the forces between the molecules, it is useful and meaningful in molecular crystals to differentiate between the internal modes of the molecules and their translational and librational motion. In general, the internal modes of molecules give rise to absorption in the near and medium infra-red rather than in the far infra-red. However, some internal modes in molecules containing either a large number of atoms or heavy atoms do occur at low frequencies. For instance in iodoform CHI_3, the CI_3 symmetric deformation mode occurs at 110.8 cm^{-1}. The half width of the band is less than 2 cm^{-1}, which is perhaps surprising in view of its proximity to the frequency of the lattice modes whose spectrum has been observed in combination with the (C–H) stretching mode in the near infra-red. The out-of-plane vibrations involving the motion of aromatic rings in heterocyclics also occur in the far infra-red. The "butterfly flapping" mode of naphthalene occurs at 178 cm^{-1} and shifts on deuteration to 160 cm^{-1}. A non-planar skeletal mode is found at 194 cm^{-1}. Two other bands arising from lattice modes occur at 103 cm^{-1} and 72 cm^{-1}. In the Raman

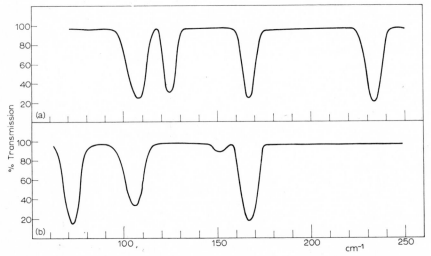

Fig. III, 7. The far absorption spectra of (a) anthracene and (b) tetracene recorded at 100° K.

spectrum the values 124, 109, 73 and 45 cm^{-1} have been obtained. In analogy with naphthalene the "butterfly flapping" mode would appear to be associated with the three bands at 193 cm^{-1}, 182 cm^{-1} and 170 cm^{-1} in azulene. The frequencies found (Fig. III, 7) in other polycyclic aromatic compounds include:

Anthracene (234 cm^{-1}, 167 cm^{-1}, 125 cm^{-1}, 108 cm^{-1})
Tetracene   (167 cm^{-1}, 106 cm^{-1}, 72 cm^{-1})
Pentacene   (208 cm^{-1}, 199 cm^{-1}, 109 cm^{-1}, 73 cm^{-1}).

In rhombic sulphur the internal modes of the puckered octahedron that occur below 220 cm^{-1} have been assigned as follows[12]: $\nu_8 = 184$ cm^{-1}, $\nu_9 = 151$ cm^{-1}, $\nu_2 = 218$ cm^{-1}, $\nu_6 = 191$ cm^{-1}. Lattice modes are found at 75 cm^{-1}, 96 cm^{-1}, 108 cm^{-1} and 150 cm^{-1}.

The simplest molecular crystals for investigation are produced by condensing small polyatomic molecules from the gas phase. Thin films of such molecules as HCl, DCl, HBr, CO_2, OCS, CS_2, Cl_2, Br_2, H_2O, H_2S and NH_3 condensed at liquid nitrogen temperature have been studied in the far infra-red. Most show two low frequency translational modes and broader bands at higher frequencies due to librational modes; the assignment of the latter is verified in such cases as HCl by deuteration, in which case the frequencies are reduced approximately in the ratio 1:1.4. Using a Debye type of approximation for the specific heats, good agreement with the calorimetric values have been obtained.

Typical values for these modes are 66.5 cm^{-1} and 113 cm^{-1} for CO_2 (Fig. III, 8) and 170 cm^{-1} for HCl, all measured as thin films on crystal quartz at 90° K (author's laboratory).

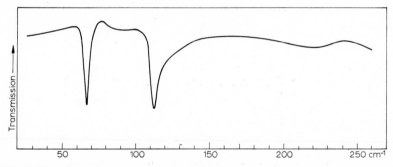

Fig. III, 8. The absorption spectrum of solid carbon dioxide recorded at 100° K showing two bands at 66.5 cm^{-1} and 113 cm^{-1}.

Crystals containing hydrogen bonds reveal many absorption bands in the far infra-red region. It is hoped that an analysis of these bands will show if the zero vibrational level has been split due to a double minimum in the potential field for the hydrogen bonded proton.

Long chain ketones have been shown to have a sequence of low frequency absorption bands[13]. Szigeti had predicted that if a polar group such as (C=O) were added to a paraffin chain, the torsional modes of the chain would become active. Many of the long chain ketones have been studied and reveal a characteristic pattern, although the absorption is not very intense.

Organo-metallic and related complexes might be expected to have frequencies in this region and their investigation promises to add to our knowledge of the metal–carbon, etc. bond.

In general, organic polymers such as polyethylene, polyethylene tereph-thalate and nylon have low absorption in the 1—200 cm⁻¹ region. However, the absorption is not zero but is spread over a wide range. This fact of course accords with the very low power factor in the microwave region, e.g. for polyethylene $\varepsilon'' = 0.0013$ at 25,000 megacycles (1.2 cm⁻¹). This corresponds to an absorbance α of 0.005 in that region. It is probable that the value for really pure material is very much lower than this. The chief impurities in such polymers result from excitation and hence lead to the introduction of polar groups which increase the infra-red activity of the torsional modes of the polymer chains, much as in the case of the long chain ketones. Polytetrafluoroethylene (PTFE) has an absorption band at 203 cm⁻¹ (at 90° K) due to the (CF₂) rocking mode. A PTFE sheet about ½ mm in thickness is useful as a means of checking scattered radiation at this frequency.

(ii) Ionic crystals

Ionic crystals such as the alkali halides have intense absorption in the far infra-red. The main resonance is due to the excitation of transverse optic

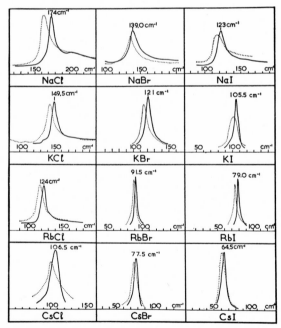

Fig. III, 9. The far infra-red absorption spectra of thin films of alkali halides (sublimed films on quartz) recorded at 90° K (———) and 300° K (· · · · · ·).

modes, in which alternate positive and negative ions move in opposite directions. As the absorption coefficients in the alkali halides vary over the frequency range 1—500 cm^{-1} by a factor of 10^4, samples of thickness 1 cm to 1μ are necessary. Detailed measurements are also necessary on the reflection spectra.

A large number of investigations have been made on the vibrational spectra of the alkali halides. The absorption spectra of thin films produced by subliming alkali halides on crystal quartz are shown in Fig. III, 9. It may be noticed that on cooling, the peaks shift to higher frequency due to the contraction of the lattice. In addition to the main band due to the transverse optic mode there are a number of subsidiary maxima both in the absorption and reflection spectra. The subsidiary bands which are more pronounced in crystals of low ionic mass are due to combination of the transverse optical vibration with the other modes of vibration which the lattice possesses. These other modes are the transverse and longitudinal acoustic vibrations

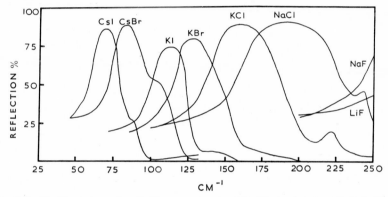

Fig. III, 10. Far infra-red reflection spectra (reststrahlen) of some alkali halides.

in which the direction of motion of the ion is independent of its ionic charge, and finally the longitudinal optical mode in which the ions vibrate in the same direction as the direction of propagation of the wave. The existence of subsidiary maxima which correspond in the theory of harmonic forces between the ions to forbidden infra-red transitions, has been attributed to anharmonicity in the binding forces and to the presence of a second order electric moment (Fig. III, 10).

A typical set of results for the dielectric constants of sodium chloride which has been obtained by combining both absorption and reflection spectra is shown in Fig. III, 11. The shapes of the curves are approximately Lorentzian and clearly show that only a single resonance is necessary to account for the main features of the absorption in the far infra-red.

The far infra-red absorption and reflection spectra of many other ionic crystals have been studied. MgO is typical of those having the same structure as NaCl but with doubly charged ions. Its main absorption occurs at 410 cm^{-1} at 100° K. CaF_2 has a less sharp maximum at 275 cm^{-1}, whilst the

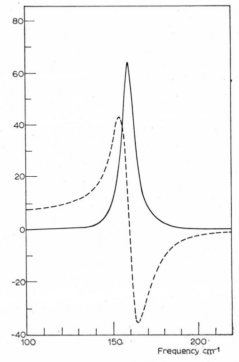

Fig. III, 11. The dielectric constants $\varepsilon' = n^2 - k^2$ (- - - - - - -) and $\varepsilon'' = 2nk$ (————) of sodium chloride at 300° K.

partially ionic crystal ZnS has a peak absorption almost as high as that of the alkali halides at 277 cm^{-1}. The effect of cooling on the infra-red absorption spectrum of sapphire is shown in Fig. III, 12.

(iii) Covalent crystals

Diamond is the prototype covalent structure. In the far infra-red it has negligible absorption (unless of the semiconductor class with low resistance) and hence forms an excellent material for detector windows. Germanium, which has a similar structure to diamond, has weak absorption bands; the peak is nearly a thousand times weaker than that in ZnS which also has a structure similar to germanium but is partially ionic.

α-Quartz is partially covalent and partially ionic. Intense absorption bands which are paralleled by high reflectivity, occur in the region 240—500 cm^{-1} (Fig. III, 13). Below 220 cm^{-1}, with the exception of one band, quartz has good transmission. The 129 cm^{-1} absorption is highly anisotropic and has maximum absorption when the electric vector of the radiation is perpendicular to the optic axis. The mode may be associated with the

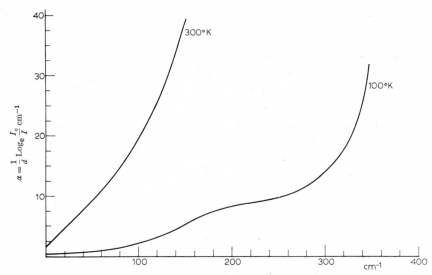

Fig. III, 12. The far infra-red absorption spectrum of sapphire (Al_2O_3) showing the marked change in the absorption on cooling.

motion of the oxygen about the (Si–Si) direction. The bands shift to 132 cm^{-1} on cooling to 90° K.

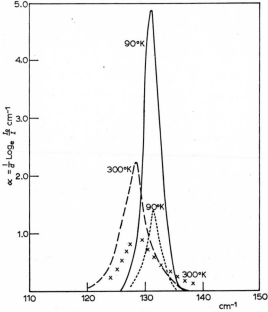

Fig. III, 13. The anisotropy of the absorption of α-quartz in the 130 cm^{-1} region obtained using polarized radiation. Maximum absorption occurs when the electric vector of the radiation is perpendicular to the optic axis. The peak absorption shifts from 127 cm^{-1} to 130 cm^{-1} on cooling from 300° K to 90° K.

References pp. 109–110

(iv) Semiconductors[14]

Impurities sometimes give rise to shallow electronic levels in semiconductors. Electronic transitions have been observed in the far infra-red region and have been further studied by applying a magnetic field and observing the Zeeman splitting e.g. phosphorus in germanium. From the splitting, Boyle has obtained the effective mass m^* of the weakly bound electron. Studies of the ionisation energies and effective electron mass can be made by measuring the oscillating magneto-absorption, which is field dependent. Cyclotron resonance provides one of the most accurate methods of determining the effective mass of such electrons. The resonance condition is given by the expression

$$\nu = \frac{eH}{2\pi m^* c}$$

However, for satisfactory measurement of the resonance it is important that $\omega\tau \gg 1$ where ω is the angular frequency and τ the collision free time of the electron. Cyclotron resonance is normally observed in the microwave region; however, if τ is very short even at liquid helium temperature, it is highly desirable to observe the resonance at the highest possible frequency. Hence, if a sufficiently high magnetic field can be obtained, it is advantageous to carry out the experiments in the far infra-red region.

The effective mass of electrons may also be computed by observing the Faraday effect. This entails the measurement of the angle of rotation of the electric vector of the far infra-red radiation as a function of the applied magnetic field. The Faraday effect is essentially a measure of the dispersion caused by cyclotron resonance.

(v) Magnetic resonance

With the introduction of superconductivity magnets capable of producing magnetic fields in excess of 300,000 oersted, it will be possible to carry out many more resonance experiments in the far infra-red.

BLOOR and MARTIN[15] have observed the zero field antiferromagnetic resonance in MnF_2 at 8.8 cm^{-1} and 5.5° K. The resonance was found to shift to 7.2 cm^{-1} on increasing the temperature to 42° K.

(vi) Metals

Tinkham has measured the energy gap in superconductors using far infra-red radiation. Observations were made on the onset of absorption due to the excitation of electrons across the energy gap. The frequency of the onset of absorption is then a direct measure of the energy gap.

(3C) Liquids

The spectra of liquids may be determined experimentally in the far infra-red region using polyethylene, polyethylene terephthalate or quartz cells.

The theory of the vibrational spectra of liquids is extremely difficult to deal with. A static disordered lattice presents a great problem. In liquids one has the further complexity of the thermal motion — both translational and librational — of the molecules. The thermal energy of molecules is of the same order of magnitude as the energy of the photons used for observation. Some severe approximations are consequently necessary. The distinction can be made between absorption due to internal modes of the molecules and that due to molecular reorientation. The latter has long been studied by dielectric loss methods in the radio and microwave regions.

Solvents with high transmission in the region below 200 cm^{-1} include benzene, with a 70 per cent transmission in cells of 1 mm, hexane, carbon tetrachloride, chloroform and carbon disulphide. Liquids with strong hydrogen bonds have very strong absorption bands extending over a wide range of the far infra-red.

(4) Conclusions

Whilst real progress in studying the rotational spectra of gases in the far infra-red must await the development of a variable-frequency coherent source, much can be achieved with the resolution at present available by the study of torsional modes, and in the study of solids and liquids for which high resolution is frequently not necessary. For solids and liquids it is usually more important to be able to record spectra over a wide frequency range with good quantitative accuracy in a short time, than to have extremely high resolution. With commercial instruments coming onto the market many more spectroscopists will be able to obtain spectra in the far infra-red.

REFERENCES

[1] E. D. PALIK, *J. Opt. Soc. Am.*, 50 (1960) 1329, gives a complete set of references to infra-red work to 1959.
[2] K. D. FROOME, *Nature*, 184 (1959) 808.
[3] K. D. FROOME, *Nature*, 193 (1962) 1170.
[4] I. KAUFMAN, *Proc. Inst. Radio Engrs.*, 47 (1959) 381.
[5] S. J. FRAG AND J. F. C. OLIVER, *J. Opt. Soc. Am.*, 36 (1959) 195.
[6] H. A. GEBBIE, *Proceedings of the Symposium on Interferometry*, National Physical Laboratory, June 1959, H. M. S. O., 1961.
   H. A. GEBBIE, *Advances in Quantum Electronics* II, ed. J. R. SINGER, Columbia University Press, 1961, p. 155.
   H. A. GEBBIE AND J. VANASSE, *Nature*, 178 (1956) 432.
   H. A. GEBBIE, *National Physics Laboratory Report, Basic Physics Group*, 1962.
[7] J. U. WHITE, *J. Opt. Soc. Am.*, 37 (1947) 713.
[8] G. HERZBERG, *Infra-red and Raman Spectra of Polyatomic Molecules*, Van Nostrand, New York, 1945.

C. H. Townes and A. L. Schawlow, *Microwave Spectroscopy*, McGraw Hill, New York, 1955. These two books give the theory of pure rotation of molecules; the latter also describes microwave techniques.

[9] E. D. Palik and K. N. Rao, *J. Chem. Phys.*, 25 (1956) 1174.

[10] A. Dante and R. C. Lord, *J. Chem. Phys.*, 30 (1959) 1310.

[11] C. Kittel, *Introduction to Solid State Physics*, Wiley, New York, 1957. This book also contains an elementary discussion of the dielectric and magnetic properties of solids.

[12] Unpublished work from the author's laboratory.

[13] S. Field and D. Martin, *Proc. Phys. Soc.*, 78 (1961) 625.

[14] *Progress in Semiconductors*, Vol. 5, Heywood, London, 1960.

[15] D. Bloor and D. Martin, *Proc. Phys. Soc.*, 78 (1961) 774.

Acknowledgements

Figs. III, 1(a) and 1(b) are reproduced with permission from National Physical Laboratory Reports. Fig. III, 3 is reproduced with permission from the Perkin-Elmer Corporation. The other figures are from work carried out in conjunction with Dr. C. S. Smart and Mr. S. A. Inglis at King's College, London.

Chapter IV

The Infra-red Spectra of Simple Molecules

W. JEREMY JONES

Fellow of Trinity College, Cambridge

Extensive experimental study has shown that the energy changes observed in molecular spectra are, in general, of three types: rotational, vibrational and electronic energy. The molecular energy is the sum of these components and changes in them give rise to emission or absorption spectra in the far infra-red (rotational energy changes), the near infra-red (vibrational) and in the visible or ultra-violet regions (electronic). The present chapter will be concerned principally with vibrational spectra which usually occur in the region 200 to 4000 cm^{-1} (wavelengths of 50 to 2.5 microns). This region embraces most of the fundamental vibrational frequencies within simple molecules and it is of very great value in the study of molecular structure. Transitions between electronic energy levels corresponding to much larger energy changes (*i.e.* higher frequencies) will be mentioned only in so far as they assist in the interpretations of vibrational spectra.

One of the main advantages of studying molecules by means of their infra-red spectra is that they may readily be examined in all three phases. Of these by far the most important is the vapour. In this state the majority of molecular substances exist as monomers and there is little or no association or interaction with neighbouring molecules. Further, in this state, at low gas pressures, the molecules are able to rotate freely and the rotational energy levels are but little affected by molecular interactions.

In order to simplify the discussion, the pure vibrational spectra will first be treated and the rather more complex vibration-rotation spectra examined in the light of the general information derived from that treatment.

(1) The Vibrational Energies of Molecules

For a system of N freely independent particles (atoms) the total thermal energy consists of N terms of the kinetic energy form $\frac{1}{2}m_i(\dot{x}_i^2+\dot{y}_i^2+\dot{z}_i^2)$; there are thus $3N$ "squared terms" in all. If these particles come together to form a rigid system (molecule), that aggregate will have only three "squared terms" for its translational energy, $\frac{1}{2}M(\dot{x}^2+\dot{y}^2+\dot{z}^2)$, where the velocities $\dot{x}$, $\dot{y}$, $\dot{z}$, are those of the centre of mass, and M is the total mass. Having, with these terms, completely abstracted the translational energy, the remaining energy must arise from forms in which the centre of mass does not move. Rotation about the centre of mass can contribute three "squared terms", $\frac{1}{2}(I_P\dot{\theta}_P^2+I_Q\dot{\theta}_Q^2+I_R\dot{\theta}_R^2)$, where I_P, $\dot{\theta}_P$, etc. are the moments of inertia and angular velocities about the principal axes P, Q, R. A theorem due to Boltzmann shows that the total energy in the system must still be representable by $3N$ "squared terms". The $(3N-6)$ remaining "squared terms" accordingly represent the vibrational energy within the rigidly bonded system: they define the limited number of vibrational modes (the normal modes) from which any vibrational motion within the system can be compounded by superposition. A "normal mode" or "normal vibration" of a polyatomic system may be defined as a vibrational state in which each atom carries out a simple harmonic motion about its equilibrium position, each atom having the same frequency of oscillation and, in general, moving in phase.

A linear molecule will have rotational energy about the line of nuclei only by virtue of nuclear spin or electronic motion — which are not included in the thermal energy of the molecule: *i.e.* a linear molecule has (thermal) rotational energy only about the two axes perpendicular to the internuclear axis and so it has one more, or a total of $(3N-5)$, internal vibrational modes. Similarly, a molecule which has r internal rotational degrees of freedom will have $(3N-6-r)$ purely vibrational modes.

The dynamics of such normal vibrations may be treated by classical methods yielding expressions relating the frequencies of vibration to the masses of the atoms and the forces binding them (see Chapter V). In order to obtain the sequence of energy levels associated with these vibrations, however, it is necessary to apply a rather fuller quantum mechanical approach, and, assuming the harmonic oscillator approximation, it is possible to solve the wave equation giving for the total vibrational energy:

$$E \text{(in ergs)} = \sum_i E_i = \sum_i h\nu_i(v_i+d_i/2) \tag{1}$$

where v_i, the vibrational quantum number, $= 0, 1, 2, \ldots$, and ν_i is the vibration frequency of the ith normal mode. d_i is the degree of degeneracy of ν_i and is equal to the number of normal modes having exactly the same frequency. Introducing the term value $G(v_1, v_2, \ldots)$, *i.e.* the energy levels *expressed in wavenumbers*, for a molecule possessing only non-degenerate vibrations we have:

$$G(v_1, v_2, \ldots) = E(v_1, v_2, \ldots)/hc = \omega_1(v_1+\tfrac{1}{2})+\omega_2(v_2+\tfrac{1}{2})+ \ldots \tag{2}$$

$\omega(= \nu/c)$ is the vibrational frequency in reciprocal centimetres. In the ground vibrational state $(v_1 = v_2 = \ldots = 0)$ the energy is not zero as the molecule possesses "zero point" vibrational energy:

$$G(0, 0, \ldots) = \tfrac{1}{2}\omega_1 + \tfrac{1}{2}\omega_2 + \ldots \tag{3}$$

In order that a vibrating molecule should interact with the fluctuating electrical field of electromagnetic radiation the molecular electrical dipole moment must change its magnitude or orientation with respect to a fixed coordinate system during the motion. It is the magnitude of this change of dipole moment which determines the intensity of a transition. For harmonic oscillators, transitions between the various energy levels are governed by the selection rules $\Delta v_i = \pm 1$. The frequent observation of overtones and combination tones of these vibrations corresponding to changes $\Delta v = 2, 3$, etc., albeit very much weaker than the fundamentals, is a consequence of the anharmonic nature of the normal modes.

(1A) Heteronuclear diatomic molecules

The relevant features for these molecules have already been delineated in Chapter I, p. 2 et seq.

(1B) Polyatomic molecules

While the normal vibrations of non-symmetrical molecules are generally associated with dipole changes, those of molecules possessing some symmetry (such as a plane or centre of symmetry) are not necessarily active as absorptions in the infra-red. The behaviour of the normal modes with respect to the elements of symmetry is the determining factor in the spectroscopic activity of a particular vibration.

A molecule may possess a number of symmetry elements, each element being a symmetry operation which will produce a configuration of the nuclei indistinguishable from the original. In the vibrating molecule, however, when such symmetry operations are carried out, the mode concerned does not necessarily lead to self-coincidence; the various normal modes may thus be symmetric or antisymmetric with respect to the symmetry elements. The basic symmetry operations will be summarized below although fuller details may be obtained from texts[1] which cover the theory in more detail than can be attempted here.

Four types of symmetry element need be considered to describe the symmetry of a molecule, the plane of symmetry, the centre of symmetry, the rotation axis, and an alternating rotation–reflection axis. The symbol used to describe the symmetry element may also be used to signify the operation corresponding to that element. Thus C_2 might indicate a two-fold rotation axis or a rotation by 180° about this axis.

The plane of symmetry (σ) Where all atoms lying off a plane are symmetrically placed about that plane, such that a perpendicular dropped on to the plane from any atom and continued an equal distance on the other side of the plane coincides with another similar atom, that plane is termed a plane of symmetry. A typical example would be the plane passing through the deuterium and nitrogen atoms in the molecule NH_2D and bisecting the angle between the two hydrogen atoms, which would then be placed symmetrically about this plane. All planar molecules possess a plane of symmetry, the molecular plane.

The centre of symmetry (i) The symmetry operation i corresponding to this element involves a reflection of all the particles through the centre of symmetry to produce a nuclear configuration indistinguishable from the original. Thus the *trans* form of planar dichlorethylene has a centre of symmetry (Fig. IV, 1).

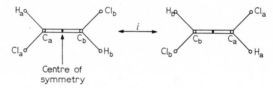

Fig. IV, 1. The molecule of *trans* dichlorethylene — the operation i.

Rotation axes (C_p or D_p) p is the order of the rotation axis. The operation C_p for this element of symmetry is a rotation by an angle $360°/p$ about this axis, which transforms the molecule into itself. Thus ammonia (Fig. IV, 2) has a three-fold rotation axis — a rotation by 120° about this

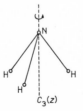

Fig. IV, 2. The molecule of ammonia, illustrating the C_3 rotation axis.
$r_0(N–H) = 1.00_8Å$, $\widehat{HNH} = 107.3°$.

axis produces a configuration indistinguishable from the original. A rotation axis can have orders from 1 to ∞. If $p = 1$ we have the identity operation I, as rotation by 360° must transform the molecule into itself. The identity is a trivial element which all molecules possess and is included in the group character tables merely for mathematical completeness. The order p is infinite for a linear molecule. If a molecule has a p-fold axis C_p and p two-fold axes perpendicular to the C_p at equal angles to one another, it has dihedral symmetry $\boldsymbol{D_p}$: *e.g.* benzene has symmetry $\boldsymbol{D_{6h}}$. $\boldsymbol{D_1}$ is identical with $\boldsymbol{C_2}$ although it is generally not considered as a dihedral point group. $\boldsymbol{D_2}$, frequently called $\boldsymbol{V}$, has three two-fold axes mutually perpendicular to one another.

Rotation–reflection axes (S_p)   This symmetry element is less easy to visualize as it involves a rotation about the S axis by an angle $360°/p$ followed by a reflection at a plane perpendicular to this axis. Thus the planar molecule *trans* dichlorethylene has a two-fold rotation–reflection axis lying along the (C=C) bond (and another orthogonal to this in the plane of the molecule). The sequence of operations is given in Fig. IV, 3, from which it may be seen that the final configuration is indistinguishable from the initial.

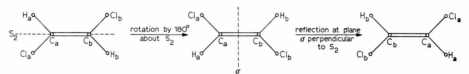

Fig. IV, 3. The molecule of *trans* dichlorethylene — the operation S_2.

A molecule may possess more than one symmetry element (*e.g. trans* dichlorethylene) and, in general, certain combinations of these elements automatically confer others. Thus water has two symmetry planes, the plane of the molecule and a plane at right angles to this one and bisecting the (H–O–H) angle. The line of intersection of these two planes must, in consequence, be an axis of symmetry — C_2. It is, therefore, not always necessary to specify all the symmetry elements.

It can be shown mathematically that only certain combinations of the symmetry elements are possible; these are the symmetry types or species. The symmetry group (or point group) to which the molecule belongs is determined by the symmetry elements it possesses. These elements (for a finite structure) must intersect at a point which is unchanged by their operation: the molecule exhibits point-symmetry and the groups of symmetry elements are known as point groups. The symmetry axis of highest order (*i.e.* principal axis) is considered as the vertical (z) axis, and planes of symmetry perpendicular to (*i.e.* horizontal), and containing (*i.e.* vertical), this axis are termed σ_h and σ_v respectively. A molecule with a three-fold symmetry axis and three symmetry planes passing through this axis has point group $\boldsymbol{C_{3v}}$ — a typical example being ammonia. In the same way water is of point group $\boldsymbol{C_{2v}}$. A two-fold rotation axis with two two-fold axes orthogonal to it is written $\boldsymbol{D_2}$; the presence of horizontal symmetry planes at right angles to these axes convert it to point group $\boldsymbol{D_{2h}}(=\boldsymbol{V_h})$ — a typical example being ethylene.

Any vibration which is unchanged by the complete set of operations characteristic of the symmetry of the equilibrium configuration is termed "totally symmetric". Symmetry species that are symmetric or antisymmetric with respect to a centre of symmetry receive the subscripts g or u respectively.

(i) Selection rules

In a first approximation the dipole moment of a vibrating molecule is

$$\mu = \mu_0 + (\mathrm{d}\mu/\mathrm{d}Q)\,\Delta Q, \qquad\qquad (4)$$

where μ_0 is the permanent dipole moment and Q is a coordinate or coordinates defining the motion of the nuclei. If a particular vibrational mode is excited the dipole moment oscillates with the frequency of vibration. In order that a vibrational mode shall interact with radiation it is necessary that the dipole moment should change during the vibration, *i.e.* $\mathrm{d}\mu/\mathrm{d}Q \neq 0$. This condition will hold only if at least one of the components $\mathrm{d}\mu_x/\mathrm{d}Q$, $\mathrm{d}\mu_y/\mathrm{d}Q$, or $\mathrm{d}\mu_z/\mathrm{d}Q$, along the coordinate axes, changes during the vibration. A quantum mechanical treatment of the problem shows that a vibration will be infra-red active provided at least one component of the dipole moment μ (or of $\mathrm{d}\mu/\mathrm{d}Q$) has the same symmetry species as that of the vibration. More correctly, it is the product of the vibrational symmetry species of the two states combining in the transition which is of significance, but for transitions from the ground to an upper vibrational state it is the species of the upper state which matters because the ground state is always totally symmetric. The species of the dipole moment components are the same as the species of translations along these axes — species which are usually given in the group character table. A vibration will be infra-red active if its symmetry species is the same as that of at least one of the dipole moment components.

As for heteronuclear diatomic molecules the harmonic oscillator approximation restricts transitions to one quantum of vibrational energy but, due to the anharmonic nature of vibrations, this selection rule is by no means rigid. Overtones and combination tones are usually very much weaker than the parent fundamentals but the intensities of fundamentals (depending on the magnitude of $\mathrm{d}\mu/\mathrm{d}Q$) may vary so widely that it is not uncommon for an overtone of one mode to be stronger than the fundamental of another.

Similar selection rules may be formulated for the Raman spectra where, in place of the transition dipole moment, it is the species of the components of the polarizability tensor determining the induced dipole moment which decides the spectral activity of a vibration.

The main problem of vibrational spectroscopy is, of course, to derive information concerning molecular structures by analysis of their spectra. Interpretation of the spectrum requires that the observed frequencies should be assigned to particular normal modes of the molecule concerned. As it is usually not possible to give a convincing explanation of the finer details of infra-red and Raman spectra on the basis of an incorrect molecular structure, the overall consistency of the assignments will provide a significant test for a proposed configuration.

In examining the suitability of a particular structure it is essential first to recognize the elements of symmetry and to ascertain the point group to which the molecule belongs. To minimize confusion relating to the assignment of the vibrational frequencies it is conventional to number the normal modes in the order of their decreasing symmetry and frequency. Thus the vibrational modes are divided into groups according to their correct symmetry species and the groups are arranged in the same order as in the group character table. Within a group of particular symmetry species, the normal modes are arranged in order of decreasing frequency, a procedure which may be considerably aided by reference to similar molecules where the normal modes are already characterized. Having arranged the normal modes in their correct order they are then numbered from 1 to $(3N-6)$.

The assignment of the observed frequencies to the normal modes proceeds through detailed interpretations of vibration-rotation bands, coincidences between infra-red and Raman spectra, and even apparent similarities with spectral features of structurally related molecules. Where a molecule possesses a centre of symmetry, the "g" modes are infra-red inactive, the "u" modes are Raman inactive. Thus the observation that there are no coincidences between the infra-red and Raman fundamentals establishes the presence of a centre of symmetry.

Of the $(3N-6)$ normal modes of a polyatomic acyclic system, $(N-1)$ may be described as primarily bond stretching vibrations, usually represented by ν, together with additional details relating to the form of the vibration. Thus $\nu_a(H_2O)$ describes a stretching mode of the water molecule which is antisymmetric with respect to rotation by $180°$ about the symmetry axis, $\nu_s(H_2O)$ represents the other stretching mode, which is symmetric with respect to all the permitted symmetry operations of this group. The remaining $(2N-5)$ modes are then angle bending vibrations, usually designated by a symbol such as δ, or γ, depending on the form of the normal vibration. The third fundamental vibration of the water molecule, essentially the in-plane (H–O–H) angle deformation mode, is termed $\delta(H_2O)$.

It will be convenient to examine a number of simple molecules belonging to a variety of different point groups to illustrate the manner in which these representations are used in particular instances.

(ii) Molecules possessing only non-degenerate vibrations

(a) Water (point group C_{2v})   This non-linear symmetric molecule (Fig. IV, 4) possesses two necessary symmetry elements which may be considered as

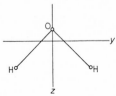

Fig. IV, 4. The molecule of water. $r_e(O–H) = 0.957$Å, $\widehat{HOH} = 104.5°$.

the C_2 axis (z) and the plane $\sigma_v(yz)$ of the molecule*. The molecule is thus of point group C_{2v} and there will be four symmetry species corresponding to vibrations which may be symmetric or antisymmetric with respect to the two necessary symmetry elements (the other element $\sigma_v(xz)$ is a consequence of these two necessary symmetry elements).

There are three $(= 3N-6)$ fundamental vibrations, the forms of which may be obtained by a normal coordinate calculation (see Chapter V) and are indicated in Fig. IV, 5.

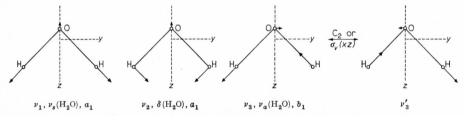

$\nu_1, \nu_s(H_2O), a_1$ $\qquad$ $\nu_2, \delta(H_2O), a_1$ $\qquad$ $\nu_3, \nu_a(H_2O), b_1$ $\qquad$ ν'_3

Fig. IV, 5. The normal modes of water (schematic).

For a non-linear triatomic molecule there can be no genuine vibrations which are antisymmetric with respect to the plane of the molecule, for such motions would correspond to rotations about the y or z axes. ν_1 and ν_3 are primarily bond stretching modes and may be considered as combinations of two isolated $\nu(O–H)$ vibrations, coupled in an in-phase and out-of-phase manner with respect to the C_2 axis (Fig. IV, 6).

$\delta(H_2O)$, in the absence of a common O-atom for the two (O–H) groups, would correspond to rotations of these groups.

* In this chapter an attempt has been made to adhere to the conventions proposed by the International Commission for Spectroscopy regarding the use of spectroscopic symbols and the labelling of symmetry axes[2]. These conventions may account for slight differences in the use of certain symbols in this chapter and in Herzberg's comprehensive text[3] on molecular spectroscopy.

The modes ν_1 and ν_2 are symmetric with respect to all permitted operations $\sigma_v(yz)$, $\sigma_v(xz)$, and C_2, $i.e.$ reflection in the planes (yz) and (xz), and

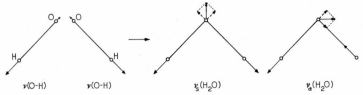

$\nu(O\text{-}H)$ $\nu(O\text{-}H)$ $\nu_s(H_2O)$ $\nu_a(H_2O)$

Two $\nu(O\text{-}H)$ modes in-phase   Two $\nu(O\text{-}H)$ modes out-of-phase

Fig. IV, 6. The normal modes of two "isolated" (O–H) groups combining in an in-phase
and out-of-phase manner (with respect to C_2 or $\sigma_v(xz)$) to yield two normal modes of water.

rotation by 180° about the C_2 axis (z). For these modes at the extreme of
the vibration, the molecule still retains the symmetry properties of the
equilibrium configuration of the nuclei. ν_3' is obtained by carrying out the
operations $\sigma_v(xz)$ or C_2 (reflection in the (xz) plane or rotation by 180°
$(360°/2)$ about the C_2 axis) on ν_3. The two modes are out of phase by 180°
and so are antisymmetric for these operations. The characters (χ) for these
normal modes, $+1$ or -1, according as a vibration is symmetric or antisymmetric for an operation, are given in Table IV, 1 together with the
characters for the symmetry species of this point group.

TABLE IV, 1

SYMMETRY SPECIES AND CHARACTERS FOR POINT GROUP $\boldsymbol{C_{2v}}$

$\boldsymbol{C_{2v}}$	I	$C_2(z)$	$\sigma_v(yz)$	$\sigma_v(xz)$	Non-genuine vibrations—translation and rotation
A_1	$+1$	$+1$	$+1$	$+1$	T_z
A_2	$+1$	$+1$	-1	-1	R_z
B_1	$+1$	-1	$+1$	-1	T_y, R_x
B_2	$+1$	-1	-1	$+1$	T_x, R_y
ν_1	$+1$	$+1$	$+1$	$+1$	
ν_2	$+1$	$+1$	$+1$	$+1$	
ν_3	$+1$	-1	$+1$	-1	

I is the identity operator, with respect to which all vibrations are symmetric.
$C_2(z)$ is a rotation by $2\pi/2$ about the z axis, $\sigma_v(yz)$ and $\sigma_v(xz)$ reflections in
the yz and xz planes respectively. A_1, A_2, B_1 and B_2, of point group $\boldsymbol{C_{2v}}$,
are the four symmetry species to one of which all possible modes of vibration
for molecules of this symmetry must belong. The characters (χ) of the
totally symmetric species A_1 are

$$\chi(I) = \chi(C_2) = \chi(\sigma_v(yz)) = \chi(\sigma_v(xz)) = +1$$

while for the B_1 species the characters are

$$\chi(I) = \chi(\sigma_v(yz)) = +1; \ \chi(C_2) = \chi(\sigma_v(xz)) = -1.$$

The A_1 sets have the same characters as would a simple translation T_z along the z axis. As the transition moment may have a component of this type, all vibrational modes of this species will be infra-red active (see p. 116 *et seq.*). The A_2 species have the same characters as the rotation about the z axis, while the B_1 and B_2 species have the same characters as translations along the y and x axes respectively — vibrational modes of species b_1 and b_2 will thus be infra-red active.

It is clear from Table IV, 1 that ν_1 and ν_2 have a_1 character, and that ν_3 has b_1 character. There are no genuine vibrations antisymmetric to the plane of the molecule, species a_2 or b_2, although there are rotations and translations of these species. The a_1 and b_1 modes, to which species all overtones and combination tones (simultaneous excitation of two or more vibrations) belong, are infra-red and Raman active. The a_1 transitions having dipole changes along the principal axis are termed parallel bands (||), while the b_1 modes having transition moments perpendicular to this, the highest-fold, axis are termed perpendicular bands ($\perp$). Table IV, 2 gives the wavenumbers of the infra-red vapour phase bands in the region below 4000 cm^{-1}.

TABLE IV, 2

INFRA-RED BANDS[4] OF H_2O VAPOUR BELOW 4000 CM^{-1}

$\nu_{observed}$ cm^{-1}	Band type	Quantum numbers of state						Species	ω cm^{-1}
		Lower (ground) state			Upper state				
		v_1	v_2	v_3	v_1	v_2	v_3		
1595.0	||	0	0	0	0	1	0	a_1	1653.9
3151.4	||	0	0	0	0	2	0	a_1	—
3651.7	||	0	0	0	1	0	0	a_1	3825.3
3755.8	$\perp$	0	0	0	0	0	1	b_1	3935.6

When account is taken of the anharmonic nature of the vibrations the term value for a molecule possessing only non-degenerate vibrations is

$$G(v_1, v_2, \ldots) = \sum_i \omega_i(v_i + \tfrac{1}{2}) + \sum_i \sum_{k \geq i} x_{ik}(v_i + \tfrac{1}{2})(v_k + \tfrac{1}{2}), \qquad (5)$$

and for the three fundamental vibration frequencies we have:

$$\nu_1 = \omega_1 + 2x_{11} + \tfrac{1}{2}x_{12} + \tfrac{1}{2}x_{13}; \qquad \nu_2 = \omega_2 + 2x_{22} + \tfrac{1}{2}x_{12} + \tfrac{1}{2}x_{23};$$

$$\nu_3 = \omega_3 + 2x_{33} + \tfrac{1}{2}x_{13} + \tfrac{1}{2}x_{23}.$$

By observing sufficient overtones and combination tones — not an easy task since they are normally extremely weak compared to the fundamentals — it is possible to estimate the nine parameters, ω_i and x_{ik}. The x_{ik} are negative, which results in the frequencies of overtones and combination tones being slightly less than would be expected from the frequencies of the fundamentals. Where the normal mode requires a large amplitude of vibration, as for the hydrogen atoms in this instance, the anharmonicity is very pronounced (note the discrepancy between ν and ω in Table IV, 2). However, for vibrations not involving hydrogen the x_{ik} are usually very small compared with the ω_i and little error is introduced by using the observed frequencies in place of the ω_i.

The forms of the normal vibrations of the water molecule shown above (as for all the molecules discussed in this chapter) are represented in terms of symmetry coordinates rather than true displacement coordinates. Thus the actual a_1 normal modes are strictly combinations of the two depicted modes $\nu_s(H_2O)$ and $\delta(H_2O)$, although the normal modes approximate closely to those shown.

(b) Nitrosyl chloride — NOCl (Point group C_s)   Simple valence theory suggests to the chemist that nitrosyl chloride will be a non-linear structure, which is immediately confirmed by the fine structure of its vibration–rotation bands. Because of the difference between the oxygen and chlorine atoms joined to the nitrogen, the molecule has only one element of symmetry — it is necessarily planar (point group $C_s \equiv C_{1v} \equiv C_{1h}$). All molecules possess a C_1 axis (no symmetry), for rotation by 360° about such an axis produces the identical configuration. Where a molecule possesses a symmetry plane at right angles to this axis (σ_h) it is of point group C_{1h}. However, such a molecule is also of point group C_{1v} for if the C_1 axis is considered to be in the molecular plane, the plane of the molecule passes through this axis. Neither C_{1v} nor C_{1h} alone adequately describes the point group and it is conventional to term such point groups C_s.

As in the case of water, there can be no vibrations which are anti-symmetric with respect to the plane of the molecule and accordingly all vibrations have species a', being completely symmetric to the only permitted operation. With the convention indicated earlier the highest frequency fundamental is termed ν_1, the next highest ν_2, and the lowest frequency band ν_3. $\nu_1 \equiv \nu_a(NOCl)$, $\nu_2 \equiv \nu_s(NOCl)$, $\nu_3 \equiv \delta(NOCl)$. $\nu_a(NOCl)$ may be imagined as being largely localized in the (N=O) group, *i.e.* $\nu(N=O)$, while $\nu_s(NOCl)$ may be described approximately as $\nu(N-Cl)$, descriptions which may only be justified because of the considerably different frequencies expected for the isolated (N=O) and (N–Cl) group vibrations. The fundamentals of the molecule have all been observed in the gas phase[5] at:

$$\nu_1 = 1799 \text{ cm}^{-1}, \quad \nu_2 = 592 \text{ cm}^{-1}, \quad \nu_3 = 329 \text{ cm}^{-1},$$

all the quoted frequencies being those of the ^{35}Cl isotopic species.

(c) Ethylene, C_2H_4 (Point group $V_h \equiv D_{2h}$)   As is well known, and as may be deduced from its infra-red and Raman spectra, ethylene is a planar molecule containing a centre of symmetry (Fig. IV, 7).

It has three necessary symmetry elements which may be considered as the three symmetry planes; all other symmetry elements arise as a consequence

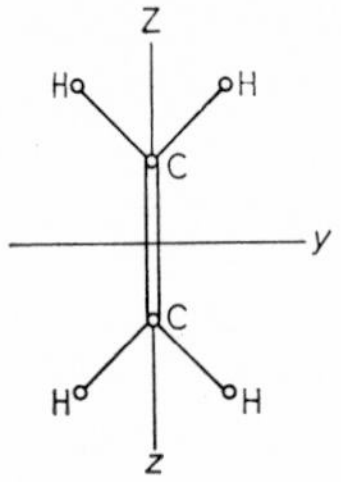

Fig. IV, 7. The molecule of ethylene — yz is chosen as the plane of the molecule. $r_0(\text{C–H}) = 1.08_6\text{Å}$, $r_0(\text{C=C}) = 1.33_9\text{Å}$, $\widehat{\text{HCH}} = 117.5°$.

of these three mutually perpendicular planes. While the group character table indicates the behaviour of the different symmetry types with respect to all permissible operations, for our purposes it is adequate to describe the behaviour with respect to the three symmetry planes. The eight symmetry types then describe the differing behaviour of a mode — symmetric or antisymmetric — with respect to reflections in these planes. To determine approximately the form of the normal vibrations it is convenient to treat the molecule as if it were composed of two isolated non-linear (CH_2) groups. Each group would then have three normal modes of a form given in Fig. IV, 8 (*cf.* the modes for water).

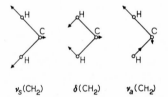

$\nu_s(CH_2)$ $\delta(CH_2)$ $\nu_a(CH_2)$

Fig. IV, 8. The three normal modes of an "isolated (CH_2) group".

When the two groups are brought together, as in ethylene, we should have six modes according as the vibrations are coupled in a symmetric or antisymmetric fashion with respect to the symmetry plane $\sigma(xy)$ dividing the two groups (Fig. IV, 9a). In addition there will be six vibrational modes which, in the absence of any force binding the two (CH_2) groups, would be considered as rotations or translations of these groups (Fig. IV, 9b).

These modes account for the twelve normal vibrations of ethylene — there being no other genuine vibrations. ν refers to a stretching vibration, δ and r to in-plane bending and rocking modes, and t and γ to out-of-plane torsion and bending vibrations respectively. The signs $+$ and $-$ indicate atomic displacements above and below the plane of the molecule during the vibra-

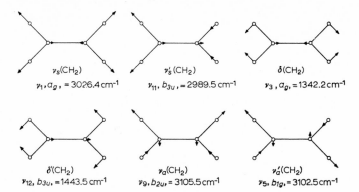

$\nu_s(CH_2)$ $\nu_1, a_g, = 3026.4\,cm^{-1}$ $\nu_s'(CH_2)$ $\nu_{11}, b_{3u}, = 2989.5\,cm^{-1}$ $\delta(CH_2)$ $\nu_3, a_g, = 1342.2\,cm^{-1}$

$\delta'(CH_2)$ $\nu_{12}, b_{3u}, = 1443.5\,cm^{-1}$ $\nu_a(CH_2)$ $\nu_9, b_{2u}, = 3105.5\,cm^{-1}$ $\nu_a'(CH_2)$ $\nu_5, b_{1g}, = 3102.5\,cm^{-1}$

Fig. IV, 9a. The approximate forms of the six normal modes of ethylene derived from the three normal modes of two "isolated (CH_2) groups". The gas phase frequencies, species and numbers, are given below the individual modes.

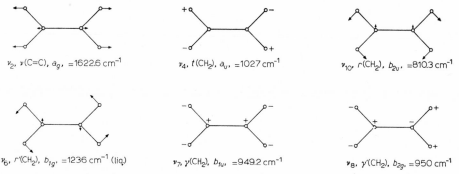

$\nu_2, \nu(C=C), a_g, = 1622.6\,cm^{-1}$ $\nu_4, t(CH_2), a_u, = 1027\,cm^{-1}$ $\nu_{10}, r(CH_2), b_{2u}, = 810.3\,cm^{-1}$

$\nu_6, r'(CH_2), b_{1g}, = 1236\,cm^{-1}$ (liq) $\nu_7, \gamma(CH_2), b_{1u}, = 949.2\,cm^{-1}$ $\nu_8, \gamma'(CH_2), b_{2g}, = 950\,cm^{-1}$

Fig. IV, 9b. The approximate forms of the six remaining normal modes of ethylene. The gas phase frequencies, species and numbers are given below the individual modes.

tion, the arrows indicating similar displacements in the molecular plane. The behaviour of each of these modes with respect to the three necessary symmetry operations $\sigma(xz)$, $\sigma(yz)$, and $\sigma(xy)$, is indicated by the characters $+1$ or -1 in Table IV, 3 in which is also given the behaviour of each of the eight symmetry types with respect to these operations.

Comparison of the characters of the modes with those of the symmetry types enable the species of the vibrations to be determined readily. These species are given in Table IV, 3. For convenience, the modes are arranged in order of decreasing symmetry and frequency — this is readily done, for stretching modes are higher in frequency than the bending modes δ, which are usually higher in frequency than the rocking (r) and out-of-plane bending modes, t and γ. The vibrations are then numbered from ν_1 to ν_{12}. The number of modes of each species is thus (R, Raman active; I, infrared active; ia., inactive in both spectra):

$3a_g(R); \ 1a_u(\text{ia.}); \ 2b_{1g}(R); \ 1b_{1u}(I); \ 1b_{2g}(R); \ 2b_{2u}(I); \ 0b_{3g}(R); \ 2b_{3u}(I),$

TABLE IV, 3

CHARACTERS OF THE VIBRATIONAL MODES OF ETHYLENE AND THE SYMMETRY
SPECIES OF POINT GROUP V_h

$D_{2h} \equiv V_h$	$\sigma(yz)$	$\sigma(xz)$	$\sigma(xy)$	Vibrational mode	$\sigma(yz)$	$\sigma(xz)$	$\sigma(xy)$	Species of vibration	Number of mode
A_g	+1	+1	+1	$\nu_s(CH_2)$	+1	+1	+1	a_g	ν_1
A_u	−1	−1	−1	$\nu(C{=}C)$	+1	+1	+1	a_g	ν_2
B_{1g}	+1	−1	−1	$\delta(CH_2)$	+1	+1	+1	a_g	ν_3
B_{1u}	−1	+1	+1	$t(CH_2)$	−1	−1	−1	a_u	ν_4
B_{2g}	−1	+1	−1	$\nu'_a(CH_2)$	+1	−1	−1	b_{1g}	ν_5
B_{2u}	+1	−1	+1	$r'(CH_2)$	+1	−1	−1	b_{1g}	ν_6
B_{3g}	−1	−1	+1	$\gamma(CH_2)$	−1	+1	+1	b_{1u}	ν_7
B_{3u}	+1	+1	−1	$\gamma'(CH_2)$	−1	+1	−1	b_{2g}	ν_8
				$\nu_a(CH_2)$	+1	−1	+1	b_{2u}	ν_9
				$r(CH_2)$	+1	−1	+1	b_{2u}	ν_{10}
				$\nu'_s(CH_2)$	+1	+1	−1	b_{3u}	ν_{11}
				$\delta'(CH_2)$	+1	+1	−1	b_{3u}	ν_{12}

a sequence verified by a consideration of Table 35 of reference 3. b_{1u}, b_{2u} and b_{3u} modes, which have the same species as translations (and hence transition dipole moments) along the x, y and z axes, are infra-red active, while a_g, b_{1g}, b_{2g}, and b_{3g} modes are Raman active. a_u is inactive in both spectra.

By consideration of the analogous vibration of water, the anti-symmetric stretching vibration ν_9, b_{2u}, is assigned to the highest frequency fundamental band observed in the infra-red at 3105.5 cm^{-1}, while the other stretching vibration $\nu_{11}[\nu'_s(CH_2)]$, b_{3u}, is assigned to a band at 2989.5 cm^{-1}. The bending vibrations ν_7, ν_{10} and ν_{12} are then assigned to bands at 949.2 cm^{-1}, 810.3 cm^{-1} and 1443.5 cm^{-1}, assignments which are confirmed by the characteristic features of the vibration–rotation spectra[6] (see p. 154 *et seq.*). The frequencies of the other fundamentals are given below the individual modes and are determined from analysis of the Raman spectrum and various infra-red combination bands.

(iii) Molecules possessing doubly degenerate vibrations — linear molecules
For certain molecules possessing axes of order three or higher, two, or even three normal modes may possess identical frequencies, a phenomenon which is termed degeneracy. We consider first molecules possessing doubly degenerate vibrations. Whilst these vibrations may occur in an infinite number of directions at right angles to the principal axis, they are representable by suitable combinations of modes in two mutually perpendicular directions, *i.e.* two degrees of vibrational freedom. These degenerate vibrations are designated e modes (or π modes for linear molecules).

Linear molecules are the simplest class possessing degenerate vibrations, and their linearity is generally readily established by observing the fine structure details, or the band contours, of their gas phase vibration–rotation spectra. They are conveniently subdivided into centro-symmetric and non-symmetric types. Carbon dioxide and carbonyl sulphide, representative molecules of these types, will be considered in some detail.

(d) Carbonyl sulphide (Point group $C_{\infty v}$)   This molecule has an infinite-fold axis of symmetry, C_{∞}, and an infinite number of symmetry planes ($\infty\,\sigma_v$) passing through this axis, *i.e.* it has point group $C_{\infty v}$.

The bending vibration of this linear molecule can occur in one of two mutually perpendicular directions, both modes giving rise to identical frequencies of vibration — they are doubly degenerate. By analogy with centro-symmetric carbon dioxide (to be described later), the lowest frequency bond stretching vibration is termed ν_1 and the doubly degenerate bending vibration ν_2, the higher frequency stretching mode is then ν_3. This system of numbering the vibrational modes of linear triatomic molecules departs from the convention suggested earlier (p. 117), and is retained only because of its widespread use.

The forms of the four fundamental vibrations ($3N-5$), two stretching and two bending, are given below (Fig. IV, 10).

ν_1, ν(C=S), σ ν_2, δ(OCS), π ν_2', δ'(OCS), π ν_3, ν(C=O), σ

Fig. IV, 10. The approximate forms of the normal modes of OCS.

Because of the considerably different frequencies expected for the (C=S) and (C=O) isolated group vibrations, ν_1 may be described very approximately as ν(C=S) and ν_3 as ν(C=O). Inspection of the modes indicates that there will be a change of dipole moment during all four vibrations (only three fundamental frequencies), and consequently all will be infra-red (and Raman) active. The observed gas phase frequencies[7] are;

$$\nu_1 = 863.4\ \text{cm}^{-1}, \quad \nu_2 = 523.1\ \text{cm}^{-1}, \quad \nu_3 = 2062.2\ \text{cm}^{-1}.$$

The parallel bands, involving dipole changes along the symmetry axis, are of symmetry species σ^+ (generally abbreviated to σ for there are no normal modes[2] of species σ^-), the perpendicular bands with transition dipole moments at right angles to this axis have species π, the degenerate species.

(e) Carbon dioxide (Point group $D_{\infty h}$)   In addition to the infinite-fold symmetry axis, carbon dioxide possesses a plane of symmetry σ_h at right angles to it, and consequently is of point group $D_{\infty h}$. Produced as a result of C_{∞} and σ_h, the molecule has a centre of symmetry and an infinite number of C_2 axes in the σ_h plane. The fundamental vibrations of molecules belonging to this point group are similar in type to those of the non-symmetrical

linear molecules, but in this instance they may also be symmetric or anti-symmetric to the centre of symmetry, and there may thus be σ_g, σ_u, π_g and π_u vibrational modes.

The structure of this molecule is readily established, for no coincidences are observed between the infra-red and Raman active fundamentals — confirmation of the linear centro-symmetric structure. As for carbonyl sulphide there are two stretching and two bending vibrations (degenerate), the forms of which are given in Fig. IV, 11.

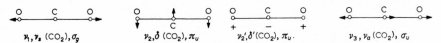

$\varkappa_1, \varkappa_s$ (CO_2), σ_g ν_2, δ (CO_2), π_u ν_2', δ'(CO_2), π_u. ν_3, ν_a (CO_2), σ_u

Fig. IV, 11. The approximate forms of the normal modes of CO_2.

Both the antisymmetric mode ν_3 and the degenerate mode ν_2 involve changes in the dipole moment during the vibration and are infra-red active, the transition moments having the same species as translations along the z, and the x and y axes respectively.

The π_u degenerate vibration, observed as a strong perpendicular type band at 667.3 cm⁻¹ in the infra-red, is termed ν_2: while the designation of this mode as ν_2 is at variance with the convention suggested earlier for numbering the modes (Π_u being preceded by Σ_u^+ in the group character table), its use is so widespread that it has come to be generally accepted. The original convention (p. 117) is usually adhered to for all molecules other than the linear triatomic ones[2]. ν_3, σ_u, the antisymmetric stretching vibration of the (C=O) groups, is observed as a very strong parallel-type band at 2349.3 cm⁻¹.

The σ_g mode, ν_1, is Raman active and is assigned to the higher frequency component of a doublet band in the Raman spectrum at 1388.3 cm⁻¹ and 1285.5 cm⁻¹ [3]. The latter band is due to the first overtone ($v = 0 \rightarrow 2$) of the ν_2 fundamental and is enhanced in intensity by Fermi resonance with the adjacent fundamental band ν_1 (see benzene, p. 131).

The separation of about 1000 cm⁻¹ between ν_1 and ν_3 indicates the degree to which two similar groups may give different frequencies as a result of coupling when linked directly, and in this case, of course, it is not possible to interpret any band as being associated with one isolated diatomic grouping.

The overtones of the infra-red active fundamentals exhibit certain unusual features: thus the first ($v = 0 \rightarrow 2$) and third ($v = 0 \rightarrow 4$) overtones of such modes do not appear in the infra-red, while the second ($v = 0 \rightarrow 3$) and fourth ($v = 0 \rightarrow 5$) overtones are active. Further, the overtone $2\nu_2(v = 0 \rightarrow 2)$ appears in the Raman spectrum. This behaviour is entirely consistent with the $\boldsymbol{D}_{\infty h}$ point group, for the even vibrational levels

$(v = 0, 2, 4, \ldots)$ of normal σ_u modes have species σ_g, the odd levels having species σ_u. Even for the π_u modes the even levels are symmetric, the odd antisymmetric, with respect to the centre of symmetry. As the g modes are infra-red inactive, the u Raman inactive, the observed behaviour is readily understood. For normal g states the modes are centro-symmetric for all v. This behaviour is generally true for molecules possessing a centre of symmetry and may frequently provide useful confirmation of such a structure. It should be realized, though, that overtones (and combination tones) are normally much weaker than the fundamentals and their absence from a spectrum is not necessarily a consequence of molecular symmetry.

(f) Acetylene (Point group $D_{\infty h}$) This centro-symmetric molecule possesses seven normal vibrations $(3N-5)$, of which 3, $(N-1)$, are bond stretching vibrations. By the methods indicated earlier for ethylene the forms of the vibrational modes may be deduced and are given in Fig. IV, 12.

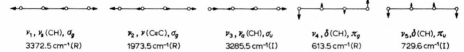

ν_1, ν_s(CH), σ_g	ν_2, ν(C≡C), σ_g	ν_3, ν_a(CH), σ_u	ν_4, δ(CH), π_g	ν_5, δ(CH), π_u
3372.5 cm⁻¹(R)	1973.5 cm⁻¹(R)	3285.5 cm⁻¹(I)	613.5 cm⁻¹(R)	729.6 cm⁻¹(I)

Fig. IV, 12. The normal modes and gas phase frequencies of acetylene. R and I denote Raman active and infra-red active respectively.

As for CO_2 and OCS, the π modes are doubly degenerate as they may take place in two mutually perpendicular directions. The frequencies are readily assigned by observation of the infra-red and Raman spectra although ν_4, not being a totally symmetric mode, is extremely weak in the Raman effect. The gas phase frequencies[8] are given below the individual modes.

(iv) Molecules possessing doubly degenerate vibrations — Symmetric top molecules

In these the moments of inertia about two mutually perpendicular axes are identical and different from that about the third, which is not zero. These symmetric top conditions represent an important class of molecular structures; and they also possess degenerate vibrations. They may be further subdivided according to the symmetry elements present and we consider first those possessing a three-fold symmetry axis.

(g) The methyl halides (Point group C_{3v}) The normal modes of molecules of point group C_{3v} may be of symmetry types a_1, a_2 or e. The operations corresponding to the symmetry elements present are rotation by $2\pi/3$ about the principal (C_3) axis and reflection in the three symmetry planes passing through this axis. All modes of species a_1 and a_2, the non-degenerate species, are symmetric to rotation about the C_3 axis but differ in their behaviour with respect to reflection in the three σ_v planes; a_1 modes are

symmetric, a_2 modes antisymmetric with respect to reflections in all three planes. The a_1 and a_2 modes have the same species, respectively, as translation along and rotation about the principal axis. The degenerate class e vibrations may take place in one of two mutually perpendicular directions orthogonal to the symmetry axis, and are not adequately described by the characters $+1$ or -1; they are represented in the group character table by the characters $+2$, $2 \cos 2\pi/3$ ($=-1$), and 0, for the operations I, C_3, and σ_v, respectively[3].

TABLE IV, 4

CHARACTERS AND SYMMETRY TYPES FOR MOLECULES OF POINT GROUP C_{3v}

C_{3v}	I	$2C_3(z)$	$3\sigma_v$	Non-genuine vibrations
A_1	$+1$	$+1$	$+1$	T_z
A_2	$+1$	$+1$	-1	R_z
E	$+2$	$2 \cos 2\pi/3$	0	T_x, T_y, R_x, R_y

For the methyl halides there are no normal vibrations of species a_2. Of the nine ($=3N-6$) fundamental modes (only six unique frequencies) there will be four, ($=N-1$) essentially bond stretching vibrations, two totally symmetric a_1 modes and one degenerate class e mode: the forms of these and the other modes are given in Fig. IV, 13.

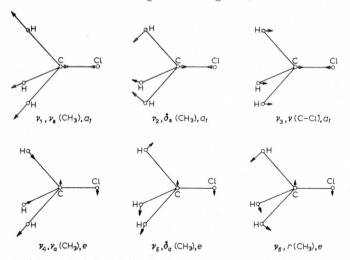

Fig. IV, 13. The normal modes of CH_3Cl. Only side views and one component of each degenerate vibration are given.

The vapour phase frequencies for methyl chloride (containing the ^{35}Cl isotope) are: $\nu_1 = 2966$ cm^{-1}, $\nu_2 = 1355$ cm^{-1}, $\nu_3 = 732$ cm^{-1}, $\nu_4 = 3042$ cm^{-1}, $\nu_5 = 1455$ cm^{-1}, $\nu_6 = 1015$ cm^{-1}. Herzberg (reference 3, Chapter 2) illustrates the manner in which the approximate form of the normal vibrations may be obtained. Comparison of the observed fundamentals in the series of methyl halides[3] indicates that for certain vibrations the frequencies remain approximately constant, suggesting that the modes concerned are essentially isolated within the (CH_3) group and do not depend upon the nature of the rest of the molecular framework. Such instances of approximate constancy of frequency have given rise to the concept of localized group vibrations, about which more will be said later. The modes involving a large amplitude of vibration for the halogen atom, primarily v_3 and v_6, give frequencies which are different for each individual molecule.

The a_1 totally symmetric modes are readily assigned, for in the Raman effect they give rise to strong polarized lines (Chapter VI) and in the infrared their vapour phase band contours are easily interpreted. Type e bands — the doubly degenerate bands — are also readily assigned by their band contours but, while they are allowed in the Raman, non-totally-symmetric vibrations are generally extremely weak. Even in the liquid phase, where the molecules appear to retain a certain degree of rotational freedom, the a_1 and e type bands can often be distinguished by an examination of their shapes and widths[9]. Observation of only six fundamentals, in place of the nine expected for a non-symmetrical molecule, provides very strong support for these molecular structures.

Certain molecules may have normal vibrations of species a_2, $e.g.$ the torsional vibration of the (CH_3) group against (CCl_3) in 1, 1, 1-trichlorethane. This is normally of little spectroscopic consequence, however, for the vibration would be expected to be very low in frequency and is, in any case, infra-red and Raman inactive.

(h) Ammonia (Point group C_{3v}) In symmetry character this molecule is entirely analogous to the methyl halides and its four fundamental vibrational modes may be likened to v_1, v_2, v_4 and v_5 of CH_3X:

$$v_1 \equiv v_s(NH_3); \quad v_2 \equiv \delta_s(NH_3); \quad v_3 \equiv v_a(NH_3); \quad v_4 \equiv \delta_a(NH_3).$$

All four fundamentals have been observed in the infra-red and the spectrum may be interpreted entirely on the basis of these four frequencies.

Even under poor resolution the $v_2[\delta_s(NH_3)]$, a_1, band at 950 cm^{-1} is seen to be a doublet. This structure arises from the finite probability that the molecule will invert its configuration during the vibration. As a result of this "umbrella" effect, each vibrational level will be split into two sub-levels, the lower symmetric and the upper antisymmetric, corresponding to symmetric and antisymmetric combinations of the wave functions belonging to the two equilibrium configurations. The form and height of the potential barrier restricting inversion will be different in appearance for all four normal modes. As the probability of barrier tunnelling is small for levels considerably below the potential barrier but quite large near the top, the splitting of the sublevels will depend markedly on the vibrational quantum number as well as on the form and frequency of the mode considered.

The quantum mechanical treatment of the problem assumes a one-dimensional oscillation of the nitrogen atom through the (H_3) plane. None of the vibrations of ammonia conforms to this condition although it is approximated by v_2, as shown by the marked splittings of 0.79 cm^{-1} and 35.7 cm^{-1} of the $v_2 = 0$ and $v_2 = 1$ levels (Fig. IV, 14). In the infra-red

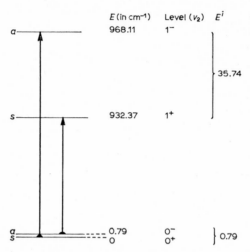

Fig. IV, 14. Energy levels and allowed transitions of the inversion doubling components for the v_2 fundamental of ammonia.

we have the selection rules $\Delta v = 1$, $s \leftrightarrow s$, $a \leftrightarrow a$, $s \leftrightarrow a$ (the signs $\leftrightarrow$ and $\leftrightarrow\!\!\!\!\!/$ indicate transitions which can or cannot take place), while in the Raman $\Delta v = 1$, $s \leftrightarrow s$, $a \leftrightarrow a$, $s \leftrightarrow\!\!\!\!\!/ a$. In the infra-red, therefore, the splitting of the v_2 band, the sum of the splittings in the ground and the first excited vibrational states, is 36.5 cm^{-1}, the zero positions of the bands being found at 931.58 cm^{-1} and 968.11 cm^{-1}.

For $v_1[v_s(NH_3)]$, a_1, the splitting of the $v_1 = 1$ vibrational energy level (E_i^i) is only 0.99 cm^{-1}, even though the fundamental frequency is 3336 cm^{-1}, suggesting a far greater displacement from the top of the barrier for this mode than is found for v_2. The inversion splittings E^i and frequencies for the normal modes of ammonia are presented in Table IV, 5.

The analysis of the detailed fine structure in the perpendicular type e bands is less easily carried out than for the parallel type a_1 bands but has been achieved recently; the inversion splitting of the $v_4 = 1$ and $v_3 = 1$ levels is found to be 1.01 and 0.36 cm^{-1}, the latter splitting being less than that observed for the ground state. For ND$_3$ the inversion splitting is considerably less than for NH$_3$, being less than 4 cm^{-1} for the $v_2 = 1$ level.

TABLE IV, 5

ENERGY LEVELS AND INVERSION SPLITTINGS FOR THE FUNDAMENTAL BANDS OF
GASEOUS AMMONIA[3, 10, 11]

v_1	v_2	v_3	v_4	Energy (in cm^{-1})	Inversion splitting E^i (in cm^{-1})	Mean frequency for the fundamental band ($v = 0 \rightarrow 1$)
0	0^s	0	0	0.00		
0	0^a	0	0	0.79	0.79	—
1^s	0	0	0	3336.2		
1^a	0	0	0	3337.2	0.99	3336.21
0	1^s	0	0	932.37		
0	1^a	0	0	968.11	35.74	949.85
0	0	1^s	0	3443.59		
0	0	1^a	0	3443.94	0.36	3443.38
0	0	0	1^s	1626.27		
0	0	0	1^a	1627.28	1.01	1626.38

(i) Benzene (Point group D_{6h})   This molecule possesses a centre of symmetry as has been shown by a careful analysis of the infra-red and Raman spectra (reference 3 gives a review of the evidence), which are entirely consistent with the D_{6h} structure. The D_{6h} point group implies a six-fold symmetry axis (the z axis) with a symmetry plane at right angles to it. For any structure of lower symmetry, such as a puckered ring configuration, more frequencies would be infra-red active than are observed as fundamentals. By following a procedure suggested by Herzberg (reference 3, section II. 4) the number of modes of each species may be determined — there are in all twelve species. The number of modes of each type is given below: $2a_{1g}$(R), $0a_{1u}$, $1a_{2g}$(ia.), $1a_{2u}$(I), $0b_{1g}$, $2b_{1u}$(ia.), $2b_{2g}$(ia.), $2b_{2u}$(ia.), $1e_{1g}$(R), $3e_{1u}$(I), $4e_{2g}$(R), $2e_{2u}$(ia.), where R, I, and ia., denote Raman active, infra-red active, and inactive in both spectra, respectively.

The class e vibrations are doubly degenerate, the class a and b vibrations non-degenerate. Consequently there are ten non-degenerate and ten doubly degenerate modes, a total of thirty normal vibrations as expected.

More than two alternative systems for numbering the normal modes have arisen, one follows WILSON[12], and another follows HERZBERG[3]. They differ from each other primarily because of the different orders of the symmetry species in the group character tables used by these authors. For general consistency in this chapter Herzberg's system will be followed although this is not now the standard sequence. The forms, species, and designations of the infra-red active modes are given in Fig. IV, 15, the numbering system of E. B. WILSON[12] being given in parentheses.

For only two of the species, a_{2u} and e_{1u}, does the dipole moment change during the vibration (as indicated by the translations T_z, and T_x and T_y, which are of these species). Accordingly, all other symmetry modes are infra-red inactive. From the character table (Table 22 of reference 3) it is seen that the a_{2u} mode is antisymmetric to the plane of the molecule (xy) and to inversion but symmetric with respect to a rotation by $60°$ $(2\pi/6)$

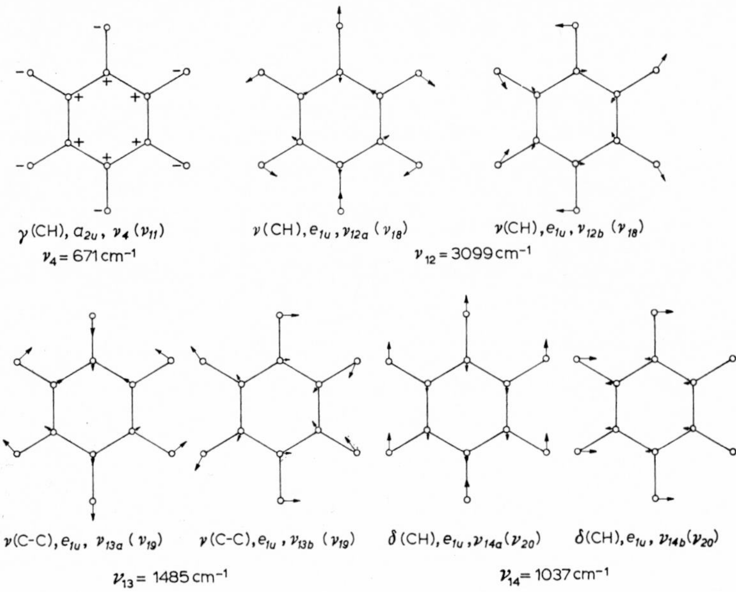

γ(CH), a_{2u}, ν_4 (ν_{11})　　　　ν(CH), e_{1u}, ν_{12a} (ν_{18})　　　　ν(CH), e_{1u}, ν_{12b} (ν_{18})
$\nu_4 = 671$ cm^{-1}　　　　　　　　　　　　$\nu_{12} = 3099$ cm^{-1}

ν(C-C), e_{1u}, ν_{13a} (ν_{19})　　ν(C-C), e_{1u}, ν_{13b} (ν_{19})　　δ(CH), e_{1u}, ν_{14a}(ν_{20})　　δ(CH), e_{1u}, ν_{14b}(ν_{20})
$\nu_{13} = 1485$ cm^{-1}　　　　　　　　　　　　　　　$\nu_{14} = 1037$ cm^{-1}

Fig. IV, 15. The approximate forms of the infra-red active fundamental vibrations of benzene — the two components of each degenerate vibration are given. The frequencies, species and numbers of the vibrations are given below the individual modes. The numbers in parentheses are the alternative numberings used by WILSON[12].

about the C_6 axis — a mode which is readily visualized and, from the sequence of the symmetry species above, is numbered ν_4. The e_{1u} modes are symmetric with respect to the plane of the molecule σ_h, degenerate to C_6 and antisymmetric with respect to inversion; from the sequence of the species given above the modes must be numbered ν_{12}, ν_{13} and ν_{14}. ν_4 is an out-of-plane bending mode of the (CH) groups, while ν_{12} and ν_{14} are in-plane stretching and bending modes of these groups, ν_{13} being a stretching mode of the C_6 skeleton.

Five strong bands are observed in the infra-red spectrum of the vapour[13], two of them constituting a fairly close doublet at 3045 cm^{-1} and 3099 cm^{-1}. The higher frequency component is assigned as ν_{12}, the other at 3045 cm^{-1} being interpreted as a combination of two skeletal vibrations, ν_{13} and ν_{16}, the latter an infra-red inactive fundamental of species e_{2g} assigned to a band in the Raman at 1585 cm^{-1}. One of the components of this combination has species e_{1u} and while this transition would normally be extremely weak, it is enhanced in intensity by resonance with the neighbouring e_{1u} fundamental ν_{12} at 3099 cm^{-1}. This resonance, termed Fermi resonance, arises when two close-lying energy levels are of the same species: the wave functions describing the two states mix and the energy levels tend to "repel" one another, whilst at the same time a sharing of the absorption intensities occurs. Confirmation of this interpretation is obtained from the study of C_6D_6, for which one strong fundamental only, at 2293 cm^{-1}, is observed in the (C–D) stretching region[13].

ν_4, ν_{13} and ν_{14} have been assigned to bands at 671 cm^{-1}, 1485 cm^{-1}, and 1037 cm^{-1}, respectively. The two strongest, completely polarized lines at 3061.9 cm^{-1} and 991.6 cm^{-1} in the Raman spectrum of the liquid[13], are interpreted as the completely symmetric a_{1g} vibrations, the higher a (C–H) stretching vibration ν_1, the lower a "ring breathing" mode ν_2. As a consequence of the very high symmetry, nine of the fundamentals are infra-red and Raman inactive and cannot be observed directly.

(v) Molecules possessing triply degenerate vibrations

In certain molecules possessing very high symmetry there may be, in addition to doubly degenerate, one or more triply degenerate modes, designated as f states. These molecules must of necessity be spherical tops, having identical moments of inertia about three mutually perpendicular axes: the prime example is methane.

(j) Methane (Point group T_d) Because of the chemical and structural identity of the four hydrogen atoms, methane has no dipole moment and is spherically symmetrical, a deduction which is confirmed by the complete absence of a pure rotational infra-red or Raman spectrum. The basic symmetry characteristics are four three-fold axes tetrahedrally directed. There are in all five symmetry species, to three of which the normal vibrations belong, a_1, e and f_2, although higher vibrational levels may also have species a_2 and f_1. The a are the non-degenerate, e the doubly degenerate,

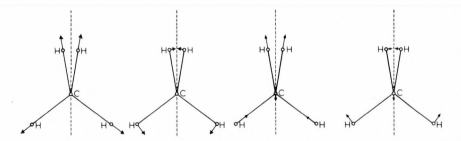

$\nu_1, a_1, (R) = 2916.5$ cm^{-1} $\nu_2, e, (R) = 1533.6$ cm^{-1} $\nu_3, f_2, (I,R) = 3018.8$ cm^{-1} $\nu_4, f_2, (I,R) = 1306.2$ cm^{-1}

Fig. IV, 16. The approximate forms of the normal modes of methane. The gas phase frequencies, species and numbers of the vibrations are given below the individual modes. R and I denote Raman active and infra-red active respectively.

and f the triply degenerate species. The normal modes of this molecule are given in Fig. IV, 16, all the vibrations being bending or stretching modes of the (C–H) bonds, one component only of each degenerate vibration being given.

The f_2 modes have the same species as translations along the three axes x, y and z, and consequently are active in the infra-red. The stretching frequency will of course occur at a higher frequency than the bending vibration and is assigned[14] to the strong infra-red band centred at $3018.8\,\mathrm{cm^{-1}}$; ν_4 is then assigned[3, 10] to a band at $1306.2\,\mathrm{cm^{-1}}$, transitions which are also observed in the Raman effect[15]. While it is forbidden by symmetry, ν_2 appears as a very weak band in the infra-red[10, 16], a result of Coriolis vibration–rotation interaction[3] between ν_2 and ν_4. This perturbation causes a mixing of the wave functions describing the two vibrational states and leads to a breakdown of the operative selection rules. The strong sharp Raman line at $2916.5\,\mathrm{cm^{-1}}$ is assigned unambiguously as ν_1, for this mode is totally symmetric and the line is completely polarized.

(1C) Isotopic substitution

In attempting to assign the fundamental frequencies of molecules a useful check is often obtained by studying the spectrum of the species in which one or more of the atoms is replaced by an isotope. This procedure does not alter the forces binding the individual atoms but due to the different masses of the isotopic species the frequencies of vibration are changed. This effect may readily be calculated for heteronuclear diatomic molecules from the equations

$$\nu_e = \frac{1}{2\pi}\sqrt{\frac{k}{\mu}}\,; \quad \mu = \frac{m_1 m_2}{m_1 + m_2}$$

giving:

$$\nu^i = \nu\left(\frac{\mu}{\mu^i}\right)^{\frac{1}{2}} = \nu\left[\frac{m_1 \cdot m_2}{m_1^i \cdot m_2^i} \cdot \frac{(m_1^i + m_2^i)}{(m_1 + m_2)}\right]^{\frac{1}{2}}, \tag{6}$$

where i refers to the isotopically substituted species. This expression is frequently of use even for polyatomic molecules where an estimated frequency shift of a particular vibration on isotopic substitution is required. Thus an isolated (O–H) or (C–H) stretching vibration may be considered as a vibration of the hydrogen atom against the molecular framework, and for deuterium substitution of the hydrogen atom the total mass of the molecule changes so little that equation (6) may be approximated by the expression,

$$\nu(\mathrm{X–D}) = \nu(\mathrm{X–H}) \cdot (m_\mathrm{H}/m_\mathrm{D})^{\frac{1}{2}} \tag{7}$$

This expression is not expected to be accurate and the observed shift is less than that calculated. Table IV, 6 gives values of the $\nu(X\text{–}H)/\nu(X\text{–}D)$ ratio for a number of different molecules, the calculated value being 1.41.

TABLE IV, 6

VALUES OF THE $\nu(XH)/\nu(XD)$ RATIO FOR SOME SIMPLE MOLECULES

$\nu(HF)/\nu(DF)$	$\nu(HCl)/\nu(DCl)$	$\nu(HBr)/\nu(DBr)$	$\nu(CH_3OH)/\nu(CH_3OD)$	$\nu(CHCl_3)/\nu(CDCl_3)$
1.36	1.38	1.39	1.35	1.34

(i) The Teller-Redlich product rule

A major advance in interpreting the effects of isotopic substitution was due to TELLER[17] and REDLICH[18] who showed that for all the vibrations of a particular species the product of the ω^i/ω values depends only on the masses of the atoms and the geometrical structure and is independent of the potential constants. They suggested the general formula:

$$\frac{\omega_1^i}{\omega_1} \cdot \frac{\omega_2^i}{\omega_2} \cdots = \left[\left(\frac{m_1}{m_1^i}\right)^\alpha \left(\frac{m_2}{m_2^i}\right)^\beta \cdots \cdots \left(\frac{M^i}{M}\right)^t \left(\frac{I_x^i}{I_x}\right)^{\delta x} \left(\frac{I_y^i}{I_y}\right)^{\delta y} \left(\frac{I_z^i}{I_z}\right)^{\delta z} \right]^{\frac{1}{2}} \quad (8)$$

M is the total molecular mass, and m_1, m_2, etc., are the masses of the individual atoms in sets of identical nuclei. The α and β terms are the numbers of vibrations contributed by each set of atoms to the symmetry species considered; they are the factors of m, m_0, etc., introduced from Tables 35 and 36 of reference 3, which are contributed by each set of nuclei; t is the number of translations of the species considered, and δx, δy, δz (the powers to which the moment of inertia ratios are raised) are 1 or 0 depending upon whether rotation about these axes has this symmetry or not. In all the above considerations degenerate vibrations, whether genuine or non-genuine, are counted only once.

The manner in which equation (8) may be used can best be illustrated by a particular example. Thus for $^{12}C_2H_2$ and $^{12}C_2D_2$ there are four species to which the normal vibrations may belong (p. 127): σ_g, σ_u, π_g and π_u. Each set of hydrogen atoms and carbon atoms contributes 1 to the term m_∞ (Table 36, reference 3), the number of sets of equivalent atoms on C_∞, but as we are not concerned with the isotopic substitution of carbon the term containing the mass of the carbon atom need not be considered. Then the set of hydrogen atoms contributes one vibration to each of the four symmetry species (*i.e.* one H–stretching vibration of species σ_g, one of species σ_u, and one H–bending vibration for each of π_g and π_u) *i.e.* α is unity for each species considered. From the group character table[3] there are no translations or rotations having species σ_g and so $t = \delta x = \delta y = \delta z = 0$. For the σ_u modes only T_z has this species, and so $t = 1$, $\delta x = \delta y = \delta z = 0$, and, as the doubly degenerate translations (T_x, T_y) count as only one, these parameters hold also for the π_u mode. For the other degenerate mode π_g, the doubly degenerate rotations also count as one, so that $t = \delta z = 0$, $\delta y = 1$. The product rule then gives:

$$\sigma_g; \quad \frac{\omega_1^D \, \omega_2^D}{\omega_1^H \, \omega_2^H} = \left[\frac{m_H}{m_D}\right]^{\frac{1}{2}} \qquad \sigma_u; \quad \frac{\omega_3^D}{\omega_3^H} = \left[\frac{m_H \cdot M_D}{m_D \cdot M_H}\right]^{\frac{1}{2}}$$

$$\pi_g; \quad \frac{\omega_4^D}{\omega_4^H} = \left[\frac{m_H \cdot I_{C_2D_2}}{m_D \cdot I_{C_2H_2}}\right]^{\frac{1}{2}} \qquad \pi_u; \quad \frac{\omega_5^D}{\omega_5^H} = \left[\frac{m_H \cdot M_D}{m_D \cdot M_H}\right]^{\frac{1}{2}} \tag{9}$$

where $M = (2m_C + 2m_H)$. In deriving this substitution rule, Teller and Redlich assumed the harmonic oscillator approximation and so in equations (8) and (9) the zero-order frequencies should strictly be used. However, as may be seen from Table IV, 7, little error is introduced when the observed fundamentals, ν, are used, and in these cases the observed ratio should be slightly greater than that calculated.

TABLE IV, 7

COMPARISON OF OBSERVED AND CALCULATED "PRODUCT RULE" RATIOS FOR C_2H_2 AND C_2D_2

	$\sigma_g,\ \nu_1^D \nu_2^D / \nu_1^H \nu_2^H$	$\sigma_u,\ \nu_3^D / \nu_3^H$	$\pi_g,\ \nu_4^D / \nu_4^H$	$\pi_u,\ \nu_5^D / \nu_5^H$
Calculated	0.707	0.734	0.834	0.734
Observed	0.715	0.738	0.825	0.739

If the isotopic substitution lowers the symmetry of the molecule then the product rule holds only for the species of the lower symmetry type. Thus in C_2HD only the σ and π species could be considered, giving:

$$\sigma; \quad \frac{(\omega_1\omega_2\omega_3)^{C_2HD}}{(\omega_1\omega_2\omega_3)^{C_2H_2}} = \left[\frac{m_H \cdot M^{C_2HD}}{m_D \cdot M^{C_2H_2}}\right]^{\frac{1}{2}} \qquad \pi; \quad \frac{(\omega_4\omega_5)^{C_2HD}}{(\omega_4\omega_5)^{C_2H_2}} = \left[\frac{m_H \cdot M^{C_2HD}}{m_D \cdot M^{C_2H_2}} \cdot \frac{I^{C_2HD}}{I^{C_2H_2}}\right]^{\frac{1}{2}}$$

$$\tag{10}$$

relations which are found to explain adequately the observed frequencies. Of course, when isotopic substitution changes the symmetry of a molecule, the operative selection rules refer to this new point group and the normal modes will not necessarily have the same form as those of the unsubstituted species.

In addition to the product rule of Teller and Redlich, there is another useful relation given by Decius and Wilson[19] called the sum rule. This rule may be used when the frequencies of isotopic species obeying chemical exchange reactions of the form $H_2O + D_2O = 2\,HDO$ (or $C_2H_2 + C_2D_2 = 2\,C_2HD$) are known. In these instances the sum rule may be expressed in the form:

$$\sum_i \nu^2(H_2O) + \sum_i \nu^2(D_2O) = 2 \sum_i \nu^2(HDO) \tag{11}$$

Mizushima[10] examines in detail these isotopic substitution rules and introduces others which are of value in comparing the frequencies of the different rotational isomers of a particular compound.

(1D) Localized group vibrations

For the molecules discussed above it is possible to assign the observed frequencies with very little ambiguity to particular normal modes of vibration. For more complex molecules of low symmetry it is difficult to determine the form of the vibration and most, if not all, of the modes are infra-red and Raman active. While it is very difficult in these instances to assign the observed frequencies completely, considerable aid in this direction is often obtained because certain groups of atoms give rise to vibrations at or near the same frequencies irrespective of the molecule in which the group occurs. Such groups are terminal groups such as (O–H), (C–H), (C=O), or (N=O), although certain internal groupings, such as (C≡C), also illustrate the effect. These characteristic frequencies arise when the normal mode is largely localized in the group considered and its frequency is sufficiently different from the frequencies of the rest of the molecular framework to remain largely unaffected by them.

By careful observations of series of compounds containing certain groups, the frequency ranges of large numbers of these group vibrations have been determined, the values of which may be obtained by reference to suitable texts on the subject and will be discussed more fully in Chapter VII. Within a particular frequency range the changes may be a consequence of the surrounding molecular framework, and these variations may even provide evidence concerning the environment of a particular group. The bending vibrations are, with a few exceptions, less well characterized and tend to be more sensitive to environmental effects, partly because they are inevitably less localized and possibly because they occur at lower frequencies and can interact more with other vibrations of similar frequency. Even for the stretching vibrations, where neighbouring groups are similar in character, coupling of vibrations may occur to such an extent that the concept of localized group vibrations becomes invalid (cf. CO_2, p. 125).

Where symmetry elements exist these should of course always be taken into account, for they lead to extremely useful subdivisions of the molecular vibrations as already described. It may be found that hydrogen atoms lying slightly off an axis or plane of symmetry lead to an effective lowering of the molecular symmetry and in these instances it is convenient to consider the vibrations of the hydrogen atoms and the heavy atom skeleton separately. For the latter the hydrogen and the atom to which it is attached are regarded as a rigid group. Even for fairly large molecules considerable use may be made of localized or group symmetry, which is frequently of value in interpreting relatively complex spectra.

(2) Vibration–Rotation Spectra

To a first approximation the total energy of a molecule carrying out simultaneous rotation and vibration may be expressed as the sum of two factors:

$$T_{vr} = E_{vr}/hc = G(v_1, v_2, \ldots) + F_{(v)}(J, K), \tag{12}$$

where the term value $G(v_1, v_2, \ldots)$ is given by a general expression for the vibrational levels of the molecule and $F_{(v)}(J, K)$ gives the energy levels associated with each vibrational state. $v_1, v_2, \ldots$ are the vibrational quantum numbers of the individual modes and J and K are quantum numbers associated with the rotation of the molecule. Ignoring the anharmonic nature of the modes, the following formula is obtained for the energy levels of a molecule with degenerate vibrations:

$$G(v_1, v_2, \ldots) = \sum_i \omega_i(v_i + d_i/2) \tag{13}$$

Here ω_i is the fundamental vibration frequency of the ith normal mode, and d_i is the degree of degeneracy.

The rotational term values for the principal molecular types have been given in Chapter III and are summarized below for linear, spherical top, and symmetric top molecules in nondegenerate vibrational states.

Linear molecules $(I_A = 0,\ I_B = I_C)$:

$$F_{(v)}(J) = B_{(v)}J(J+1) \tag{14}$$

Spherical top molecules $(I_A = I_B = I_C)$:

$$F_{(v)}(J) = B_{(v)}J(J+1) \tag{15}$$

Symmetric top molecules:

(i) Prolate tops $(I_A < I_B = I_C)$:

$$F_{(v)}(J, K) = B_{(v)}J(J+1) + (A_{(v)} - B_{(v)})K^2 \tag{16}$$

(ii) Oblate tops $(I_A = I_B < I_C)$:

$$F_{(v)}(J, K) = B_{(v)}J(J+1) + (C_{(v)} - B_{(v)})K^2 \tag{17}$$

The energy levels of an asymmetric top molecule $(I_A \neq I_B \neq I_C)$ are considerably more complex and cannot in general be given by simple expressions of this sort. The constants $A_{(v)}$, $B_{(v)}$ and $C_{(v)}$, are termed the rotational constants and, given in wavenumbers, are defined by the relations;

$$A_{(v)}(\text{in cm}^{-1}) = h/8\pi^2 c I_A; \text{ etc.} \tag{18}$$

with $I_A \leq I_B \leq I_C$ (i.e. $A_{(v)} \geq B_{(v)} \geq C_{(v)}$). h and c are Planck's constant ($= 6.625 \cdot 10^{-27}$ erg sec) and the velocity of light ($= 2.99793 \cdot 10^{10}$ cm sec^{-1}) respectively. I, the moment of inertia, is defined by the relation

$$I = \sum_i m_i r_i^2 \ \text{g cm}^2 \qquad (19)$$

m_i = (atomic weight of ith atom)$\cdot 1.66 \cdot 10^{-24}$ g .

r_i = distance of ith atom from the axis.

Interaction of vibration and rotation is primarily manifested in the fact that the rotational constants differ very slightly for the various vibrational levels. This dependence of $A_{(v)}$, etc. on the vibration of the molecule is signified by the use of the subscript (v) to indicate the vibrational level concerned.

If, as is usually the case, the interaction of vibration and rotation is not too large, the selection rules are the same as those of the pure rotation and vibration spectra separately: in this case, however, it must be remembered that for the rotational selection rules it is the direction of the change of the dipole moment during the vibration rather than the direction of the permanent dipole moment which is of significance. Accordingly, we may attempt to interpret the vibration–rotation spectra in the light of the information derived from the earlier sections. Analysis of the vibration–rotation bands generally provides strong support for a proposed assignment and frequently values may be obtained for the rotational constants (and hence moments of inertia) which can lead to accurate estimates of some or all of the internuclear distances (Chapter III).

Centrifugal distortion will not be considered here as it is observable only for very small molecules, or for very high J values of other molecules.

(2A) Linear molecules ($I_A = 0$, $I_B = I_C$)

Diatomic and linear polyatomic molecules are treated together, for the expressions for their rotational levels are the same and the same general conclusions apply.

The total vibrational and rotational energy is given by:

$$T_{vr} = E_{vr}/\boldsymbol{hc} = \sum_i \omega_i(v_i + d_i/2) + B_{(v)} J(J+1) \qquad (20)$$

The spectral activity of a particular vibration in the infra-red is governed by the symmetry considerations given in Section I. Provided a mode is infra-red active it is sufficient for discussion of the fine structure or band contour to consider any vibrational transition as a single sharp line of frequency ν_0 (not ω_i which is the fundamental frequency for infinitesimal vibrational amplitude). The shape of the band is then determined by the rotational selection rules operating.

Provided the dipole change is along the symmetry axis, the transitions between the rotational levels are governed, as for the pure rotational spectra, by the selection rule

$$\Delta J = \pm 1 \qquad (21)$$

For the pure rotational spectra studied in absorption (Chapter III) only the transitions $\Delta J = +1$ are significant. There the transitions $\Delta J = -1$ correspond to emission. For the vibration–rotation spectra they have to be taken into account. The transition frequencies for absorption from a lower state (v'', J'') (usually considered as the ground vibrational state, $v'' = 0$) to an upper state (v', J') are given by:

$$\nu = \nu_0 + [B'J'(J'+1) - B''J''(J''+1)],$$

where $B' (= h/8\pi^2 c I'_B)$ and B'' are the rotational constants in the upper and lower levels of the vibrational state considered. With selection rule $\Delta J = \pm 1$, this yields expressions for two series of lines, the R and P branches respectively.

$$\Delta J = J' - J'' = +1;$$
$$R(J'') = \nu_0 + B'(J''+1)(J''+2) - B''J''(J''+1),$$
$$= \nu_0 + 2B' + (3B' - B'')J'' + (B' - B'')J''^2; \quad J'' = 0, 1, 2, \ldots \qquad (22)$$

$$\Delta J = J' - J'' = -1;$$
$$P(J'') = \nu_0 + B'(J''-1)J'' - B''J''(J''+1),$$
$$= \nu_0 - (B' + B'')J'' + (B' - B'')J''^2; \quad J'' = 1, 2, \ldots \qquad (23)$$

If $B' = B'' (= B)$, as is very closely the case for most fundamentals, equations (22) and (23) reduce to:

$$R(J'') = \nu_0 + 2B(J''+1); \quad J'' = 0, 1, 2, \ldots \qquad (24)$$

$$P(J'') = \nu_0 - 2BJ''; \quad J'' = 1, 2, \ldots \qquad (25)$$

The first transition of the R branch occurs from the level $J'' = 0$ of the ground vibrational state to the level $J' = 1$ of the upper vibrational state, while for the P branch the first transition from the ground state cannot occur from $J'' = 0$, but only from $J'' = 1$ to the $J' = 0$ level of the upper vibrational state. The line frequencies in the P and R branches are:

$$R(J''); \ \nu_0 + 2B, \ \nu_0 + 4B, \ \nu_0 + 6B, \ldots; \ P(J''); \ \nu_0 - 2B, \ \nu_0 - 4B, \ \nu_0 - 6B, \ldots \ (26)$$

That is, each branch represents a series of lines of separation $2B$, the R branch occurring on the high frequency side, the P branch on the low frequency side of the band centre.

Examination of equations (24) and (25) indicates that there is no transition corresponding to ν_0, the fundamental frequency itself. Such a line would only occur if the transition $\Delta J = 0$ were allowed, in which case a strong sharp line (the Q branch) should be observed at the fundamental frequency. Such a transition is allowed for linear molecules, but only if the vibrational level considered possesses an angular momentum about the

C_∞ axis. Nitric oxide exhibits such a Q branch in its vibration–rotation spectrum, arising because the molecule in its ground state possesses an odd electron and there is an electronic angular momentum about the axis. The line frequencies of this Q branch are:

$$\Delta J = 0; \quad Q(J'') = \nu_0 + B'J''(J''+1) - B''J''(J''+1)$$

$$Q(J'') = \nu_0 + (B'-B'')J'' + (B'-B'')J''^2 \tag{27}$$

If $B' = B''$ this series of lines coincide at a frequency ν_0.

No other heteronuclear diatomic or linear polyatomic molecule possesses odd electrons and the parallel bands (transitions along the symmetry axis) of such molecules do not exhibit Q branches. However, the perpendicular modes (transitions at right angles to the symmetry axis) of linear polyatomic molecules are associated with an angular momentum about the symmetry axis by virtue of the motions of the nuclei perpendicular to that axis, and consequently they exhibit Q as well as P and R branches. For these bands the selection rules are $\Delta J = 0, \pm 1$, and the line frequencies are given by equations (22), (23) and (27). Thus the parallel bands of linear molecules consist of P (low frequency) and R (high frequency) branches, each having lines of spacing $2B$. The band centre is shown by a line missing at the frequency ν_0, the separation of the first line of the R branch from the first line of the P being $4B$. For the perpendicular bands of linear molecules, P, Q, and R branches are present, the P and R branches reproducing the previous pattern.

When measured accurately, the P and R line separations are not quite constant and the Q branch, if present, is found to consist of a series of very closely spaced lines. These effects arise because B' and B'' are not quite equal and the full equations for the line frequencies, (22), (23) and (27), have to be considered. If $B' < B''$, as is usually the case for parallel bands, the lines of the R branch will converge towards the high frequency side, those of the P branch will diverge towards the low frequency side following equations (22) and (23). B' and B'' are accurately determinable from the frequency differences of selected pairs of lines in the P and R branches. Thus the lines in the branches are numbered according to the J'' value in the lower state, the first line of the R branch being $R(0)$, the next $R(1)$, etc., the first line of the P branch being $P(1)$, etc. From (22) and (23) then;

$$R(J'') - P(J'') = 2B'(2J''+1) \tag{28}$$

$$R(J''-1) - P(J''+1) = 2B''(2J''+1) \tag{29}$$

Further, if the lines of the Q branch are resolved it is possible to determine $(B'-B'')$ very accurately from equation (27).

Fig. IV, 17 illustrates a typical parallel vibration–rotation band of a linear molecule, the fundamental band of the diatomic molecule hydrogen chloride at 2886 cm^{-1}.

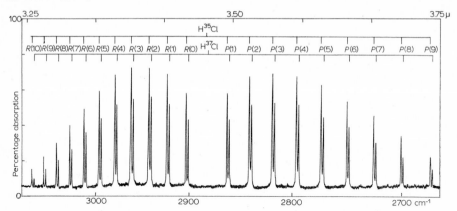

Fig. IV, 17. The fundamental absorption band of hydrogen chloride under high resolution. Pressure = 70 mm Hg in a 10-cm cell.

The lines are of approximately constant spacing with a gap in the band centre corresponding to the absence of the $\Delta J = 0$ transition. The splitting of each of the "lines" into two components is due to the two chlorine isotopes, ^{35}Cl and ^{37}Cl, the separation of the two band centres agreeing very well with that calculated[20] from the equation $\nu_e = (1/2\pi)\sqrt{k/\mu}$ (= 2.1 cm^{-1}). From the frequencies of the lines and relations (28) and (29) the rotational constants for both species in the ground and first vibrational levels are given. By observing a number of overtones it is possible to measure the $B_{(v)}$ values for the higher vibrational levels. Typical values of $B_{(v)}$ are given below:

$$H^{35}Cl; \quad B_0 = 10.44 \text{ cm}^{-1}, \ B_1 = 10.14 \text{ cm}^{-1}, \ B_2 = 9.83 \text{ cm}^{-1}$$
$$H^{37}Cl; \quad B_0 = 10.43 \text{ cm}^{-1}, \ B_1 = 10.12 \text{ cm}^{-1}, \ B_2 = 9.78 \text{ cm}^{-1}$$

These constants can be represented by the equation

$$B_{(v)} = B_e - \alpha(v + \tfrac{1}{2}), \tag{30}$$

where α is the vibration–rotation interaction constant and B_e is the rotational constant for the hypothetical vibrationless state. The B_0 values have been established most precisely from microwave data. In order to determine the B_e values, however, it is essential to determine values for $B_{(v)}$ in an excited vibrational state. The B_e values as measured from infra-red spectroscopy[20] for $H^{35}Cl$ and $H^{37}Cl$ are 10.594_3 cm^{-1} and 10.578_5 cm^{-1} respectively.

Fig. IV, 18 indicates a perpendicular band of a linear molecule, the doubly degenerate bending vibration ν_5 of acetylene: as is apparent from this figure, P, Q and R branches are present, the Q branch being very pronounced.

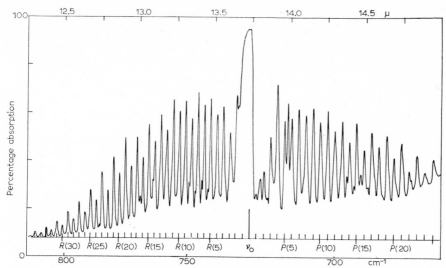

Fig. IV, 18. The ν_5 fundamental band of acetylene under high resolution.
Pressure = 31 mm Hg in a 10-cm cell.

The influence of vibration–rotation interaction reflected in the dependence of $B_{(v)}$ upon v is partly a result of the anharmonic nature of the vibrations, and partly a result of harmonic nuclear motions[3]. The measured moments of inertia are values averaged over the whole of the vibrational motion and consequently vary from one vibrational level to another.

Where there are a number of different vibrational modes the rotational constants are governed by the expression

$$B_{(v)} = B_e - \sum_i \alpha_i (v_i + d_i/2) \qquad (31)$$

Thus the $B_{(v)}$ values for hydrogen cyanide are given by the formula[3]
$B_{(v)} = 1.4878 - 0.0093(v_1 + \frac{1}{2}) + 0.0007(v_2 + 1) - 0.0108(v_3 + \frac{1}{2})\text{cm}^{-1}$. ν_2 is the doubly degenerate (HCN) bending vibration, and in this case $d_i = 2$; v_1 and v_3 are the quantum numbers of the non-degenerate $\nu(\text{C}\equiv\text{N})$ and $\nu(\text{C–H})$ modes respectively. It is seen that α is of the order of $10^{-2}B_e$ to $10^{-3}B_e$. For parallel vibrations α is usually positive while for degenerate modes it may be positive or negative.

In determining precise internuclear distances from rotational constants the B_e values should be used. This is particularly important when it is necessary to resort to isotopic substitution to determine these parameters. The rotational constants as measured from the analysis of the pure rotational spectra invariably refer to the ground vibrational state B_0, and without measurements of the rotational constants in other vibrational states it is not possible to determine B_e, and hence true r_e values. It is this particular fact which limits the accuracy of internuclear distances determined by microwave techniques to a few parts in 10^{-3}Å. The vibration–rotation spectra may not in principle suffer from this disadvantage, but the measurements themselves are inherently less accurate except for the very smallest molecules.

The intensity distribution of the rotational lines is determined by the thermal population of the molecules among the rotational levels of the lower vibrational state. As indicated earlier (Chapter III, p. 96) this thermal distribution for linear molecules is governed by the expression

$$N_J \propto (2J+1) \cdot e^{-hcBJ(J+1)/kT} \tag{32}$$

The maximum of this relation occurs at the J_{max} value given by

$$(J_{max}+\tfrac{1}{2}) = (kT/2hcB)^{\frac{1}{2}} \tag{33}$$

Accordingly, even if the individual rotational lines are not resolved, it is still possible to obtain a rough estimate of the rotational constant from the separation of the maxima of the P and R branches, and if T is the temperature of observation this separation is given by

$$\Delta\nu = (8kTB/hc)^{\frac{1}{2}} = 2.358(TB)^{\frac{1}{2}} \text{ cm}^{-1} \tag{34}$$

(i) Statistical weights of the rotational levels

If the molecule studied is of point group $\boldsymbol{D}_{\infty h}$, the rotational wavefunction may be symmetric (s) or antisymmetric (a) with respect to an exchange of the identical nuclei present. Alternate rotational levels are then symmetric or antisymmetric in character and have different statistical weights according to the pairs of identical nuclei present. Atomic nuclei frequently possess nuclear spin, and it is this factor which produces an alternation in the statistical weights, and hence populations, of the symmetric and antisymmetric levels. Where all nuclei, excepting possibly that at the centre of symmetry, have zero spin, as is the case for carbon dioxide, the antisymmetric rotational levels are completely absent.

For acetylene, which has one pair of identical nuclei (H) of spin $I = \tfrac{1}{2}$, the antisymmetric levels have three times the statistical weight of the symmetric levels, as is the case for hydrogen (H_2) itself. While transitions may occur between levels of the same symmetry, transitions between symmetric and antisymmetric levels are strictly forbidden: accordingly, as for hydrogen, there are *ortho* and *para* species. The symmetry properties of the rotational levels in the σ_g and σ_u states, the combining states for parallel bands, are given in Fig. IV, 19. The possible transitions are also indicated and two typical $(\sigma_u - \sigma_g)$ bands, for carbon dioxide and acetylene, are illustrated diagrammatically, no account being taken of the thermal populations of the different levels.

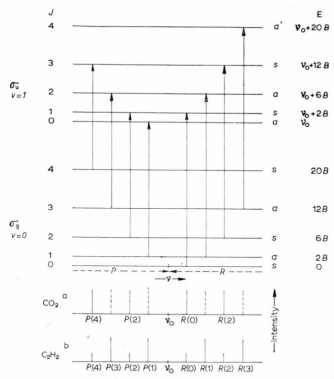

Fig. IV, 19. Energy level diagram for $\sigma_u - \sigma_g$ bands of linear polyatomic molecules, giving schematic spectra for CO_2 and C_2H_2. (a) Broken lines indicate missing lines. (b) Statistical weights of $s : a$ in the ratio $1 : 3$. For $\pi_u - \sigma_g$ bands a strong Q branch is found at ν_0 corresponding to $\Delta J = 0$.

For carbon dioxide all lines corresponding to transitions from the lower state with J'' odd are absent. Further, the zero gap in CO_2 is not $4B$, as for non-symmetric linear molecules, but $6B$, the first $[P(1)]$ line of the P branch being absent. In addition, the separation of successive lines is now not $2B$ but $4B$. For acetylene it is apparent that there is an intensity alternation of the rotational lines of the type strong, weak, strong, weak, etc.. This intensity alternation is apparent in the perpendicular band, ν_5, of acetylene at 729 cm^{-1} (Fig. IV, 18).

The presence or absence of such intensity alternations is usually sufficient to show whether or not a linear molecule possesses a centre of symmetry. Thus the absence of an intensity alternation for the fundamental bands of N_2O shows that it cannot possess a centro-symmetric structure.

(2B) Symmetric top molecules

Symmetric tops consist of those molecules having two identical moments of inertia, the third moment of inertia being different but not equal to zero.

If the unique moment of inertia is less than the other two the molecule is termed a prolate symmetric top, if it is greater it is an oblate symmetric top. Methyl chloride and benzene, two representative molecules of these classes, are shown in Fig. IV, 20, which depicts the axes of inertia associated with them.

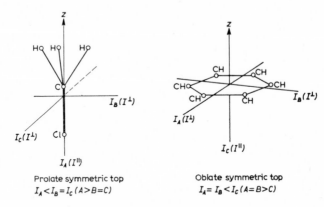

Prolate symmetric top
$I_A < I_B = I_C \, (A > B = C)$

Oblate symmetric top
$I_A = I_B < I_C \, (A = B > C)$

Fig. IV, 20. Axes of inertia for methyl chloride and benzene.

The energy levels of a symmetric top molecule in a non-degenerate vibrational state, according to equations (12), (16) and (17), are:
Prolate symmetric top;

$$T_{vr} = E_{vr}/hc = G(v_1, v_2, \ldots) + B_{(v)} J(J+1) + (A_{(v)} - B_{(v)}) K^2 \qquad (35)$$

Oblate symmetric top;

$$T_{vr} = E_{vr}/hc = G(v_1, v_2, \ldots) + B_{(v)} J(J+1) + (C_{(v)} - B_{(v)}) K^2 \qquad (36)$$

The quantum numbers are governed by the restriction $J \geq K$, i.e.

$$J = K, \; K+1, \; K+2, \ldots; \quad J = 0, 1, 2, \ldots \qquad (37)$$

and all levels with $K > 0$ are doubly degenerate corresponding to the two directions of rotation about the figure axis[3].

For general simplicity the band structures of the prolate symmetric tops will be examined: the same methods may be used for the oblate symmetric tops and the results are closely similar. As for the linear molecules, the rotational constants $A_{(v)}$, $B_{(v)}$ and $C_{(v)}$ differ slightly for each vibrational level considered and their values in the different vibrational levels are governed by expressions such as (31).

(i) Parallel type fundamentals

All allowed infra-red transitions between two non-degenerate vibrational states[3] (parallel type fundamentals) have for the rotational selection rules:

$$\Delta K = 0, \; \Delta J = \pm 1, \text{ if } K = 0; \quad \Delta K = 0, \; \Delta J = 0, \pm 1, \text{ if } K \neq 0. \qquad (38)$$

For these bands the dipole change occurs in the direction of the figure axis (the z axis in Fig. IV, 20) and cannot therefore be modulated by the rotation about this axis, *i.e.* only rotational levels of the same K value may combine with one another. For a particular K level, according to $\Delta J = 0, \pm 1$, there are three simple branches P, Q, and R, with the same equations relative to the zero position ν_0^{sub} of this sub-band as equations (22), (23) and (27) for linear molecules, the $K = 0$ level having no Q branch. The complete parallel ($\|$) band is obtained by a superposition of a number of such sub-bands, corresponding to the various values of K populated at the temperature of observation. Such a parallel band is shown schematically in Fig. IV, 21.

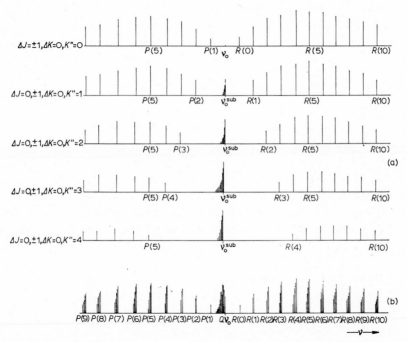

Fig. IV, 21. Sub-bands of a $\|$ band and complete $\|$ band of a symmetric top — the sub-bands in (a) are directly superimposed in (b). In both (a) and (b) only a slight difference between $(A'-B')$ and $(A''-B'')$ is assumed. The heights of the lines indicate the intensities calculated on the basis of the assumption that $A'' = 5.25$, $B'' = 1.70$ cm^{-1}, and $T = 144°$ K. The intensities indicated for the sub-band $K = 0$ should be divided by 2. (*Adapted from G. Herzberg, Molecular Spectra and Molecular Structure, copyright van Nostrand, 1950³*).

Due to the differences of the rotational constants in the various vibrational levels, the origins of the sub-bands ($J = 0$) do not coincide exactly but vary according to the relation:

$$\nu_0^{\text{sub}} = \nu_0 + [(A'_{(v)} - A''_{(v)}) - (B'_{(v)} - B''_{(v)})] K''^2 \qquad (39)$$

If $B'_{(v)} = B''_{(v)}$ and $A'_{(v)} = A''_{(v)}$ then all the lines of the Q branches of each sub-band coincide, as do the various rotational lines of the different sub-bands. The whole band thus consists of a sharp Q branch, and lines of the P and R branches with a spacing of $2B$. If $B'_{(v)}$ and $A'_{(v)}$ differ slightly from $B''_{(v)}$ and $A''_{(v)}$ then the sub-bands will no longer exactly coincide and the P and R branches will show a convergence similar to that for the linear molecules. By the methods described earlier for the linear molecules, the $B_{(v)}$ values of the upper and lower states may be measured.

The observed parallel type bands of prolate symmetric tops are very similar in appearance to the perpendicular type fundamentals of linear molecules (*e.g.* Fig. IV, 18). The main difference arises from the fact that the individual rotational "lines" are now multiplets arising from the superposition of all the lines of the different sub-bands; generally, however, the splitting due to this effect is not resolved. Observation of such a simple band structure for a non-linear molecule establishes, at least to a good approximation, that the molecule is a symmetric top. For the higher vibrational levels, $B'_{(v)}$ and $A'_{(v)}$ may differ markedly from $B''_{(v)}$ and $A''_{(v)}$ and such a band structure would not be apparent.

The relative intensity of the Q to the P and R branches varies with the ratio I_A/I_B. The smaller this ratio the lower the relative intensity of the Q to the P and R branches, until for the parallel band of a linear molecule, having $I_A/I_B = 0$, the Q branch is completely absent.

Inversion doubling, for molecules such as ammonia which have very low potential barriers restricting inversion, produces a splitting of the individual rotational lines, the magnitude of which is the sum of the splittings of the lower and upper vibrational states (Section I, p. 129).

(ii) Perpendicular type fundamentals

When the vibrational transition moment occurs in a direction at right angles to the highest-fold symmetry axis, the resulting bands are termed perpendicular bands. The perpendicular type fundamentals, for molecules which are symmetric tops by virtue of their symmetry, occur by transitions from the non-degenerate ground state to the doubly degenerate first $(v_i = 1)$ vibrational level. For these bands the rotational selection rules are:

$$\Delta J = 0, \pm 1, \quad \Delta K = \pm 1 \qquad (40)$$

Corresponding to every value of K and ΔK we have a sub-band, consisting of a P, Q, R, series arising from the associated transitions $\Delta J = 0, \pm 1$. The frequencies of the lines of such a sub-band are the same relative to the zero position of the sub-band, $\nu_0^{sub}(J = 0)$, as found earlier for the parallel bands. However, in this instance, even when $B'_{(v)} = B''_{(v)}$ and $A'_{(v)} = A''_{(v)}$, due to the selection rule $\Delta K = \pm 1$ the zero positions of the sub-bands, ν_0^{sub}, do not coincide. For the frequencies of $\nu_0^{\mathrm{sub}}(J = 0)$ we obtain:

$$\nu_0^{\mathrm{sub}} = \nu_0 + (A'_{(v)} - B'_{(v)})(K'' \pm 1)^2 - (A''_{(v)} - B''_{(v)})K''^2$$

$$\nu_0^{\mathrm{sub}} = \nu_0 + (A'_{(v)} - B'_{(v)}) \pm 2(A'_{(v)} - B'_{(v)})K'' + [(A'_{(v)} - B'_{(v)}) - (A''_{(v)} - B''_{(v)})]K''^2$$

$$(41)$$

For simplicity it will be assumed that $A'_{(v)} = A''_{(v)} = A$, and $B'_{(v)} = B''_{(v)} = B$, in which case equation (41) reduces to:

$$\nu_0^{\mathrm{sub}} = \nu_0 + (A - B) \pm 2(A - B)K'' \qquad (42)$$

where K'' is the quantum number of the lower (ground) vibrational state, and ν_0 the fundamental vibrational frequency. The $(+)$ sign in equation (42) refers to the positive sub-bands (R branch, $\Delta K = +1$) for which $K'' = 0$, 1, 2, . . ., and the $(-)$ sign to the negative sub-bands (P branch, $\Delta K = -1$) for which $K'' = 1, 2, \ldots$. Equation (42) gives the frequencies of the zero

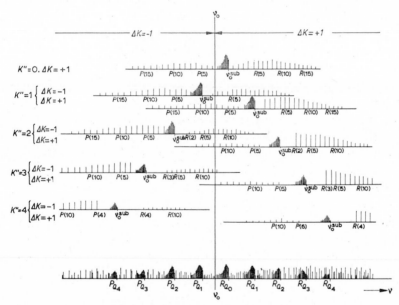

Fig. IV, 22. Sub-bands of a $\perp$ band and complete $\perp$ band of a symmetric top — the complete band is shown in the bottom strip. The spectrum is drawn on the assumption that $A' = 5.18$, $A'' = 5.25$, $B' = 0.84$, $B'' = 0.85$ cm^{-1} and $\zeta_i = 0$. The intensities were calculated for a temperature of 144° K. It should be realized that if the lines of an individual Q branch are not resolved, the resulting line would stand out much more prominently than might appear from the spectrum given. (*Adapted from G. Herzberg, Molecular Spectra and Molecular Structure, copyright van Nostrand, 1950³*).

positions of the various sub-bands, and represents a series of Q branches separated by $2(A - B)$. The structure of such a sub-band is shown diagrammatically in Fig. IV, 22.

From every K'' level populated at the temperature of observation, apart from the $K'' = 0$ level, there arise two sub-bands, the one to the high frequency side of the band centre corresponding to $\Delta K = +1$, the other to the low frequency side corresponding to $\Delta K = -1$. The individual rotational lines of the sub-bands are clearly apparent, and, as for the parallel bands, with increasing K values, many lines are missing near the sub-band centres corresponding to the restriction $J \geq K$. Also the intensity of corresponding lines in the P and R branches of the sub-bands for larger K values is no longer approximately the same, lines with $\Delta J = \Delta K$ having the greater intensity[3].

As the individual rotational lines of the different sub-bands corresponding to transitions $\Delta J = \pm 1$ overlap to such an extent, they generally form a complex, weak, and usually unresolved background. The individual Q branches form the most pronounced feature of these perpendicular bands. The intensities of the Q branches decrease from the centre and the band appears to have a diffuse contour, with a broad maximum at its centre, upon which is superposed a Q branch sequence of separation $2(A-B)$.

The Q branches are labelled $^{R}Q_{K''}$ or $^{P}Q_{K''}$ (corresponding to transitions $\Delta K = +1$ and $\Delta K = -1$ respectively), where K'' is the rotational quantum number of the lower vibrational level from which the transition occurs. Thus the first line of the positive sub-band is $^{R}Q_{0}$, the second $^{R}Q_{1}$, etc., and the first line of the negative sub-band is $^{P}Q_{1}$, the second $^{P}Q_{2}$, etc.. The centre of this band then occurs, according to equation (42), midway between the first lines of the ^{P}Q and ^{R}Q sequences, the separation between these two lines being $2(A-B)$, the same as all subsequent separations, *i.e.* there is no zero gap. For prolate symmetric tops the ^{R}Q series occurs to the high frequency side of the band centre.

When the differences between the rotational constants in the upper and lower states are considered, the expression obtained accounts satisfactorily for the slight convergence of the Q branches. The fine structure details of the Q branches are due to the slight differences in the $B_{(v)}$ values of the upper and lower vibrational states.

Fig. IV, 23 illustrates a typical perpendicular fundamental of a prolate symmetric top molecule, methyl iodide, in which the series of Q branches is readily seen, the average separation being 7.7 cm^{-1}. Equation (42) predicts that the separation of the Q branches should be the same for all three perpendicular fundamentals of methyl iodide. In fact the separation of 7.7 cm^{-1} observed for this, the (CH_3) rocking fundamental ν_6, is considerably different from the values of 11.7 cm^{-1} and 9.0 cm^{-1} observed for the other two perpendicular bands $\nu_5[\delta_a(CH_3)]$ and $\nu_4[\nu_a(CH_3)]$. This discrepancy is a result of a specific interaction of vibration and rotation termed Coriolis interaction, which produces marked changes between bands which would be expected to have virtually identical structures. The coupling occurs as a result of certain forces, the Coriolis forces, which

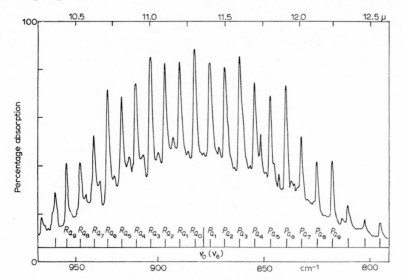

Fig. IV, 23. The ν_6 fundamental band of methyl iodide under high resolution. Gas pressure = 240 mm Hg in a 10-cm cell.

arise when a system of particles (molecule) is both rotating and vibrating. The Coriolis forces, directed at right angles to the direction of motion of each particle and at right angles to the axis of rotation, are proportional to the masses of the particles, their apparent velocities with respect to a coordinate system rotating with the molecule, and the angular velocity of this rotating coordinate system with respect to a fixed coordinate system[3]. If one of the components of the doubly degenerate vibrations is excited, e.g. ν_6 of CH_3I, the Coriolis forces produced, acting at right angles to the directions of motion of the nuclei and to the axis of rotation, act in the same directions as the displacement vectors of the other component ν_6' of this perpendicular vibration. As the frequencies of these two degenerate modes are identical, in the rotating molecule the transition from the one to the other mode of vibration will occur very quickly if the one mode is first excited. As a result the nuclei do not move in straight lines during the vibration but in ellipses, which are the flatter the smaller the coupling between the two components of the degenerate mode.

Because of Coriolis interaction the nuclei in these degenerate modes acquire an additional, vibrational, angular momentum $\zeta_i h/2\pi$ $(0 \leq |\zeta_i| \leq 1)$ about the symmetry axis. As this vibrational angular momentum may act in the same way or oppose the rotational angular momentum, each K rotational level is split into two sub-levels, a splitting which increases with increasing rotation (K) about the top axis and is zero for $K = 0$.

Accordingly, the rotational term value of a symmetric top molecule in which one degenerate vibration is singly excited is:

$$F_{(v)}(J, K) = B_{(v)}J(J+1) + (A_{(v)} - B_{(v)})K^2 \mp 2A_{(v)}\zeta_i K \qquad (43)$$

$$T_{vr} = E_{vr}/\boldsymbol{hc} = G(v_1, v_2, \ldots) + B_{(v)}J(J+1) + (A_{(v)} - B_{(v)})K^2 \mp 2A_{(v)}\zeta_i K \qquad (44)$$

ζ_i is a constant, the Coriolis constant, whose value depends on the mode considered. This expression (44) differs from the previous expression (35) which gives the rotational energy levels in non-degenerate vibrational states, by the factor $\mp 2A_{(v)}\zeta_i K$. Equation (42) deduced previously for the Q branch sequences is valid provided $\zeta_i = 0$, *i.e.* the nuclei possess no vibrational angular momentum in the degenerate state. Where this is not the case, the frequencies of the Q branch sequences may be obtained from a consideration of expressions (40), (35) and (44), the selection rules and the rotational energies in the ground (non-degenerate) and degenerate first vibrational levels. Although Coriolis interaction produces a splitting of the K levels into two sub-levels it does not produce a splitting of the rotational lines, for the transition with the selection rule $\Delta K = +1$ from the ground state may only occur to the level of expression (44) having the term $-2A_{(v)}\zeta_i K'$; the transition with the selection rule $\Delta K = -1$ may only occur from the ground state to the rotational level of the degenerate state having the term $+2A_{(v)}\zeta_i K'$. The frequencies of the Q branches are given by the expression:

$$\nu_0^{\text{sub}} = \nu_0 + A(1-2\zeta_i) - B \pm 2(A(1-\zeta_i) - B)K'' \qquad (45)$$

This expression is closely analogous to (42) and represents a series of Q branches separated by $2(A(1-\zeta_i)-B)$; the $^RQ_0$ line occurs at a frequency $\nu_0 + A(1-2\zeta_i) - B$, the $^PQ_1$ line at $\nu_0 - (A-B)$, so that the centre of the band, ν_0, occurs at a distance $(A-B)$ from the first line of the P branch.

As ζ_i may vary between -1 and $+1$ for each perpendicular band it is not possible to determine A or B unambiguously from a measurement of the Q branch separations of one band. However, if the values of the Q branch spacings are measured for all perpendicular fundamentals such a determination is possible, for while the ζ_i's are different for each mode considered, their sum is a constant: for the methyl halides this sum for the three perpendicular modes $\nu_4(\nu_a(\mathrm{CH_3}))$, $\nu_5(\delta_a)(\mathrm{CH_3}))$ and $\nu_6(r(\mathrm{CH_3}))$, is[3]:

$$\zeta_4 + \zeta_5 + \zeta_6 = B/2A \qquad (46)$$

Then,

$$\Delta\nu_4 + \Delta\nu_5 + \Delta\nu_6 = 2(A(1-\zeta_4) - B) + 2(A(1-\zeta_5) - B) + 2(A(1-\zeta_6) - B)$$

and,

$$\Delta\nu_4 + \Delta\nu_5 + \Delta\nu_6 = 6A - 7B \qquad (47)$$

For methyl iodide this sum is 28.4 cm^{-1}, and as $B(= 0.28$ cm$^{-1})$ is known from the analysis of a parallel band, A is 5.06 cm^{-1}, and then[3] $\zeta_4 = 0.058$, $\zeta_5 = -0.216$, $\zeta_6 = 0.187$. A sufficiently accurate estimate of B, which is generally much less than A, is frequently obtained from the P and R separation of a parallel band[21].

From Fig. IV, 23 it is seen that the Q branches exhibit an intensity alternation of the type strong, weak, weak, strong, etc. This arises because of the symmetry properties of the rotational levels. For molecules of symmetry C_{3v} possessing three identical nuclei of spin $I = \frac{1}{2}$, such as CH$_3$I, the ground state rotational levels with $K = 0, 3, 6, 9$, etc., have twice the statistical weight of the levels with $K = 1, 2, 4, 5$, etc. As the intensities depend on the thermal population of the levels in the ground state, the perpendicular bands exhibit the intensity alternation observed. Observation of such an intensity alternation in a Q branch sequence is sufficient to establish that the rotating species has C_3 symmetry about the axis of rotation. The first line $^R Q_0$ of the Q branch series always forms a strong line near the band centre and this is of considerable value in correctly placing the band origin.

For molecules which are symmetric tops not on account of geometric symmetry but because two moments of inertia happen accidentally to be equal, this sort of strong Coriolis interaction does not occur. The perpendicular bands of such molecules thus may have a series of Q branches as indicated above but with a spacing of $2(A-B)$ and not $2(A(1-\zeta_i)-B)$.

(2C) Spherical top molecules $(I_A = I_B = I_C)$

The total energy of these molecules in the non-degenerate ground vibrational state is:

$$F_{(0)}(J) = B_0 J(J+1), \tag{48}$$

where B_0 is the rotational constant averaged over the ground vibrational state. For molecules of point group T_d, e.g. methane, only the class f_2 fundamentals are infra-red active, and for these modes again Coriolis interaction is possible between the three degenerate components of each vibration. This interaction results in a splitting of the rotational levels to give three sub-levels, designated $F^{(+)}$, $F^{(0)}$ and $F^{(-)}$, levels. The term values for these levels are:

$$F_{(v)}^{(+)}(J) = B_{(v)} J(J+1) + 2 B_{(v)} \zeta_i (J+1) \tag{49}$$

$$F_{(v)}^{(0)}(J) = B_{(v)} J(J+1) \tag{50}$$

$$F_{(v)}^{(-)}(J) = B_{(v)} J(J+1) - 2 B_{(v)} \zeta_i J \tag{51}$$

where ζ_i is again the Coriolis interaction constant. For transitions between the ground and first vibrational levels the selection rules are:

$$\Delta J = 0, \pm 1 \tag{52}$$

$$\Delta J = 0, \; a_1 \leftrightarrow F_{(v)}^{(0)}; \quad \Delta J = +1, \quad a_1 \leftrightarrow F_{(v)}^{(-)}; \quad \Delta J = -1, \; a_1 \leftrightarrow F_{(v)}^{(+)} \tag{53}$$

a_1 represents the symmetry of the vibrational level involved (ref. 3, p. 452). If $B'_{(v)} = B''_{(v)}$, as is almost the case for fundamentals, the selection rules, with the above restrictions, give:

$$R(J) = \nu_0 + 2B(1-\zeta_i) + 2B(1-\zeta_i)J''; \; J'' = 0, \; 1, \; 2, \ldots \tag{54}$$

$$Q(J) = \nu_0 \tag{55}$$

$$P(J) = \nu_0 - 2B(1-\zeta_i)J''; \; J'' = 1, \; 2, \ldots \tag{56}$$

These three branches represent a band structure identical with the perpendicular bands of linear molecules, except that in this case the line separation is not $2B$ but $2B(1-\zeta_i)$. The observed structures of these bands is in fact almost identical with a typical perpendicular band of a linear molecule or a parallel band of a symmetric top. When account is taken of the difference between $B'_{(v)}$ and $B''_{(v)}$ the expression obtained explains the convergence of the lines of the P and R branches and the multiplicity of lines in the Q branch.

For a molecule such as methane there are but two triply degenerate f_2 vibrations, ν_3 and ν_4 (Section I), and in such cases the sum $(\zeta_3 + \zeta_4)$ is equal to $\frac{1}{2}$. Accordingly, if the line separation $2B(1-\zeta_i)$ in each band is measured the value of B may be obtained, and hence the (C–H) internuclear distance. For ν_3 and ν_4 of methane, ζ_3 and ζ_4 are 0.05 and 0.45 respectively, the line spacings being 9.9 cm^{-1} and 5.7 cm^{-1} at the band centre. The B value determined by this means is 5.22 cm^{-1}, while correction for the dependence of $B_{(v)}$ on v gives[3, 10] $B_{(0)} = 5.249$ cm^{-1}.

(2D) Asymmetric top molecules $(I_A \neq I_B \neq I_C)$

To simplify the discussion of the band structures of these molecules, which will in any case be restricted to the fundamentals, the rotational constants will be assumed to be independent of the vibrational level considered. As before we have,

$$I_A < I_B < I_C, \text{ and therefore } A > B > C.$$

The observed bands may be divided into three distinct types, A, B and C, depending on whether the dipole moment change occurs along the axis of least, intermediate, or greatest moment of inertia. For molecules of low symmetry, hybrid bands resulting from the superposition of components of all these types may occur.

If the three moments of inertia are considerably different then the resulting bands are indeed extremely complex, and the very simple water molecule is one of the very few cases for which a complete analysis has been achieved. It is only in the limiting cases where the molecule approximates to a symmetric top or a linear molecule that any regularity of fine structure can be expected. In these cases the band structures are determined according to the ratio $\rho = I_A/I_B = B/A$ for planar molecules, structures which obey the condition,

$$I_A + I_B = I_C. \tag{57}$$

For these planar molecules, if $\rho = 1$, then $I_A = I_B < I_C$, which is the condition for an oblate symmetric top; for $\rho = 0$ on the other hand, $I_A = 0$ and hence $I_B = I_C$, so that this represents a linear molecule. Further, when ρ is very small (≈ 0.1), $I_B \approx I_C$ and then $I_A < I_B \approx I_C$, which of course approximates to a prolate symmetric top. Accordingly, depending on the agreements between the different values of the moments of inertia, the band contours for dipole transitions along the A, B, and C, axes resemble the parallel or perpendicular type bands of symmetric top or linear molecules. The type of band of a symmetric top molecule which the A, B, and C, type bands of planar asymmetric top molecules will resemble are given in Table IV, 8 for ρ near 0 and 1.

TABLE IV, 8

SYMMETRIC TOP BANDS CORRESPONDING TO THE A, B, AND C, TYPE BANDS OF PLANAR ASYMMETRIC TOP MOLECULES FOR $\rho \approx 1$ AND $\rho \approx 0$

	Near oblate symmetric top $A \approx B > C$, $\rho \approx 1$	Near prolate symmetric top $A > B \approx C$, $\rho \approx 0.1$	Near linear molecule $B \approx C$, $\rho \approx 0.0$
Dipole vibration of asymmetric top along the axis (below)	Band type of corresponding oblate symmetric top	Band type of corresponding prolate symmetric top	Band type of corresponding linear molecule
A	$\perp$	$\parallel$	$\parallel$
B	$\perp$	$\perp$	$\perp$
C	$\parallel$	$\perp$	$\perp$

Then for the near oblate symmetric top, where $I_A \approx I_B$, transitions along the A and B axes resemble the perpendicular bands of the oblate symmetric top (having $I_A = I_B$), while dipole changes along the unique C axis correspond to the parallel bands. It can easily be seen that for the near prolate symmetric top only the A-type band will resemble the parallel band of the corresponding symmetric top. The near prolate tops are perhaps of rather more general interest than the others, primarily because they frequently have one very small moment of inertia and hence widely spaced rotational lines, and also because interesting molecules such as ethylene and formaldehyde belong to this class.

The vibration–rotation spectrum of ethylene will be considered in some detail. The term value for a molecule of this type is:

References pp. 164–165

$$F(J, K) = \frac{(B+C)}{2} \cdot J(J+1) + \left(A - \frac{(B+C)}{2}\right)K^2 \qquad (58)$$

Type-A bands, for which the selection rules are $\Delta J = 0, \pm 1;\ \Delta K = 0$, as for the symmetric tops, resemble the parallel type bands of the prolate symmetric top — a pronounced central Q branch, and P and R branches with "lines" of spacing $2(B+C)/2$. The type-B and type-C bands, with selection rules $\Delta J = 0, \pm 1;\ \Delta K = \pm 1$, resemble the perpendicular bands of the symmetric top, *i.e.* a series of Q branches with, in this case, a separation of $2(A - \frac{1}{2}(B+C))$. Towards the outsides of the bands the Q branches of

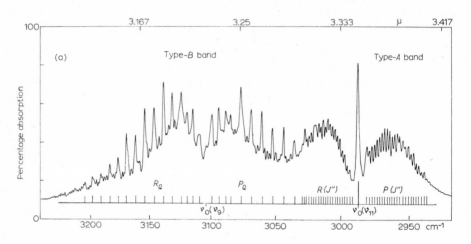

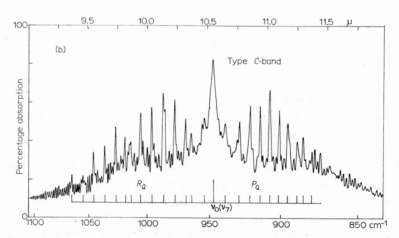

Fig. IV, 24. Observed type-A, type-B and type-C fundamental bands of ethylene. (a) The **3.3** micron region, gas pressure = 80 mm Hg in a 10-cm cell, illustrating the type-A and type-B bands ν_{11} and ν_9. (b) The 10 micron region, gas pressure = 40 mm Hg in a 10-cm cell, illustrating the type-C band ν_7.

the type-B and -C bands have very similar structures. However, near the band centres these structures are very different. This arises because with increasing ρ the type-C band goes over into a parallel type band of a symmetric top in which the Q branches collect in the band centre, while the type-B band remains a perpendicular type band for all values of ρ and there is no piling up of Q branches in the band centre. Thus for $\rho = 0.16$, as in this case, certain of the Q branches have collected in the centre and the type-C band contains a very strong central maximum. The type-B band contains no central maximum for any value of ρ, in fact there is a slight decrease in intensity of the Q branches near the band centre.

Fig. IV, 24 illustrates typical A, B and C, type bands of ethylene, for which A is the (C=C) axis, and C the axis perpendicular to the plane of the molecule. In contrast with the type-B band, the type-A and -C bands possess strong central maxima which are frequently more pronounced for the type-C than the type-A bands. From the line separations, type-A bands yield values for $(B+C)/2$, while both type-B and type-C bands yield $2[A-(B+C)/2]$, which for small values of ρ as in this case $(B \ll A)$, is nearly equal to $2A$.

For larger molecules, which are not necessarily planar, and where fine structure details are usually absent, BADGER and ZUMWALT[22] have represented the A, B and C, type band contours of asymmetric tops in terms of two parameters $\rho = (A-C)/B$ and $s = (2B-A-C)/(A-C)$. In general contour these bands resemble those given above, both type-A and type-C bands having pronounced central Q branches, that of the C-type normally

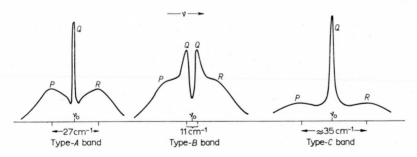

Fig. IV, 25. Typical A, B and C type band contours, drawn to scale for nitromethane, $A \approx 0.41$ cm^{-1}, $B \approx 0.37$ cm^{-1}, $C \approx 0.19$ cm^{-1}; $\rho = (A-C)/B = 0.59$,
$$s = (2B-A-C)/(A-C) = 0.64.$$

being very much stronger relative to the P and R branches, while the type-B band has a doublet Q branch. Typical A, B and C, type band contours are given in Fig. IV, 25.

While it is not possible to determine moments of inertia accurately from these band contours, they are frequently of very considerable value in confirming the structure of a molecule or in determining the symmetry class of a particular vibration.

(2E) Overtone bands and combination bands

In addition to the fundamental bands of a molecule, a number of bands arising from multiple excitation of one or more vibrations — overtones or combination tones — are observed. While they are considerably weaker than the fundamentals, the intensities of the fundamentals may vary to such a degree that the combination bands of certain fundamentals may be more intense than other weak fundamentals. Overtones normally occur from the ground vibrational state to the second or higher level of a vibration v_i, their intensities decreasing very rapidly with increasing vibrational quantum number. Combination bands may be of two types: summation bands, simultaneous excitation of two (or more) vibrations of frequency v_i and v_k from the ground state to give a band of frequency v_i+v_k; difference bands occur by transitions from molecules already in a vibrational state v_i by absorption of radiation to a higher vibrational state v_k — the frequency of the transition being (v_k-v_i). As there are initially very few molecules in the state v_i, the fraction depending on the Boltzmann factor $e^{-hcv_i/kT}$, and as the transition is a binary combination ($\sum_i |\Delta v_i| = 2$), difference bands of this sort are very weak and are rarely observed unless v_i is very low. The intensities of the bands vary markedly with temperature. As a result of anharmonicity, their frequencies differ slightly from the values expected from the frequencies of the fundamentals, being usually somewhat lower.

The symmetry species of the overtones and combination tones are obtained readily from the species of the fundamentals (HERZBERG[3], Chapter II.3). It should be remembered that because a fundamental is infra-red inactive it does not follow that a combination tone involving this fundamental is also infra-red inactive (and *vice versa*). For the higher levels of degenerate vibrations the overtones (and combination tones) may consist of a number of components of different species. Thus for the first overtone of the e type fundamentals of the methyl halides there are two active component levels, a_1 and e, of slightly different energy (a result of anharmonicity) — the bands generally overlapping one another. Providing the species of the transition is determined, the expected rotational structure is readily obtained, for the selection rules are the same for all vibrations of a particular symmetry class, although slight differences occur as a result of vibration–rotation interaction. In particular, where Coriolis interaction is significant, the values of ζ_i for the higher vibrational levels are not the same as for the fundamentals, although they are frequently multiples of these values.

(i) "Hot" bands

Where an appreciable fraction of the molecules exist in an excited vibrational state ν_i, one frequently observes what are termed "hot" bands. For simple harmonic motion of a molecule in the state ν_i the probability of its transferring to a state $2\nu_i$ (i.e. $v_i = 1$ to 2) is the same as for the transition from $v_i = 0$ to $v_i = 1$. As there are considerably fewer molecules in this state than in the ground state, the transition will be weaker than the fundamental, but for low values of ν_i (less than 1000 cm^{-1}) it may still be appreciable. These bands are usually observed where a Q branch is prominent in a vibration–rotation band, the transition $v_i = 1 \rightarrow 2$ giving a band of similar structure, its weaker Q branch being somewhat displaced from the main Q branch. The displacement of the two band centres gives a measure of the anharmonicity of the vibration.

An unusual type of "hot" band occurs when one low frequency vibration ν_i is excited in the lower and upper states in addition to another vibration ν_k in the upper state — the resulting band being of frequency $(\nu_k + \nu_i - \nu_i)$. As the change in quantum number Δv_k is only 1, the transition probability is the same as for the fundamental (ν_k) band, the intensity ratios depending on the number of molecules in each state. As a result of coupling of ν_i and ν_k the two bands do not quite coincide, and many such bands have been observed.

(3) Condensed Phase Spectra

In determining molecular structures it is advisable to study the spectra of molecules which are essentially unaffected by external influences such as specific molecular interactions. The nearest approach to this state of affairs occurs in the gas phase where at low gas pressures ($< 10^{-2}$ atmosphere) neighbouring molecules can affect but little the molecular energy levels. Even at pressures in excess of 1 atmosphere, however, such interactions are frequently insignificant as is reflected by the extreme sharpness of the rotational fine structure lines: at these pressures certain highly polar molecules tend to interact, usually as a result of hydrogen bonding, but such interactions generally decrease very rapidly with decreasing gas pressures or increasing temperatures. With increasing pressure of gas the rotational lines become progressively broader until finally they blur out completely. The bands still retain traces of their P, Q and R type contours until even these at very high pressures finally coalesce to give a broad band with a pronounced maximum in the band centre. At these pressures the gas density is generally approaching that of the liquid and the behaviour of the rotational fine structure lines with increasing density indicates the sort of changes which might be observed in the spectra on passing to the liquid state.

In the liquid and solution phases the vibrational bands frequently possess a comparatively simple form, usually consisting of a single maximum at the appropriate vibrational frequency. The shape of the band can normally be *approximated* by a Lorentz-type curve[23], rotational fine structure is almost invariably absent and the bands have half-widths (width at half peak height) of 5–15 cm^{-1}, caused, as in the high pressure gas, by frequent collisions and specific short-lived molecular interactions. On passing to the solid state the molecules have far less freedom of movement and the lines tend to be somewhat narrower — a phenomenon which increases markedly with decreasing temperature.

In certain cases, notably those involving hydrogen bonding, there may be a very marked interaction between the molecules in the condensed phase, an effect which produces a change in the whole character of the spectrum. This change is not surprising for the absorbing species may not now be a monomer but a multimer, such as a carboxylic acid dimer, which would not be expected to have a spectrum identical with that of the monomer: many similarities arising from certain functional groups may still exist and the most marked changes will occur for those groups directly involved in the hydrogen bonding, in particular the ν(X–H) vibration. Such complex (multimeric) species may frequently be broken down to the monomer, most easily by dilution in a non-interacting solvent; these aspects of condensed phase spectra will be considered in more detail in Chapter XII.

Apart from factors affecting the widths and shapes of bands in the condensed states, certain other features become apparent: thus the vibrational bands are not found at the same frequency as for the corresponding band in the gas but are displaced somewhat, normally to low frequencies, the frequencies decreasing in the order

$$\nu_{gas} > \nu_{solution \ (non-polar \ solvent)} > \nu_{liquid} > \nu_{solid}$$

The shifts may be as much as several per cent but are generally very much less; some typical values are given in Table IV, 9.

Attempts have been made to correlate such frequency shifts with bulk parameters, such as the dielectric constant or refractive index of the medium, but in the more polar media specific molecular interactions assume increasing importance and do not allow of a simple interpretation of these frequency displacements (Chapter XII).

In addition to such frequency displacements it is found that certain bands, both fundamentals and higher harmonics, which would normally be inactive or at least very weak, become apparent in the spectra. To a certain extent this is due to the fact that in these states the intensity is not spread over the whole of the rotational band contour but is concentrated at one particular frequency and hence the band is sharper and more no-

TABLE IV, 9

FUNDAMENTAL VIBRATION FREQUENCIES IN THE GASEOUS, LIQUID AND SOLID
STATES[3]

Molecule	Vibrational mode	ν_{gas} (cm^{-1})	ν_{liquid} (cm^{-1})	ν_{solid} (cm^{-1})
HCl		2886	2785	2768 (100° K)
CO₂	ν_1, σ_g	1388.3	1387.5	1388
	$2\nu_2$, σ_g	1285.5	1285.5	1285
	ν_2, π_u	667.3		656
	ν_3, σ_u	2349.3		2288 (87° K)
SO₂	ν_1, a_1	1151.2	1144.3	
	ν_2, a_1	519	524.5	
	ν_3, b_1	1361	1336	
CHCl₃	ν_1, a_1	3033	3018.9	
	ν_2, a_1	672	668.3	
	ν_3, a_1	363	365.9	
	ν_6, e	262	262	

ticeable. However, this is not the only reason, as is apparent from the fact that certain bands arise in the condensed states which are forbidden in the gas at normal pressures.

In crystalline states the activity of a particular vibration is dependent not only upon the molecular symmetry but also on the structure of the unit cell. It is the symmetry and number of molecules in the unit cell which is of significance in determining the activity of a particular mode in the solid state. As these factors usually lower the effective symmetry, more vibrations become infra-red active than would be anticipated if the symmetry of the isolated molecule were considered. These effects lead to an appreciable coupling of vibrations and frequently marked splittings of what would be expected to be simple bands — aspects of solid state spectra which will be discussed in Chapter VIII.

The molecules in a liquid have no preferred orientation but have a range of environments. In this state the molecules have considerable freedom of movement and it is possible for the molecular symmetry to be distorted during close collisions with other molecules. Unlike the case of the solid, where the crystal gives rise to a set of selection rules that are generally rigidly obeyed although they may be different from those of the free molecule, in the liquid there is no preferred orientation and during close collisions the molecular symmetry may be completely removed so that all vibrations to some degree become infra-red active. The molecular symmetry, however, is still of very great value, for even with such distortions the infra-red forbidden bands of a particular substance will still be comparatively weak compared with the allowed bands.

The profusion of bands in the liquid and crystal spectra of benzene cast doubt for some considerable time upon its D_{6h} point group, until INGOLD *et al.*[13], and subsequently MAIR and HORNIG[24], succeeded in establishing this high symmetry. In the crystal state the observation of large numbers of fundamental and overtone bands which would, from the normal molecular symmetry, be inactive, were shown to be allowed transitions when the crystallographic site-symmetry of the molecule was discussed.

(3A) Rotation of molecules in the condensed phase

Perhaps the most noticeable changes between gas and condensed phase spectra arise as a result of the disappearance of discrete rotational fine structure lines or characteristic band contours. While the rotational fine structure lines, with one notable exception, are blurred out completely, there is considerable evidence to suggest that certain molecules possess rotational energy even if it does not establish that changes in this motion are quantized.

By their observation of rotational lines in the Raman spectrum of liquid hydrogen McLENNAN and McLEOD[25] showed that quantized rotations persisted in that liquid. ALLIN, HARE and MacDONALD[26] later found that the fundamental frequency was weakly active in the infra-red and that there were numerous rotational lines corresponding to $\Delta J = 0, \pm 2$: selection rules which correspond to those of the Raman effect. The explanation is that the molecular symmetry is distorted during close collisions so that the fundamental frequency becomes infra-red active. The dipole moment induced during these close collisions depends on the polarizability of the molecule so that the operative selection rules are effectively those of the Raman rather than the infra-red spectra. VAN KRANENDONK and BIRD[27] were able to interpret the spectra successfully and to account for the forces giving rise to the induced absorption.

"Induced absorptions" have also been observed by KETELAAR[28] and COULON *et al.*[29] in high pressure mixtures of hydrogen with various gases such as N_2 and CO_2. Further, in mixtures of such gases, new bands due to simultaneous transitions are observed at frequencies which are the sum (and difference) of frequencies of both component molecules. These simultaneous transitions are also observed in liquid mixtures. Some typical values of these combination frequencies are given in Table IV, 10.

For molecules larger than hydrogen, for which the rotational lines are more closely spaced, fine structure is almost invariably absent in the condensed phase. However, even for certain of these cases, there is the possibility that rotational-type motions may contribute to the shapes of the infra-red bands (*cf.* the spectra of highly compressed gases). Such cases would inevitably refer to molecules having at least one very low moment of inertia, and even in these cases it would be essential that hydrogen bond or dipolar interactions should be absent, for such effects would certainly prevent the quasi-free rotation. Accordingly, it is only as dilute solutions

TABLE IV, 10

SIMULTANEOUS VIBRATIONAL TRANSITIONS IN HIGH PRESSURE GAS MIXTURES[28]

(all frequencies in cm^{-1})

Mixture A B	ν_A involved	ν_B involved	Calculated frequency $(\nu_A + \nu_B)$	Observed frequency
$N_2 + H_2$	2331	4155	6486	6500
$HCl + H_2$	2886	4155	7041	7050
$HBr + H_2$	2559	4155	6714	6720
$CO_2 + H_2$	2349	4155	6504	6510
$CO_2 + N_2$	2349	2331	4680	4670
$CO_2 + N_2$	667	2331	2998	2996

in non-polar solvents, or for non-polar substances in the other states as well, that such motions might become apparent. Methane[30], the methyl halides[9], and the hydrogen halides in inert solvents[31], are among many examples where the shapes of the absorption bands have been attributed to such rotational motions: their band shapes are frequently closely analogous to those found in the gas but without the detailed fine structure lines. One characteristic feature of them is that while they may retain P and R branches with maxima virtually undisplaced from their equilibrium positions, there is invariably a strong broad branch in the band centre which, presumably, arises from the pure vibrational transition of a species in which the rotation is largely restricted. As the temperature is lowered the intensity of this central branch increases relative to the P and R, for the rotational motions will tend to decrease in significance as the higher rotational levels become depopulated.

In the solid state, particularly at low temperatures, rotation is usually completely eliminated. Even in this state, however, for very small molecules rotational motions may still be present, and fine structure details in the infra-red spectra of ammonia and water in inert gas matrices[32] have been attributed to the rotation of the molecules.

(3B) Rotational isomerism

Among many other effects which occur on passing from the gaseous to liquid and solid states are changes in the relative proportions of any rotational isomers which may be present. In certain molecules internal rotation about one or more single bonds may occur to yield conformations which are of comparable stability. If the energy barrier restricting the rotation about the bond is not large — as is usually the case for single bonds — then the rotational isomers will be able to transform from the one to the other fairly readily and a dynamic equilibrium will be set up. The relative proportions of the species will depend on the physical environment. It has been found that the spectra of systems which are complex in the gaseous and liquid states because a number of isomers are present often become comparatively simple in the solid state. In the latter state, in general, one conformation forms a stable lattice more readily than another. Thus for 1, 2-dichlorethane in the solid state, the molecule has the *trans* rather than the *gauche* form[10]. As the separate isomers each have their own characteristic infra-red or Raman spectra, and as the relative proportions of the species may change with the physical state or the temperature, infra-red spectroscopy provides an invaluable means of studying this phenomenon[33]. Many such studies have been carried out and values obtained for the differences in internal energy of the rotational isomers.

REFERENCES

[1] E. B. WILSON, J. C. DECIUS and P. CROSS, *Molecular Vibrations*, McGraw-Hill, London, 1955.
   H. EYRING, J. WALTER and G. E. KIMBALL, *Quantum Chemistry*, Wiley, New York, 1949.
   J. R. PARTINGTON, *Treatise on Physical Chemistry* (Vol. 5), Longmans, London, 1954, p. 201 *et seq.*,
   H. WEYL, *Symmetry*, Princeton Univ. Press, Princeton, 1952.
   S. BHAGAVANTAM AND T. VENKATARAYADU, *Theory of Groups and its Applications to Physical Problems*, 2nd Ed., Andhra Univ. Press, Waltair (India), 1951.
   G. PLACZEK, *Handbuch der Radiologie*, Bd. VI/2, Akademische Verlag, Leipzig, 1934.
[2] *Report on Notation for the Spectra of Polyatomic Molecules*, J. Chem. Phys., 23 (1955) 1997.
[3] G. HERZBERG, *Molecular Spectra and Molecular Structure*, II, *Infra-red and Raman Spectra of Polyatomic Molecules*, Van Nostrand, New York, 1945.
[4] H. H. NIELSEN, *Phys. Rev.*, 59 (1941) 565; 62 (1942) 422.
[5] W. G. BURNS and H. J. BERNSTEIN, *J. Chem. Phys.*, 18 (1950) 1669.
   W. H. EBERHARDT and T. G. BURKE, *J. Chem. Phys.*, 20 (1952) 529.
[6] B. L. CRAWFORD, J. E. LANCASTER and R. G. INSKEEP, *J. Chem. Phys.*, 21 (1953) 678.
   T. FELDMAN, J. ROMANKO and H. L. WELSH, *Can. J. Phys.*, 34 (1956) 737.
   D. H. RANK, E. R. SHULL and D. W. E. AXFORD, *J. Chem. Phys.*, 18 (1950) 116.
   B. P. STOICHEFF, *Advances in Spectroscopy* (Vol. 1), Editor, H. W. THOMPSON, Interscience, London, 1959.
[7] C. R. BAILEY and A. B. D. CASSIE, *Proc. Roy. Soc.* (London), *Ser. A*, 135 (1932) 375.
   H. C. ALLEN, E. K. PLYLER and L. R. BLAINE, *J. Chem. Phys.*, 26 (1957) 400.
   H. J. CALLOMON, D. C. McKEAN and H. W. THOMPSON, *Proc. Roy. Soc. (London), Ser. A*, 208 (1951) 341.
[8] T. FELDMAN, G. G. SHEPHERD and H. L. WELSH, *Can. J. Phys.*, 34 (1956) 1425.
   E. E. BELL and H. H. NIELSEN, *J. Chem. Phys.*, 18 (1950) 1382.
[9] W. J. JONES and N. SHEPPARD, *Trans. Faraday Soc.*, 56 (1960) 625.
[10] J. LECOMTE, *Encyclopedia of Physics* (Vol. XXVI *Light and Matter* II), Editor, S. FLÜGGE, Springer-Verlag, Berlin, 1958. *Spectroscopie dans l'infrarouge.*
   S. MIZUSHIMA, *ibid., Raman effect.*
[11] J. S. GARING, H. H. NIELSEN and K. N. RAO, *J. Mol. Spectry.*, 3 (1959) 496.
   W. S. BENEDICT, E. K. PLYLER and E. D. TIDWELL, *J. Chem. Phys.*, 29 (1958) 829; 32 (1960) 32.
[12] E. B. WILSON, *Phys. Rev.*, 45 (1934) 706.
[13] C. R. BAILEY, J. B. HALE, C. K. INGOLD and J. W. THOMPSON, *J. Chem. Soc.*, (1936) 931.
   W. R. ANGUS, C. R. BAILEY, J. B. HALE, C. K. INGOLD, A. H. LECKIE, C. G. RAISIN, J. W. THOMPSON and C. L. WILSON, *J. Chem. Soc.*, (1936) 971.
[14] D. R. J. BOYD, H. W. THOMPSON and R. L. WILLIAMS, *Proc. Roy. Soc. (London), Ser. A*, 213 (1952) 42.

[15] T. FELDMAN, J. ROMANKO and H. L. WELSH, *Can. J. Phys.*, **33** (1955) 138.
B. P. STOICHEFF, C. CUMMING, G. E. ST. JOHN and H. L. WELSH, *J. Chem. Phys.*, **20** (1952) 498.

[16] J. S. BURGESS, E. E. BELL and H. H. NIELSEN, *J. Opt. Soc. Amer*, **43** (1953) 1058.

[17] E. TELLER, quoted in W. R. ANGUS, C. R. BAILEY, J. B. HALE, C. K. INGOLD, A. H. LECKIE, C. G. RAISIN, J. W. THOMPSON and C. L. WILSON, *J. Chem. Soc.*, (1936) 978.

[18] O. REDLICH, *Z. physik. Chem. (Leipzig)*, B **28** (1935) 371.

[19] J. C. DECIUS and E. B. WILSON, *J. Chem. Phys.*, **19** (1951) 1409.

[20] I. M. MILLS, H. W. THOMPSON and R. L. WILLIAMS, *Proc. Roy. Soc. (London), Ser. A*, **218** (1953) 29.
J. PICKWORTH and H. W. THOMPSON, *Proc. Roy. Soc. (London), Ser. A* **218** (1953) 37.

[21] S. L. GERHARD and D. M. DENNISON, *Phys. Rev.*, **43** (1933) 197.

[22] R. M. BADGER and L. R. ZUMWALT, *J. Chem. Phys.*, **6** (1938) 711.

[23] R. N. JONES, *Technique of Organic Chemistry (Chemical Applications of Spectroscopy)* Editor, A. WEISSBERGER, Interscience, New York, 1956.

[24] R. D. MAIR and D. F. HORNIG, *J. Chem. Phys.*, **17** (1949) 1236.

[25] J. C. McLENNAN and J. H. McLEOD, *Nature*, **123** (1929) 160; *Trans. Roy. Soc. Can.*, **23** (1929) 19.

[26] E. J. ALLIN, W. F. J. HARE and R. E. MacDONALD, *Phys. Rev.*, **98** (1955) 554.

[27] J. VAN KRANENDONK and R. B. BIRD, *Physica*, **17** (1951) 953.

[28] J. P. COLPA and J. A. A. KETELAAR, *Mol. Phys.*, **1** (1958) 14.
J. FAHRENFORT and J. A. A. KETELAAR, *J. Chem. Phys.*, **22** (1954) 1631.
J. A. A. KETELAAR, *Infra-red Spectra of Compressed Gases. Pressure Induced and Simultaneous Transitions*, Instituto superiore di Sanità, Rome, Vol. II, Part III (1959).

[29] R. COULON, J. ROBIN and B. VODAR, *Compt. rend.*, **240** (1955) 956.

[30] M. F. CRAWFORD, H. L. WELSH and J. H. HARROLD, *Can. J. Phys.*, **30** (1952) 81.

[31] J. LASCOMBE, P. V. HUONG and M. JOSIEN, *Bull. soc. chim. France*, (1959) 1175.
M. O. BULANIN and H. D. ORLOVA, *Optika i Spektroskopiya*, **4** (1958) 569.

[32] D. E. MILLIGAN, R. M. HEXTER and K. DRESSLER, *J. Chem. Phys.*, **34** (1961) 1009.
E. CATALANO and D. E. MILLIGAN, *J. Chem. Phys.*, **30** (1959) 45.

[33] N. SHEPPARD, *Advances in Spectroscopy* (Vol. 1), Editor, H. W. THOMPSON, Interscience, London, 1959.
S. MIZUSHIMA, *Structure of Molecules and Internal Rotation*, Academic Press, New York, 1954.

Chapter V

Force Constant Calculations for Small Molecules

IAN M. MILLS

Lecturer in Chemistry, University of Reading

The vibration frequencies and the form of the $(3N-6)$ normal vibrations of an N atomic molecule are evidently characteristic of two features of the molecular structure:

(i) the atomic masses and the geometrical distribution of the vibrating nuclei,

(ii) the force field which tends to restore the molecule to its internal equilibrium configuration during any distortion.

The atomic masses and equilibrium geometry of the molecule must be known before any force constant calculations can be attempted. Fortunately this information is generally available for the molecules of interest, from studies of the rotational spectra (see Chapters III and IV), and in some cases from electron and X-ray diffraction studies. Occasionally force constant calculations have been used as supporting evidence for the molecular geometry, but in general the controlling feature (i) above is known in advance. The force field, or potential field, (ii) above, is not generally known, and indeed the immediate object of a force constant calculation is to determine this field. The force field arises from changes in the energy of the electrons which bind the molecule together, and in principle it can be calculated *a priori* by solving the electronic wave equation, and hence determining this energy, as a function of the nuclear configuration. However, theoretical physics has not yet advanced to the point where useful *a priori* calculations of force constants can generally be made: the mathematical difficulties are too great. Hence we attempt to deduce the force field by calculation from the observed vibration frequencies, as determined from the infra-red and Raman spectra, and thus obtain empirical information on the electronic binding in the molecule.

There are other reasons why we wish to determine this force field, in addition to our desire to understand the electronic structure. Experience shows that the force constants are strongly characteristic of the chemical groups with which they are associated, so that it is possible to make useful predictions about the force field in a large molecule from the known force fields of smaller molecules in which the same chemical groups occur. This can be a great aid to understanding the vibration spectra of large molecules (Chapter VII). Also it is sometimes important to know the mode of vibration, *i.e.* the form of the normal coordinate, associated with each vibration frequency: this is essential, for instance, in the interpretation of absolute intensity studies (Chapter X). Unlike the vibration frequencies, the normal coordinates cannot be directly observed — in fact they can only be determined from a force constant calculation, since a knowledge of the normal coordinates implies a detailed knowledge of the force field.

The mathematical representation of the force field may be developed as follows. Suppose that we define $(3N-6)$* internal displacement coordinates R_i, $i = 1$ to $(3N-6)$, which are just sufficient to specify completely the internal configuration of the molecule. By "internal" we mean that these coordinates take no account of overall translation and rotation of the molecule (which evidently do not alter the potential energy and hence do not give rise to any forces); by "displacement coordinates" we mean that these coordinates measure displacements from the equilibrium configuration, so that every $R_i = 0$ in equilibrium. Examples of these coordinates will be given in Section 1, but they will frequently be chosen to be displacements in the bond lengths and interbond angles. Then the total potential energy of the molecule as a function of the coordinates, $V(R_i)$, may always be expanded in a Taylor series about the equilibrium configuration:

$$V = V_e + \sum_i \left(\frac{\partial V}{\partial R_i}\right)_e R_i + \tfrac{1}{2}\sum_i \sum_j \left(\frac{\partial^2 V}{\partial R_i \, \partial R_j}\right)_e R_i R_j \qquad (1)$$

$$+ \text{(terms of order } R^3 \text{, and higher powers)}$$

The first term, V_e, is trivial since it merely defines the (arbitrary) zero of the energy scale; moreover, the coefficients of R_i in the second term are all zero since the derivatives are all to be taken in the equilibrium configuration, in which, by definition, V is a minimum with respect to all the R_i. The coefficients in the third term, being second derivatives in the equilibrium configuration, are the harmonic force constants, and are normally written:

$$\left(\frac{\partial^2 V}{\partial R_i \, \partial R_j}\right)_e \equiv \left(\frac{\partial^2 V}{\partial R_j \, \partial R_i}\right)_e = F_{ij} \qquad (2)$$

The coefficients of cubic and higher terms in R are the anharmonic force constants; they are generally neglected in calculations on polyatomic molecules, on the grounds that for small displacements, terms in R^3 are small compared to those in R^2, and also for the more practical reason that no general theory of force constant calculations incorporating anharmonic terms has yet been developed.

* The correct number would be $(3N-5)$ for a linear molecule; see p. 112, Chapter IV.

In practice, the harmonic approximation, in which cubic and higher terms in eqn. (1) are neglected, generally represents the potential energy to within ± 4 per cent over the amplitudes of vibration associated with most fundamental vibrations, and within ± 10 per cent for hydrogen atom vibrations, in which the amplitudes are exceptionally large. Calculated vibration frequencies are rather better than this, since the force constants are related to the squares of the vibration frequencies. It is convenient to use the symbol ν for the observed fundamental vibration frequencies of the molecule, and ω for the harmonic frequencies with which the molecule would vibrate in the absence of cubic and higher terms in the force field. We shall generally confine our discussion to the harmonic approximation, and retain only second order terms in the force field, eqn. (1), and we shall thus use the symbol ω for the calculated values of the vibration frequencies. In Section 2 below we return to the problem of anharmonicity, and the resulting distinction between the observed frequencies ν and the harmonic frequencies ω.

The force constants F_{ij} thus define the harmonic force field, and it is these force constants that we wish to determine from the observed vibration frequencies. In Section 1 of this chapter we consider the calculation of vibration frequencies and normal modes from an assumed set of force constants, and the (known) atomic masses and equilibrium geometry of the molecule. In Section 2 we consider the much more difficult procedure of calculating the force constants and normal modes from the observed vibration frequencies. Finally, in Section 3, we review briefly the results of calculations on small molecules, and we discuss certain specialized force fields which are frequently assumed to apply in force constant calculations.

One general simplifying feature, which must be mentioned at this stage, is the effect of symmetry. The examples of the last chapter showed how the normal vibrations always reflect the symmetry properties of a molecule: in the simple cases every normal mode is either symmetric or antisymmetric with respect to each element of symmetry. Another result of symmetry, related to this, is that the number of independent force constants is reduced, since symmetrically equivalent force constants are required to be equal to each other, and others may be required to be zero. The proper development of this subject is the application of group theory to molecular vibrations[1], and is beyond the scope of this chapter; however, we shall indicate by examples how symmetry simplifies the calculations.

(1) **Calculation of Vibration Frequencies from Force Constants**

We shall now suppose that we know, or have assumed, values for the harmonic force constants that define the force field, and consider how to calculate the frequencies and normal modes of the corresponding vibrations. The full development of this subject is complex, and is treated comprehensively in a textbook by WILSON, DECIUS and CROSS[2], and in many other references[3-6], to which the serious student is referred; in the present treatment we can do little more than outline the nature of the calculation. An elementary knowledge of matrix algebra is invaluable[7], and to encourage the beginner in this subject some of the equations of this section are written in both conventional and matrix notation, the latter being confined to the paragraphs in small print. A detailed understanding of the equations of this section is not essential for reading the later sections of the chapter, although it is helpful.

The first step towards solving the equations of motion of any system, in either classical or quantum mechanics, consists of deriving expressions for the kinetic and potential energies in terms of some convenient set of coordinates describing the system. We consider later a number of possible choices for these coordinates, with their advantages and disadvantages. Since, however, the calculation is basically similar in any set of coordinates, we shall develop the equations in terms of a set of $(3N-6)$ internal displacement coordinates R_i, as introduced in the last section, which are just sufficient to define the internal configuration of the atoms in the molecule. The potential energy V is then given by equation (1) of the last section, which reduces in the harmonic approximation to the form:

$$2V = \sum_i \sum_j F_{ij} R_i R_j \tag{3}$$

For small displacements of the atoms the kinetic energy T may be shown to be given by a rather similar expression, involving the time derivatives of the coordinates $\dot{R}_i = (\partial R_i / \partial t)$:

$$2T = \sum_i \sum_j M_{ij} \dot{R}_i \dot{R}_j \tag{4}$$

The coefficients M are functions of the atomic masses and equilibrium geometry of the molecule; when the masses and geometry are known their determination is in principle straightforward, but may in practice be quite tedious. Partly for this reason, the kinetic energy is often characterized by an alternative equation involving the momenta P, conjugate to the coordinates R:

$$2T = \sum_i \sum_j G_{ij} P_i P_j \tag{5}$$

The coefficients G are evidently related to the coefficients M; indeed, by making use of the definition of the momenta

$$P_i = (\partial T / \partial \dot{R}_i) = \sum_j M_{ij} \dot{R}_j \tag{6}$$

to substitute for P in (5), it is easy to show that

$$\sum_j G_{ij} M_{jk} = \delta_{ik} \tag{7}$$

where $\delta_{ik} = 1$ if $i = k$, and $\delta_{ik} = 0$ if $i \neq k$.

Equations (3) through (7) can all be written in a simpler form by making use of matrix notation, as is done below:

$$2V = \mathbf{R'FR} \tag{3}$$
$$2T = \mathbf{\dot{R}'M\dot{R}} = \mathbf{P'GP} \tag{4, 5}$$
$$\mathbf{P} = \mathbf{M\dot{R}} \tag{6}$$
$$\mathbf{GM} = \mathbf{I}, \text{ or } \mathbf{M} = \mathbf{G}^{-1} \tag{7}$$

In these equations $\mathbf{R}$, $\mathbf{\dot{R}}$ and $\mathbf{P}$ denote single column matrices (vectors of order $n = 3N-6$) of the coordinates, their time derivatives, and their conjugate momenta, and the transpose of a matrix $\mathbf{R}$ is denoted by $\mathbf{R'}$. $\mathbf{F}$, $\mathbf{M}$ and $\mathbf{G}$ denote square matrices (of order $n \times n$) composed of the coefficients F_{ij}, M_{ij} and G_{ij} respectively; all three are symmetric matrices. $\mathbf{I}$ denotes the identity matrix (of order $n \times n$), and eqn. (7) shows that $\mathbf{M}$ and $\mathbf{G}$ are inverse matrices.

The set of coefficients F_{ij} define the force field, and the set M_{ij} (or G_{ij}) define the kinetic properties of the system; these are the two features of the molecular structure that control the frequencies and modes of the normal vibrations. The numerical values of the coefficients depend, of course, on the choice of coordinates, and in general there will be non-zero cross terms in the expressions for both V and T. However, the form of eqns. (3), (4) and (5) is always the same, in any set of coordinates.

There are now several ways of deriving equations for the modes and frequencies of the normal vibrations, but the most illuminating approach is to look for a new set of n displacement coordinates Q, in terms of which the expressions for V and T are both "diagonal", i.e. have zero coefficients for all the cross terms. We define the new coordinates Q by a linear transformation from the original coordinates R:

$$R_j = \sum_k L_{jk} Q_k, \quad j = 1 \text{ to } n, \tag{8}$$

involving n^2 transformation coefficients $L_{jk} = (\partial R_j/\partial Q_k)$. It can be shown that this transformation can always be chosen in such a way that the expressions for V and T take the form:

$$2V = \sum_k \lambda_k Q_k^2 \tag{9}$$
$$2T = \sum_k \dot{Q}_k^2 \tag{10}$$

In addition to being free of cross terms, the coefficients of the diagonal terms in eqn. (10) have been chosen to be unity: the form of eqns. (9) and (10) then prove to be just sufficient fully to define the coordinates Q. It is easy to show that in terms of these coordinates the molecular vibrations take the form of n independent simple harmonic motions, one in each coordinate Q_k, the frequency ω_k of the kth vibration being given by:

$$4\pi^2 \omega_k^2 = \lambda_k \tag{11}$$

Solution of the Schrödinger equation for the system gives a wave function which is a product of harmonic oscillator wave functions in the independent coordinates, and the corresponding sum of harmonic oscillator energy terms is:

$$E = \sum_k E_k = \sum_k h\omega_k(v_k + \tfrac{1}{2}) \tag{12}$$

The n quantum numbers v_k define the state of the system, and the parameters ω_k define the frequencies of the fundamental transitions.

The key to our problem is thus to determine the normal coordinates Q : $i.e.$ to find the frequency parameter λ_k (eqns. (9) and (11)), and the transformation coefficients $L_{jk} = (\partial R_j/\partial Q_k)$, $j = 1$ to n (eqn. (8)), for each coordinate Q_k. These define, respectively, the vibration frequency ω_k, and the relative contributions of the internal coordinates R_j, for the kth normal vibration. These frequency parameters and transformation coefficients prove to be given by the following set of linear equations:

$$\sum_j [F_{ij} - \lambda M_{ij}] L_j = 0, \quad i = 1 \text{ to } n \tag{13}$$

involving the coefficients F and M of eqns. (3) and (4). Since (13) has the form of n equations in the n unknowns L_j, there is a condition of self-consistency which requires that the determinant of their coefficients be zero:

$$\begin{vmatrix} F_{11} - \lambda M_{11} & F_{12} - \lambda M_{12} \dots \\ F_{12} - \lambda M_{12} & F_{22} - \lambda M_{22} \dots \\ \quad \cdot \\ \quad \cdot \\ \quad \cdot \end{vmatrix} \equiv |F_{ij} - \lambda M_{ij}| = 0 \tag{14}$$

This "secular equation" is a polynomial of degree n in λ, whose n roots, λ_k, are the desired frequency parameters; by substituting λ_k for λ in the set of equations (13), the corresponding set of transformation coefficients L_{jk}, $j = 1$ to n, may be determined. (Solution of (13) will give only the ratio of the coefficients L_j to one another; they must then be normalized to satisfy eqns. (9) or (10) as described in reference 5). The λ's and L's are known as the characteristic roots and vectors of the secular determinant (14).

If the coefficients G of eqn. (5) are used to characterize the kinetic energy, we find, in place of (13):

$$\sum_j [(GF)_{ij} - \lambda \delta_{ij}] L_j = 0, \quad i = 1 \text{ to } n \tag{15}$$

where

$$(GF)_{ij} = \sum_l G_{il} F_{lj}$$

This gives the secular equation:

$$\begin{vmatrix} (GF)_{11}-\lambda & (GF)_{12} & \cdots \\ (GF)_{21} & (GF)_{22}-\lambda & \cdots \\ \cdot & & \\ \cdot & & \\ \cdot & & \end{vmatrix} \equiv |(GF)_{ij}-\lambda\delta_{ij}| = 0$$

(16)

Again, the roots of (16) give the λ_k's, and the corresponding L_{jk}'s are obtained by back-substitution in eqn. (15).

Equations (15) and (16), of course, give the same solutions as equations (13) and (14) (as may be proved by making use of eqn. (7)); the use of one or the other set of equations is a matter of convenience, depending on whether the kinetic energy has been characterized by the coefficients M or G.

As before, eqns. (8) through (16) may all be more simply written in matrix notation. We define a column vector Q of normal coordinates by:

$$R = LQ,$$

(8)

in terms of which V and T take the form:

$$2V = Q'\Lambda Q$$

(9)

and

$$2T = \dot{Q}'\dot{Q}$$

(10)

Λ being a diagonal matrix of the frequency parameters λ_k. Using (8) to substitute for R in eqns. (3) and (4), and comparing the result with (9) and (10), we find:

$$L'FL = \Lambda$$

and

$$L'ML = I$$

Combining these two equations gives:

$$FL = ML\Lambda$$

(13)

— which is identical with the previous eqn. (13) when expanded and broken down into terms relating to the individual roots. Finally, on premultiplying (13) by $G = M^{-1}$, we obtain

$$GFL = L\Lambda$$

(15)

which is equivalent to the previous eqn. (15).

The secular equations (14) and (16), which specify the acceptable values of the diagonal elements λ_k of Λ may be written:

$$|F-\lambda M| = 0$$

(14)

and

$$|GF-\lambda I| = 0$$

(16)

The problem of calculating the molecular vibration frequencies and normal coordinates from the force constants thus reduces to the problem of determining the roots and vectors of a secular equation, in one of the two alternative forms (14) or (16). This may involve a lengthy calculation, particularly if the determinant is of high order, but the procedure is in principle straightforward[7] and the availability of electronic computers has largely removed this problem, so that we shall not discuss it further. There is also the problem of determining the set of coefficients M_{ij} or G_{ij} from the atomic masses and molecular geometry; this in itself can involve some tedious calculation, and may influence the initial choice of coordinates as discussed below, but a full discussion is again beyond the scope of this chapter. Detailed discussions of all these points are given in references 2–6.

It is interesting to observe the effect of the cross terms in F and M (or G), in the original expressions for the potential and kinetic energies, on the form of the normal vibrations. It is these cross terms that cause the original coordinates R_j to mix together to form the normal coordinates Q_k in which the vibrations occur.

For if the cross terms were zero, the potential and kinetic energies would already be diagonal: thus the Q's would be essentially identical to the R's (since this is their defining property), and there would be no mixing of the coordinates R in the normal vibrations. It can therefore be said that the coordinates R mix together to form the normal vibrations due to two distinct causes: (i) the presence of cross terms in the kinetic energy, or "kinetic effects", and (ii) the presence of cross terms in the potential energy, or effects of the force field. We shall see later that when the R's are chosen to be pure bond stretching and angle bending coordinates, the cross terms in the potential energy are often small compared to the diagonal terms; however, even if the force field is *completely diagonal* in a particular set of coordinates, there will still generally be some mixing of these co-ordinates to form the normal vibrations, owing to the kinetic effects. This fact is often not fully appreciated in qualitative discussions of the form of normal vibrations.

It remains to discuss the choice of the initial coordinates R in terms of which the solution for normal coordinates is carried out. The three con-siderations which influence this choice are: (i) ease of calculation of the coefficients M_{ij} or G_{ij}, (ii) ease of solution of the secular equation (14) or (16), and (iii) the physical significance of the force constants F_{ij} in terms of the chosen coordinates. Some alternative choices, with the relative merits of each, are described below, and are illustrated using the water molecule (Fig. V, 1) as an example.

(i) Cartesian displacement coordinates, for each atom in the molecule, in X, Y and Z directions, are chosen in some convenient way relative to the equilibrium configuration. These have the advantage that the coefficients M are extremely simple, being the atomic masses for the diagonal elements

and zero for the cross terms; in fact:

$$2T = \sum_t^N m_t(\dot{x}_t^2 + \dot{y}_t^2 + \dot{z}_t^2) \tag{17}$$

where m_t is the mass of the tth atom. Cartesian coordinates have two serious disadvantages. Firstly, there are six too many of them, $3N$ instead of $(3N-6)$; in fact, they include the six overall translations and rotations of the molecule, in which we are not really interested. This leads to six superfluous zero roots in the secular equation. For the H_2O molecule, for example, it is necessary to solve a 9×9 secular equation to obtain the three vibration frequencies. Secondly, the physical significance of the force constants in terms of cartesian coordinates is inconvenient and hard to visualize, and is complicated by the six redundant coordinates. For these reasons, they are rarely used to set up the secular equation.

(ii) Internal valence coordinates; these are displacements in the bond lengths and inter-bond angles in the molecule. Because they are *internal* coordinates, only $(3N-6)$ are required, and the redundant coordinates are avoided*. Moreover, in terms of changes in bond lengths and inter-bond angles, the force constants have the most convenient chemical significance, since the diagonal terms give directly the resistance to the stretching and bending of the bonds. The disadvantage of these coordinates is the difficulty of deriving expressions for the kinetic coefficients M_{ij}, but this has been circumvented by Wilson, who has described a straightforward method of calculating the coefficients G_{ij} which is always applicable. The secular equation may thus be set up and solved in the form (15), and this is, in fact, how most normal coordinate calculations are now carried out. A further advantage of internal valence coordinates is that the force field is approximately diagonal for most molecules in this form, cross terms generally being rather small in magnitude (see Section 3 below). It should be noted, however, that the kinetic energy is not generally diagonal, so that there is always some mixing to form the normal vibrations. This should be remembered when using the terminology "H-stretching", "CH_2-deformation", "CH_2-rock" etc., as descriptive of the normal vibrations; strictly this terminology should be reserved for the internal coordinates, and should only be used for a normal vibration when the corresponding internal coordinate R_j predominates in the form of the vibration.

For the water molecule, $(3N-6) = 3$, and there are 3 vibration frequencies and 3 internal coordinates. The latter are chosen to be changes in the two bond lengths and the inter-bond angle, δr_1, δr_2 and $\delta \alpha$ (Fig. V, 1).

---

* It is sometimes convenient to define more than $(3N-6)$ internal coordinates in symmetrical molecules in order to use complete symmetrical sets of coordinates. The resulting redundancies are generally removed in transforming to symmetry coordinates (see below, and reference 6).

The secular equation then involves a (3×3) determinant, whose roots would give the three vibration frequencies, and whose vectors would give

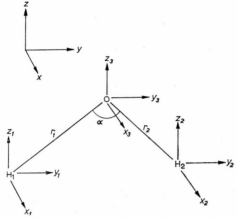

Fig. V, 1. Coordinates for the water molecule.
Cartesian coordinates: $[x_1\, y_1\, z_1\, x_2\, y_2\, z_2\, x_3\, y_3\, z_3]$.
Internal valence coordinates: $[\delta r_1,\ \delta r_2,\ \delta\alpha]$.

Symmetry coordinates: $\left[S_1 = \dfrac{1}{\sqrt{2}}\,(\delta r_1 + \delta r_2),\ S_2 = \delta\alpha,\ S_3 = \dfrac{1}{\sqrt{2}}\,(\delta r_1 - \delta r_2) \right].$

All of these coordinates measure displacements from the equilibrium configuration.

the relative contributions of $(O\text{–}H_1)$ and $(O\text{–}H_2)$ stretching, and $(\overset{\frown}{H O H})$ bending, to each normal vibration.

(iii) Symmetry coordinates: the use of symmetry   These are simple linear combinations of the previous internal coordinates chosen to take advantage of the molecular symmetry. They are chosen to have the simplest possible transformation properties under the rotations and reflections that leave the equilibrium configuration unaltered; this means, for example, that the effect of a two-fold rotation or a plane of reflection on any symmetry coordinate is either to reverse its sign or to leave it unaltered. (The effect of three-fold, and higher, rotation axes is more complicated and will not be discussed here). In the water molecule there are two planes of symmetry: the (XZ) and the (YZ) planes, and one two-fold rotation axis: the Z axis (Fig. V, 1). The symmetry coordinates S might be chosen to be:

$$S_1 = \frac{1}{\sqrt{2}}\,(\delta r_1 + \delta r_2)$$

$$S_2 = \delta\alpha \tag{18}$$

$$S_3 = \frac{1}{\sqrt{2}}\,(\delta r_1 - \delta r_2)$$

We observe that S_1 and S_2 are symmetric — *i.e.* are unaltered — by reflection

in the (XZ) plane or by two-fold rotation about the Z axis, but S_3 changes
sign under these symmetry operations, since they have the effect of inter-
changing the two hydrogen atoms. Thus S_3 has different symmetry properties from S_1 and S_2, and is said to be of a different species; the symbols
A_1 and B_2 (p. 119) are the conventional notations for the symmetry species
in this case. In a similar way the symmetry coordinates of any molecule
can be divided into groups, or species, having different symmetry properties, as shown by the examples discussed in Chapter IV.

The advantage of symmetry coordinates lies in the fact that, as indicated earlier, the normal vibrations and normal coordinates also have
these simple symmetry properties, and may be similarly divided into
species; this means that the normal coordinates of a particular species are
obtained by combining symmetry coordinates *of that species only*. The
secular equation (14) or (16) factorizes in terms of symmetry coordinates
by breaking into non-zero blocks along the main diagonal with zero cross
terms connecting the blocks: the cross terms F_{ij} and M_{ij}, or G_{ij}, are always
zero between two coordinates S_i and S_j of different species. Thus the

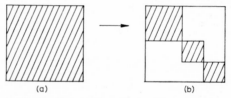

(a)   (b)

Fig. V, 2. Diagrammatic illustration of the effect of symmetry coordinates in factorizing
the secular determinant: non-zero blocks are shaded. (a) Internal coordinates. (b) Symmetry
coordinates.

problem of solving the original $(3N-6)$ square secular equation reduces to
several smaller problems which are correspondingly simpler; this is illustrated diagrammatically in Fig. V, 2. For the water molecule, the (3×3) equa-
tion in terms of $(\delta r_1,\ \delta r_2$ and $\delta\alpha)$ factorizes into a (2×2) equation in S_1 and
S_2 and a (1×1) equation in S_3. (The normal coordinate Q_3 is thus identical
to the symmetry coordinate S_3, apart from a normalization factor, since
there is no other coordinate of the same symmetry with which S_3 could mix).

It may also be shown that in molecules containing necessarily degenerate
vibrations, the block of the secular equation corresponding to the degenerate
species can be further factorized into d identical sub-blocks, where d is
the degeneracy[2]; thus, in effect, only one of each set of degenerate vibrations
(or coordinates) need be considered.

Further advantages of symmetry coordinates, which will become
apparent in the next section, follow from the fact that it is generally possible
to assign the observed vibrations to their symmetry species from their
infra-red and Raman activity, and from the rotational structure which

divides them into parallel and perpendicular bands, or type A, B and C bands (see Chapter IV). Also, the reduction in the number of independent force constants, which always results from the presence of symmetry, appears in these coordinates only in the zero cross terms connecting different species: the remaining force constants are truly independent.

Symmetry coordinates are generally used as a half-way stage in solving the secular equation, the problem being first set up, for example, in terms of internal valence coordinates, and then transformed into terms of internal valence symmetry coordinates in order to factorize the secular equation. The correct way of choosing symmetry coordinates is not always as obvious as in the example of the water molecule above; again, see reference 2.

In order to set up the secular equation in terms of symmetry coordinates, it is necessary to convert the kinetic and potential energies into terms of these coordinates. If the transformation matrix U defines the symmetry coordinates S in terms of the coordinates R:

$$S = UR, \tag{19}$$

and if

$$2V = R'FR = S'\mathfrak{F}S, \tag{20}$$

$$2T = \dot{R}'G^{-1}\dot{R} = \dot{S}'\mathfrak{G}^{-1}\dot{S}, \tag{21}$$

where $\mathfrak{F}$ and $\mathfrak{G}$ characterize V and T in terms of the symmetry coordinates, then the necessary relations are easily obtained by substituting from (19) in (20) and (21). They are:

$$\mathfrak{F} = U'^{-1}FU^{-1} \tag{22}$$

and

$$\mathfrak{G} = UGU' \tag{23}$$

If, moreover, U has been chosen to be an orthogonal transformation (as is generally done), then $U^{-1} = U'$, giving a further simplification of eqn. (22).

Solution of the secular equation

$$\mathfrak{G}\mathfrak{F}\mathfrak{L} = \mathfrak{L}\Lambda \tag{24}$$

will now give the transformation matrix $\mathfrak{L}$ that defines the normal coordinates in terms of the symmetry coordinates:

$$S = \mathfrak{L}Q \tag{25}$$

To obtain the normal coordinates in terms of the original internal coordinates, we must combine (19) and (25) to obtain

$$R = LQ = U^{-1}\mathfrak{L}Q = U'\mathfrak{L}Q \tag{26}$$

the last equality holding only if U is an orthogonal matrix.

(iv) Other coordinates We should observe that it is possible to choose internal coordinates that always give a diagonal expression for the kinetic energy, (unlike the valence coordinates described in *(ii)* above); generally these are closely related to the cartesian coordinates of the atoms. Obviously this simplifies the secular equation, and also makes it easier to derive the kinetic coefficients M_{ij}. It is also possible to form symmetry combinations of such coordinates. The disadvantage of these coordinates to the

chemist lies in the loss of simple physical significance of the force constants, and in the fact that the force field rarely has the approximately diagonal form that goes with valence coordinates (see Section 3 below). Another closely related set of coordinates that are occasionally useful for a special purpose (see for example ref. 8) are external cartesian symmetry coordinates, in which the symmetry factorization has been carried out but the six zero roots corresponding to translation and rotation have deliberately not been removed.

A worked example The general theory described in this section is best illustrated by considering a numerical example: we choose the water molecule, illustrated in Fig. V, 1, to which reference has already been made above in considering examples of coordinates.

We choose as internal valence coordinates $(\delta r_1, \delta r_2, r_e\delta\alpha)$. These are essentially the same as those introduced under *(ii)* above, except that the angle bending coordinate α has been "scaled" by multiplying by the equilibrium (O–H) bond length r_e. This scaling of angle bending valence coordinates gives all the coordinates the same dimensions, and simplifies the numerical representation of the matrices.

We write the potential field in the form:

$$2V = f_r(\delta r_1{}^2 + \delta r_2{}^2) + f_\alpha(r_e\delta\alpha)^2 + 2f_{rr}\delta r_1\delta r_2 + 2f_{r\alpha}(r_e\delta\alpha)(\delta r_1 + \delta r_2)$$

$$= [\delta r_1\, \delta r_2\, r_e\delta\alpha] \begin{bmatrix} f_r & f_{rr} & f_{r\alpha} \\ & f_r & f_{r\alpha} \\ \text{(sym.)} & & f_\alpha \end{bmatrix} \begin{bmatrix} \delta r_1 \\ \delta r_2 \\ r_e\delta\alpha \end{bmatrix}$$

This is in the form of eqn. (3), the middle factor in the final expression being the **F** matrix in terms of internal coordinates. The standard methods of references 2 and 4 give the **G** matrix (eqn. (5)) in terms of these coordinates to be:

$$\mathbf{G}: \quad \begin{array}{c} r_1 \\ r_2 \\ r_e\alpha \end{array} \begin{bmatrix} (\mu_H + \mu_O) & C\alpha \cdot \mu_O & -S\alpha \cdot \mu_O \\ & (\mu_H + \mu_O) & -S\alpha \cdot \mu_O \\ \text{(Sym.)} & & 2\mu_H + 2(1 - C\alpha)\mu_O \end{bmatrix} \begin{array}{c} r_1 \\ r_2 \\ r_e\alpha \end{array}$$

where μ_H and μ_O are the inverse masses of the H and O atoms, α_e is the equilibrium HOH bond angle, and $C\alpha$, $S\alpha$ are abbreviations for $\cos\alpha_e$ and $\sin\alpha_e$ respectively. Since the **G** and **F** matrices are always symmetrical, we have only entered elements on and above the diagonal.

If we introduce symmetry coordinates as defined in eqn. (18), the **U** matrix defining the transformation, eqn. (19), becomes:

$$\begin{bmatrix} S_1 \\ S_2 \\ S_3 \end{bmatrix} = \begin{bmatrix} +\dfrac{1}{\sqrt{2}} & +\dfrac{1}{\sqrt{2}} & 0 \\ 0 & 0 & +1 \\ +\dfrac{1}{\sqrt{2}} & -\dfrac{1}{\sqrt{2}} & 0 \end{bmatrix} \begin{bmatrix} \delta r_1 \\ \delta r_2 \\ r_e\delta\alpha \end{bmatrix}$$

where S_1 and S_2 are of species A_1, and S_3 is of species B_2.

Evaluating the symmetrized $\mathfrak{G}$ and $\mathfrak{F}$ matrices according to eqns. (22) and (23) we find:

$$\mathfrak{F}: \quad \begin{array}{c} S_1 \\ S_2 \\ S_3 \end{array} \left[\begin{array}{cc|c} (f_r + f_{rr}) & +\sqrt{2}f_{r\alpha} & 0 \\ & f_\alpha & 0 \\ \hline \text{(sym.)} & & (f_r - f_{rr}) \end{array} \right]$$

$$\begin{array}{ccc} S_1 & S_2 & S_3 \end{array}$$

$$\mathfrak{G}: \quad \begin{array}{c} S_1 \\ S_2 \\ S_3 \end{array} \begin{array}{ccc} S_1 & S_2 & S_3 \\ \left[\begin{array}{ccc} \mu_H + \mu_O(1 + C\alpha) & -\sqrt{2}\,S\alpha \cdot \mu_O & 0 \\ & 2\mu_H + 2\mu_O(1 - C\alpha) & 0 \\ (\text{sym.}) & & \mu_H + \mu_O(1 - C\alpha) \end{array}\right] \end{array}$$

As anticipated, we find zero cross terms between coordinates of different symmetry species. On substituting the following numerical values for the force constants,* and for the atomic masses and equilibrium geometry:

$$f_r = \quad 8.45 \text{ mdyne Å}^{-1} \qquad \mu_H = 0.992 \quad (\text{a.m.u.})^{-1}$$
$$f_{rr} = -0.09 \text{ mdyne Å}^{-1} \qquad \mu_O = 0.0625 \ (\text{a.m.u.})^{-1}$$
$$f_\alpha = \quad 0.76 \text{ mdyne Å}^{-1} \qquad \alpha_e = 104° \ 30'$$
$$f_{r\alpha} = \quad 0.26 \text{ mdyne Å}^{-1} \qquad (\text{a.m.u.} = \text{atomic mass unit, on scale } {}^{16}O = 16.00)$$

— we find the following numerical values for the $\mathfrak{G}\mathfrak{F}$ matrix product:

$$\begin{array}{c} \underline{\mathfrak{G}\mathfrak{F}} \\ (\text{a.m.u.})^{-1}(\text{mdyne Å}^{-1}) \end{array} \begin{array}{c} S_1 \\ S_2 \\ S_3 \end{array} \begin{array}{ccc} S_1 & S_2 & S_3 \\ \left[\begin{array}{ccc} 8.652 & +0.314 & 0 \\ +0.06 & 1.604 & 0 \\ 0 & 0 & 9.149 \end{array}\right] \end{array}$$

The secular equation (16) thus factorizes into a (2×2) block involving S_1 and S_2, and a (1×1) block involving S_3. Multiplying out the determinant $|\,\mathfrak{G}\mathfrak{F} - \lambda I\,|$, we find that the acceptable values of λ are given by the roots of the secular equation to be

$$A_1 \text{ species: } \begin{cases} \lambda_1 = 8.654 \ (\text{a.m.u.})^{-1} \text{ mdyne Å}^{-1} \\ \lambda_2 = 1.600 \ (\text{a.m.u.})^{-1} \text{ mdyne Å}^{-1} \end{cases}$$

for the quadratic block, and

$$B_2 \text{ species: } \quad \lambda_3 = 9.149 \ (\text{a.m.u.}^{-1}) \text{ mdyne Å}^{-1}$$

for the linear equation. Converting the units of λ according to the relation:

$$\frac{\lambda}{(\text{a.m.u.})^{-1}(\text{mdyne Å}^{-1})} = 10^{-5} \left(\frac{N_0}{\text{a.m.u.g}^{-1}}\right)^{-1} \left(\frac{\lambda}{\text{sec}^{-2}}\right)$$

where N_0 is Avogadro's number, and applying eqn. (11) in the form

$$\frac{\lambda}{\text{sec}^{-2}} = 4\pi^2 \left(\frac{\omega}{\text{sec}^{-1}}\right)^2 = 4\pi^2 \left(\frac{c}{\text{cm sec}^{-1}}\right)^2 \left(\frac{\omega}{\text{cm}^{-1}}\right)^2$$

where c is the velocity of light, we find for the calculated harmonic vibration frequencies:

$$A_1 \text{ species: } \begin{cases} \omega_1 = 3833.5 \text{ cm}^{-1} \\ \omega_2 = 1648.6 \text{ cm}^{-1} \end{cases}$$
$$B_2 \text{ species: } \quad \omega_3 = 3941.6 \text{ cm}^{-1}$$

These may be compared with the observed harmonic vibration frequencies, which are found to be 3832.2, 1648.5 and 3942.5 cm^{-1} for ω_1, ω_2 and ω_3 respectively[9]. The force constants given here were adjusted to fit these observed frequencies (see Table V, 1, p. 188).

On substituting the roots λ_1, λ_2 and λ_3 in turn into eqn. (15), we can solve for the corresponding columns of the $\mathfrak{L}$ matrix; when these are appropriately normalized, the complete $\mathfrak{L}$ matrix which defines the normal coordinates in terms of the symmetry coordinates is found

---

* These force constants have actually been deduced from the harmonic vibration frequencies of H_2O, D_2O and HDO according to methods described in Section 2 below.

to be:

$$
\begin{array}{c}
\underline{\mathfrak{L}:} \\
\mathrm{(a.m.u.)^{-\frac{1}{2}}}
\end{array}
\begin{array}{c}
\\
S_1 \\
S_2 \\
S_3
\end{array}
\begin{array}{ccc}
Q_1 & Q_2 & Q_3 \\
\left[\begin{array}{cc|c}
+1.017 & -0.065 & 0 \\
+0.009 & +1.463 & 0 \\
\hline
0 & 0 & +1.035
\end{array}\right]
\end{array}
$$

Thus the normal coordinate Q_1 involves simultaneous displacements of $(S_1: S_2: S_3)$ in the ratio $(+1.017: +0.009 : 0.0)$, etc. The fact that S_3 is not involved in Q_1 or Q_2 is, of course, a necessary result of their different symmetry properties. Making use of eqn. (26) to obtain the complete transformation matrix between the normal coordinates and internal coordinates $(\delta r_1,\ \delta r_2$ and $r_e \delta \alpha)$, we find:

$$
\begin{array}{c}
\underline{L = U'\mathfrak{L}:} \\
\mathrm{(a.m.u.)^{-\frac{1}{2}}}
\end{array}
\begin{array}{c}
\\
\delta r_1 \\
\delta r_2 \\
r_e\, \delta \alpha
\end{array}
\begin{array}{ccc}
Q_1 & Q_2 & Q_3 \\
\left[\begin{array}{ccc}
+0.719 & -0.046 & +0.732 \\
+0.719 & -0.046 & -0.732 \\
+0.009 & +1.463 & 0.0
\end{array}\right]
\end{array}
$$

Again, the columns of this matrix tell us the ratio of displacements in the three coordinates $(\delta r_1:\ \delta r_2:\ r_e \delta \alpha)$ for each normal mode. Thus the 3833 cm^{-1} H-stretching vibration Q_1 is seen to involve a small amount of angle bending, α increasing slightly as the bonds stretch; the 1648 cm^{-1} bending vibration involves some H-stretching, the (O–H) bonds contracting as the angle opens up; but the antisymmetric 3941 cm^{-1} (O–H) stretching vibration involves no change in the bond angle. The forms of the normal coordinates implied by the above L matrix are illustrated in Fig. V, 3.

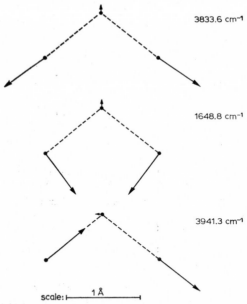

3833.6 cm^{-1}

1648.8 cm^{-1}

3941.3 cm^{-1}

scale: ⊢——1 Å——⊣

Fig. V, 3. Atomic displacement vectors in the normal vibrations of the H$_2$O molecule. The bonds are represented by dotted lines, and the atomic displacements by solid arrows; in each case these represent a unit displacement in the appropriate normal coordinate. For the 3833 and 3941 cm^{-1} vibrations the displacements are approximately twelve times larger than the classical vibration amplitude due to zero point energy, and for the 1648 cm^{-1} vibration they are approximately seven times larger.

It is interesting to observe how small the mixing between stretching and bending vibrations is in this molecule. A similar result holds for all hydrogen stretching vibrations, owing to the very light mass of the hydrogen atom[2]; evidently the practice of referring to the normal coordinates as "H-stretching" and "HOH bending" is justified in this case. Descriptions of this kind are common, and have been adopted in many places in other chapters of this book, but it should be remembered that sometimes the valency coordinates mix heavily in forming the normal coordinates, particularly when two or more vibrations of the same symmetry occur at closely similar frequencies.

(2) Calculation of Force Constants from Vibration Frequencies

The calculation of vibration frequencies and normal coordinates from the force constants is a straightforward procedure; as we have seen in the last section it involves setting up and solving a secular equation, whose roots determine the vibration frequencies and whose vectors determine the form of the normal coordinates. In practice, however, it is the vibration frequencies that are observed, and the force constants and normal coordinates that we wish to determine. This reverse calculation is much more difficult, for several reasons. Firstly, there are in general more unknown force constants than observed vibration frequencies, so that a unique solution for the force constants can only be obtained by introducing some extra data. The necessary extra data are not always available, and in this situation it is common practice to assume some specialized force field which reduces the number of unknown force constants and thus makes the problem soluble; however, such a solution is not really unique, since the type of specialized force field assumed is a matter of choice. The second difficulty is of a computational nature: the explicit equations which relate the roots of the secular equation (*i.e.* the observed vibration frequencies) to the unknown force constants, are generally complicated non-linear equations of varying order which are difficult to solve in any systematic way, and — when they are solved — may have more than one solution. This complexity of the calculation often tends to obscure the first difficulty about inadequacy of the data, so that it is difficult to know whether or not a particular set of force constants is unique in reproducing the observed vibration frequencies. Finally there is the problem of anharmonicity: the observed vibration frequencies ν differ from the harmonic frequencies ω with which the molecule would vibrate if the potential function contained no cubic and higher order terms, and thus some correction should really be applied to the ν's before they are used as data in a force constant calculation. These aspects will now be discussed in rather more detail.

In an N-atomic molecule there are $n = (3N-6)$ normal vibrations, but $\frac{1}{2}n(n+1)$ independent force constants F_{ij} in the most general harmonic potential field.* Except when $n = 1$ the number of force constants thus exceeds the number of vibrations, so that it is not possible to determine the force field uniquely from the observed vibration frequencies. If the molecule has symmetry, the number of independent force constants is reduced: for a symmetry species σ containing n_σ normal vibrations there are $\frac{1}{2}n_\sigma(n_\sigma+1)$ force constants, in terms of symmetry coordinates, from the considerations of the last section. The observed vibrations can generally be assigned to their various symmetry species from the rotational structure of the bands and their infra-red and Raman activities. The problem of determining the force constants in the molecule may thus be broken down into several smaller independent problems: to determine the force constants in each symmetry species, from the vibrations of that species. However, unless $n_\sigma = 1$ for all σ, there will still be more unknown constants then observed frequencies; to be specific, a symmetry species containing one vibration will involve only one force constant, but two vibrations will involve three force constants, three vibrations will involve six force constants, and so on.

It is thus necessary to obtain some extra data. These are generally sought in the form of observed vibration frequencies for isotopically substituted molecules. Since the force field is a function of the electronic structure of the molecule, and since this is influenced by the charges *but not the masses* of the constituent nuclei (under the Born–Oppenheimer approximation) the molecular force field is unaltered by isotopic substitution in the molecule. The atomic masses, and hence the kinetic coefficients M_{ij} and G_{ij} in eqns. (4) and (5), are altered, however, and this alters the secular equation and hence changes the frequency, and generally the form, of the normal vibrations. The changed vibration frequencies, when they are observed, thus provide extra equations involving the same (unknown) force constants, and thus help to solve the difficulty of insufficient data.

This method of supplementing the data is not as successful in practice as one might have hoped. Unless the change in mass of the isotopic nucleus is very large, the forms of the normal coordinates remain essentially unaltered and only the amplitudes of the vibrations — *i.e.* the scales of the coordinates — are changed. In these circumstances the extra equations obtained in the unknown force constants prove to be nearly "parallel" to the equations from the original molecule, so that almost any set of force constants that fit the frequencies of the original molecule will also fit the frequencies of the isotopic derivative. Even in the most favourable cases, there are a number of *isotope rules* which relate the vibration frequencies of a molecule to the frequencies of its isotopic derivatives *independently of the*

---

* The number $\frac{1}{2}n(n+1)$ is obtained as follows: There are evidently n diagonal terms F_{ii}, since $i = 1$ to n. The number of cross terms F_{ij} is $\frac{1}{2}n(n-1)$, since $F_{ij} = F_{ji}$. Hence the total number of terms $= n+\frac{1}{2}n(n-1) = \frac{1}{2}n(n+1)$.

force field; evidently these must reduce the information obtainable from the isotopic frequencies. The best known of these isotope rules is the Teller–Redlich product rule[10], which states that the product of the vibration frequencies of a molecule bears a constant ratio, which is independent of the force field, to the same product for an isotopic derivative. If the molecule has symmetry the rule applies separately to the product of the frequencies in each symmetry species.

The product rule can be readily proved from the secular equation in the form (16). On expanding the determinant a polynomial in λ of order n is obtained, the coefficient of λ^n being equal to (± 1) and the coefficient of λ^0, *i.e.* the constant term, being equal to the product of the roots, $\prod_k \lambda_k$. This constant term is obtained by putting $\lambda = 0$ in (16), whence

$$\prod_k \lambda_k = |GF| = |G| \cdot |F| \tag{27}$$

the last equality holding by virtue of a standard theorem of matrix algebra[7]. If we write eqn. (27) for an isotopically substituted molecule:

$$\prod \lambda_k^i = |G^i| \cdot |F|$$

(remembering that F is unaltered by isotopic substitution), and then divide one equation by the other, we obtain

$$\frac{\prod \lambda_k}{\prod \lambda_k^i} = \frac{|G|}{|G^i|} = \left[\frac{\prod \omega_k}{\prod \omega_k^i} \right]^2 \tag{28}$$

which is the product rule, since the ratio of the determinants of the G matrices does not involve the force constants. Evidently this derivation applies equally to each block of a symmetry-factorized secular equation. This form of the product rule may be shown to be equivalent to eqn. 8, p. 135.

Other isotope rules involve three or more isotopically equivalent molecules, and are more complex, but they all have the effect of reducing the independent information obtainable from isotopic frequencies[8, 11].

By far the most useful isotopic substitution in force constant calculations is that of hydrogen by deuterium, owing to the large percentage change of mass; this technique has been successfully applied to determining the force field of many small hydride molecules, as illustrated by the examples discussed in Section 3.

There are other observable data, in addition to the vibration frequencies, which provide information on the force field. The most useful are certain vibration–rotation interaction constants, which may be determined from studies of vibration–rotation structure in gas-phase infra-red and Raman spectra. These constants are of two kinds: those which characterize the centrifugal stretching of the molecule when it is in a high rotational state, denoted by the symbol $D(D_J, D_{JK}$ etc.), and those which characterize the mutual interaction of pairs of normal vibrations due to Coriolis forces in the rotating molecule, called Coriolis zeta constants and denoted by the symbol

ζ (see Chapter IV). In an elementary way it is easy to see that the ζ's and D's are functions of the force constants*, but the functional relationships are complicated[12, 13] and will not be presented here. The complexity of the relations adds to the computational difficulties when these data are used as information on the force field. Also there are relatively few molecules for which these data are available, and for all these reasons they have not been used very often in force constant calculations. Nonetheless, recent calculations have demonstrated their usefulness, as discussed in Section 3 below. Mean amplitudes of vibration, determined from precise electron diffraction studies, have also been used as data on the force field[14]. There are still other observable data which are known to be functions of the force constants, but none that have been used in force constant calculations, either because the data have not been sufficiently accurately observed or because the functional relationship to the force constants is not completely understood.

Even when all the available data discussed above are used in a force constant calculation, it still frequently happens that the data are not sufficient to determine uniquely all the force constants in the most general harmonic potential field. Indeed, this situation is the rule rather than the exception in force constant calculations on polyatomic molecules. In these circumstances it is still possible, of course, to find a force field that fits the vibration frequencies: the problem is rather to choose between a whole family of possible solutions to the force field. The choice is generally made on the basis of our general expectations about the molecular structure: by fitting the force field to some simplified model of the molecule which we expect to apply, or by transferring some of the constants from other molecules containing the same chemical group, or by some combination of both these methods. This problem is discussed in more detail in Section 3 below, for the choice is by no means easy, and it is still the source of considerable disagreement in force constant calculations — as well as being one of the most interesting features of this subject. The important thing is to realize that *some choice has been made* whenever a set of force constants are deduced from an insufficient number of observed data.

We must now return to the computational problem, and discuss how explicit equations for the force constants can be obtained in terms of the observed vibration frequencies. The problem can be illustrated by examining a (2×2) secular equation of the form of eqn. (16):

$$\begin{vmatrix} (GF)_{11}-\lambda & (GF)_{12} \\ (GF)_{21} & (GF)_{22}-\lambda \end{vmatrix} = 0 \qquad (29)$$

---

* In the case of a diatomic molecule the dependence of the centrifugal stretching constant D on the one force constant is implied in the equation on p. 9, Chapter I.

On expanding the determinant the following equations are obtained for the sum and product of the two roots:

$$\lambda_1\lambda_2 = (G_{11}G_{22}-G_{12}^2)(F_{11}F_{22}-F_{12}^2) \tag{30}$$

$$\lambda_1+\lambda_2 = (G_{11}F_{11}+2G_{12}F_{12}+G_{22}F_{22}) \tag{31}$$

If the vibration frequencies (*i.e.* λ_1 and λ_2) and the G elements are known, these provide two equations in the three unknown force constants, one of 1st order and one of 2nd order in the F's. As they stand they are not soluble, but if a second pair of equations are available for an isotopically substituted molecule, in which the G elements and the λ's are different, the equations are soluble* — although there will generally be two alternative solutions because (30) is a second order equation. The choice between these must be made on physical grounds, as discussed in the previous paragraph, if no other data are available. A (3×3) secular equation will evidently give equations of up to the third order in the F's, and so on; the solution of equations of this kind becomes impractical, even for a (3×3) determinant, without some simplification of the force field, or some other simplifying feature. The use of data on ζ's and D's introduces further problems in setting up and solving the equations for the force constants.

Because of these difficulties, a different and more powerful method of calculating force constants has been developed, usually referred to as the *force constant refinement procedure*. As the name implies, the force constants are obtained by an iterative method, in which some set of approximate constants (which are usually easy to guess) are made to converge upon the true force constants by the following cycle of operations:

(i) The approximate F's are used to calculate values for all the vibration frequencies ω_k (and for any other data that may be used in the calculation), and for the derivatives $(\partial\omega_k/\partial F_{ij})$ for every datum ω_k and every force constant F_{ij}.

(ii) These derivatives are used to set up linear equations which give the small changes in the calculated values of the data that result from any set of small changes in the force constants:

$$\delta\omega_k = \sum_{ij} (\partial\omega_k/\partial F_{ij}) \cdot \delta F_{ij} \tag{32}$$

If the $\delta\omega_k$ are identified with the difference between the calculated and observed values of the various data, the solution of eqns. (32) for the δF's gives the first order corrections to the force constants, which should make the calculated and observed values of the data agree. Since the

---

* It should be noted that eqn. (30) for the isotopic molecule will give no new information, because of the product rule: compare with eqn. (28) above. Only eqn. (31) for the isotopic molecule will provide useful information.

equations are linear, they are relatively easy to solve. The data must, of course, be more numerous than the unknown force constants, and the equations are then generally solved by the method of least squares.

(iii) The first order corrections δF_{ij}, obtained from the solution of (32), are applied to the original force constants, and the cycle is re-entered at stage (i).

This method of calculation has recently been applied, with minor variations, to a number of molecules; it has many advantages, the most important of which is that it is a systematic procedure which can be programmed for use on an electronic computer. Extra data, of any kind, are readily incorporated: it is only necessary to be able to calculate from the F's the expected values of the data and the necessary derivatives, and to include the results as extra linear equations in (32). It is also possible to determine the probable errors in the final values of the force constants implied by the experimental uncertainty in the original data, and by their mutual consistency, when they are sufficiently numerous to overfix the force field. The method is not without its difficulties, but it is the best answer to the computational problem of determining force constants which has yet been provided. For further discussion the reader is referred to the original papers[15–17].

Finally we must return to the problem of anharmonicity. Up to the present time, force constant calculations on polyatomic molecules have been almost entirely confined to the harmonic approximation, owing to the present limitations in the study of anharmonic vibrations, and also the absence of data, for most molecules, which might provide information on the anharmonic force constants. However, the observed vibration frequencies ν are undoubtedly influenced by the anharmonic force constants, as is shown by the few small molecule calculations in which proper corrections for anharmonicity have been made. Also the observed frequencies of a molecule and its isotopic derivatives, when they are available, generally fail to fit the product rule (eqn. (28)) by more than the experimental error in the data: this is attributed to the use of ν's rather than ω's in the equation. Thus it is evident that some correction should really be applied to the observed ν's in order to obtain the harmonic ω's for use in a force constant calculation.

In principle these anharmonicity corrections can be determined from data on the frequencies of the overtone and combination transitions in the vibration spectrum, as described, for example, in HERZBERG[18]. In practice this method has been applied to all diatomic molecules, but to very few polyatomic molecules, owing to the difficulty of obtaining sufficient data on the overtones. Dennison has proposed a set of semi-empirical rules for making the corrections in the absence of these data[19], making use of the fact that the harmonic frequencies ω for isotopic molecules must fit the product rule exactly; in this way the corrections have been made for perhaps fifteen or twenty of the smaller polyatomic molecules. Hydrogen stretching vibrations show by far the largest effects of anharmonicity, owing to the large amplitudes of the vibrations: for these the corrections are usually around 5 per cent, and for most other vibrations around 2 per cent, ω almost always being larger than ν. Because of this difference it is sometimes profitable to make anharmonicity corrections to the hydrogen stretching vibrations only.

For the majority of polyatomic molecules, however, there simply are not sufficient data to determine the anharmonicity corrections, even using Dennison's rules, and there is little likelihood of the data soon becoming available. In this situation the observed ν's are used without correction as data on the harmonic force constants; this, in fact, is how the majority of force constant calculations have been performed. It may be argued that this corresponds to obtaining the best average fit of a harmonic potential function to the true (anharmonic) function over the amplitudes of the fundamental vibrations, rather than obtaining an exact fit at the equilibrium configuration. However, it should be remembered that force constants calculated from ν's will generally differ from those calculated from ω's, the largest differences occurring for hydrogen stretching vibrations; moreover no harmonic force field will exactly fit the observed ν's when isotopic data are used, owing to the product rule difficulty referred to above.

Centrifugal stretching constants D and Coriolis zeta constants ζ should, of course, also be corrected for the effects of anharmonicity before they are used as data on the force constants. No such corrections have so far been made, owing to the lack of both theory and data for making them. There are, however, reasons for believing that these corrections should be small[17].

(3) Significance of Results: Simplified Force Fields

There must be over 1000 force constant calculations on polyatomic molecules published in the literature of vibrational spectroscopy. Of these, perhaps 30 or 40 represent serious attempts to determine all the constants in the most general harmonic force field, such calculations being confined to small molecules of high symmetry — for which the number of independent force constants is reduced to the minimum. Even for some of these there is doubt as to whether the solution obtained is unique; this is a measure of the difficulties discussed in the last section. In all the remaining cases some simplifying assumptions have been made about the nature of the force field. Although the purist will regret that the inadequacy of the experimental data requires one to make these simplifying assumptions, they are of great interest to chemists, since they are generally based on some relatively simple model of the valence forces in the molecule. It would be a great advance to have a reliable model. In this section we briefly review some of the results and interpretations of force constant calculations on small molecules, and some of the simplified force fields which have proved successful in application.

We start by considering some examples of calculations in which the most *general harmonic force field* (G.F.F.) has been obtained: in Table V, 1

TABLE V, 1

G.F.F. CALCULATIONS FOR CO_2, H_2O, C_2H_2 AND SiH_4

For each molecule the number of independent vibration frequencies, with their division into symmetry species, is given first, followed by the number of independent force constants in the G.F.F. This is followed by the valency coordinate definitions, and then by a table of numerical force constants for the given coordinates. Units are:

$$10^5 \quad \text{erg cm}^{-2} = \text{mdyne Å}^{-1} \quad \text{for (str.)} \times \text{(str.) constants;}$$
$$10^{-3} \quad \text{erg cm}^{-1} = \text{mdyne} \quad \text{for (str.)} \times \text{(bend) constants;}$$
$$10^{-11} \quad \text{erg} \quad = \text{mdyne Å} \quad \text{for (bend)} \times \text{(bend) constants.}$$

CO_2   3 independent vibrations, $\Sigma_g^+ + \Sigma_u^+ + \Pi_u$.
     3 force constants in G.F.F.

Internal coordinates:

Force constant	Coefficient in V		
f_r	$\frac{1}{2}(r_1^2 + r_2^2)$	15.9_8	mdyne Å^{-1}
f_{rr}	$r_1 r_2$	$+2.2_2$	mdyne Å^{-1}
f_θ	$\frac{1}{2}\theta^2$	0.78_3	mdyne Å

Data fitted: ω's from reference 19.

H_2O   3 independent vibrations, $2A_1 + B_2$
     4 force constants in G.F.F.

Internal coordinates:

Force constant	Coefficient in V		
f_r	$\frac{1}{2}(r_1^2 + r_2^2)$	8.45	mdyne Å^{-1}
f_{rr}	$r_1 r_2$	-0.09	mdyne Å^{-1}
f_α	$\frac{1}{2}\alpha^2$	0.70	mdyne Å
$f_{r\alpha}$	$(r_1\alpha + r_2\alpha)$	$+0.25$	mdyne

Data fitted: ω's for H_2O, D_2O and HDO from ref. 19.
(These force constants are identical to those given on p. 179 although the units are different. Both the calculated and observed ω's are given on p. 179).

C_2H_2   5 independent vibrations, $2\Sigma_g^+ + \Sigma_u^+ + \Pi_g + \Pi_u$.
     6 force constants in G.F.F.

Internal coordinates:

TABLE V, 1 (continued)

Force constant	Coefficient in V	Eggers[20]	Mills[21]	
f_r	$\frac{1}{2}(r_1^2+r_2^2)$	6.37	6.40	mdyne Å^{-1}
f_R	$\frac{1}{2}R^2$	16.4	16.4$_8$	mdyne Å^{-1}
f_{rr}	$r_1 r_2$	0	$+0.00_5$	mdyne Å^{-1}
f_{rR}	$R(r_1+r_2)$	-0.03	-0.01_9	mdyne Å^{-1}
f_θ	$\frac{1}{2}(\theta_1^2+\theta_2^2)$	0.25$_6$	0.26$_0$	mdyne Å
$f_{\theta\theta}$	$\theta_1\theta_2$	$+0.09_2$	$+0.09_6$	mdyne Å

Data fitted: ω's for C_2H_2 and C_2D_2 in both cases.

SiH$_4$ 4 independent vibrations, A_1+E+2F_2
5 force constants in G.F.F.

Internal coordinates: $r_1\, r_2\, r_3\, r_4$ (Si–H) stretching coordinates,
$\alpha_{12}\,\alpha_{34}\,\alpha_{13}\,\alpha_{24}\,\alpha_{14}\,\alpha_{23}$ (H–Si–H) bend coordinates.

Typical symmetry coordinates

Species $A_1 : S_1 = \frac{1}{2}(r_1+r_2+r_3+r_4)$

$\qquad E \; : S_2 = (12)^{-\frac{1}{2}}(\alpha_{13}+\alpha_{24}-\alpha_{14}-\alpha_{23})$

$\qquad F_2 : \begin{matrix} S_3 = \frac{1}{2}(r_1+r_2-r_3-r_4) \\ S_4 = (2)^{-\frac{1}{2}}(\alpha_{34}-\alpha_{12}) \end{matrix}$

Symmetry force constant	Coefficient in V	Ref. 22 (1942)	Ref. 23 (1956)	Ref. 24 (1957)	Ref. 21 (1961)
F_{11}/mdyne Å^{-1}	$\frac{1}{2}S_1^2$	2.84$_5$	2.98	2.84$_5$	2.84$_0$
F_{22}/mdyne Å	$\frac{1}{2}S_2^2$	0.40$_9$	0.41	0.40$_8$	0.41$_1$
F_{33}/mdyne Å^{-1}	$\frac{1}{2}S_3^2$	2.70$_3$	2.63	2.71$_9$	2.74$_2$
F_{34}/mdyne	$S_3 S_4$	-0.04_2	$+0.26_9$	-0.21_1	-0.03_4
F_{44}/mdyne Å	$\frac{1}{2}S_4^2$	0.49$_4$	0.55$_0$	0.50$_6$	0.50$_4$

Data fitted					
ν's for $\{$		SiH$_4$	SiH$_4$ SiD$_4$	SiH$_4$ SiD$_4$	SiH$_4$ SiD$_4$
ζ's for $\{$		SiH$_4$			SiH$_4$ SiD$_4$
SiH$_4$ $\begin{matrix}\zeta_3 \text{ calc.} \\ \zeta_3 \text{ obs.}\end{matrix}$ $\{$		$+0.038$	$+0.246$ $+0.046$	-0.065	$+0.044$

Equations relating symmetry force constants F_{ij}, and internal coordinate force constants f_{ij} for SiH$_4$ (from eqn. (22)):

$$F_{11} = f_r + 2f_{rr}$$
$$F_{22} = f_\alpha - 2f_{\alpha\alpha} + f_{\alpha\alpha'}$$
$$F_{33} = f_r - f_{rr}$$
$$F_{34} = \sqrt{2}(f_{r\alpha} - f_{r\alpha'})$$
$$F_{44} = f_\alpha - f_{\alpha\alpha}$$

the results of calculations on CO_2, H_2O, C_2H_2 and SiH_4 are summarized. CO_2, a linear symmetric molecule, is a very simple example, since the symmetrized secular equation factorizes into three (1×1) blocks (see the discussion in Chapter IV); because of this there are only three independent constants in the G.F.F. and these are determined without difficulty from the three observed vibration frequencies. (Actually there are 4 vibrations and 4 (1×1) blocks in the secular equation, one of the frequencies and one of the blocks being duplicated owing to degeneracy, but we need only consider independent vibration frequencies and blocks in discussing the force constants). Anharmonicity corrections were made in this calculation, the force constants being determined from the ω's.

The H_2O molecule has a lower symmetry than CO_2, since it is non-linear in its equilibrium configuration; this results in the symmetrical stretching vibration and the bending vibration being of similar symmetry properties, so that they form a (2×2) block in the secular equation (see Chapter IV, p. 118). There are thus four independent force constants, but only three vibration frequencies in the molecule. However, in this case there is an abundance of data on overtone and combination bands, and on the isotopic species HDO and D_2O: this allows a precise determination of the ω's for all three molecules. The data are then more than sufficient to fix uniquely the four independent force constants, and the results are given in Table V, I. The calculation of the vibration frequencies for H_2O, from these force constants, is used as an example in Section 1 above.

C_2H_2, also a linear symmetric molecule, is more complicated, since the secular equation factorizes into one (2×2) and three (1×1) blocks by symmetry (excluding degeneracy); there are thus six G.F.F. constants to be determined from the five observed vibration frequencies. (The symmetry forms of the normal vibrations are illustrated in Chapter IV, Fig. 12, p. 127.) Fortunately a sufficient number of overtone and combination bands have been observed to allow rather precise corrections for anharmonicity, and when these are combined with similar data available for the vibration frequencies of C_2D_2, the force constants can be determined without much ambiguity. The agreement between the two independent calculations of Table V, 1 illustrates this; such differences as there are between the two calculations arise from slightly different anharmonicity corrections.

The fourth example, SiH_4, a regular tetrahedral molecule, is more complicated still. It has been chosen to illustrate the value of extra data, other than the vibration frequencies; in this case the Coriolis ζ constants. The secular equation factorizes into two (1×1) blocks and a (2×2) block (again excluding degeneracy): thus there are five G.F.F. constants to be determined from four vibration frequencies. The necessary frequencies of SiD_4 have been observed, as have many of the frequencies of the intermediate isotopes, so that the situation is apparently no worse than for C_2H_2. The results of four independent force constant calculations are compared in Table V, 1, the force constants being presented in terms of symmetry coordinates; although most of the results agree well, there are large differences in the values obtained for the cross term F_{34}. This difficulty with SiH_4 arises from "parallelism" in the equations for the force constants, and from the fact that no anharmonicity corrections have been made to the vibration frequencies: the inconsistency in the ν's, when they are used without correction, gives rise to considerable uncertainty in the force constants of the (2×2) block. Inclusion of the observed zeta-constants in the data for this symmetry species removes this difficulty, as is shown by the agreement between the results of the two calculations which made use of these data, and the incorrect values of ζ which are calculated from the other two sets of results. Indeed, it is evident that the zeta-data are much more valuable than the isotopic data in this instance.

It would be helpful to give an example of a molecule containing a (3×3) block in the secular equation for which all the constants in the G.F.F. have been unambiguously determined, but it is doubtful (in the author's opinion) if there is such a case. Some of the methyl halide molecules, in which the secular equation factorizes into two (3×3) blocks, come closest; the CH_3F molecule has recently been the subject of such a G.F.F. calculation[17]. It is evident that general harmonic force constant calculations will always be very restricted in application: future developments in this field depend mainly on (i) the use of extra data, other than vibration frequencies, and (ii) improved methods, and data, for estimating the effect of anharmonicity.

We now turn to the simplified, or specialized force fields, which are used — of necessity — in the vast majority of force constant calculations. There are two assumptions which underly all such simplified force fields: one is the approximation of the *valence force field* (V.F.F.), in which it is assumed that there are no interactions between the stretching and bending of different bonds in the molecule, *i.e.* that the force field is diagonal (all cross terms are zero) when it is written in terms of valence internal coordinates; the other is the assumption that such valence force constants are *transferable* between molecules, *i.e.* that they are characteristic of the chemical group with which they are associated, rather than the whole molecule. The latter assumption appeals to the intuition of the chemist, since chemists are inclined to think in terms of more or less independent chemical groups — and even of independent bonds — in a molecule, but the experimental justification is the constancy of characteristic group vibration frequencies observed for the same chemical group in different molecules (see Chapter VII). Actually these characteristic group frequencies demonstrate both the transferability of force constants, and the smallness of the interactions

TABLE V, 2

SOME APPROXIMATE VALENCY STRETCHING FORCE CONSTANTS

These constants show correlations to bond length, bond order, and position of the bonding atoms in the Periodic Table. Stretching force constants f(mdyne Å^{-1}), and equilibrium bond lengths r_e(Å), are given. The force constants are average values prepared by the author from many published V.F.F. treatments on a variety of molecules; they are all obtained by fitting to *observed* vibration frequencies v, and are never more significant than $\pm$ 0.1 mdyne Å^{-1}. The equilibrium bond lengths are mainly taken from ref. 35.

(A) ---- X–H FORCE CONSTANTS AND BOND LENGTHS

Group IV	f	r_e	Group V	f	r_e	Group VI	f	r_e	Group VII	f	r_e
>C–H	4.9	1.10									
>C–H	5.3	1.08	>N–H	6.2	1.02	/O–H	7.5	0.96	F–H	8.8	0.92
≡C–H	5.9	1.06									
–Si–H	2.8	1.48	>P–H	3.1	1.42	/S–H	3.8	1.34	Cl–H	4.8	1.27
–Ge–H	2.6	1.53	>As–H	2.9	1.52				Br–H	3.9	1.41
			>Sb–H	2.3	1.71				I–H	2.9	1.61

(B) ---- C–X FORCE CONSTANTS AND BOND LENGTHS

	Bond order	Group IV	f	r_e	Group V	f	r_e	Group VI	f	r_e	Group VII	f	r_e
1st Period	Single	>C–C<	4.5	1.54	>C–N<	4.7	1.47	>C–O\	5.1	1.43	>C–F	5.7	1.39
		>C–C≡	5.2	1.46							≡C–F	9.3	1.27
	Double	>C=C<	10.8	1.34				>C=O	12.1	1.21			
		=C=C<	11.2	1.31				=C=O	15.5	1.16			
	Triple	–C≡C–	16	1.20	–C≡N	18	1.16						
2nd Period	Single	>C–Si<	2.8	1.87							>C–Cl	3.4	1.78
3rd Period	Single										>C–Br	2.9	1.93
4th Period	Single										>C–I	2.3	2.14

between remote groups; they thus provide evidence for both of the above assumptions. It is less obvious that interactions between the stretching and bending of *neighbouring* bonds and interbond angles will be negligibly small, however appealing such a simple model may be. In the examples of Table V, 1 the constants f_{rr} in CO_2, f_{rr} and $f_{r\alpha}$ in H_2O, f_{rr} and f_{rR} in C_2H_2, and f_{rr}, $f_{r\alpha}$, $f_{r\alpha'}$, $f_{\alpha\alpha}$ and $f_{\alpha\alpha'}$ in SiH_4 should all be zero in the V.F.F. approximation (for SiH_4 this requires that $F_{11} = F_{33}$, $F_{22} = F_{44}$, and $F_{34} = 0$). It will be observed that none of these cross terms is zero, although they are all small compared to the diagonal terms. Such comparisons with G.F.F. calculations provide the most searching test of simplified force fields (when the G.F.F. is known to be reliable); however, the number of independent force constants in a V.F.F. is always less than or equal to the number of observed vibration frequencies, so that the V.F.F. assumption can generally be tested with frequency data only. In HERZBERG[18], pp. 168 to 186, the V.F.F. is tested in this way for a large number of small molecules. All these tests lead to the same general conclusion: that, although the V.F.F. approximation is close to the truth for almost all molecules, small but definite interactions do occur between neighbouring bond-stretch and angle-bend coordinates. Rather similar conclusions are reached for the assumption of transferability of valency force constants: small but real changes do take place in different chemical surroundings. These conclusions are also reasonable from a valence theory point of view, although there have been only some few attempts to make specific predictions about the interactions on a purely theoretical basis. (See Chapter VII).

Despite its limitations, the V.F.F. approximation is of fundamental importance. For this reason some approximate V.F.F. stretching force constants are assembled in Table V, 2, for various chemical bonds, along with the corresponding equilibrium bond lengths. It should be emphasized that these force constants are only approximate: just as the limitation of the bond energy hypothesis places a fundamental limitation on the accuracy of tables of bond energies, so the limitations of the V.F.F. approximation limit the accuracy of the force constants in Table V, 2. Certain correlations, however, stand out from this table, notably the correlation of force constant with bond length and bond order, and with the group and period of the bonding atoms in the Periodic Table. Badger[34] has discussed these effects in diatomic molecules.

Evidently it is desirable to find some refinement of the V.F.F. which recognises the existence of small interactions. From a practical point of view we want a simplified force field that contains more adjustable constants than the V.F.F., but fewer than the G.F.F.; from a theoretical point of view we want a model that will enable us to understand and correctly predict the interactions that occur in a valency coordinate force field.

Almost all attempts to satisfy this need are built on the basic model of the
V.F.F., with extra interaction terms introduced — either empirically,
because certain cross terms are found to be necessary to fit the data, or
according to some theoretical model of interactions between the valency
coordinates.

The majority of force constant calculations are of the first type, being
empirical modifications of the V.F.F., generally referred to as modified
valence force fields (M.V.F.F.). It is assumed that certain cross terms only in
a valency coordinate force field are zero, the others being given non-zero
values which are adjusted to fit the data. The *number* of non-zero cross terms
is also chosen to be sufficient to fit the available data. The question of
which cross terms are chosen to be adjusted is obviously crucial, but it is
rarely justified by theoretical arguments. Thus it is commonly assumed that
all cross terms involving the interaction of hydrogen stretching with other
coordinates are zero: not because there is any theoretical reason for ex-
pecting this result, but because the data generally tend to be insensitive
to these force constants*. In fact, the few reliable G.F.F. calculations that
have been made suggest that this assumption is not generally true; moreover
the values obtained for the other force constants are undoubtedly correlated
to such assumptions about cross terms. Sometimes there is general agreement about the importance of certain interaction constants: an example is
provided by the $R=CH_2$ and $R-CH_3$ groups, where it has been found in
many different molecules that stretching the (R–C) bond tends to open up
the (CH_2) or (CH_3) interbond angles, as shown by the corresponding cross
term in the valency coordinate force field. But, in general, M.V.F.F. calculations which are not based on any definite model of the valence forces do
not really allow conclusions about the valency structure; the most that we
can say is that they provide a force field that fits the data.

The alternative is to look for some simple model of the valency interactions, which can be used to determine the non-zero cross terms in terms
of an appropriate number of adjustable parameters. The following examples
illustrate the most important theoretical considerations which are believed
to cause such valency interactions[25].

(i) Resonance effects   In the CO_2 molecule, for example, it is to be expected that stretching one (C–O) bond will tend to induce a contraction in the
other, since resonance contributions of the form $(\overset{+}{O} \equiv C - \overset{-}{O})$ and $(\overset{-}{O} - C \equiv \overset{+}{O})$
tend to favour such a distortion. The positive value of f_{rr} found in the
G.F.F. calculation of Table V, 1 shows that there is just such an interaction
in CO_2, and similar effects may be expected in other cases.

---

* This is a result of the fact that hydrogen stretching vibrations may generally be approximately factorized from the secular equation, owing to the small mass of the hydrogen atom
and correspondingly high frequency of the vibration[2].

(ii) Rotation and rehybridisation of orbitals   There are certain combinations of bending coordinates for which it is possible to "follow" the distortion by partially rotating the orbitals around a central atom; certain others for which the distortion can be followed by rehybridizing the orbitals about a central atom; and yet others for which neither of these effects can take place. Such effects can be used to make qualitative predictions about valency interactions: they have been incorporated into model force field calculations particularly by LINNETT et al.[26, 27], and are generally referred to as orbital-following effects. We will quote two examples. In both the C_2H_4 and the C_2H_6 molecules, the in-phase rocking vibration of the two end groups occurs at a much lower frequency than the corresponding out-of-phase vibration[28], and this can only be attributed to a valency interaction between the rocking coordinates in the two end groups. It may be understood by observing that the in-phase vibration may be followed by rotating the orbitals around the carbon atoms, but the out-of-phase vibrations may not. The other example concerns the bending coordinates of XH_4 molecules, in which the bonds are formed from sp^3 hybrids on the central atom. It has been shown[27] that the triply degenerate coordinate (S_4 of SiH_4 in Table V, 1) may be followed by rehybridizing the orbitals around the central atom in such a way that some of the bonds increase in p character and others in s character. The doubly degenerate coordinate (S_2 of SiH_4) cannot be followed by any s–p rehybridization. Accordingly, one would expect $(3/2) F_{22}$ to be larger than F_{44} (the factor $3/2$ arises because unit displacements in S_2 and S_4 do not lead to the same changes of angle). This is indeed found to be true for CH_4, SiH_4, and GeH_4.

(iii) Stretch-bend interactions due to rehybridization   Whenever angle bending coordinates can be followed by rehybridizing the orbitals, we may expect a secondary interaction with the bond stretching coordinates, since it is known that increasing the s content of a hybrid orbital tends to shorten the bond, and increasing the p content tends to lengthen it [25]. Thus, in the H_2O molecule, opening the (HOH) angle will tend to increase the s content of the (O–H) bonds (towards the sp linear arrangement): we should therefore expect the (O–H) bonds to shorten, *i.e.* we expect $f_{r\alpha}$ to be positive. Again, this agrees with the observed result of the G.F.F. calculation on the water molecule in Table V, 1. Similar considerations for CH_4 and SiH_4 predict that F_{34} should be negative, as is observed for both molecules (see ref. 29 and Table V, 1). The observed interaction between (=CH_2) and (–CH_3) symmetrical deformations and the (R-C) stretching coordinate (mentioned earlier in this section) may also be understood in this way.

(iv) Repulsion between non-bonded atoms   It often happens that the distance between two atoms in a polyatomic molecule, which are not

directly bonded together, is less than the estimated sum of the van der Waals radii of the atoms. It seems reasonable to suppose that there will be a repulsion between atoms in this situation, and that in the equilibrium configuration this is counterbalanced by attractive forces set up through the chemical bonds, which indirectly link the atoms. It is easy to see that this model will give rise to valency interactions in the force field, since a change imposed in one of the valency coordinates will alter some of the non-bonded repulsions, and thus induce changes in the other coordinates.

This last effect has been made the basis of a model force field for poly-atomic molecules, known as the *Urey–Bradley force field* (U.B.F.F.) after its original proponents[30]. Recently the U.B.F.F. has been widely applied, and it generally gives both a satisfactory fit to the observed data, and numerical force constants which appear to be moderately transferable between similar chemical groups in different molecules.

The necessary algebra for this force field is straightforward, but lengthy, and the serious student should refer to the original papers[16, 30, 31]. We will illustrate it by giving the form of the U.B.F.F. for a bent triatomic molecule (such as NOCl):

$$
\begin{aligned}
2V(\text{U.B.F.F.}) = \; & K_1' r_1 \cdot \delta r_1 + K_1 \cdot \delta r_1^2 \\
& + K_2' r_2 \cdot \delta r_2 + K_2 \cdot \delta r_2^2 \\
& + H' \cdot \delta\alpha \; + H \cdot \delta\alpha^2 \\
& + F' q \cdot \delta q \; + F \cdot \delta q^2
\end{aligned}
\tag{33}
$$

Here r_1, r_2 and α are the two equilibrium bond lengths and interbond angle, and q is the equilibrium distance between the non-bonded atoms; δ is used to denote displacements in these coordinates. The use of K, H and F for bond stretching, angle bending, and non-bonded stretching force constants respectively is conventional, and convenient. The linear terms in the force field are necessary in this case, since the coordinates are redundant, and hence the molecule will generally exist in a state of internal tension in its equilibrium configuration. If the redundancy relation between the four coordinates (δr_1, δr_2, $\delta\alpha$ and δq) is used to eliminate δq from eqn. (33), the linear terms that remain may be equated to zero, and the expression for V will reduce to the form of eqn. (3) in the coordinates (δr_1, δr_2 and $\delta\alpha$), involving only the force constants K_1, K_2, H, F and F'. It is only with the application of this redundancy condition and the elimination of the linear terms that the U.B.F.F. achieves the necessary condition of representing the equilibrium configuration free from unbalanced force. The model is generally further simplified by assuming that $F' = -0.1\ F$, for all non-bonded repulsions, which has been shown to be a reasonable assumption in certain cases[31], and is necessary in order to reduce the number of adjustable parameters in other cases. In this form the U.B.F.F. must be regarded as at least partly empirical in its origin.

The U.B.F.F. has a well defined mathematical form, which is readily applied to any molecule, whereas some of the other effects discussed above are difficult to incorporate into a systematic model force field; moreover, for most molecules, the U.B.F.F. has approximately the desirable number of adjustable parameters to fit the available data. Nonetheless, it is not without its difficulties. Thus the observed interaction between the rocking coordinates of C_2H_4 and C_2H_6, mentioned earlier, cannot be explained by the

U.B.F.F.[28]. For CH_3F, the results of a recent U.B.F.F. calculation[33] do not agree well with the results of an even more recent G.F.F. calculation[17] which made use of extra data on the ζ's and D's; also the fact that the (C–F) bond length in CH_3F is longer than that in CF_4, where the non-bonded repulsions are stronger, is hard to understand in terms of a Urey–Bradley model of valency interactions.

It seems probable that all of the effects discussed above may be important in causing valency interactions, and that no one effect will be paramount. This suggests that model force fields must always be regarded as to some extent empirical. In the end, the most that we can ask of any force field is that it should fit all the available data, give more or less transferable force constants, and — we hope — should not be at variance with the expectations of chemical valence theory. If two different force fields for the same molecule satisfy all these requirements, then we can only conclude that there is no way of choosing between them until some further data become available.

REFERENCES

1 The following general references are recommended on symmetry and group theory:
  H. WEYL, *Symmetry*, Princeton University Press, Princeton, 1952.
  B. HIGMAN, *Applied Group Theoretic and Matrix Methods*, Oxford University Press, Oxford, 1955.
  F. D. MURNAGHAN, *The Theory of Group Representations*, Johns Hopkins University Press, Baltimore, 1938.
  And the following deal particularly with the application of group theory to molecular vibrations:
  E. B. WILSON, J. C. DECIUS AND P. C. CROSS, *Molecular Vibrations*, McGraw Hill, New York, 1955.
  J. ROSENTHAL AND G. M. MURPHY, *Rev. Modern Phys.*, 8 (1936) 317.
2 E. B. WILSON, J. C. DECIUS AND P. C. CROSS, *Molecular Vibrations*, McGraw Hill, New York, 1955.
3 E. B. WILSON AND J. B. HOWARD, *J. Chem. Phys.*, 4 (1936) 260.
  B. T. DARLING AND D. M. DENNISON, *Phys. Rev.*, 57 (1940) 128.
4 E. B. WILSON, *J. Chem. Phys.*, 7 (1939) 1047; 9 (1941) 76.
5 B. L. CRAWFORD AND W. H. FLETCHER, *J. Chem. Phys.*, 19(1951) 141.
6 C. E. SUN, R. G. PARR AND B. L. CRAWFORD, *J. Chem. Phys.*, 17 (1949) 840.
  S. CALIFANO AND B. L. CRAWFORD, *Z. Electrochem.*, 64 (1960) 571.
  See also ref. 2, pp. 140, 172.
7 A. C. AITKEN, *Determinants and Matrices*, Oliver and Boyd, London, 1954.
  R. A. FRAZER, W. J. DUNCAN AND A. R. COLLAR, *Elementary Matrices*, Cambridge University Press, Cambridge, 1952.
  W. L. FERRAR, *Determinants and Matrices*, Oxford University Press, Oxford, 1953.
8 S. BRODERSON AND A. LANGSETH, *Kgl. Danske Videnskab. Selskab, Mat. Fys. Skrifter*, 1, No. 5 (1958); No. 7 (1959); *J. Mol. Spectry.*, 3 (1959) 114, 450.
  J. HEICKLEN, *J. Chem. Phys.*, 36 (1962) 721.
9 W. S. BENEDICT, N. GAILAR AND E. K. PLYLER, *J. Chem. Phys.*, 24 (1956) 1139.
10 O. REDLICH, *Z. physik. Chem. (Leipzig)*, B. 28 (1935) 371.
  E. TELLER, quoted by ANGUS *et al.*, *J. Chem. Soc. (London)*, 1936, 971.
  See also ref. 2.

[11] J. C. DECIUS AND E. B. WILSON, *J. Chem. Phys.*, 19 (1951) 1409.
See also ref. 2.

[12] D. KIVELSON AND E. B. WILSON, *J. Chem. Phys.*, 21 (1953) 1229.

[13] J. H. MEAL AND S. R. POLO, *J. Chem. Phys.*, 24 (1956) 1126.

[14] S. J. CYVIN, *Acta. Chem. Scand.*, 13 (1959) 2135; 14 (1959) 960; *J. Mol. Spectry.*, 3 (1959) 467.
Y. MORINO, Y. NAKAMURA AND T. IIJIMA, *J. Chem. Phys.*, 32 (1960) 643.

[15] D. E. MANN, T. SHIMANOUCHI, J. H. MEAL AND L. FANO, *J. Chem. Phys.*, 27 (1957) 51.

[16] J. OVEREND AND J. R. SCHERER, *J. Chem. Phys.*, 32 (1960) 1289, 1296.

[17] J. ALDOUS AND I. M. MILLS, *Spectrochim. Acta*, 18 (1962) 1073.

[18] G. HERZBERG, *Infrared and Raman Spectra of Polyatomic Molecules*, Van Nostrand, New York, 1945.

[19] D. M. DENNISON, *Rev. Modern Phys.*, 12 (1940) 175.

[20] D. F. EGGERS, I. C. HISATSUME AND L. VAN ALTEN, *J. Phys. Chem.*, 59 (1955) 1124.

[21] Calculations carried out in the author's laboratory, to be published.

[22] C. H. TINDAL, J. W. STRALEY AND H. H. NIELSEN, *Phys. Rev.*, 62 (1942) 151.

[23] J. H. MEAL AND M. KENT WILSON, *J. Chem. Phys.*, 24 (1956) 385.

[24] I. F. KOVALEV, *Opt. i Spektroscopiya*, 2 (1957) 310.

[25] J. DUCHESNE, *Acad. Roy. Belg. Classe. Sci. Mem.*, 26 (1952) 3.
C. A. COULSON, J. DUCHESNE AND C. MANNEBACK, *Victor Henri Memorial Volume*, Maison Desoer, Liège, (1948) 33.

[26] D. F. HEATH AND J. W. LINNETT, *Trans. Faraday Soc.*, 44 (1948) 556, 561, 873, 878, 884; 45 (1949) 264.

[27] J. W. LINNETT AND P. J. WHEATLEY, *Trans. Faraday Soc.*, 45 (1949) 33, 39.

[28] T. SHIMANOUCHI, *J. Chem. Phys.*, 26 (1956) 594.

[29] I. M. MILLS, *Spectrochim. Acta*, 16 (1960) 35.

[30] H. C. UREY AND C. A. BRADLEY, *Phys. Rev.*, 38 (1931) 1969.

[31] T. SHIMANOUCHI, *J. Chem. Phys.*, 17 (1949) 245, 734, 848.

[32] S. CALIFANO AND J. HEICKLIN, *Spectrochim. Acta*, 17 (1961) 900.

[33] J. OVEREND AND J. R. SCHERER, *J. Chem. Phys.*, 33 (1960) 446.

[34] R. M. BADGER, *J. Chem. Phys.*, 2 (1934) 128.

[35] *Interatomic Distances*, ED. L. E. SUTTON, Special Publication of the Chemical Society, No. 11, The Chemical Society, London, 1958.

Chapter VI

Raman Spectroscopy

J. C. EVANS

The Dow Chemical Company, Midland, Michigan

Molecular scattering of light in a transparent medium has long been known and extensively studied. Scattering without change in wavelength during the scattering process is now usually known as Rayleigh scattering, Rayleigh being one of the earliest and most active investigators of the phenomenon. In 1928, another type of scattering was first identified experimentally — scattering accompanied by a change of wavelength. RAMAN[1] found that when an intense beam of monochromatic light was incident upon a transparent medium, in the first instance a liquid, the spectrum of the scattered light contained in addition to the relatively intense Rayleigh line, new but much weaker lines which were characteristic of the scattering medium. The effect was independently discovered in the solid phase, in quartz, by LANDSBERG and MANDELSTAM[2], and soon afterwards it was shown to occur in the vapour phase. The importance of these observations was immediately recognized and the development of this new tool for studying molecular rotation and vibration was rapid. Before the advent of automatic-recording infra-red spectrometers, the Raman spectrum was more widely used than the infra-red in solving molecular structure problems, and its apparent eclipse in recent years in the organic structure field is due only to the ease with which infra-red spectra can now be obtained with almost any type of sample. Likewise, the rotational Raman spectrum can be as informative as the simple microwave absorption spectrum but it is not so easily obtained.

(1) Theory of Rayleigh and Raman Scattering

An understanding of the nature of the Raman effect is inseparable from a knowledge of the nature of Rayleigh scattering, the classical picture of which we shall first review. When a light wave with electric vector E which oscillates with frequency ν and hence is representable by $E = E_0 \cos 2\pi\nu t$ (where E_0 is the amplitude and t is the time), is incident upon a molecule, the electrons are forced into oscillations of the same frequency. The dipole

References p. 225

moment, **P**, which is induced, is proportional to the electric field, the proportionality constant **α** being termed the *polarizability* of the molecule. Then,

$$\boldsymbol{P} = \boldsymbol{\alpha}\boldsymbol{E} = \boldsymbol{\alpha}\boldsymbol{E}_0 \cos 2\pi vt \tag{1}$$

Classical electromagnetic theory states that an oscillating dipole radiates energy and it is this radiation, which in general occurs in all directions, that constitutes the scattered light. Furthermore, the total intensity or the average rate of total radiation is given by

$$I = \frac{16\pi^4}{3c^3} v^4 \cdot \boldsymbol{P}_0^2 \tag{2}$$

where *c* is the velocity of light and $\boldsymbol{P}_0$ is the amplitude of **P** *i.e.*, $\boldsymbol{\alpha}\boldsymbol{E}_0$. The term v^4 shows that I varies rapidly with the frequency. This fact, taken together with the spectral emission curve of the sun and the wave-length-dependent sensitivity of the eye, explains the blue colour of the sky.

Equation (2) shows that for a rigid molecule the scattered light will have the same frequency as the incident light. However, suppose the molecule to be vibrating with one normal vibration of frequency v_k and normal coordinate Q_k. During the vibration the polarizability is assumed to change and, to a first approximation, the polarizability may be expressed by

$$\boldsymbol{\alpha} = \boldsymbol{\alpha}_0 + \left(\frac{\partial\boldsymbol{\alpha}}{\partial Q_k}\right) Q_k \tag{3}$$

for small oscillations about the equilibrium position. $(\partial\boldsymbol{\alpha}/\partial Q_k)$ is the rate of change of polarizability with Q_k, and $\boldsymbol{\alpha}_0$ is the polarizability of the molecule in its equilibrium configuration. Q_k varies with the frequency of the molecular vibration and is expressible as $Q_k = Q_k^0 \cos (2\pi v_k t)$, neglecting the phase factor. By substitution in (3) followed by substitution in (1) and some rearrangement, the induced dipole moment is found to be

$$\boldsymbol{P} = 2\boldsymbol{\alpha}_0 \boldsymbol{E}_0 \cos 2\pi vt + \boldsymbol{E}_0 Q_k^0 \left(\frac{\partial\boldsymbol{\alpha}}{\partial Q_k}\right) [\cos 2\pi(v+v_k)t + \cos 2\pi(v-v_k)t] \tag{4}$$

which shows that, in addition to the Rayleigh scattering component, the induced dipole moment has two components which oscillate, and so emit radiation, with frequencies $(v+v_k)$ and $(v-v_k)$. The spectrum of the scattered light should show three lines, the intense Rayleigh line and two equally displaced weaker lines; weaker, because $\boldsymbol{\alpha}_0$ will in general be greater than $Q_k^0(\partial\boldsymbol{\alpha}/\partial Q_k)$. The relative intensities of emission of the two displaced lines is given, by reference to equation (2), by

$$\frac{I_{\text{Stokes †}}}{I_{\text{Anti-Stokes}}} = \left(\frac{\nu - \nu_k}{\nu + \nu_k}\right)^4 \tag{5}$$

This is close to unity since ν is usually of the order of twenty times the value of ν_k; also, it predicts that the anti-Stokes line will always be more intense than the Stokes with the discrepancy increasing in favour of the anti-Stokes line as ν_k increases. The earliest experimental observations showed that the expression (5) was not valid, the Stokes lines being found to be more intense than the anti-Stokes with the discrepancy increasing so rapidly with the value of ν_k, that above about 700 cm^{-1} the anti-Stokes lines were hardly ever observed. The classical picture, while correctly predicting that the Raman effect will occur, is thus inadequate for a quantitative account.

However, about five years prior to Raman's observation, SMEKAL[3] predicted that both elastic and inelastic collisions between molecules and light quanta could occur. The elastic collisions result in a change of direction of the photons but no change of energy; this is Rayleigh scattering. The inelastic collisions may be of two types,

$$\boldsymbol{h}\nu + \text{M} \rightarrow \boldsymbol{h}\nu' + \text{M}^* \quad \text{with } \boldsymbol{h}\nu > \boldsymbol{h}\nu' \tag{6a}$$

$$\boldsymbol{h}\nu + \text{M}^* \rightarrow \boldsymbol{h}\nu' + \text{M} \quad \text{with } \boldsymbol{h}\nu < \boldsymbol{h}\nu' \tag{6b}$$

In (6a), the molecule in its lowest energy level (or ground state), M, accepts from the photon the energy $\boldsymbol{h}(\nu - \nu')$, which is just sufficient to raise it to an excited level, M*, while the modified photon appears with lower energy $\boldsymbol{h}\nu'$, and a lower frequency ν'. In (6b), an excited molecule donates to the photon the amount of energy which it must discard to fall to its ground state. This picture immediately explains why the Stokes line (process 6a) is more intense than the anti-Stokes line (process 6b). The concentrations of M and M* are determined by the Boltzmann factor and at the usual temperatures of observation the populations of excited levels, M*, are less than that of the ground level.

Before proceeding with the next step, which is the quantitative application of quantum mechanics to the theory, it is desirable to enlarge the previous discussion of the polarizability of a molecule. Consider a stationary molecule within which rectangular coordinate axes x, y and z are fixed. When plane polarized radiation with electric vector $\boldsymbol{E}$ strikes the molecule it can in the general case be resolved into components E_x, E_y and E_z along the three axes. The induced dipole moment $\boldsymbol{P}$ is not necessarily parallel to $\boldsymbol{E}$ and it can also be resolved into three components P_x, P_y and P_z along the three axes. Since P_x will contain contributions from each of the three

---

† The terms Stokes and Anti-Stokes lines refer to the displaced lines $(\nu - \nu_k)$ and $(\nu + \nu_k)$ respectively; they were taken from the older field of fluorescence spectroscopy.

components of E, three proportionality constants are required. Thus,

$$P_x = \alpha_{xx}E_x + \alpha_{xy}E_y + \alpha_{xz}E_z \qquad (7)$$

Similarly,

$$P_y = \alpha_{yx}E_x + \alpha_{yy}E_y + \alpha_{yz}E_z \qquad (8)$$

and,

$$P_z = \alpha_{zx}E_x + \alpha_{zy}E_y + \alpha_{zz}E_z \qquad (9)$$

In matrix notation, $\boldsymbol{P} = \boldsymbol{\alpha E}$, which in expanded form is

$$
\begin{vmatrix} P_x \\ P_y \\ P_z \end{vmatrix} = \begin{vmatrix} \alpha_{xx} & \alpha_{xy} & \alpha_{xz} \\ \alpha_{yx} & \alpha_{yy} & \alpha_{yz} \\ \alpha_{zx} & \alpha_{zy} & \alpha_{zz} \end{vmatrix} \times \begin{vmatrix} E_x \\ E_y \\ E_z \end{vmatrix} \qquad (10)
$$

and, since it may be shown that $\alpha_{xy} = \alpha_{yx}$, etc., $\boldsymbol{\alpha}$ is a symmetric matrix or tensor. $\boldsymbol{\alpha}$ is usually known as the *polarizability tensor* of the molecule with components or matrix elements $\alpha_{\rho\sigma}$ which, although dependent on the directions of the coordinate axes within the molecule, are independent of the directions of E and P. It may be shown that there exists within the molecule a set of axes such that all the off-diagonal elements of the polarizability tensor are zero. This means that by appropriate choice of the x, y, and z directions, equations (7), (8) and (9) simplify to $P_x = \alpha_{xx}E_x$, $P_y = \alpha_{yy}E_y$, and $P_z = \alpha_{zz}E_z$ and the induced moments are parallel to the perturbing electric vectors along these axes. These axes are known as the *principal axes* of the polarizability ellipsoid which is defined as the ellipsoid obtained by plotting from the origin of the principal axes the value of $1/(\alpha)^{\frac{1}{2}}$ in each direction. For symmetrical molecules the directions of the principal axes are easily found because they must coincide with the symmetry axes, *e.g.* for chloroform which has C_{3v} symmetry the threefold axis must coincide with one principal axis, say the z axis. The other two axes must be at right angles to this and to one another but, in this case, are not otherwise restricted since the ellipsoid is a rotational ellipsoid about the z axis.

It is convenient to resolve the polarizability into two parts, a symmetrical or isotropic part α^s, and the anisotropic part α^a, such that,

$$\boldsymbol{\alpha} = \alpha^s + \alpha^a \qquad (11)$$

where

$$3\alpha^s = (\alpha_{xx} + \alpha_{yy} + \alpha_{zz}) \qquad (12)$$

and

$$2[\alpha^a]^2 = [(\alpha_{xx} - \alpha_{yy})^2 + (\alpha_{yy} - \alpha_{zz})^2 + (\alpha_{zz} - \alpha_{xx})^2 + 6(\alpha_{xy}^2 + \alpha_{yz}^2 + \alpha_{zx}^2)] \qquad (13)$$

This is equivalent to considering the total polarizability matrix to be the sum of two matrices;

$$\begin{vmatrix} \alpha_{xx}^s + \alpha_{xx}^a & \alpha_{xy}^a & \alpha_{xz}^a \\ \alpha_{yx}^a & \alpha_{yy}^s + \alpha_{yy}^a & \alpha_{yz}^a \\ \alpha_{zx}^a & \alpha_{zy}^a & \alpha_{zz}^s + \alpha_{zz}^a \end{vmatrix} = \begin{vmatrix} \alpha_{xx}^s & 0 & 0 \\ 0 & \alpha_{yy}^s & 0 \\ 0 & 0 & \alpha_{zz}^s \end{vmatrix} + \begin{vmatrix} \alpha_{xx}^a & \alpha_{xy}^a & \alpha_{xz}^a \\ \alpha_{yx}^a & \alpha_{yy}^a & \alpha_{yz}^a \\ \alpha_{zx}^a & \alpha_{zy}^a & \alpha_{zz}^a \end{vmatrix} \quad (14)$$

The values of α^s and $[\alpha^a]^2$ are the *invariants of the polarizability tensor*, so called because their values are independent of the relative orientation of the principal axes and the fixed coordinate system.

As will be evident from the later discussion, the vibrational Raman effect requires a discussion of the partial derivatives of each of the components of the polarizability tensor with respect to each normal coordinate. This matrix is known as the *derived polarizability tensor*, its elements being $(\partial \alpha_{\rho\sigma}/\partial Q_k)$ where Q_k is the normal coordinate and ρ and σ are independently x, y or z. The invariants of this matrix have a form similar to (12) and (13) but with the partial derivative substituted for each $\alpha_{\rho\sigma}$. Since these differentials need not always be positive it is sometimes not possible to define the derived polarizability ellipsoid.

At this point, we shall return to the development of the theory of the Raman effect. The detailed development of the quantitative quantum mechanical treatment is beyond the scope of this chapter and the reader is referred to the original account[4]. However, it is instructive to look at the resulting expression for the intensity. The treatment used the classical description of the radiation with the quantized energy level picture of the molecule. The intensity of light, incident with intensity I_0 and frequency v_0, which is scattered at a frequency $(v_0 + v_{mn})$ while the molecule passes from the vibrational level m to the vibrational level n, $(v_{mn} = v_m - v_n)$ is given, after averaging over all orientations of the molecule, for 4π solid angle by

$$I_{mn} = \frac{2^7 \pi^5}{3^2 c^4} I_0 (v_0 + v_{mn})^4 \sum |(\alpha_{\rho\sigma})_{mn}|^2 \quad (15)$$

where the sum goes over $\rho = x$, y and z and $\sigma = x$, y and z independently and $\alpha_{\rho\sigma}$ is the $\rho\sigma$th matrix element of the polarizability tensor for the transition $m \to n$. The significance of these matrix elements is made clearer if their relationship to the induced dipole moment $\boldsymbol{P}$ is illustrated. Just as the permanent dipole moment of a molecule is expressed as a matrix with elements, $\int \boldsymbol{\Psi}_n \boldsymbol{M} \boldsymbol{\Psi}_m^* \, d\tau$ where $\boldsymbol{M}$ is a vector with components $M_x = \sum e_i x_i$, $M_y = \sum e_i y_i$, $M_z = \sum e_i z_i$, e_i being the charge and x_i, y_i and z_i the coordinates of particle i, and $\boldsymbol{\Psi}_n$ and $\boldsymbol{\Psi}_m$ are the time-dependent wave functions of the states n and m, so can the induced dipole moment be expressed as the matrix with elements

$$P_{nm} = \int \boldsymbol{\Psi}_n \boldsymbol{P} \boldsymbol{\Psi}_m^* \, d\tau \quad (16)$$

The wave functions $\Psi_n = \psi_n \cdot e^{2\pi i (E_n/h)t}$, and the complex conjugate $\Psi_n^* = \psi_n^* \cdot e^{-2\pi i (E_n/h)t}$ consist of two parts, ψ_n and the exponential term, where ψ_n is the time-independent wave-function. The time-independent part, or the amplitude, of (16) is then

$$P_{nm}^0 = \int \psi_n P^0 \psi_m^* \, d\tau \tag{17}$$

and the probability of the transition $n \to m$ is proportional to the square of P_{nm}^0; here P^0 is the amplitude of $\boldsymbol{P}$ and the three components of P_{nm}^0 are given in terms of α and E by expressions such as

$$[P_x^0]_{nm} = E_x^0 \int \psi_n \alpha_{xx} \psi_m^* \, d\tau + E_y^0 \int \psi_n \alpha_{xy} \psi_m^* \, d\tau + E_z^0 \int \psi_n \alpha_{xz} \psi_m^* \, d\tau \tag{18}$$

These six integrals, $\int \psi_n \alpha_{\rho\sigma} \psi_m^* \, d\tau$, are the matrix elements encountered in equation (15). At least one of these components must be non-zero if the transition $n \to m$ is to be active in the Raman effect and I_n is to be non-zero. This is the basic selection rule governing the Raman effect; we shall return to this in the next section, but in the meantime, let us consider the expression derived by Kramers and Heisenberg for the elements $[\alpha_{\rho\sigma}]_{mn}$;

$$[\alpha_{\rho\sigma}]_{mn} = \frac{1}{h} \sum \left[\frac{(M_\rho)_{rn}(M_\sigma)_{mr}}{\nu_{rm} - \nu_0} + \frac{(M_\rho)_{mr}(M_\sigma)_{rn}}{\nu_{rn} + \nu_0} \right] \tag{19}$$

where h = Planck's constant and the M are the amplitudes of the transition moments, e.g. $(M_\rho)_{rn}$ is the amplitude or time-independent part of the transition moment $(\boldsymbol{M}_\rho)_{rn}$ between the levels r and n,

$$(M_\rho)_{rn} = \int \psi_r M_\rho \psi_n^* \, d\tau \tag{20}$$

The sum in equation (19) extends over all the vibrational levels of all the excited electronic states r, so that each level should be identified by two subscripts to describe its electronic and its vibrational character. However, for our purpose, which is to examine the form of the expression, this is not essential. Six equations of the form of (19) give the six elements of the polarizability tensor. For any of these elements to be non-zero and hence contribute to the Raman intensity, it is apparent that there must exist at least one excited level, r, which can combine with (i.e. has finite transition moments to) both the initial, m, and final, n, vibrational levels of the ground state. This does not mean that an actual transition to the excited level occurs; on the contrary, ν_0 is chosen to be much less than any ν_{rm} and the theory is not valid when ν_0 is close to ν_{rm}.

In general, the summation in equation (19) which extends over all energy levels cannot be evaluated. However, PLACZEK[5, 6] introduced experimentally attainable quantities by making use of the expansion of the polarizability in a Taylor series in the vibrational coordinates (see equation (3)). The matrix element $[\alpha_{\rho\sigma}]_{mn}$ was replaced by the classical expression $(\partial\alpha_{\rho\sigma}/\partial Q_{mn})\cdot Q^0_{mn}$, which is the product of the derivative of the polarizability with respect to the normal coordinate Q_{mn}, and the amplitude. In this way Placzek was able to express the Raman scattering intensity in terms of the invariants of the polarizability derivatives,

$$I_n = \text{constant} \cdot \frac{(\nu_0+\nu_{mn})^4}{\nu_{mn}} \cdot \frac{NI_0}{(1-e^{-h\nu_{mn}/kT})} \cdot [45(\alpha'_s)^2+13(\alpha'_a)^2] \qquad (21)$$

where N is the number of molecules in the initial energy state and other terms are defined earlier. The constants 45 and 13 arise in the averaging over all configurations and depend on the geometry of the experimental arrangement, *i.e.* light scattered per unit solid angle at right angles to the incident direction is observed. Furthermore, the ratio of Stokes to anti-Stokes intensity is

$$\frac{I_{\text{Stokes}}}{I_{\text{Anti-Stokes}}} = \left(\frac{\nu_0-\nu_k}{\nu_0+\nu_k}\right)^4 \cdot e^{h\nu_k/kT} \qquad (22)$$

which has been verified experimentally when the assumptions upon which the derivation depends are valid. These are, (a) $(\nu_{rm}-\nu_0)$ is large and $(\nu_0 \gg \nu_k)$, which means that the exciting frequency is much less than the frequency of the first electronic absorption band and much greater than the nuclear vibrations, and (b) the ground electronic state is non-degenerate, which is true for almost all molecules. Most of the published work on Raman intensities has been done on the basis of Placzek's polarizability theory but, recently, more work has been done in the region outside the theory's limitations. Some discussion of this will be given later.

(2) Selection Rules

The selection rule for the vibrational Raman effect has already been quoted; it is that at least one of the six matrix elements of the polarizability tensor for the transition $m \to n$ must be non-zero if the transition is to be active *i.e.*

$$\int \psi_m \alpha_{\rho\sigma} \psi_n^* \, d\tau \neq 0$$

The symmetry of the molecule in its equilibrium position determines whether this is so or not, since, for the integral to be non-zero, the integrand must not change sign during any symmetry operation permitted by the molecular symmetry. Thus, $\alpha_{\rho\sigma}$ must have the same symmetry properties as the product $\psi_m \psi_n^*$, which for the fundamental transition $0 \to 1$ is the symmetry of the upper state since the ground state is totally symmetric. Furthermore, since the symmetry of the molecular vibration is the same as

References p. 225

that of the upper level of the transition, the selection rule may be stated as follows: "a vibration whose symmetry is the same as that of one of the six components of the polarizability will appear as a fundamental in the Raman spectrum". The symmetry species of the six polarizability components have been determined and tabulated for all the common point groups[7].

(3) Depolarization Ratio

It was shown in the discussion of the polarizability that P is not in general parallel to E but depends on the symmetry of the polarizability. One might expect then that a knowledge of the polarization properties of the scattered light could give information about the polarizability ellipsoid in the case of Rayleigh scattering and about the symmetry of the molecular vibrations in the case of the Raman bands. This is indeed so, and the value of the depolarization ratio of a Raman band is frequently very informative. The depolarization ratio ρ is defined as the ratio of the intensity of the scattered light polarized perpendicular to the xy plane, $I_\perp$, to that polarized parallel to this plane, $I_\parallel$, when the incident light approaches along the z axis and the scattered light is observed at right angles to the z axis,

$$\rho = \frac{I_\perp}{I_\parallel} \tag{23}$$

When the incident light is unpolarized and the required intensities are computed and averaged over all possible orientations of the molecule, ρ is found to be, for Rayleigh scattering

$$\rho = \frac{6(\alpha^a)^2}{45(\alpha^s)^2 + 7(\alpha^a)^2} \tag{24}$$

while for Raman scattering under the same conditions,

$$\rho = \frac{6(\alpha'_a)^2}{45(\alpha'_s)^2 + 7(\alpha'_a)^2} \tag{25}$$

the primes representing the derivatives. The totally symmetrical part of the polarizability only changes when the molecule is distorted in a totally symmetrical manner. According to (25), this means that ρ for all vibrations which are not in the totally symmetric species will be 6/7, while only those in the totally symmetric species can have a value of ρ less than 6/7. This property is extremely useful, particularly in liquid phase spectra, in identifying the totally symmetric vibrations; there is no comparable source of such information in the infra-red spectrum.

(4) **Rotational Raman Spectra**

The emphasis so far has been entirely upon the vibrational Raman effect, because the major part of the published literature has been devoted to the vibrational spectra of molecules in condensed phases, usually in the liquid phase. However, the quantized rotation of molecules in the vapour phase manifests itself in two ways — in the appearance of purely rotational Raman lines in the immediate vicinity of the Rayleigh line and in the appearance of fine structure in the vibrational Raman bands. The purely rotational scattering is particularly important because it provides the means for obtaining the rotational spectra of those molecules which do not possess permanent electric dipole moments; this property precludes the observation of rotational transitions in absorption in the microwave region. As was described in Chapter IV, knowledge of the rotational spectrum of a molecule and several of its isotopic derivatives can yield accurate moments of inertia from which precise molecular dimensions may be calculated.

A polarizability change during a rotation must occur if the rotational transitions are to contribute to the scattering. A glance at the equations 11 to 14 and the definitions of the invariants of the polarizability suffices to show that the symmetric part will not contribute to the rotational scattering. However, a change in the anisotropic part during rotation will always occur unless the molecule has spherical symmetry. All molecules not in this latter class will show rotational Raman lines. It follows from the expression for the depolarization ratio, which is of the same form as equation (25), that all rotational lines will have $\rho = 6/7$ for the geometrical set-up described, and this is then not of diagnostic use.

The rotational structure of vibration–rotation bands in the vapour spectra of small molecules can be very informative, as was shown in the case of infra-red bands in Chapter IV. The selection rules in the Raman spectrum are, of course, different, and in general the changes in J, the quantum number measuring the total angular momentum, may be $J = 0$, ± 1, ± 2 yielding five branches, O, P, Q, R, S. However, high resolution studies of vibration–rotation structure in the Raman effect are even more difficult than pure-rotation studies because of their low intrinsic intensities, and the number of such studies is not large[8].

(5) **Experimental**

Raman scattering is usually weaker by at least a factor of 10^3 than the Rayleigh scattering, and it is then a rare occasion when the experimenter is embarrassed by a surfeit of intensity. In general, all possible means are used to increase the intensity of the scattering, the efficiency of collecting the scattered radiation and the sensitivity of the detecting system. The various parts of the experimental equipment are inter-dependent and depend also on the nature of the sample. Fig. VI, 1 shows a schematic diagram of the general apparatus and Fig. VI, 2 illustrates some typical

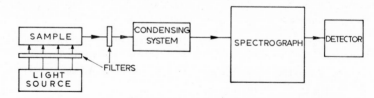

Fig. VI, 1. Schematic representation of the general Raman apparatus.

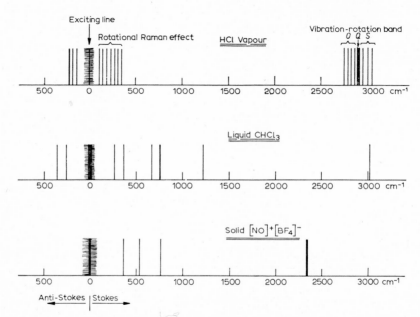

Fig. VI, 2. Line diagrams of Raman spectra recorded photographically. The exciting line is broadened mainly by over-exposure, although in liquids there is also a continuous wing extending to about 50 cm⁻¹ from the exciting line.

spectra. We shall discuss the various parts in order, starting with the light source.

(5A) Light source

Raman and his co-workers initially employed an intense beam of sunlight as the exciting source, placing complementary filters in the incident and scattered light beams to separate the Raman radiation. They quickly turned to more nearly monochromatic sources and employed mercury arcs which emit several intense atomic lines in the ultraviolet, visible and even in the infra-red. Most investigators have used mercury arcs, and most have preferred the 4358Å line. Frequently, the absorption of the sample or its fluorescence emission prohibits the use of this exciting line and a longer wavelength line must be used. Lines in the green, 5461Å mercury; the yellow, 5776Å helium; the red, 6438Å cadmium and near infra-red, 8224Å argon, have been used. At the other extreme, the very convenient mercury resonance line at 2537Å is probably the shortest wavelength to be used. The earlier discussion has emphasized the increase of Raman band intensity with the exciting line frequency.

The type and shape of lamp chosen depend upon the nature of the sample. For vapours, especially for rotational spectra, a narrow exciting line is required and a low-pressure light source must be used to prevent pressure broadening of the emission line. High-current, direct-current, mercury arcs in which the discharge and mercury-pool electrodes are water cooled were developed for this purpose at the University of Toronto and are known as "Toronto" sources. The light output at 4358Å is high, the background emission is low and the exciting line is sharp. This type of lamp is also much used in exciting liquid-phase Raman spectra, although in this case the somewhat more convenient, alternating-current, hot-cathode, medium-pressure mercury arcs are very useful. The exciting line is broader but is still much narrower than the vibrational Raman bands of liquids. For polycrystalline solids where little is gained by having a large sample, the higher pressure arcs provide the small, bright source which is most convenient.

In recent years a new source of very intense monochromatic light in the red region has been developed — the laser or optical maser. It promises to be very useful in exciting Raman spectra[8a].

(5B) Sample cell and filters

The sample-phase determines the type of cell required. Vapours require large cells merely to enable an adequate number of molecules to be irradiated since pressures in excess of one atmosphere lead to pressure-broadening and consequent line overlapping. Multiple-reflection cells about 1 metre long and about 10 cm in diameter are surrounded by several water cooled lamps and the entire system is enclosed in a container with highly reflecting walls to increase the efficiency. Spurious light scattered from the mirrors and walls of the sample tube is reduced as much as possible with light baffles mounted within the tube.

Liquids are usually placed in glass tubes which are irradiated along their lengths, the scattered light emerging through a strainless, flat end-window being collected. The other end is blackened so that the meniscus is covered; efficiency is increased by having a mirror mounted at this end. A sample tube of volume about 5 ml is mounted within concentric filter and cooling jackets surrounded by several straight a.c. medium-pressure arcs or by a single helical Toronto arc. A 'light-furnace' surrounds the entire set-up. Solution filters are normally used to remove radiation of shorter and longer wavelength than the exciting line, *e.g.* the 4358Å line may be isolated with an aqueous sodium nitrite solution to remove shorter wavelengths and an alcoholic solution of Rhodamine dye to remove longer wavelengths. In general, a complementary filter in the scattered light beam is not required for liquid samples.

Solids, however, if encountered in the polycrystalline powder form, require good filtering in both beams: otherwise, the high intensity of reflected light from the numerous crystal faces entering the spectrograph becomes overwhelming. Nowadays, narrow-band, multilayer interference filters are available. These give high transmission over a narrow band and high reflectivity elsewhere, and may be made to transmit at any wavelength over the entire range of wavelengths used to excite Raman spectra. The filters, however, do require that the incident light be parallel, since the wavelength of the peak transmission varies with the angle of incidence. An arrangement for exciting Raman spectra of solids is illustrated in Fig. VI, 3. The first filters, F_1 and F_2, serve to isolate the exciting line,

Fig. VI, 3. An arrangement for exciting Raman spectra of powdered solids.
A, light source; L, lenses; F, filters; S, sample; H, spectrograph.

which is condensed onto the sample S. This is in the form of a pressed pellet, the thickness of which may be of the order of 1 mm. The scattered radiation emerging from the far side is collected, rendered parallel, and freed of the exciting line by reflection on filters F_3 and F_4. These are chosen so that they transmit the exciting line when the light is incident at a small angle, the Raman radiation being reflected and then collected by the spectrograph.

(5C) Condensing systems

The most effective means of transferring the Raman radiation to the spectrograph must be employed. Various lens systems and image-slicers have been described and the problem has been treated theoretically. It is found that the optimum filling of the spectrograph slit and collimator is achieved when the condensing lens system is chosen so that it images the near-end of the Raman sample tube onto the collimator lens while the far end is imaged onto the slit; the volume-image of the illuminated sample should just fill the collimator. One or two lens systems are normally used to achieve this[9].

Raman sample tubes are usually cylindrical so that the circular image falling on the narrow, rectangular spectrograph slit is not being used to the best advantage. Image-slicers have been developed to improve the matching of tube and slit. The circular aperture of the Raman sample tube is sliced optically into a number of thin slices which are re-arranged end-to-end to match the entrance slit. In the instrument to be described in the next section, twenty such slices are used to illuminate a slit 10 cm long.

(5D) Spectrographs and detectors

The requirements here depend again on the problem, although one general rule applies; the largest aperture instrument with the necessary resolution should be used. Most of the Raman spectra in the literature were obtained using photographic recording but, with the advent of photomultiplier tubes, direct photoelectric recording became possible. Linear response, excellent reproducibility and convenience are the chief advantages of the latter method, and improved intensity and depolarization measurements are possible. However, less efficient use is made of the scattered light. While the photographic plate records all wavelengths at the same time, the photoelectric detector must scan the spectrum. The higher intrinsic sensitivity of the photoelectric surface alleviates this disadvantage to a considerable extent, but photoelectric instruments require careful designing with the emphasis on the total light flux transmitted rather than, as with the photographic instrument, on the light density. The important features are well-illustrated in Fig. VI, 4, which is a schematic diagram, (with explanatory notes), of the optics of a particularly powerful photoelectric Raman instrument. The exceptionally long slits and twin-slit system are made possible by the use of the double monochromator which also removes an irritating problem with single monochromator instruments *viz*, scattered light, which becomes serious with samples which exhibit Tyndall scattering by small particles in suspension, or with powdered solid samples. Direct photoelectric recording of the spectra of liquids, solids and vapours is possible with an instrument such as this.

Other instruments are commercially available[10] and several arrangements have been described by various workers[11, 12]. While the experimental details of recording spectra will depend largely on the type of sample, the instrument used, and the spectral region in which the Raman spectrum is excited, it may be of interest to describe briefly the conditions under which liquid or solution samples excited in the blue region are examined. About

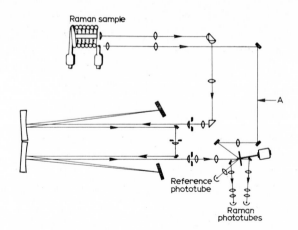

Fig. VI, 4. A commercial photoelectric recording Raman instrument.
(Courtesy of Applied Physics Corporation, Monrovia, Calif.).

Raman cell. 4.5 cc volume, 22 cm illuminated length, with ground joint tubulation and cap

Monochromator. Two-grating twin-slit double monochromator collimated by off-axis spherica
mirrors in Czerny-Littrow arrangement with corrector lenses to flatten the field. Focal length
1000 mm, slit height 100 mm, aperture 100 mm × 100 mm. Entrance, exit and intermediate
slits simultaneously variable over range 0.0—1.0 mm. Gratings ruled 1200 lines/mm blazed
for 4500 Å in first order. Wave number counter reading to 1.0 cm⁻¹; wavelength drive by
synchronous motor giving speeds of 0.005, 0.01, 0.025, 0.05, 0.1, 0.25, 0.5, 1.0, 2.5, 5.0 and
10.0 cm⁻¹/sec with a quick return speed of 50 cm⁻¹/sec.

Mounting. Cell and source unit independently mounted on optical bench.

Cell optical system. Non-centred coated system employing image slicer to make maximum
use of cell radiation.

Excitation source. Water-cooled Toronto type mercury arc in form of horizontal helix surrounding cell, with d.c. power supply for 220 V, 3 phase, 60 c.p.s. operation. Arc enclosed in an
air-cooled reflector. Filter assembly between arc and cell arranged to circulate fluid for temperature control of cell.

Auxiliary optical system (Beam marked A in Figure). The auxiliary optical system takes a
sample of exciting radiation from the Raman arc, chops it by the rotating semicircular mirror
and directs it to a separate phototube for the development of a reference signal. The recording
system responds to the ratio of the Raman signal and reference signal, so that recorded results
are essentially independent of arc intensity.

Recording system. Strip chart recorder using 11-inch wide paper. Marker pen for wavenumber
calibration. Chart speeds 10, 20, 40, 100, 200 cm⁻¹ per inch. Maximum pen speed 1.0 second
across chart. Approximately critically damped response with natural period adjustable
from 0.5 sec to 60 sec.

Photometric system. Double phototube 30 c.p.s. chopped radiation system employing electrical
null balance against reference signal developed by auxiliary phototube. Calibrated electrical
attenuators for changing scale sensitivity by factors of 1, 2, 5, 10, 20, 50, 100, 200, 500, 1000.
Calibrated electrical attenuator covering threefold range. Provision for inserting absorbing
filter after exit slit to permit scanning Rayleigh line. Optical attenuator for reference system.

5 ml of sample yields a Raman spectrum which may usually be photo-graphed with less than a minute's exposure or recorded photoelectrically $(50-4000 \text{ cm}^{-1})$ in about thirty minutes. Spectral slit-widths are usually of the order of 5 cm^{-1}. Smaller samples, of the order of 0.1 ml, require longer exposure or scanning times.

(6) Applications

Molecular structure determinations constitute the most important and most studied application of the Raman effect. Information is derived both from frequency data and from intensity data, and, although the separation is artificial and will not be strictly adhered to, we shall consider first applications of frequency data and then proceed to discuss intensities.

(6A) Applications based on Raman frequencies

Earlier it was indicated that precise molecular dimensions are derived from rotational Raman spectra. This has been done for a number of important, non-polar molecules, an outstanding example being benzene[13]; data for C_6H_6 and C_6D_6 enabled the bond lengths to be determined, $(C-C) = 1.397_3 \pm 0.001$Å, $(C-H) = 1.084 \pm 0.006$Å.

Experimental factors, in particular the spacing of the rotational lines, confine these studies to the relatively small molecules. The reader is referred to STOICHEFF's recent comprehensive account of this field[8]; this account also covers the progress made in high resolution studies of vibration–rotation Raman bands which can also yield precise rotational constants.

Most applications of the Raman effect, however, do not yield molecular dimensions but yield, what is frequently of equal importance, information about the molecular symmetry which can then usually determine the molecular configuration. Infra-red data are essential to make full use of this procedure, which can be illustrated by means of a simple example. In the case of a molecule whose empirical formula is known, the probable structures are written and their symmetries used to deduce the activities (infra-red and/or Raman) of the various fundamental modes. For fairly simple molecules with a high degree of symmetry, the numbers of the modes active in the Raman, in the infra-red and in both spectra may suffice to eliminate some structures. Particularly favourable are those molecules which possess a centre of symmetry, since the rule of mutual exclusion applies here *i.e.* modes active in the Raman are inactive in the infra-red and *vice versa*, the Raman active modes being those which are symmetrical with respect to the centre of symmetry. For example, the isomeric molecules *cis*- and *trans*- dichloroethylene are quite different in their activities (see Table VI, 1).

TABLE VI, 1

SPECTRAL ACTIVITY OF *cis*- AND *trans*- DICHLOROETHYLENE

trans *Dichloroethylene* (C_{2h})			cis *Dichloroethylene* (C_{2v})		
Species	Number of modes	Activity	Species	Number of modes	Activity
A_g	5	Raman (polarized)	A_1	5	Raman (polarized) Infra-red
A_u	2	Infra-red	A_2	2	Raman (depolarized)
B_g	1	Raman (depolarized)	B_1	4	Raman (depolarized) Infra-red
B_u	4	Infra-red	B_2	1	Raman (depolarized) Infra-red

The *trans* molecule with its centre of symmetry should show much simpler spectra, and this is found to be the case. It so happens, in this example, that the number of polarized Raman bands is the same in the two molecules, but this additional information is frequently of great value. Most arguments of this nature in the literature lean heavily on the Raman data because the infra-red data are very often incomplete and the far infra-red data are usually lacking. Only recently has the low-frequency infra-red region received the attention which it deserves.

Structural deductions based on symmetry properties are of particular importance in the study of compounds which exist in several molecular forms or conformations which are of closely similar energies and cannot be separated. A good example is the study of rotational isomers of flexible molecules. In fact, the first experimental evidence for the existence of such isomers came from KOHLRAUSCH's Raman studies of the alkyl halides[14], the spectra being too complex to be due to one molecular species. Since then the halogenated derivatives of ethane have probably received the most attention, and the vibrational spectroscopic studies have helped determine the stable isomers, their energy differences, and the shapes of the potential barriers.

As an example of these studies the case of 1,2-dibromoethane will be reviewed briefly. Spectra, both Raman and infra-red, obtained in the solid, liquid and vapour phases showed the presence of isomers, probably two in number. Relative band intensities are temperature dependent within the fluid phases where the two isomers exist, but, in the crystalline spectrum, many fewer bands were observed. Furthermore, the number of bands and the lack of coincidence between strong Raman and strong infra-red bands showed that the one isomer present in the solid possessed a centre of symmetry, and must, therefore, be the *trans* form, of symmetry C_{2h}, Fig. VI, 5.

The spectra of the *trans* molecule obtained in the solid phase enabled the spectra of the other isomer to be identified in the liquid and vapour phases.

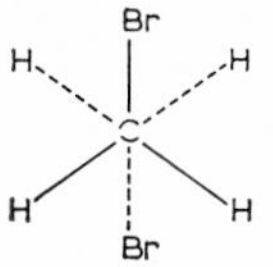

Fig. VI, 5. *trans* 1,2-Dibromoethane, viewed along the (C–C) axis.

The numbers of bands and their Raman polarization properties showed that the symmetry of this isomer was lower, and the measurements of band intensities of the isomers at various temperatures yielded equilibrium constants and energy difference values. The *trans* form was found to be more stable by about 1.5 kcal/mole in the vapour phase and by about 0.7 kcal/mole in the liquid phase. However, there was early disagreement as to the configuration of the higher-energy isomer because the symmetries of the possible forms are low and selection rules are not of much help; the possibilities are the *cis* form, C_{2v}, and two forms of symmetry C_2 (Fig. VI, 6). This difficulty was overcome by NEU and GWINN[15] who made use of symmetry in a more subtle fashion.

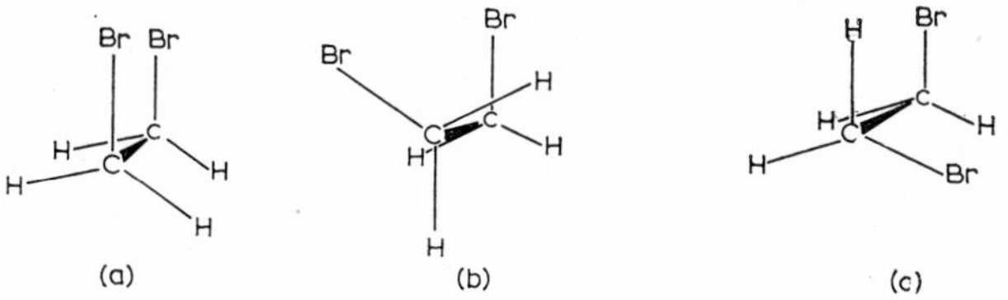

Fig. VI, 6. The forms of 1,2-dibromoethane.
(a) *cis*, C_{2v}. (b) *gauche*, C_2. (c) eclipsed, C_2.

Deuterium substitution for one hydrogen atom on the C_{2v} structure yields the same molecule whichever hydrogen is replaced, since the hydrogens are equivalent. This is not the case for the C_2 models which contain two types of hydrogens. Substitution by one deuterium atom would yield two equally stable isomers whose spectra would be expected to differ. The observed spectra proved that the high-energy form possessed C_2 symmetry.

Of the two C_2 forms the *gauche* is certainly the more probable since it is a staggered form, and evidence accumulated from the spectra of other series, together with evidence from other methods, has proved this conclusively. Before leaving this aspect of molecular configuration determination, it should be emphasized that the selection rules apply strictly only to the isolated molecules and that quite frequently forbidden bands do appear weakly in liquid spectra due to the intermolecular perturbations.

References p. 225

When the molecular configuration has been determined or is already well known, the Raman data may be used along with the infra-red data in making a complete vibrational assignment. It cannot be emphasized too strongly that an assignment based only on the Raman data or on infra-red data must be regarded with suspicion even when the molecular symmetry is such that all modes are allowed in one spectrum. Frequently, the dipole moment change or the polarizability change during a normal mode is so small that the overtones or combination tones of other modes are considerably more intense: this can lead to an incorrect choice of fundamental frequencies. However, it also happens that the two spectra are complementary and that the fundamental modes give rise to strong bands in one or the other spectrum, making the assignment straightforward.

The complete vibrational assignment, once obtained, is extremely useful since it may be used to study the forces between the atoms within the molecule, and it may be used to calculate the thermodynamic properties of the free molecule in the vapour phase. The former application has been fully discussed in Chapter V. In the latter application it is assumed that the molecule is a collection of independent harmonic oscillators and that it is a rigid rotator. It is known from statistical mechanics that the contributions made by the many degrees of freedom of the isolated molecule, the translational, rotational and the vibrational, can be considered separately and summed to obtain the total. In this way, expressions derived for each contribution to the entropy, heat capacity, free energy and heat content may be numerically evaluated if the vibrational frequencies and moments of inertia are known. Such calculations have been made for many molecules and many comparisons with the experimentally measured heat capacities and entropy values have been obtained.

As the molecular complexity increases, arguments based on symmetry become less useful and normal coordinate calculations rapidly become unmanageable. It is then that the use of group frequencies or characteristic frequencies becomes an important tool in determining structures. The uses and limitations of the group frequency concept in the infra-red are discussed in Chapter VII; in the Raman, the situation is similar except that the emphasis is not on the same group frequencies. It is true that many groups show characteristic bands which are strong in both infra-red and Raman, e.g. $(C=O)$, (NO_2), $(C-H)$, (SO_2), $(C-halogen)$ and there are many groups which may be identified by different characteristic frequencies in the two spectra, e.g. phenyl. Others are best determined in either one or the other spectrum. Groups which are more easily identified in the Raman spectrum than in the infra-red are those which are easily polarizable e.g. $(R-C\equiv C-R')$, $(C-S)$, $(C=C)$, $(S-H)$, $(C-halogen)$.

Another important type of molecule or group is that in which the atoms are so heavy that the vibrational frequencies lie beyond the experimental long-wave limit of most infra-red spectrometers. This limitation is rapidly being removed but there are many inorganic molecules (Fig. VI, 7) for which all the fundamental modes lie below 300 cm^{-1}, which is the practical limit for a CsBr-prism infra-red instrument.

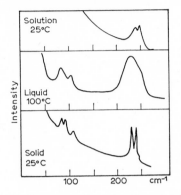

Fig. VI, 7. Raman spectra of antimony tribromide.

As an illustration of the type of problem which may be solved using group-frequency arguments, the elucidation of the structure of a one-component liquid obtained as a reaction product will be described. The molecule was known to contain carbon, hydrogen and chlorine and the structure was thought to be $CH_2(CCl_3)_2$. The Raman spectrum recorded photoelectrically is reproduced in Fig. VI, 8. The outstanding features are

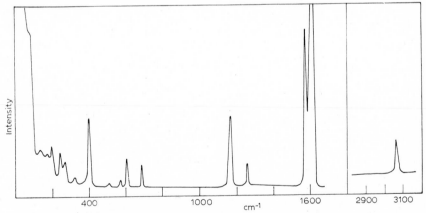

Fig. VI, 8. Raman spectrum of an unknown liquid.

the two intense bands in the (C=C) region near 1600 cm^{-1}; their positions indicate the presence of two conjugated (C=C) bonds with several Cl atoms attached. However, the possibility remained that one of these bands was a fundamental mode while the other was an overtone or combination tone deriving its intensity from Fermi resonance with the fundamental. This interpretation was readily disposed of by a measurement of the depolarization ratios of these bands. One, the more intense band at 1611 cm^{-1}, is highly polarized ($\rho = 0.3$) while the other is almost depolarized ($\rho > 0.8$). The high intensities of the two bands show that the two (C=C) bonds are conjugated, and further, but less reliable support, is drawn from the assignment of the strong band at 1164 cm^{-1} to the stretching mode of the intermediate (C–C) bond. The presence and position of one band in the (C–H) stretching region indicates the presence of one H atom attached to the double-bond system, and this is further supported by the assignment of the

1254 cm^{-1} band to the in-plane bending mode of the $\left(=\mathrm{C}\diagup^{\mathrm{H}}\right)$ group. The spectrum below 800 cm^{-1} shows the absence of the (CCl$_3$) group since this group yields readily recognizable bands, but the pattern is not in disagreement with the structure based on the higher frequency data;

$$\mathrm{\underset{H}{\overset{Cl}{>}}C=C\underset{\underset{\underset{Cl}{\diagdown}C=C\underset{Cl}{\overset{\diagup Cl}{\diagdown}}}{\diagup}}{\overset{\diagup Cl}{\diagdown}}}$$

Steric hindrance prevents complete coplanarity in this molecule.

A standard spectrum of this compound was not available but subsequent quantitative chlorine-analysis and reconsideration of the reaction supported the structure. In this example, the infra-red spectrum which was also obtained as a matter of course, was of but little assistance. The coincidence of the single Raman and single infra-red bands in the ν(C–H) region confirms the presence of only one (C–H) group, while the relative intensities of the (C=C) bands are markedly different in the infra-red, the 1570 cm^{-1} band being strong, while the 1611 cm^{-1} is very weak and partly obscured. This reversal of intensities is expected for the proposed structure.

A sound application of group-frequency methods to structure determination requires a large number of standard spectra of many families of molecules. References 16 and 17 give such a compilation of spectra, and characteristic bands are pointed out. A recent discussion of group frequencies in both the infra-red and Raman, with many references, is also valuable[18].

(6B) Applications based on Raman intensities

The absolute intensities of Raman bands are not obtained directly and what is always measured when such data are required is the ratio of the Raman band intensity to the Rayleigh intensity. In terms of Placzek's polarizability theory, considering for simplicity only a totally symmetrical vibrational mode ν_k and confining the discussion to the symmetrical or isotropic contributions to the scattering, the ratio

$$\frac{\text{Intensity of Raman band}}{\text{Intensity of Rayleigh line}} = \left(\frac{\nu_0 - \nu_k}{\nu_0}\right)^4 \left(\frac{\partial \alpha^s / \partial Q_k}{\alpha^s}\right)^2 \cdot \frac{h}{8\pi^2 \nu_k} \cdot \frac{1}{\left(1 - e^{-h\nu_k/kT}\right)} \quad (26)$$

where all symbols have been previously defined and transverse observation is used. The polarizability α^s may be calculated for the vapour phase using the relation

$$2\pi\alpha^s N = n-1 \quad (27)$$

where n is the refractive index in the visible and N the number of molecules per unit volume. Thus, for a spherically symmetrical molecule like methane, expression (26) holds for ν_1, the totally symmetrical stretching mode, and $(\partial\alpha/\partial Q_k)$ may be obtained if the intensity ratio is measured. The experimental technique for obtaining such data in the vapour phase, where intermolecular effects are minimized, is not easy, and numerous corrections must be applied. The first photoelectrically-recorded vapour phase spectra were reported in 1958 by YOSHINO and BERNSTEIN[19] who applied to the observed intensities and depolarization ratios a number of corrections: (a) allowance for the variation in sensitivity of the instrument with frequency; (b) for the non-ideality of the irradiation set-up in which the incident light is not uniformly distributed about the sample and is not strictly at right angles to the direction of observation; (c) for the polarization produced by the multiple reflection sample cell; (d) for the dependence of the transmission of spectrograph and detector sensitivity upon the polarization of the light. Once the ν_1 band of methane had been placed on the absolute scale by comparison with a Rayleigh line, other Raman bands were measured by comparison with this standard Raman band. Values of $(\partial\alpha/\partial Q_k)$ were determined for a number of molecules, but, since the normal coordinates are different for each molecule, these values are not comparable and further assumptions have to be made in order to proceed. WOLKENSTEIN[20] proposed that the polarizability change during a normal mode be considered to be made up of contributions from all the changes in the polarizabilities of the constituent bonds; furthermore, when a bond is stretched, the only change in polarizability is localized in this bond. Accepting this assumption, further progress requires knowledge of the form of Q_k, which can only be obtained from a complete normal coordinate analysis of the molecule; this yields the transformation from normal coordinates to the internal coordinates.

Since the experimental data yields $(\partial\alpha^s/\partial Q_k)^2$, the sign is undetermined. Good arguments for choosing the positive value can be presented and on this basis Yoshino and Bernstein obtained the very interesting result that for methane, ethane, neopentane, ethylene and benzene the values of $(\partial\alpha^s/\partial r_{CH})$, the rate of change of polarizability upon stretching the (C–H) bond, are all very close together at $1.0 \cdot 10^{-16}$ cm^2. For the (C–C) bonds the values of $(\partial\alpha^s/\partial r_{\rm CC})$ are almost in the ratio of the multiplicities of these bonds. In addition, $(\partial\alpha^s/\partial r_{\rm CC})$ divided by the bond multiplicity yielded values near $1.0 \cdot 10^{-16}$ cm², indicating that the numbers of bonding electrons determine the values of $(\partial\alpha^s/\partial r_{\rm CH})$ and of $(\partial\alpha^s/\partial r_{\rm CC})$. Relative-intensity data for the liquid or solution phase are more readily obtained than are the vapour phase data but their interpretation is complicated by several effects which are absent in the vapour phase. Intermolecular interactions are present, while the refractive index of the sample influences the effective volume of the liquid irradiated, the spread of the scattered light cone leaving the sample tube, and the reflection losses at the sample-to-glass interfaces. In addition, the internal field effect, or the change in the radiation field in the liquid dielectric, is determined by the refractive index (*cf.* with infra-red intensities in liquids). This means that although the Raman band intensity should show a linear dependence on the concentration of a solute in a solution, this will not be observed unless the intermolecular effects are small and the refractive index remains almost constant over the concentration range of interest. Fig. VI, 9 shows an example of the type of

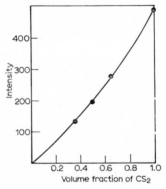

Fig. VI, 9. Intensity variation with concentration of the 650 cm⁻¹ Raman doublet of carbon disulphide in cyclopentane solutions.

intensity *versus* concentration curve encountered; the implications in quantitative analyses are obvious. Intensity changes with temperature change have been shown to be anomalous in many liquid systems *i.e.* they do not obey equation (21). However, in the vapour phase some of these same systems conform with (21), showing that intermolecular interactions are responsible for the anomalous behaviour in the liquid.

Considerable attention has been given to the experimental factors influencing liquid-phase Raman intensities, the most thorough treatments being references 21 and 22. An intensity scale has been developed which is based on the integrated intensity of the 459 cm⁻¹ Raman band of CCl_4; this is given the value 100. Observed spectra are corrected for the effects of refractive index, sample colour, spectral sensitivity, and convergence of the incident radiation. At the present time, however, the indications are that the refractive index effects are not fully understood[23]. These may, however, be avoided by employing an internal standard, e.g. the use of CCl_4 as solvent. This technique has been used in measuring intensities for the purpose of calculating derived bond polarizabilities for ions in aqueous solution[24]. The totally symmetrical modes of the ions $(ClO_4)^-$, $(NO_3)^-$, $(SO_4)^{2-}$, $(CO_3)^{2-}$, $(PO_4)^{3-}$ were measured, the comparison with CCl_4 being made via the $(ClO_4)^-$ ion by means of a solution containing CCl_4 and $HClO_4 \cdot 0.5 H_2O$ in ethanol. Values of α^s in the range 0.9 to $1.73 \cdot 10^{-16}$ cm^2 were obtained and the trends could not be explained without accepting appreciable π-bonding in the ions; e.g. in going through the series $(PO_4)^{3-}$ (0.91), $(SO_4)^{2-}$ (1.37), and $(ClO_4)^-$ (1.73), where the α values are bracketed, increased π-bonding is indicated. Furthermore, it appears that the π- and σ-bonding contributions to the polarizability derivatives are not always equal[19]. This aspect of the subject is very promising for the study of the electronic structures of bonds.

Most measurements of relative band intensities are not made with the aim of calculating derived bond polarizabilities, but are aimed at providing empirical data which can be used in molecular structure determinations. Probably the widest investigations are those by SHORYGIN et al.[25] who based their intensity scale on the 313 cm^{-1} band of CCl_4. Most of the spectra were photographically recorded and an accuracy of the order of ± 10 per cent is quoted for the integrated band intensities. Some of their most interesting findings are summarized as follows; (a) band intensity measurements of group vibrations of compounds in a homologous series or series of similar compounds show that these band intensities are approximately the same and are proportional to the number of such groups present, except (b) when the group is involved in conjugation with another group. In such cases the intensity increases, and in many cases this increase is very large. For example, as the number of (C=C) bonds is increased from one to three in conjugation, the band intensity increases from 30(1) to 300(2) to 3000(3); again, whereas acetone and ethyl acetate have values of 15 for the carbonyl band intensity, that for benzylidene acetone is 600; for benzonitrile the (C≡N) band intensity is ten times that for acetonitrile. A measurement of band intensity is thus a good indication of the presence or absence of conjugation; this fact was used in the example described earlier. It is noteworthy that intensity changes of this order do not arise in these cases in the infra-red spectrum.

Theoretically, these intensity changes upon increased conjugation can be qualitatively explained by reference to equation (19). Conjugation will tend to increase the numerators and decrease the denominators, since the absorption intensity (transition moments) is increased and the electronic bands are moved to lower frequency. When the process is carried to the extreme and the exciting line approaches and actually enters the absorption band, it is sometimes found that a remarkable increase in intensity occurs for some bands but not for others. Raman excitation of a dye molecule, N, N'-diethyl*pseudo*cyanine chloride, was possible within its absorption band below a dye concentration of 10^{-3} moles/litre and above 10^{-6} moles/litre. The strongest bands, an unresolved pair near 1380 cm^{-1} gave intensity values of $46 \cdot 10^6$ on the 313 cm^{-1} CCl$_4$ band scale[26]. Observations such as these are described as *resonance Raman effects* and have drawn much attention recently. ALBRECHT[27] has further developed the theory and in so doing has clarified the nature of the Raman effect under non-resonance conditions. It is well-known in electronic absorption spectroscopy that some electronic transitions are forbidden but will appear weakly in absorption because a certain molecular vibration distorts the electronic structure, and the electronic transition is 'vibrationally induced.' Similarly, such effects will occur in allowed electronic transitions although their influence is not so readily detected. Albrecht shows that these vibrationally induced components in allowed electronic transitions are responsible for the Raman effect, and, in the resonance Raman effect, it is the vibrationally induced character in the nearby electronic transition which determines the Raman band intensities. Therefore, those vibrations which have the greatest effect upon this adjacent excited electronic state will be most enhanced in their Raman activity[27a].

The resonance Raman effect promises to be of some use in the study of the properties of excited electronic states since a knowledge of the nature and symmetry of those Raman bands which are enhanced in intensity can yield information about the symmetry of the excited electronic level. As yet, only molecules which possess $\varPi \rightarrow \varPi^*$ type absorption bands have been found to show resonance Raman scattering. For other molecules the Raman intensities increase as the absorption band is approached but are rapidly lost as the band is reached and the absorption process takes over.

(6C) Applications to physical chemistry

In the previous discussion, applications were roughly separated into two classes, and the emphasis was placed on molecular structure determination. There remain a number of applications which use both frequencies and intensities and which are probably best classified under this wider title.

Numerous studies of ionic equilibria in aqueous solutions and in other solvents, which have such intense absorption in the infra-red that they are of limited use (*e.g.* sulphuric acid) have been made. The various ionic species present can be identified and their concentration changes can be followed as conditions are varied. Dissociation constants may then be determined. Much quantitative work has been done on the dissociation equilibria in strong acids, *e.g.* H_2SO_4, HNO_3; reference 28 discusses several of these in detail. Mixtures of nitric and sulphuric acid, which are of great interest in organic chemistry as nitrating agents, were shown to contain the linear nitronium ion, $(NO_2)^+$; one, strong, polarized Raman band (at 1400 cm^{-1}) was observed, in agreement with the expectation for a linear triatomic ion[29].

Association processes are also a rich source of applications for the Raman method. New complex ions arising in concentrated aqueous solutions of simpler ions are usually readily detected, *e.g.* tetrahedral complex ions $(MX_4)^{2-}$ in addition to the smaller, linear, neutral molecules have been shown to exist in aqueous solutions of Cd^{2+}, Zn^{2+} and Tl^{2+} ions with excess halide ions. A closely related field to which the Raman method is now beginning to make a contribution is that of fused salts and salt mixtures. Here again, complex ions have been found, *e.g.* in fused mixtures[30] of $ZnCl_2$ and KCl, while a series of molten nitrates showed variations in the nitrate ion spectrum which could be correlated with the polarizing power of the cation[31].

Proceeding to the weaker intermolecular interactions, we find that the changes produced by such interactions in the Raman spectrum are less pronounced, and may amount to relatively small shifts in band positions and changes in band intensities. An important interaction of this type is the hydrogen bond, to the study of which infra-red spectroscopy has contributed greatly. Raman spectral contributions have been relatively less significant although one should not overlook the importance of the direct observation of very low-frequency Raman bands which are assigned to vibrations of the hydrogen bond. In the higher frequency range of the (O–H) and (N–H) stretching modes, it is found in general that hydrogen bonding decreases the already rather weak intensities. As an example, in the case of phenol, which is believed to associate into dimers or trimers and larger multimers, the intrinsic intensity of the higher frequency, more weakly hydrogen bonded dimeric band is greater than that of the lower frequency, stronger hydrogen bonded multimer band. This is presumably due to the fact that the stronger the (O–H $\cdots\cdots$ O) bond becomes, the longer is the (O–H) distance, the more polar is the (O–H) bond and the less polarizable does it become.

Still weaker are the van der Waals interactions which are, however, readily detected in the Raman spectrum. An example is the appearance in the spectrum of CS_2 solutions, as the concentration is increased, of the Raman forbidden band of the bending mode near 390 cm^{-1}; Fig. VI, 10. The band was also observed to be polarized. The data suggest that the CS_2 molecule may, under the perturbing influence of other CS_2 molecules, tend toward C_{2v} symmetry in which case the bending mode is Raman allowed and polarized. Speculation about the geometrical arrangement of the interacting molecules may be made within these limits. Numerous investigations of van der Waals' type interactions have been made. Fig. VI, 7 illustrated how

eferences p. 225

224 J. C. EVANS VI

the liquid spectrum of $SbBr_3$ is perturbed in comparison with the solution

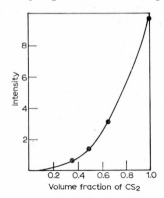

Fig. VI, 10. Intensity variation with concentration of the 390 cm⁻¹ Raman band of carbon disulphide in cyclopentane solutions.

spectrum. Also illustrated is the change on proceeding to the solid, and this brings us to the last topic for discussion.

(6D) Applications to the study of crystals

In Chapter VIII the infra-red spectra of crystals are discussed and it is shown that in addition to the symmetry of the individual molecule the symmetry of the unit cell must be considered. In favourable cases, with both Raman and infra-red data available, it is possible to decide between several possible crystal structures.

An interesting application of the Raman spectra of crystals was pointed out by HAAS and HORNIG[32] who showed that in some instances the Raman spectrum can give, by a measurement of two band frequencies, the value of $(\partial \mu / \partial Q_k)$ for the normal mode, i.e. the derivative of the dipole moment with respect to the normal coordinate. The simplest case is that of a cubic crystal in which a vibration is active in both Raman and infra-red. The Raman spectrum will show two lines, one due to longitudinal scattering (ν_l) and the other due to transverse scattering (ν_t). These are separated in frequency to an extent determined by dipole–dipole interaction. For cubic crystals the expression is:

$$\frac{\partial \mu}{\partial Q_k} = \pm \frac{3}{n_0^2 + 2} \left\{ \frac{\pi n_0^2 (\nu_l^2 - \nu_t^2)}{N} \right\}^{\frac{1}{2}} \tag{28}$$

where n_0 is the refractive index and N the number of oscillators per cm³. ν_l and ν_t may also be estimated from the infra-red reflection spectrum, but not as accurately.

(7) Conclusion

An attempt has been made to outline the theory, method and applications of Raman spectroscopy. The emphasis has been placed on those applications to which infra-red spectroscopy cannot be applied or is inadequate alone. Problems to which either method could give satisfactory answers have been avoided; usually, in such cases, the infra-red method is preferred. However, in general, the two methods should be used together for maximum effectiveness because the unexpected may manifest itself very clearly in one spectrum but be undetected in the other.

REFERENCES

[1] C. V. RAMAN, *Indian J. Phys.*, 2 (1928) 387.
[2] G. LANDSBERG AND L. MANDELSTAM, *Naturwissenschaften*, 16 (1928) 557.
[3] A. SMEKAL, *Naturwissenschaften*, 11 (1923) 873.
[4] H. A. KRAMERS AND W. HEISENBERG, *Z. Physik.*, 31 (1925) 681.
[5] G. PLACZEK, *Handbuch der Radiologie*, Akademische Verlagsgesellschaft, Leipzig, 1934, Vol. VI, Part 2.
[6] For a simplified account see S. BHAGAVANTAM, *Scattering of Light and the Raman Effect*, Chemical Publishing Co. Inc., New York, 1942.
[7] G. HERZBERG, *Infrared and Raman Spectra of Polyatomic Molecules*, Van Nostrand, New York 1945.
[8] B. P. STOICHEFF, High Resolution Raman Spectroscopy, in *Advances in Spectroscopy*, 1 (1959) 91.
[8a] See for instance: S. P. S. PORTO AND D. L. WOOD, *J. Opt. Soc. Am.*, 52 (1962) 251.
[9] J. R. NIELSEN, *J. Opt. Soc. Am.*, 37 (1947) 494.
[10] Hilger and Watts Ltd., London.
[11] D. H. RANK AND R. V. WIEGAND, *J. Opt. Soc. Am.*, 36 (1946) 325.
[12] C. H. MILLER, D. A. LONG, L. A. WOODWARD AND H. W. THOMPSON, *Proc. Phys. Soc. (London)*, 62A (1949) 401.
[13] B. P. STOICHEFF, *Can. J. Phys.*, 32 (1954) 339.
[14] K. W. F. KOHLRAUSCH, *Z. Physik. Chem. (Leipzig)*, 18 B (1932) 61.
[15] J. T. NEU AND W. D. GWINN, *J. Chem. Phys.*, 18 (1950) 1642.
[16] K. W. F. KOHLRAUSCH, *Ramanspektren, Hand- und Jahrbuch der Chemischen Physik*, Edwards Bros., Ann Arbor, 1945.
[17] J. H. HIBBEN, *The Raman Effect and its Chemical Applications*, Reinhold, New York, 1939.
[18] R. N. JONES AND C. SANDORFY, *Chemical Applications of Spectroscopy*, Vol. IX of *Technique of Organic Chemistry*, Ed., A. WEISSBERGER, Interscience, New York, 1956.
[19] T. YOSHINO AND H. J. BERNSTEIN, *J. Mol. Spectry.*, 2 (1958) 213.
[20] M. WOLKENSTEIN, *Doklady Akad. Nauk S. S. S. R.*, 32 (1941) 185.
[21] H. J. BERNSTEIN AND G. ALLEN, *J. Opt. Soc. Am.*, 45 (1955) 237.
[22] D. G. REA, *J. Opt. Soc. Am.*, 49 (1959) 90.
[23] D. G. REA, *J. Mol. Spectry.*, 4 (1960) 507.
[24] G. W. CHANTRY AND R. A. PLANE, *J. Chem. Phys.*, 33 (1960) 736.
[25] P. P. SHORYGIN, *Uspekhii Khim.*, 19 (1950) 419. *Technical Translation TT*-228, Natl. Res. Council of Canada, Ottawa.
[26] W. MAIER AND F. DOOR, *Appl. Spectroscopy*, 14 (1960) 1.
[27] A. ALBRECHT, *J. Chem. Phys.*, 34 (1961) 1476.
[27a] See also G. ECKHARDT *et al.*, *Phys. Rev. Letters*, 9 (1962) 455.
[28] T. F. YOUNG, L. F. MARANVILLE AND H. M. SMITH, *Structure of Electrolytic Solutions*, Ed. W. J. HAMER, J. Wiley Inc. New York, 1959, p. 35.
[29] C. K. INGOLD, D. J. MILLEN, AND H. G. POOLE, *J. Chem. Soc. (London)*, (1950) 2576.
[30] W. BUES, *Z. Anorg. u. Allgem. Chem.*, 279 (1955) 104; M. A. BREDIG AND E. R. VAN ARTSDALEN, *J. Chem. Phys.*, 24 (1956) 478.
[31] G. J. JANZ AND D. W. JAMES, *J. Chem. Phys.*, 35 (1961) 739.
[32] C. HAAS AND D. F. HORNIG, *J. Chem. Phys.*, 26 (1957) 707.

Chapter VII

Characteristic Features in the Spectra of Organic Molecules

DUŠAN HADŽI

University of Ljubljana, Yugoslavia

Most of the applications of infra-red spectroscopy to the structural problems of complex organic molecules are based on the appearance of characteristic bands in their spectra. Empirical studies of related compounds containing the same functional group or structural element such as (O–H), (CH$_3$), (CONH$_2$), phenyl, etc. have shown that for each structural element one or more specific bands are exhibited in the spectrum. Thus in the spectra of secondary amides in dilute solution, bands are found near 3460 cm^{-1}, and between 1670–1700, 1550–1510, and 1305–1220 cm^{-1}. The frequencies and intensities of such bands seem to be determined primarily by the nature of the atoms constituting the particular group and by the bonding conditions in the group. The influence of the molecular framework is shown in the variability of the frequencies and intensities within more or less limited ranges. The specific bands are associated with certain vibrational modes within the group and commonly described in terms of changes in bond length or bond angles, *e.g.* 3460 cm^{-1}(N–H) stretching, 1670 cm^{-1} (C=O) stretching, 1550 cm^{-1}(N–H) bending etc. This way of describing the motions of atoms in molecules is well suited to the concept of the chemical bond as developed from chemical studies. Although often incorrect, it is adequate if used only in connection with empirical correlations between spectra and structure, and in their application to qualitative analysis. We shall deal briefly with this aspect of characteristic bands in Section 6.

For the purpose of demonstrating the presence of certain structural elements in a molecule it would be desirable that the characteristic band frequencies were not subject to large variations caused by structural differences in the rest of the molecule, so that the specific bands would appear in narrow regions and hence be little overlapped by those from other groups. However, the frequencies and intensities of specific bands do depend upon the molecular environment and this leads to important investigations into the factors governing these variations. Much use has latterly been made of it in the study of the electronic effects of substituents. If the frequency and intensity variations of specific bands are to be used to follow electronic influences upon bond properties (reflected in the force constants and dipole moment derivatives) one has to be certain that the vibrational interactions with the molecular framework of the group being studied are small compared with electronic interactions. It is therefore necessary for anyone using the characteristic frequencies for either of the two purposes mentioned to be familiar with the basis of their occurrence. This is particularly so if the characteristic frequencies are used for the study of group environment effects.

It is not intended that this chapter should either systematically treat all the applications of infra-red spectroscopy to organic chemistry, or be a reference work on characteristic frequencies. It is written to give the reader an idea of the scope and limitations of the concept of characteristic frequencies and of their applicability.

(1) The Basis of Characteristic Vibrational Frequencies

The bond force constant is one of the most important physical factors reflecting the electronic structure of the bond and its variations with the bond environment. Precise values of force constants are not easily obtained even for relatively simple polyatomic molecules (*cf.* Chapter V). The factor which is readily measured is the frequency, and the question arises — in what circumstances may this be used directly for bond characterization? Strictly, this will be possible if the observed frequency depends only upon the masses constituting this bond and its force constant, as in a diatomic molecule. This situation is sometimes approached, so that contributions from other vibrations amount to less than one per cent. We shall examine briefly the conditions necessary for a vibration to be characteristic of a localized part of the molecule.

Consider the general form of the secular equation for the frequencies of a molecule (*cf.* eqn. (16), p. 172, but writing D for (GF)):

$$
\begin{vmatrix}
D_{11}-\lambda & D_{12} & D_{13}\dots\dots \\
D_{21} & D_{22}-\lambda & D_{23}\dots\dots \\
D_{31} & D_{32} & D_{33}-\lambda\,.. \\
\dots\dots & \dots\dots & \dots\dots
\end{vmatrix} = 0
$$

where $\lambda = 4\pi c^2\omega^2$, with ω the harmonic frequency in cm^{-1} and where D_{ij} are the quantities which determine the coupling between the valence coordinates. They are defined by $D_{ij} = \Sigma G_{ii}F_{tj}$, the G_{it} being the elements of the **G** matrix and F_{tj} the valence force constants. Suppose all coupling coefficients D_{1i} or D_{ij} besides D_{11} are equal to zero. One root is then obtained directly from $D_{11} = \lambda$. This means that the normal vibration with the frequency $\omega = \sqrt{D_{11}/4\pi c^2}$ involves only one coordinate. There is no coupling with other vibrations and the frequency is fully characteristic. This may arise if there is only one coordinate of the symmetry concerned. This seldom occurs with complex molecules. In general the coefficients D_{ij} are different from zero and the difference $(D_{11}-\lambda)$ has a finite value. If it is small the frequency may still be considered as characteristic to a limited extent.

Following VOLKENSTEIN, ELYASHEVITCH and STEPANOV[1], the quantity $\rho = (D_{11}-\lambda)/D_{11}$ may be taken as a measure of the vibrational independence of a frequency. To evaluate this expression one must solve the secular equation for each special case. However, general circumstances can also be deduced under which the vibrations may become characteristic. If λ is close to D_{11} we may write the approximate solution of the secular equation as follows:

$$\lambda = D_{11} + \frac{D_{12} \cdot D_{21}}{D_{11}-D_{22}} + \frac{D_{13} \cdot D_{31}}{D_{11}-D_{33}} + \ldots$$

Disregarding special cases in which single members of the right-hand side sum are large, but of opposite sign, the difference $(D_{11}-\lambda)$ will be small if each of the members is small. This will be so if either the difference $(D_{11}-D_{jj})$ is large or the product $(D_{1i} \cdot D_{i1})$ is small. The conditions which make the differences $(D_{11}-D_{jj})$ large may be found from the equations for the diagonal elements:

$$D_{11} = G_{11}F_{11}+G_{12}F_{21}+G_{13}F_{31}+\ldots$$
$$D_{22} = G_{12}F_{21}+G_{22}F_{22}+G_{23}F_{32}+\ldots$$

Members of the type $G_{ii}F_{ii}$ make the largest contribution to the value of D_{ii}, and it is therefore sufficient to discuss the difference $(G_{11}F_{11}-G_{22}F_{22})$. It should be remembered that the members of the G matrix contain the masses of the atoms and the geometrical parameters, and that the F_{ij}'s are force constants. Clearly, the difference $(G_{11}F_{11}-G_{22}F_{22})$ will be large if G_{11} and G_{22}, or F_{11} and F_{22}, are very different. In other words, there will be very little coupling between the vibration of a light atom like hydrogen and heavier atoms, provided that the force constants are similar. Thus the hydrogenic stretching vibrations will, in general, be independent of other vibrations in the same molecule, and hence highly characteristic. However, the (C–H) and (O–H) bending force constants are much smaller than the bond-stretching force constants, and therefore the GF products may become similar in magnitude to the products related to the (C–C) or (C–O) stretching. Considerable coupling therefore is possible between the bending vibrations of (X–H) and the (C–C) or (C–O) stretching.

A general discussion of the products $D_{1i} D_{i1}$ is difficult. Some empirical rules bearing upon these products may, however, be quoted[2]:

(i) Considerable coupling is possible between stretching vibrations only if the bonds have a common atom.

(ii) Coupling between angle deformation and bond stretching will occur to a considerable extent if the bond forms one side of the angle.

(iii) Angle deformation vibrations may couple only if they have a common bond.

(iv) Strong coupling may occur between angle deformation vibrations involving hydrogen and the stretching of an adjacent bond with a heavier atom. The coupling diminishes with increasing mass of the hydrogen-bearing atom.

We have considered so far characteristic vibrations involving the distortion of a single bond or angle alone. There are a number of cases known in which vibrations are localized in a group of several atoms within a larger molecule, thus giving rise to frequencies which are characteristic of the particular group. The vibrations are not necessarily localized in particular bonds or angles of the group, but may be combinations of its valence coordinates. In other words, in these normal coordinates, one or more bond lengths may change simultaneously with some angle bending, but without influencing the other molecular framework vibrations. This will be possible if the coupling coefficients between the symmetry coordinates of the group and of the framework are small. These coupling coefficients are usually not equal for all symmetry coordinates of the group and therefore not all vibrations of a particular group will be equally characteristic.

One way of assessing the degree of independence of group vibrations is to proceed with the normal coordinate analysis of a particular molecule. Since this is intractable for complex molecules, various types of model calculations are of more general interest. For example, the group frequencies and normal modes may be calculated[3] for a group X in a hypothetical molecule R–X in which the framework R is given infinite mass, and representative values for the bond lengths, angles, and force constants of the group X are used. The deviations of the frequencies of actual molecules from the frequencies of the standard molecule R–X measure the dependence of the group frequencies on the framework. If the coupling constants of the group coordinates with the framework are shown to be small, then variations in the group frequencies with different R are due to differences in the force constants within the group.

A convenient mathematical method for such calculations has recently been developed by KING and CRAWFORD[3] and applied to the methyl group. Both the symmetric and asymmetric (C–H) stretching frequencies of this group as well as the symmetric deformation frequency are due to essentially internal group vibrations. In the standard molecule these frequencies are 2932, 3051, and 1378 cm^{-1}. The degenerate deformation and the (CH$_3$)

rocking vibration (1451 and 1050 cm^{-1} in the standard molecule) are appreciably mixed. However, this is not influenced by the molecular frame-work and the degenerate deformation is also a characteristic methyl group vibration. The rocking is actually an external vibration since the R–CH$_3$ bond is involved, it is not therefore really a characteristic methyl vibration.

The carbonyl group appears in a number of different classes of com-pounds (ketones, aldehydes, acids, amides, etc.) and all these compounds exhibit, under normal conditions, a strong band in the region between 1630 and 1870 cm^{-1}, the frequency depending firstly upon the class of compound and secondly upon the substituents. The high force constant of the (C=O) group guarantees a certain degree of independence of its stretching vibration, but the interesting question is whether the large spread in frequencies is due to changes in the force constant or to vibrational coupling. HALFORD has made model calculations[4] by fixing the value of the (C=O) force constant and varying the masses of X, and the angle $\widehat{XCX}$. The influence of the mass depends on the $\widehat{XCX}$ angle, being least for an angle of 180°. With an angle of 120°, the increase in the masses X from 12 to infinity changes the carbonyl frequency by only 20 cm^{-1}. The change is still smaller if the masses X are attached to the carbonyl carbon through an intermediate carbon atom. This explains the constancy of the carbonyl frequency in saturated open chain ketones where the variations are within about 5 cm^{-1}, but it shows also that the so called carbonyl stretching vibration is characteristic not only of the (C=O) group but also of the $\begin{smallmatrix} & O \\ & \| \\ & C \\ X^{\diagup} & \diagdown X \end{smallmatrix}$ fragment. The recent work of BRATOŽ and BESNAINOU[5] illustrates this point even more clearly.

These authors resolved the "carbonyl" frequency in various classes of compounds into contributions from the (C=O) oscillator with a force constant of 10.5 md/Å and contributions from the vibrations of the next neighbours which are different for each class of compounds. Some of the results are reproduced in Table VII, 1. The differences between the calculated and the experimental frequencies reflect the changes in the force constant due to the influence of the group environment. The results show clearly that the main contribution to the carbonyl frequency, besides that of the (C=O) group itself, is from the adjoining carbon atom stretching vibrations. In the case of aldehydes the loss of one half of this contribution is com-pensated by that from the $\widehat{OCH}$ angle-bending, but the observed frequency of the aldehydes, which is some 20–30 cm^{-1} higher than in saturated ketones, suggests that the force constant in aldehydes is considerably higher than in ketones. Frequencies very similar to those for saturated ketones were calculated for chloroketones, unsaturated ketones, acids, and esters. The

TABLE VII, 1

(C=O) FREQUENCIES OF SOME CLASSES OF CARBONYL COMPOUNDS OBTAINED FROM MODEL CALCULATIONS BY BRATOŽ AND BESNAINOU[5]

The frequencies in the last column are obtained by adding the contributions from appropriate partial oscillators, each contribution being multiplied by the number of oscillators present in the particular class of carbonyl compound. The contribution of the (C=O) oscillator is 1574 cm⁻¹ in each case, based on the force constant 10.5 mdyne/Å.

Class of carbonyl compound	Contributions from partial oscillators (cm⁻¹)									
	ν C—C	ν C—H	ν C—H	δ C—C	δ (C,C)	δ C—Cl	δ C—H	δ CH$_2$	δ CH	
Saturated ketones	47.1			6.8	7.2				2.5	1706
Unsaturated ketones	47.1			6.8	7.4				10.2	1717
Chloroketones	47.1			6.8	7.2	1.8			2.5	1705
Cyclobutanone	78.9	−0.6		4.9				2.0	2.3	1752
Aldehydes	59.5	−11.8		7.4	7.1		47.9		2.5	1689
p-Quinones (symmetrical and asymmetrical frequency)	23.5			3.4	3.6					1696

structural differences involved evidently do not influence the carbonyl frequency. Strong coupling arises between the two carbonyl groups in *o*-quinones, but very little in *p*-quinones. This is understandable, for in the first case the two carbonyl groups are close together, whereas in the second they are separated by several atoms. A particularly interesting result is obtained with cyclobutanone which exhibits a higher frequency than

is found in open chain ketones as a result of the reduced

angle in the strained cyclic compound. Thus the higher frequencies of the carbonyl band in small cyclic ketones and lactones have a simple mechanical

explanation. Variations in the force constant controlling the

angle and the (C–C) stretching will also influence the carbonyl frequency. The increase in either of them will cause a rise in the latter as shown by the calculations of MIRONE and CHIORBOLI[6].

In the absence of detailed calculations, suitable experimental data can be used to determine whether a frequency is characteristic of a particular bond or of a more extended group. Ethylene has a band at 1623 cm^{-1} which might be taken as characteristic of the (C=C) stretching vibration. However, in propene the frequency is 1642 cm^{-1}, and this is the average frequency for a number of hydrocarbons of the type $\diagdown CH_2$–CH=CH$_2$, the limiting values being 1639 and 1647 cm^{-1}. In asymmetrically substituted ethylenes the frequency tends to be slightly higher, with the average 1650 cm^{-1}. With substitution on both sides of the double bond (di- and trisubstituted ethylenes) the frequency is still higher, up to 1678 cm^{-1}. Differences between *cis* and *trans* isomers of disubstituted ethylenes exist, the *trans* isomers absorbing at an average of 20 cm^{-1} higher than the *cis* isomers[7]. These values may be different if the substituents are large. These data indicate that the so called (C=C) stretching frequency includes contributions from other vibrations. The band at 1623 cm^{-1} is a characteristic frequency of ethylene only, but the value 1642 cm^{-1} characterizes the structural unit $\diagdown CH_2$–CH=CH$_2$, and the other frequencies quoted characterize the respective structural types since they are insensitive to further lengthening of the aliphatic chain of the substituents on the double bond. These qualitative conclusions are in agreement with model calculations[8].

Information on coupling may be obtained also from band shifts on isotopic substitution. In the case of vibrations affecting only a bond or angle, only the corresponding bands should shift on substitution of the respective atom by its isotope. Most often the substitution of deuterium for hydrogen is used; the ratio of the band frequencies should then equal $\sqrt{2}$.

The methyl group will be taken as an example. In methanol[9], the symmetric methyl stretching vibration is at 2845 cm^{-1} and the asymmetric one at 2973 cm^{-1}. In CH_3OD the corresponding frequencies are shifted to 2840 and 2965 cm^{-1}. This indicates a slight coupling between the (O–H) stretching and the (C–H) stretching vibrations. The (CH_3) bending modes (symmetrical and asymmetrical of a' and a'' species) have slightly higher frequencies, and the (C–O) stretching is also higher in CH_3OD (1041 cm^{-1}) than in CH_3OH (1034 cm^{-1}). The (CH_3) rocking vibration of the a' species shifts from 1116 to 1160 cm^{-1} on deuteration, whereas the ratio of the so-called (O–H) and (O–D) bending frequencies is 1.55 instead of the theoretical value 1.36. This shows appreciable coupling between all these vibrations, the strongest being between the a' methyl rocking and (O–H) bending.

As mentioned before, the (CH_3) rocking should be most prone to coupling with other vibrations in the molecule. This is also borne out by the experimental work of PIMENTEL and KLEMPERER[10] on n-octane and its analogue with hydrogens from both methyl groups exchanged for deuterium. The methyl bending modes shift from 1460 and 1380 cm^{-1} to 1046 and 1025 cm^{-1}, respectively. The frequency ratios of these bands are close to the theoretical value; this is also true for the b_u rocking mode, which shifts from 1083 to 806 cm^{-1}. Considerably smaller shifts are, however, shown by the pair of bands at 883 and 867 cm^{-1} in the normal compound. They appear at 742 and 716 cm^{-1} respectively in the spectrum of the deuterated compound, and are assigned to the mixed (CH_2) and (CH_3) rocking vibrations of a_u species. The coupling of the methyl-rocking vibration with the stretching of the terminal (C–C) bond is shown by the shift of a band from 1016 to 924 cm^{-1}.

In considering isotopic shifts as an indication of coupling, the possibility should be borne in mind that some frequencies may come closer together in the isotopic molecule than they were in the simple molecule, and therefore couple more strongly in the former. For example, the (C≡C) frequency in acetylene is at 1974 cm^{-1} and the (C–H) stretching frequencies are 3374 and 3287 cm^{-1}, respectively[11]. Although in aliphatic compounds there is more interaction between the (C–H) and the (C≡C) vibrations than between the (C–H) stretching and skeletal vibrations, the contribution of other vibrations to (C–H) stretching in acetylene is only about 2 per cent. In acetylene–d_2 the symmetric (C–D) stretching is at 2701 cm^{-1} and the (C≡C) stretching at 1762 cm^{-1}. The ratio of the (C–H) and (C–D) frequencies is only 1.250 and that of the (C≡C) frequencies, 1.120, which shows that the (C–D) and (C≡C) vibrations are appreciably coupled. Other examples may be found in the paper by LORD and MILLER[12].

Some other examples of characteristic group frequencies are worth examining. The spectra of alcohols have a strong band in the region between 1050 and 1150 cm^{-1} which is usually designated as the (C–O) stretching frequency. In methanol this band is at 1034 cm^{-1}, and it shifts slightly to higher frequencies in methanol-d_1 [9]. The calculated distribution of potential energy amongst normal coordinates shows no other contribution to this coordinate but (C–O) stretching [13]. Thus 1034 cm^{-1} is the frequency of (C–O) stretching in methanol. In ethanol the band is at 1053 cm^{-1} and is also in that region for higher straight chain primary alcohols [14]. The increase in frequency compared with methanol is apparently due to the coupling of the (C–O) stretching with (C–C) stretching which would by itself have a slightly lower frequency. In the spectrum of 2-propanol the band is at 1154 cm^{-1} and similar frequencies are found for other secondary alcohols. The normal coordinate giving rise to the bands about 1100 cm^{-1} in the spectra of alcohols involves the stretching of the (C–O) bond and the neighbouring (C–C) and probably (C–H) bonds. The particular frequencies are therefore characteristic of the structures shown below and not of the (C–OH) bond only. Although an appreciable coupling between the (C–O) stretching and (O–H) bending motions would be expected from the general conditions, this does not seem to be the case with alcohols.

A different situation in this respect arises in the carboxylic acids. In the spectra of this class of compound in the monomeric state there are two bands which may be connected with the (C–O) stretching and (O–H) bending motions. They appear between 1190 and 1075 cm^{-1}, and between 1380 and 1280 cm^{-1}, respectively [15]. Both shift appreciably on exchanging the hydroxylic hydrogen for deuterium, thus showing the participation of hydrogen in both normal coordinates. The calculation of the distribution of potential energy amongst coordinates of formic acid [16] has demonstrated that the higher frequency has a larger contribution from the (O–H) bending vibration whereas the lower frequency gets more from the (C–O) stretching. However, the (C–H) bending participates considerably in the coordinate with the lower frequency. In other carboxylic acids the (C–C) stretching vibrations probably couple with the (C–O) stretching, but the main coupling partner is still the (O–H) bending vibration, in contrast to the alcoholic (C—OH) group. In deuterated acids, the extent of coupling between (C–O) and (O–H) bending is very much reduced [17]. In the series of phenols there does not seem to be much coupling between the (O–H) bending and (C–O) stretching, but the former vibration couples with a vibration of the aromatic ring [18].

The spectra of secondary amides [19] exhibit several bands which were very frequently used to show the presence of the (–CONH–) group. However, the nature of the vibrations giving rise to some of these bands, particularly those near 1660, 1560 and 1270 cm^{-1}, was much disputed until recently. When (NH) is replaced by (ND) the first band shifts about 10 cm^{-1} to lower frequencies and the other two are replaced by new bands near 1450 and 950 cm^{-1}. The highest frequency band, also designated amide-I band, is closest to a (C=O) stretching, but the shift on deuteration shows a slight participation of a proton motion. Some authors attributed the band at 1560 cm^{-1} (amide-II) to the (N–H) bending vibration and the lowest frequency band (amide-III) to the (C–N) stretching. Neither this nor the converse assignment could possibly explain the deuteration shifts and it was clear that both (C–N) stretching and (N–H) bending participate in both normal coordinates.

The calculations of MIYAZAWA, SHIMANOUCHI, and MIZUSHIMA[20] have now suggested the nature of these vibrations in the case of N–methylacetamide as a simple representative of this class of compound. The amide-I band is due to a coordinate in which the (C=O) bond stretches while the (C–N) bond contracts. The energy associated with the (C=O) bond in this vibration is much larger than that associated with the (C–N) bond and therefore this frequency is said to be 80 per cent carbonyl stretching. The calculation of the displacement vectors of atoms involved in this vibration shows a large displacement of the hydrogen atom perpendicular to the (N–H) bond direction (Fig. VII, 1(a)). In the amide-II coordinate, the (C–N) bond

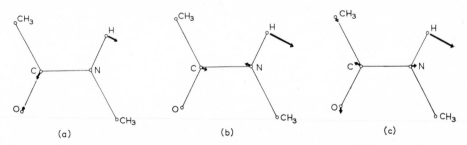

Fig. VII, 1. Atomic displacement vectors of (a) the amide-I, (b) the amide-II, and (c) the amide-III vibrations of N-methylacetamide. *(After T. Miyazawa, T. Shimanouchi and S. Mizushima, J. Chem. Phys., 29 (1958) 611.)*

stretches whilst the (C=O) bond slightly contracts, the amplitude ratio being 1.0:−0.2. The potential energy contribution of the latter bond is very small, but the contributions of (C–N) stretching and (N–H) bending are about equally large. The form of the vibration is shown in Fig. VII, 1(b). The final rating of this frequency is 60 per cent (N–H) bending and 40 per cent (C–N) stretching. The amide-III band appears to be due to a mixture of the (C–N) and (C=O) in-phase stretchings with an amplitude ratio of

1.0 : 0.45, with some (N–H) bending, the participation of the latter being slightly less than in the amide-II coordinate (Fig. VII, 1(c)). Deuterium substitution does little to simplify this complicated pattern of coupled vibrations. The amide-II′ band is due mainly to (C–N) stretching with contributions from (C–CH$_3$) and (N–CH$_3$) stretchings, (N–D) bending and (O=C–N) bending. Similarly, the amide III′ band at 950 cm^{-1} is due as much to the (N–D) bending as to the (C–CH$_3$) and (N–CH$_3$) stretching motions.

These randomly selected examples of characteristic group frequencies have mainly involved atoms other than carbon so we will now consider some hydrocarbon structural units, the vibrations of which also give rise to characteristic spectral features. Paraffin hydrocarbons containing a 2,2-dimethyl unit regularly show two strong bands near 1250 and 1200 cm^{-1}, whilst two bands near 1170 and 1145 cm^{-1} appear to be characteristic of the 2-methyl grouping. SIMPSON and SUTHERLAND[21] have made model calculations for molecules of the type

$$
\begin{array}{ccc}
\text{Z} & & \text{Z} \\
| & & | \\
\text{C} & \text{and} & \text{C} \\
\text{CH}_3 \diagup \; | \; \diagdown \text{CH}_3 & & \text{CH}_3 \diagup \; | \; \diagdown \text{CH}_3 \\
\text{CH}_3 & & \text{H}
\end{array}
$$

respectively. They used a simple valence force field neglecting the (C–H) vibrations and calculated the frequencies for different masses of Z to show the influence of increasing the length of the hydrocarbon chain. The result was that one of the A_1 species and one of the degenerate E species with frequencies 1230 and 1280 cm^{-1}, respectively, show remarkably little dependence on the mass of Z. Thus for masses from 29 to 99, corresponding to the series from 2,2-dimethylbutane to 2,2-dimethylnonane, the frequencies mentioned decrease by about 50 and 35 cm^{-1} respectively. For the model simulating the 2-methyl paraffins these authors also found two frequencies which were only slightly sensitive to the increase of chain length and were in satisfactory agreement with the observed frequencies in the spectra of this type of hydrocarbon. These examples clearly show that there are vibrations limited to certain sections of the carbon skeleton which are nearly independent of the mass of the remaining framework.

There are many other group frequencies of practical importance which it would be interesting to analyse, particularly those connected with the vibrations of the benzene ring, but it is not the aim of this chapter to treat the subject exhaustively. However, it is hoped that the examples presented will clarify the concept of characteristic frequencies.

(2) Electronic Influences on the Frequencies of Characteristic Vibrations

If mechanical influences on a group frequency are shown to be negligible then any variations in this frequency are due to changes in the force constant which are caused by the group environment. The influences on the force constant may originate from internal or external environmental effects. The latter type of effect is discussed in Chapter XII. The term "group-environment" is used in this section only in connection with effects transmitted through chemical bonds. Intramolecular effects which may modify a bond or angle force constant are of a complex nature, but empirical results have shown that simple relations exist between the variation of the frequency of a characteristic band and such quantities as are used to characterize the influence on group environment of chemical equilibria and reaction kinetics. For example, the variations in the (O–H) stretching frequency of phenols show similar electronic effects of ring substituents as do their acid dissociation constants.

It is customary in organic chemistry to distinguish two main types of electronic interaction between the reacting centre and the substituent, *i.e.* the inductive and the mesomeric or resonance effects. Either of them may be positive or negative depending on the direction of displacement of the electronic charge in the reacting group. A positive effect means a migration of charge from the substituent to the reacting group and a negative effect means a withdrawal of electronic charge by the substituent. Substituents may exhibit one type of effect or both simultaneously; in the latter case the inductive and the resonance effect may work in the same or in opposite directions. The inductive effect originates primarily from differences in electronegativity and consists in a polarization of the σ-electronic system. The resonance effect is due to delocalization in π-electronic systems.

These effects are generally measured by the magnitude of certain substituent factors[22]. One of the most used constants is the Hammett σ factor defined by the equation

$$\sigma = \log \left[\frac{K_{X \cdot C_6 H_4 COOH}}{K_{C_6 H_5 COOH}} \right] \qquad \text{where } K_{X \cdot C_6 H_4 COOH} \text{ and } K_{C_6 H_5 COOH}$$

are the ionization constants for the substituted and unsubstituted benzoic acids, respectively. A positive value of σ for a substituent indicates that it attracts electronic charge more strongly than hydrogen; substituents with negative σ values are regarded as electron donors. Hammett's σ factors embrace both the inductive and resonance effects of the substituent; they are suitable for aromatic systems in the absence of steric effects. Taft's σ^* factors are defined by the reactivity of aliphatic carboxylic acids[23]. They measure the inductive effect of the substituent and also possible steric effects. Therefore these factors may be used in connection with saturated systems and extended also to *ortho*-substituents in benzene.

Good correlations between the (O–H) stretching frequency and the

Hammett factor have been obtained by STONE and THOMPSON[24] and other authors[25, 26] for *meta*- and *para*-substituted phenols (Fig. VII, 2). The frequency decreases from 3613 to 3593 cm^{-1} as the σ values increase from

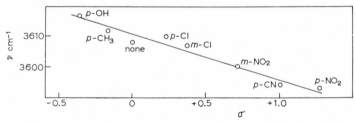

Fig. VII, 2. (O–H) stretching frequencies of substituted phenols in carbon tetrachloride solution as a function of σ. Data from ref. 24

−0.41 to +1.27. FLETT's results[27] show that condensed aromatic structures have an effect similar to the electron withdrawing substituents in phenol, *i.e.* the frequencies of polycyclic phenols are lower than that of phenol itself. The (O–H) frequency in monomeric carboxylic acids behaves similarly with respect to the electron-withdrawing tendencies of the substituents[28].

The (O–H) stretching frequency in alcohols follows a more complicated pattern. If methanol is taken as standard (3640 cm^{-1})[27], then electron-withdrawing substituents like (–CH$_2$CN) or halogens cause a decrease of frequency, *e.g.* CH$_2$CN. CH$_2$OH, 3625 cm^{-1}. However, substitution of hydrogen in the methyl group of methanol by alkyl groups, which are electron-donating, also leads to a frequency decrease, *e.g.* the (O–H) stretch-

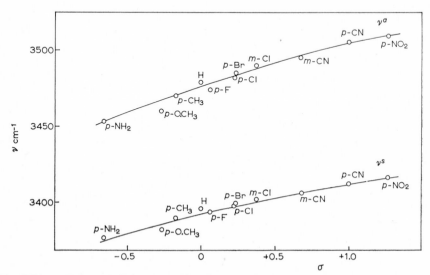

Fig. VII, 3. Frequencies of the asymmetric (ν^a) and symmetric (ν^s) (NH$_2$) stretching vibrations of substituted anilines in carbon tetrachloride solution as functions of σ. Data from ref. 30.

ing frequency in tertiary butanol is 3616 cm^{-1}. In general the (O–H) stretching frequencies of alcohols are higher than those of phenols.

The trends in (N–H) stretching frequencies are the reverse of those for the (O–H) group. Aliphatic amines have considerably lower frequencies than their aromatic analogues[29], e.g. dimethylamine 3350 cm^{-1}, N–methyl-aniline 3433 cm^{-1}. The (N–H) stretching frequencies of substituted anilines correlate well with the substituent factors,[30, 31] but here electron-withdraw-ing substituents cause a frequency increase (Fig. VII, 3). In the series of primary amines there are two (N–H) stretching frequencies corresponding to the symmetric and asymmetric vibrations, but both behave in the same way. Both frequencies may be correlated with the electronic charge on nitrogen in the series of N–heterocyclic amines and polycyclic aromatic amines[32] and it has been shown that the frequencies increase with decreasing charge on the amino nitrogen. However, the (N–H) stretching frequency in substituted acetanilides and N–methyl benzamides decreases if electron withdrawing substituents are introduced (Fig. VII, 4)[33]. The same is true of phenylhydrazones[34].

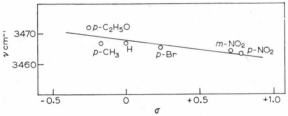

Fig. VII, 4. (N–H) stretching frequencies of substituted N-methylbenzamides in chloroform solution as a function of σ. Data from ref. 33.

The behaviour of the (S–H) stretching frequencies is qualitatively analogous to the amines, but the difference between the extreme frequencies observed[35] is less than 50 cm^{-1}.

From the theoretical point of view it would be advantageous to obtain correlations of frequencies with physically better defined quantities in the way that the electronegativities are, although even these are not uniquely defined[36]. An attempt at this kind of correlation is represented by the plot of the (Si–H) stretching frequencies of a number of trisubstituted silanes against the sum of the electronegativities of the substituents[37] (Fig. VII, 5). The plot is essentially linear, the frequency increasing with the increase of electronegativity. However, for molecules containing (SiH$_2$), (SiH$_3$) or (SiBr) large deviations appear, and SMITH and ANGELOTTI[37] have selected a set of numbers characterizing individual substituents so that their sum corre-lated well with the (Si–H) stretching frequency for any given structure. These numbers are related to Gordy's electronegativities, but not in a linear way.

From GORDY's[38] empirical relation $k = aN(x_A x_B/d^2)^{\frac{3}{4}} + b$ (k is the force constant, a and b are empirical constants, x_A and x_B are the electronegativities of the bond forming atoms, N is the bond order and d the bond

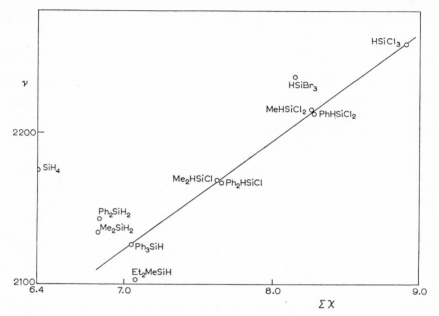

Fig. VII, 5. (Si–H) stretching frequencies as a function of the sum of the electronegativities of the silicon substituents. *(After A. L. Smith and N. C. Angelotti, Spectrochim. Acta, 15(1959) 412).*

length) it follows clearly that the force constant of a bond is not simply related to the electronegativities of the atoms involved, but that it also depends upon factors which are intimately related to the particular conditions of bonding. Thus it is not surprising that the fit of the (Si–H) stretching frequencies could be obtained only with quantities which, although related to electronegativities, seem to be specially adapted to the bonding of substituents to silicon. THOMPSON[39] has obtained a roughly linear relationship between the (Si–H) stretching frequencies and the Taft σ^* factors, although individual points deviate considerably. This result can be understood in view of the roughly linear relationship between the σ^* factors and the electronegativities adapted by Smith and Angelotti, and particularly in terms of the deviations of individual points from the line relating these two quantities[39].

There is apparently no simple relationship between the (C–H) stretching frequencies of substituted methanes and the electronegativity of the substituents. Plotting the average (C–H) frequency[40] against the sum of the σ^* constants of the substituents yields widely scattered points (Fig. VII, 6).

However, there are indications of a tendency for the (C–H) frequencies to be higher in molecules with more electronegative substituents. Thus in halogenomethanes the average (C–H) frequency is increased with respect to

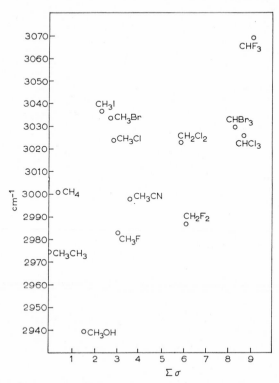

Fig. VII, 6. Plot of the average (C–H) stretching frequency of substituted methanes against the σ^* values.

methane[40]: CH_4, 2994 cm^{-1}; CH_3Cl, 3017 cm^{-1}; CH_3Br, 3027 cm^{-1}; CH_3I, 3030 cm^{-1}. An exception is CH_3F since its average is 2976 cm^{-1}. The order of increasing frequencies is the reverse of the electronegativity, which is F > Cl > Br > I. By increasing the number of halogen atoms the frequency increases markedly in some cases, such as CHF_3 (3062 cm^{-1}), but very little in others: CH_2Cl_2, 3016 cm^{-1}; $CHCl_3$, 3019 cm^{-1}. If the symmetrical and degenerate (C–H) stretching frequencies of monohalogenomethanes are plotted against the (X–H) (X = halogen) stretching frequency[41], a line with negative slope can be drawn through the points. The (X–H) frequency decreases with decreasing electronegativity of the halogen. Fig. VII, 6 also shows that in the XCH_3 molecules the average (C–H) stretching frequency decreases with increasing σ^*.

Ethylenic and aromatic (C–H) frequencies are higher than aliphatic. Substituted benzenes are suitable for the purpose of correlating (C–H) stretching frequencies with substituent, although there are actually several infra-red active vibrations of this bond. LEBAS and JOSIEN[42] have picked out the strongest one and plotted its frequency against theoretical para- meters characterizing the π-electronic charges imparted to the carbon atoms by the substituents. A definite trend of increasing frequencies with smaller charge on the carbon atoms is apparent, although the individual points are rather scattered. This is true not only of the strongest band but also of others, as shown by SCHMIDT[43]. This author used the inductive effect of the substituents as measured by their σ_I factors as evidence for the electron withdrawal from the ring.

Systematic changes of frequency with the electronegative character of the substituent also appear in the deformation vibrations of the methyl group. The symmetrical methyl deformation frequency increases with in- creasing electronegativity of the atom linked to carbon as shown by SHEPPARD[44]. The frequency increase is linear for elements belonging to the same row, but plots for elements belonging to different rows constitute a series of parallel lines (Fig. VII, 7). Bellamy and Williams have obtained

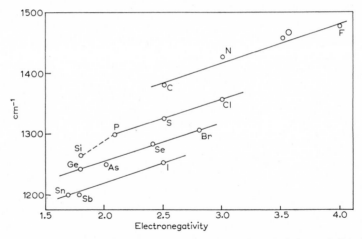

Fig. VII, 7. The frequencies of the symmetrical deformation vibrations of CH_3–X groups as a function of the electronegativity of X on Pauling's scale. *(Reproduced by courtesy of Dr. N. Sheppard and the Editor of the Transactions of the Faraday Society).*

good correlation[41] between the internal deformation frequencies of the (CH_3) group, its rocking frequency, and the (X–CH_3) stretching frequencies of the methyl halides and the (H–X) stretching frequency which may be taken as a measure of the electronegativity of X. The frequencies of other substituted methanes could also be fitted in these plots. The slope of the correlation curves is the reverse of that for the (C–H) stretching frequencies mentioned above. The straight lines correlating the square of the symmetrical (CH_3) deforma- tion and of methyl rocking frequencies of methyl halides with the electronegativity of the halogens were used by WILMSHURST[45] to obtain a set of adjusted electronegativities for various groups such as (O–H), (C≡N), (NO$_2$), etc. Similar results were also obtained for the deformation frequencies of substituted silanes[45].

Substituted benzenes exhibit several characteristic features in the region between 750 and 900 cm^{-1}, their pattern being determined primarily by the number and position of the (C–H) groups. BELLAMY[46] correlated the exact position of these bands for each type (*ortho, meta, para*) of substitution, with the sum of the σ values of the substituents, and obtained a plot consisting of three parallel lines, one for each type of substitution. These bands correspond to the (C–H) bending vibrations perpendicular to the plane of the benzene ring, their frequencies increasing with greater electron-withdrawing power of the substituents. The halogens could be fitted into the plot only if zero σ values were assigned to them.

In discussing the observed trends in (A–H) frequencies of various classes of compound we should first of all be certain that the variations are due to changes in the force constants. We may actually expect, on the ground of arguments presented in Section 1, that the (A–H) stretching frequencies would fulfil the requirements for a high degree of independence. BERNSTEIN[40] has recently shown that, in fact, the mechanical influences upon the (A–H) stretching frequencies are negligibly small compared with the influences of the group environment on the (A–H) force constant. Sometimes the Fermi resonance with the overtones of bending vibrations may interfere, but this can easily be allowed for. An *a priori* calculation of force constants is in principle possible[47, 48], but this requires the knowledge of precise molecular orbital wave functions and is therefore limited in practice to very simple molecules. Thus we shall consider some of the factors influencing the force constants of (A–H) bonds which are revealed by empirical correlations. One of them, the electronegativity, has already been shown to be of importance in this respect.

A more extended assessment of the influence of electronegativity upon the force constant may be obtained by considering the diatomic hydrides[49]. On going from left to right in a row of the Periodic Table the force constants of the hydrides increase, and they decrease from top to bottom of a column. This is approximately also the direction in which the electronegativities of the elements are changing. This fact led WALSH[49] to propose the force constants of the diatomic hydrides as a measure of the electronegativity of elements. Thus we may expect that the force constant of (A–H) which is part of a larger molecule, but behaves like a diatomic molecule, will be a function of the electronegativity of the atom A as modified by the substituents, *i.e.* of its effective electronegativity. However, as we have already seen, this proposition has to be carefully qualified.

Another factor of major importance influencing the force constant is the hybridization of the orbitals of the atom A. This is exemplified by the series of the (C–H) force constants for carbon in different hybridized states[50]. In saturated compounds with sp^3 carbon orbitals, the (C–H) force constant is about 4.9 mdyne/Å; in ethylenic and aromatic structures with sp^2 hybridized carbon it is approximately 5.1 mdyne/Å, and in acetylene with sp hybridized carbon it is 5.9 mdyne/Å. The force constant increases with increasing proportion of s orbitals in the hybridized carbon orbitals. However, changes in hybridization and in the electronegativity of carbon are not independent. The electronegativity increases with increasing s character of the orbitals[51]. It has been claimed that an increase of the s character in the (C–H) bond occurs upon increasing the electron-withdrawing power of the substituents on carbon[52]. Thus with substituents more electronegative than carbon the (C–H) force constant should be increased by two parallel mechanisms, $i.e.$ the increase both in the effective electronegativity of carbon and in the proportion of s character in the bonding orbital with hydrogen.

Whilst the foregoing account may be generally correct, the methyl halides do not fit into the pattern. BELLAMY and WILLIAMS[41] offered an explanation for this in considering also the methyl deformation frequencies, the C-halogen bond energies, and the stretching frequencies of these bonds. The trends of the latter two quantities in the series CH_3F, CH_3Cl, CH_3Br, and CH_3I suggest an increase of the p character in the carbon orbital used in bonding with the halogen. In compensation, the s character of the carbon orbital used with hydrogen is increased. This strengthens the (C–H) stretching force constant but reduces the force constant controlling the (H–C–H) angle distortion, because orbitals with more s character have less pronounced directional properties. A similar explanation could not be used for the aromatic (C–H) frequencies because here a decrease of charge on the carbon causes both the stretching and the bending frequencies to increase.

The increase of the s character in the nitrogen bonding orbitals of (N–H) may explain the increase in the (N–H) force constant in aromatic as compared with aliphatic amines. A stronger conjugation of the lone pair electrons of nitrogen with the aromatic ring in anilines with electron attracting substituents and with condensed aromatic structures is possible, if the lone pair orbitals have more p character. This causes a relative increase of s character of the orbitals bonding the hydrogen atoms and hence a strengthening of these bonds.

A similar increase in the π-electronic conjugation of the oxygen lone pair electrons certainly exists in the series alcohols–phenols–carboxylic acids. Evidence for this is the decrease of the basicity of oxygen on going from aliphatic ethers to anisole and the methoxynaphthols[53], as well as the mesomeric dipole moment of phenols[54]. However, the net effect of the structural changes in this series is to reduce the (O–H) force constant. Since the acid dissociation constants increase strongly as the force constants decrease, it is rather tempting to connect the latter with the increasing ionic character of the (O–H) link, although the ionization constants do not depend solely upon the ionic character of the bond. It is interesting to note that the (N–H) frequencies of amides and hydrazones show similar trends with the character of the substituents as the phenols, and that their hydrogens also have significant acidic character[33, 34]. The polar character of the (O–H) bond should be reduced by an electron-donating substituent on the oxygen which increases the force constant. This is exemplified in the (O–H) frequencies of hydroxides of the type Ph_3XOH, where X is C, Si, Ge, Sn, and Pb. With decreasing electronegativity of X the (O–H) frequency increases. Silicon and, to a smaller extent, germanium hydroxides have higher frequencies than expected from their electronegativity; this is explained by WEST and BANEY[55] by the dative π-bonding of oxygen to Si or Ge with subsequent increase of s character of the (O–H) bond orbital.

Many empirical correlations with structural factors also exist for the characteristic frequencies of multiple bonds, particularly the carbonyl bond. KAGARISE[56] has plotted the (C=O) stretching frequencies of acid halides and esters against the sum of Gordy's electronegativities of the atoms linked to the carbonyl carbon, and obtained good straight lines showing the increase of frequency with increasing electronegativity. Although mass effects could interfere, their influence is apparently small compared with the electronic perturbations of the carbonyl group. The clearest electronic effects may be expected when the substituents are attached to the carbonyl group through a good conducting medium like the aromatic ring. In fact, most of the work has been done on aromatic ketones[33, 57, 58], esters[59], amides[33], acids[28], and peroxides[60]. As an example, the correlation of the carbonyl frequency in substituted benzophenones and acetophenones with the σ constants of the substituents is shown in Fig. VII, 8. The increase of frequency with increasing electron-withdrawing power of the substituents is observed and this is rather general for all types of carbonyl groups[33].

Besides the polar effects, conjugation will have much influence upon the force constant of a group with π-electron bonds. This is shown qualitatively in the decrease of frequencies on going from saturated ketones (about 1710 cm^{-1}) to acetophenone (1686 cm^{-1}) and further to benzophenone (1665 cm^{-1}). A quantitative correlation is possible in the quinone series. The bond orders of the quinodimethanes corresponding to various quinones can be calculated by semi-theoretical methods[61] and these bond orders can be taken as a measure of the conjugation of the carbonyl link in quinones and correlated with the (C=O) frequencies[62]. These decrease as the bond order decreases. A semi-quantitative calculation of the bond orders of (C=O) bonds in substituted acetophenones has also been made[63], and the

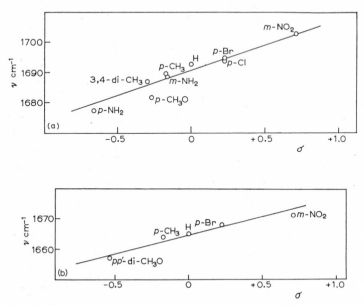

Fig. VII, 8. Carbonyl stretching frequencies of (a) acetophenones and (b) benzophenones as functions of σ. Data from ref. 59.

results correlated with the frequencies of this group; the same trends are observed as for the quinones. Thus it is clear that major variations in the carbonyl frequencies are due to two main factors: the conjugating capacity of the framework and the electronegativity of the substituents.

A more detailed analysis of the factors influencing the carbonyl force constant is possible by applying quantum mechanical methods directly to the calculation of the force constant. This can be done if changes in the distribution of the π-electrons are considered to be solely responsible for force constant changes. As the first step in their work, BRATOŽ and BES-NAINOU[64] have calculated the molecular orbitals for some representative carbonyl groups. The inductive effect of the substituents is accounted for by an appropriate choice of the matrix elements of the carbonyl carbon atom in the secular determinant, using experimentally available or estimated ionization potentials. The force constant is obtained as the second derivative of the molecular orbital energy. The general expression shows this to be a function of the bond order, the charges on the atoms, and the derivatives of the bond order operators with respect to bond length. The first two quantities characterize the bond in the ground state whereas the third expresses the rearrangement of the molecular orbital during the vibration. The application of the method to the frequency variations in the series formaldehyde–acetaldehyde–acetone yields a satisfactory agreement with the observed trend *i.e.* decreasing (C=O) frequencies. The increased avail-ability of electrons by progressive substitution with the donating methyl groups lowers the ionization potential of the carbon atom. Since the carbonyl link is already polarized in the direction (C^{+}–O^{-}) the decrease of the ef-fective electronegativity of carbon enhances the charge assymetry. This results, *inter alia*, in a decrease of the bond order. As this is the most im-portant factor in the expression for the force constant, it must be concluded that the increase in polarity of the carbonyl link results in the reduction of its force constant. Substitution with electron-attracting substituents, *e.g.* halogen, reduces the polarity of the bond and hence increases the force constant. The decrease of the force constant in molecules where conjugation of the carbonyl group occurs is due to the reduction of the bond order, as exemplified by the quinones. This effect should be more pronounced with *p*-quinones than with *o*-quinones, which is in agreement with experimental results.

Good correlations of group frequency with substituent factors have been obtained for several groups in addition to carbonyl. Thus a linear relationship of the (P=O) stretching frequency with the sum of the Taft σ^{*} factors was obtained[65] in a series of phosphonates of the type R.PO.(XY) and similar results were obtained for the frequencies of aromatic and aliphatic nitro groups[66, 67]. The frequency of the (C≡N) group in aliphatic and aromatic nitriles is only slightly sensitive to the polar effects of the substituents but decreases markedly on going from aliphatic to aromatic nitriles[68, 69].

(3) Correlation of Bond Frequencies with other Bond Characteristics

There are several characteristic bond and group properties which depend upon the same factors as the force constants; simple relationships should therefore be observed between them. A good correlation may be expected between bond frequencies and bond dissociation energies in view of the relation:

$$D = \frac{k_e(\mu_H + \mu_X)}{4x_e\omega_e}$$

developed by BERNSTEIN[40] for the case of (X–H) groups. Here, D is the dissociation energy of the (X–H) bond, $x_e\omega_e$ the anharmonic constant, k_e the equilibrium value of the (X–H) force constant and μ_H and μ_X the inverse masses of the H and X atoms. The relation between the dissociation energy and the average stretching frequency for some (C–H) bonds is shown in

Fig. VII, 9. The deviations in the case of toluene and chloroform are attributed[40] to the extra stabilization of the radicals by resonance.

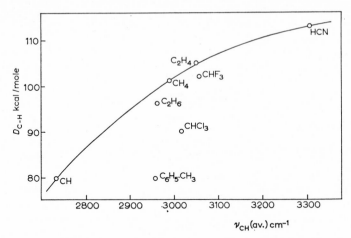

Fig. VII, 9. Relationship between the (C–H) dissociation energy and the average (C–H) frequency. *(After H. J. Bernstein, Spectrochim. Acta, 18 (1962) 166).*

There are a number of empirical relations between force constants (k) of diatomic molecules and interatomic distance (r). For several series of molecules like the hydrogen halides, oxides of the elements of particular groups of the Periodic Table, or alkali hydrides, SMITH[70] has shown that a relation $kr^2 = $ const. is satisfactory. It is to be expected that simple relationships would also exist between bond frequencies and bond lengths for groups such as (C–H), (O–H) and (N–H). Such correlation curves have frequently been given, *e.g.* by BERNSTEIN[40]. It is interesting to note that the largest departures from the curve relating the (C–H) frequencies to bond lengths are shown by some methyl halides, the (C–H) frequencies of which show the largest deviations from the values expected from the polar effects of the substituents *(cf.* p. 241 and Fig. VII, 10). Correlations between (C=O) and (C–N) frequencies and bond lengths have also been published[71].

The (O–H) stretching frequencies of phenols and of carboxylic acids correlate well with their pK_a values[72, 73]. The slopes of the lines are different for each type of hydroxylic group, but for both, the frequency decreases as the acidity increases. A correlation of the (O–H) with the (C=O) stretching frequencies of the carboxyl group shows that the latter decreases with increasing (O–H) frequency, as would be expected from the polar effects of substituents on both groups separately.

Some interesting correlations of the (C=O) frequency with quantities related to the energy of the non-bonding orbitals of the carbonyl oxygen have been made. Thus a linear relation between the ionization potential of a number of carbonyl compounds and the (C=O) frequency was found by

COOK[74]. Lines of different but positive slopes arise for compounds in which conjugation between the carbonyl group and the substituents is possible,

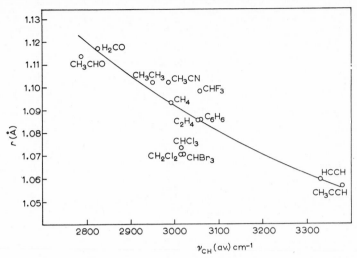

Fig. VII, 10. Relationship between the (C–H) bond length and the average (C–H) stretching frequency. *(After H. J. Bernstein, Spectrochim. Acta, 18 (1962) 166).*

and those in which this is not so. The carbonyl frequencies of benzophenones are related[58] in a simple manner to the polarographic half-wave potentials. Structural changes which reduce the polarity of the carbonyl group increase the bond order and raise both the (C=O) frequency and the energy needed to remove an electron from the carbonyl oxygen; the lone pair electrons from this carbon are thus less readily available for hydrogen bonding with hydrogen chloride or acetylene[74]. The reduced polarity of the (C=O) link by substitution of electron attracting atoms is also reflected in the smaller dipole moment[75].

It should be obvious from these examples that frequencies may be used to estimate several other bond or group characteristics which are often difficult to measure directly. Moreover, the common trends in the variation of several bond properties with structural changes contribute considerably to the confidence one may have in the interpretation of the electronic interactions between substituents and functional groups. A feature of much significance is that the proper use of characteristic frequencies has promoted the quantitative assessment of bonding conditions in complex molecules — an assessment of a type which was previously restricted to simple molecules.

(4) Electronic Influences on the Intensities of Characteristic Bands

The intensities of absorption bands arising from localized vibrations are also characteristic, *i.e.* their values are determined by the electronic properties of the bond and are influenced by the group environment to the extent to which the latter induces changes in these properties. Although both the frequencies and the intensities depend ultimately on the electronic structure of the bond there is no direct relationship between them, the former being determined by the second derivative of energy with respect to the coordinate (Q) and the latter by the dipole moment gradient, $\partial\mu/\partial Q$. A particular change in the group environment may cause the frequency and the intensity of the corresponding band to vary in opposite directions. For instance, the frequency of the (O–H) group in phenols is lowered by electron-withdrawing substituents, whereas the intensity is raised by such substituents. These two band characteristics are thus treated separately. Since the general background to the problem of the intensity of infra-red bands is given in Chapter X we may proceed by examining some of the experimental results obtained with characteristic bands.

In correlating the band intensities with substituent effects some authors prefer to plot the logarithm of the integrated band intensity A whereas others prefer the square root. The first usage is derived from the Hammett type equation $\log A = \log A_0 + \sigma\rho$ relating the intensity of a particular characteristic band to the substituent factor σ, the slope of the correlation line ρ, and its intercept A_0[30]. The use of $A^{\frac{1}{2}}$ is connected[76] with the theoretically derived relationship between the intensity and changes in the dipole moment gradient $(\partial\mu/\partial Q)$ induced by the substituents. A statistical evaluation of both types of plot showed them to be equally good[77].

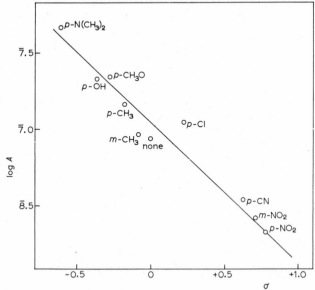

Fig. VII, 11. The intensities of (C≡N) bands of benzonitriles as a function of σ. Data from ref. 68.

For some characteristic bands the intensity variations are relatively much larger than the corresponding frequency variations. The intensity of the (C≡N) band in different nitriles may differ[78] by a factor of 60 whereas the frequencies fall in an interval of about 50 cm⁻¹. The intensities of this band correlate well with substituent constants[68, 79] (Fig. VII, 11), decreasing with increasing electron-withdrawing power of the substituent.

The correlation of the (C=O) band intensity with substituent effects in different classes of compound containing this group shows that the slopes of the lines for particular classes may differ considerably. Thus for propiophenones and benzophenones (Fig. VII, 12(b)) the slope of the line

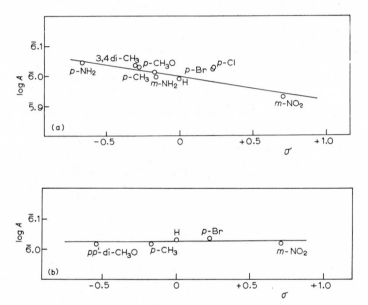

Fig. VII, 12. The intensities of the (C=O) bands of (a) acetophenones and (b) benzophenones as functions of σ. Data from ref. 59.

relating log A to Hammett's σ factors is zero, whereas it is negative for ethyl benzoates, acetophenones (Fig. VII, 12(a)), and benzaldehydes[60]. In the series of aromatic amides the slope of this line is also negative, but approximately zero for N–methylbenzamides[57]. The study of the carbonyl band intensities in compounds of the general type X.CO.Y led THOMPSON and JAMESON[57] to the conclusion that resonance factors are dominant in influencing the carbonyl intensities. Experimental results can be fitted by an equation of the form:

$$\log A = \log A_0 + \alpha \sum \sigma^* + \beta(\sigma_R^X + \sigma_R^Y) - \gamma(\sigma_R^X \cdot \sigma_R^Y)$$

where β and γ are constants depending upon the particular type of carbonyl; α measures the inductive effect and is a correspondingly small factor;

σ_R^X and σ_R^Y are substituent factors measuring the resonance effects of X and Y. The last term takes care of the resonance interactions between X and Y. The effect of the resonance stabilization of the whole molecule upon the carbonyl band intensity is shown in the correlation by BARROW[80], the intensity increasing roughly linearly with resonance energy.

Whereas the intensities of the (C=O) and (C≡N) bands generally decrease with increasing negative polar effects of substituents, the reverse is true of the (O–H), (N–H), and (S–H) stretching bands. The (O–H) stretching band intensities in substituted phenols were determined by STONE and THOMPSON[24] and a linear dependence of log A on the σ constants was obtained (Fig. VII, 13). Alcoholic hydroxyls have smaller absorption

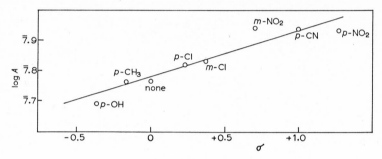

Fig. VII, 13. The intensities of the (O–H) band of substituted phenols as a function of σ. Data from ref. 24.

intensities, but here too the intensity increases with the negative polar effect of the substituents[81].

The trends in the intensities of (N–H) stretching vibrations with structural changes are qualitatively similar to those of (O–H) bands. Thus, aliphatic amines have much weaker bands than their aromatic analogues and the correlations of the (N–H) stretching band intensities with substituent σ constants in the series of anilines and methylanilines[30, 82] show the band intensity to increase with negative substituent effects (Fig. VII, 14). This is an interesting contrast to the opposite trends of the (N–H) and (O–H) frequencies. However, the (N–H) intensities of substituted acetanilides are rather insensitive towards polar effects[33]. ELLIOT and MASON determined the (N–H) stretching band intensities of N–heteroaromatic[32] and polycyclic primary[83] amines, and correlated them with the electronic charges on the nitrogen atom. The latter quantity depends on the conjugating capacity of a given position in a condensed aromatic nucleus, and the electron withdrawing power of the heterocyclic nitrogen. The intensities increase linearly with decreasing charge on the amino nitrogen atom, but the intensities of the groups in sterically hindered positions fall on a different line.

The intensity behaviour of aromatic (C–H) stretching bands in relation to the charges on the carbon atoms is the reverse of that for the (X–H) groups just mentioned. The work of SCHMIDT[43] and BELLANATO and SCHMIDT[84] demonstrates that the intensities of the (C–H) stretching bands in substituted benzenes decrease with the negative inductive effect of the

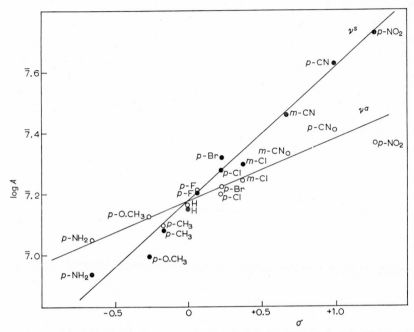

Fig. VII, 14. The intensities of the symmetric (ν^s) and asymmetric (ν^a) (N–H) bands of substituted anilines as functions of σ. Data from ref. 30.

substituents as expressed by their σ_I factors. This is true whether one considers the complex area of all (C–H) stretching bands or the peak extinction of each of the three main components. Plotting the latter quantities against the σ_I constants yields three approximately straight lines with different slope. Since each of the three peaks probably corresponds to one of the normal modes in which the *ortho*, *meta*, and *para* hydrogen atoms participate to a different extent, the difference in their slopes may be assumed to be due to the unequal spreading of the polar effect of the substituent amongst the various positions. The possibility of following, by a physical method, the influence of the substituent on the charge in different positions of the aromatic skeleton is clearly of great interest to organic chemists. In this connection the interesting work of SANDORFY *et al.*[25] should also be mentioned. They have related the variations of the frequencies and intensities of substituted phenols and benzonitriles to the charge distribution in the ring, and have shown the result to be in good agreement with the concepts of substituent effects developed from chemical experience.

There is little systematic work on the intensities of the bands of aliphatic (C–H) groups. The determination of the intensities of characteristic bands of (CH$_3$) and (CH$_2$) groups adjacent to (C=O) groups in ketones and esters, and to the ether–oxygen in esters, shows a decrease of the stretching intensities and an increase of the deformation band intensities[85]. This suggests that electron attracting substituents decrease the (C–H) stretching intensities, which agrees with FLETT's results[86] obtained on compounds of the type p-X.C$_6$H$_4$.CH$_3$ and C$_6$H$_5$.CH$_2$Y. In this work both the aliphatic and the aromatic (C–H) band intensities were correlated with Hammett's σ values for X and CH$_2$Y respectively.

The interpretation of the empirically established relationships between the characteristic band intensities and the structural effects in terms of the changes in the polar properties of the bonds is difficult in view of the variety of contributions towards $\partial \mu / \partial Q$. The problems of the *a priori* calculation of vibrational band intensities in simple molecules were lucidly described by COULSON[87], but the general conclusions may also be used for qualitative considerations. The bond dipole moment (this term is used for the sake of simplicity although the concept of the bond dipole moment in polyatomic molecules has no well-defined meaning[87]) contains contributions from the asymmetry in the charge distribution of the bonding electrons, inequalities of size of the atoms (homopolar dipole), asymmetry of the hybrid atomic orbitals, and the asymmetry of charge associated with the lone pair orbitals[88]. Most of these contributions are expected to change during the vibration and thus contribute to $\partial \mu / \partial Q$. Moreover, electronic rearrangements may occur in bonds close to the vibrating one, even though they are not coupled vibrationally. Large contributions to the intensity may arise from this source, particularly in conjugated systems. Thus the expression for $\partial \mu / \partial Q$ comprises a number of terms which may be of the same or of opposite signs and in general it is difficult to find out which of the terms is dominant and what would be the influence of a change in the environment on each term.

Only speculation is possible if merely the intensity of one vibrational mode is available. Consider for instance the large increase in the (N–H) stretching intensity between a secondary aliphatic amine such as diethyl-amine and an aromatic one such as diphenylamine. The increase is about sixty-fold[29]. One can perhaps associate this with changed hybridization in the (N–H) bond which varies from approximately sp^3 for aliphatic nitrogen towards sp^2 for nitrogen in aromatic amines[89]. In consequence there will be changes in the asymmetry of charge distribution of the bonding electrons due to the increase in the effective electronegativity of nitrogen, and in the charge of the lone pair electrons, besides other changes which may be of minor importance.

An additional factor contributing to the enhanced intensity of aromatic (N–H) bands has been proposed *inter alia*, by MASON[83]. It is, in essence, a changing during the vibration of the π-electronic orbitals of the ring due to the rehybridization of the lone pair orbitals. This mechanism should be operative only with secondary amines and in the case of the symmetric stretching band of primary amines, but not with the asymmetric stretching. Here any hybridization change in one bond during its stretching is compensated by the converse process in the other (N–H) bond. Thus, the symmetric stretching band ought always to be more intense. However, this is not borne out by experimental data (Fig. VII, 14). Apparently the reasons for the large intensity of the aromatic (N–H) bands have to be sought in the dipole moment gradient of the bond itself. In this respect the measurements of the frequency and intensity of both the fundamental and the overtones of the (N–H) stretching mode are informative. It is possible to interpret the combined data in terms of the mechanical and electrical anharmonicities and obtain information on the change of the dipole moment with bond length[29]. The plots of the dipole moments against bond length for aliphatic amines differ essentially from such plots for aromatic amines, the latter being linear as for the plot for a fully ionic bond, although with a different slope[29]. This result demonstrates that the charge distribution of the ionic type in aromatic (N–H) bonds is probably the dominant factor in the determination of the intensity.

The acidic character of the (N–H) groups in diphenylamine, pyrrole, and its homologues is to some extent connected with the increase in polar character of this link. However, it would be an oversimplification to take the acid dissociation constants as quantitative measures of the bond polarity since other factors are involved[90]. It is very likely that the larger absorption intensity of the phenolic (O–H) stretching band compared to that of alcohols is due to the increase in the charge asymmetry in the phenolic (O–H) link and that its gradient is steeper. Evidence for the greater bond polarity of the latter is found in the comparison of the intensities of the (O–D) bending bands of phenols and alcohols[91] which are in the ratio of approximately 2:1. Deuterated compounds were used for this investigation because the (O–D) bending is very much less coupled to other vibrations than the (O–H) bending. Both the acid dissociation constants and the band intensities of the (O–H) stretching vibration are enhanced by structural changes such as the change from an aliphatic to an aromatic radical and the introduction of electron-withdrawing substituents. This conforms to the parallelism[92] between the stretching of a bond polarized in the sense $(O^-\!\!-\!\!H^+)$ and the dissociation into ions $(RO^-\!\!+\!\!H^+)$. Both processes should be facilitated by structural factors in R which help to stabilize the excess negative charge on the oxygen atom. However, this parallelism does not always hold. Carboxylic acids have in general much higher dissociation constants than phenols, but the (O–H) band intensities are about the same[93].

It is sometimes assumed that the more polar the bond the stronger is the absorption. The comparison of the (C=O) and (C≡N) band intensities shows that this is not necessarily so. The dipole moment of the nitrile group is about twice as large as that of the carbonyl group[54], but the intensities of the stretching bands of (C=O) groups are on the average 10 to 50 times greater than those of the (C≡N) groups. One would expect the charge separation during the stretching to increase in the sense of (C$^+$=N$^-$). A compensating process must operate to reduce the effect of this dipole moment increase. Following the arguments of SANDORFY et al.[25] a rehybridization of the nitrogen lone pair orbitals can take place. In the ground state nitrogen is digonally hybridized, but when the (C≡N) bond stretches, the overlap with the carbon orbitals is diminished and digonal hybridization is energetically less favoured. The nitrogen atom returns partially to the unhybridized state, the lone pair being pulled back to the nucleus and the bonding electrons toward the carbon atom. This process reduces the overall electric moment of the (C≡N) group. There are thus two opposing effects on the dipole moment change during vibration, and their interplay will be strongly influenced by substituent effects; this explains the great variability of the intensity of this band.

The variations of the (C=O) band intensity as a function of structural factors may be put on a quantitative basis as shown by BESNAINOU, PRAT, and BRATOŽ[94]. The method considers the changes in the π-electron charge with bond length, the contribution to the gradient by σ electrons being obtained empirically. The other contributions to $\partial\mu/\partial Q$ are the changes in the π-electron charge on the carbonyl carbon and, possibly, on other atoms which contribute to the molecular orbitals of the (C=O) group, and the constant charge on the vibrating oxygen atom. The calculation of the former contribution follows from the molecular orbital coefficients and their derivatives with respect to the bond length. The results of the calculation of the (C=O) band intensities of several representative compounds are in satisfactory agreement with the experimental data and can also be applied to qualitative explanations of the observed trends in carbonyl band intensities. For instance, the increase of this quantity in the series formaldehyde–acetaldehyde–acetone is due to the electron donation of the methyl group which reduces the effective electronegativity of the carbonyl carbon and hence increases the bond polarity with increasing charge on the oxygen atom. Electron attracting substituents have, of course, the reverse effect. The influence of conjugation consists in the extension of the vibrating charge and therefore an increase in $\partial\mu/\partial Q$.

The semi-theoretical treatment of BROWN[76] is especially adapted to show analogies between the vibrations of functional groups and chemical reactions, and to explain the correlations between band intensities and substituent factors.

The evaluation of characteristic band intensities in terms of polar bond properties and the influence thereon of the group environment is only now being systematically undertaken and there is much scope for future theoretical work. The empirical results already obtained offer many interesting applications in the study of structural effects upon functional groups, the spreading of polar effects of the substituents, the estimation of substituent factors, and similar problems of chemical interest.

(5) Steric Effects on Characteristic Band Frequencies and Intensities

We have so far dealt with electronic effects transmitted through chemical bonds without mentioning explicitly the rôle of spatial relations between the origin of the effect and the subject group. This is probably of minor importance for the inductive effect, but it is well known that the extent of the overlapping of orbitals with p character depends largely on their mutual orientation. A change in structure such as introducing bulky substituents may force the atoms with such orbitals to take positions which are unfavourable for effective conjugation, and thus reduce the effects of conjugation on characteristic frequencies and intensities. This is one aspect of the steric effect and may be illustrated by examples from the work of JONES et al.[57] The (C=O) band of 2, 3, 5, 6-tetramethylacetophenone occurs at 1704 cm^{-1}, whereas the corresponding band of the unsubstituted or o-methyl compound is at 1690 cm^{-1}. The bulky methyl groups in the first compound force the carbonyl group out of the plane of the benzene ring and thus inhibit the resonance effect which caused the difference in the (C=O) frequency between the saturated ketones and acetophenone. Therefore, the (C=O) frequency of the sterically hindered tetramethylacetophenone assumes a value similar to that in the saturated ketones. A single methyl group does not have this effect because the (C=O) group can take an *s-trans* conformation and remain in the plane of the ring.

In the example above the steric effect of the methyl groups consisted in altering an electric effect transmitted through other bonds. Another type of steric effect is one in which polar influences between atoms and groups are transmitted through space and not through chemical bonds. The two types of polar influence cannot always be distinguished. Careful consideration of models is, of course, necessary to show that the geometry of the molecule is consistent with the operation of such effects. The observation of steric effects is connected with the existence of two or more isomers which may either be of fixed configuration or in a dynamic equilibrium, depending on the height of the potential barrier that separates the energetically more favoured conformations. The term "rotational isomerism" is used to describe a situation where two or more energetically preferred isomers exist by virtue of rotation about a bond and where the conformations with lower energy are separated by energy barriers comparable to kT. Spectroscopic methods are extremely useful in dealing with various problems associated with rotational isomerism such as the determination of the energy differences between the rotational isomers, but that is not within the scope of this chapter. The interested reader is referred to the review by SHEPPARD[95] and we shall proceed to examine some examples of the space transmitted effects on characteristic bands.

The α-halogen (X) in halogenoketones may occupy two distinct positions with respect to the carbonyl group:

s-cis   gauche   equatorial   axial

In cyclic ketones these positions are stable and called equatorial if the (C–X) bond is perpendicular to the threefold symmetry axis of the basic hydrocarbon cyclohexane, and axial if it is parallel to the axis. With an equatorial halogen, the (C=O) and (C–X) bonds are nearly coplanar and the (C=O) frequency in such bromoketones is about 20 cm^{-1} higher than in unsubstituted ketones[96]. When the halogen is axial, the frequency is only 2–3 cm^{-1} higher. Since the inductive effect should not depend on the mutual orientation of the (C=O) and (C–X) bonds, the large frequency increase in the case of parallel orientation of the bonds is ascribed to a dipole–dipole interaction transmitted through space and termed the field effect[75]. This effect is reflected also in the decrease of the (C=O) band intensity and indicates a decrease of the negative charge on the oxygen atom. This is in agreement with the increase of the force constant due to the decrease in bond polarity.

In open chain haloketones the two isomers are in dynamic equilibrium and coexist in the liquid phase. Consequently, two bands due to carbonyl groups in different environments are observed. Thus ω-chloroacetophenone exhibits the frequencies[97] 1714 and 1694 cm^{-1}. The relative intensity of these bands changes with temperature and solvent. From the temperature dependence of the relative intensity and the analogy with the spectra of chlorocyclohexanones it can be concluded that the higher frequency is due to the s-cis isomer and that this is the thermodynamically more stable one.

α, β unsaturated ketones may assume two different conformations, (I, II)

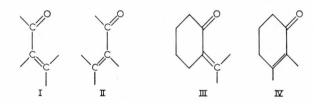

which are characterized by differences in (C=O) and (C=C) frequencies. The vibrations of these two bonds are actually coupled, but nevertheless one of the resulting normal modes will involve more of the (C=O) bond and the other predominantly the (C=C) bond, which is shown also by different solvent effects on the corresponding bands[98]. The (C=O) and the (C=C) bands in the spectra of such ketones are split or have shoulders and the assignment of these features to the particular isomer is possible by using the analogy with the cyclic unsaturated ketones of fixed configuration (III, IV)[99]. Relative to the *trans* configuration, the *cis* isomers show a greater separation between the (C=O) and (C=C) bands, a diminution of the (C=O), and an increase of the (C=C) band intensities. An interpretation of these results in terms of differences in mutual polarization of the (C=O) and (C=C) groups depending on their mutual orientation has been offered by NOACK and JONES[100].

Variations in vibrational frequencies and intensities of bonds which are related by stereoisomerism may be caused by combinations of sterically conditioned differences in electronic effects transmitted both through the bonds and space. Differences in geometry may also cause changes in the kinetic coupling; this is particularly important for bands due to less strictly localized vibrations. It is not always possible to relate observed differences in band frequencies and intensities of isomers to particular effects, but this does not impair the importance of the empirically established regularities in their application to the conformational analysis of complicated molecules.

A number of different group frequencies due to substituted isomeric cyclohexanes and more complicated alicyclic structures have demonstrated that it is possible to infer from the frequency whether the respective group is axial or equatorial. For instance, axial (C–D) groups have lower frequencies than the equatorial ones[101] — the difference may amount to 30 cm^{-1}. The examination of the spectra of a number of 3-hydroxysteroids with known orientation of the (C–OH) link revealed systematic differences in the position of a strong band in the region of 1000–1050 cm^{-1}. With the equatorial configuration of the (C–OH) group the frequency tends to be higher than if it is axial[102]. Similarly, chlorocyclohexanes with an equatorial chlorine absorb near 758–760 cm^{-1}, but when the chlorine is axial[103] the absorption will be between 708 and 737 cm^{-1}. Thus it appears that axially oriented links have lower frequencies in general [104], but this is true only of

links connected directly to the ring. Hydroxyl groups in hydroxycyclohex-
anols and triterpenoids have higher (O–H) stretching frequencies if axially
oriented. Thus *cis*-2-methylcyclohexanol absorbs at 3632 cm^{-1} (axial OH)
whereas its *trans* isomer (equatorial) has the band at 3622.5 cm^{-1}. Differences in the same direction have been observed in all examples investigated although they are sometimes smaller[105, 106]. These differences may be
related to the fact that the (O–H) frequencies of alcohols and phenols,
which have the hydroxyl group in a very "crowded" environment, are
unusually high. 2, 2, 4, 4-tetramethylpentanol-3 has the (O–H) band at
3632 cm^{-1} and tricyclohexylcarbinol[107] has it at 3652 cm^{-1}. By analogy with
simpler tertiary alcohols one would expect a much lower frequency. The
(O–H) frequencies of phenols with large alkyl groups in both *ortho* positions
are between 3650 and 3660 cm^{-1}. This high frequency is presumably not a
result of the steric inhibition of resonance or of the positive inductive effect
of the alkyl groups[108]. Thus some effect of the proximity of the (C–H)
protons to the hydroxyl group appears to be operative. An increase in the
potential resisting the (O–H) stretching may originate in α-proton–proton
repulsion[109]. A similar repulsion presumably causes the extremely high (C–H)
frequencies in fused bicycloheptanes and so-called half-cage structures[109]:

they may be as high as 3139 cm^{-1}.

A different type of no-bond interaction of the hydroxyl group is observed
in alcohols and phenols with suitably positioned substituents having
π-electrons, such as double bonds or aromatic rings. Benzyl alcohol has two
incompletely resolved bands at 3617 and 3636 cm^{-1}; allyl alcohol has an
unsymmetrical band which may be resolved into maxima at 3619 and
3634 cm^{-1}. These bands are interpreted as due to two rotational isomers in
one of which the (O–H) group is turned towards the unsaturated system
and the proton is under the influence of the π-electronic charges, which
lowers the frequency[110]. The low frequency of 2,6-diphenyl phenol (3553
cm^{-1}) is apparently due to such interaction[111]. Even stronger interactions of
acidic protons with atoms bearing lone pair electrons (O, N, halogens) may
take place under suitable steric conditions. They lead to a pronounced
lowering of (O–H) or (N–H) stretching frequencies which are indicative of
the steric arrangement of the respective groups. For instance, the triterpenic
diol urs-12-ene-3α : 24-diol has the (O–H) band at 3641 cm^{-1} whereas its
3β-isomer has two bands 3550 and 3629 cm^{-1}, respectively[112]. In the first
isomer both (O–H) groups and the methylene group are axial and there is no
possibility of interaction. The second isomer has an equatorial (O–H) group

and this may approach the oxygen of the other group sufficiently closely to interact. However, this is a type of hydrogen bond interaction (Chapter XII) and need not further be elaborated here.

(6) Application of Characteristic Features to the Determination of the Gross Structure

Thus far we have dealt with a number of bands originating in the vibrations of particular bonds or small groups, and the structural framework was involved only as a source of electronic effects. This way of considering spectral features results from a predominantly theoretical interest in the structure of molecules, but besides having a bearing on the finer details of bonding or mutual influences of groups, it constitutes a sound foundation for the more immediately practical applications of characteristic features in the structural analysis of complex molecules.

In the last two decades many data have accumulated on bands which are characteristic of various structural elements, and on empirical assignments of bands to approximate vibrational modes within complex molecules. Many such studies would have benefited from a more critical and analytical assessment. Actually, many more bands can probably be used for the detection of certain structural elements than one would expect from the limitations imposed by electronic effects. Excellent systematic accounts of the features characteristic of particular structural elements already exist[113-116]. It is impossible briefly to summarize the varied procedures open to an experienced spectroscopist in applying this large accumulation of observations to the study of molecular structural problems; only some few simple illustrations of such problems can be given.

Perhaps the most frequently encountered problem is to assess the spectral evidence for the presence of a particular group in a molecule. In principle, the appearance of a band of appropriate frequency and intensity will constitute good positive evidence. However, the absence of the expected band is not necessarily a proof that the corresponding group is absent. It is possible that the band is so weak as to escape observation. Difficulties of this kind occur sometimes with $(C\equiv N)$ and $(S-H)$ stretching modes. Alternatively, the bond force constant may be so strongly modified that the band is much displaced and is not recognized. For example, no $(C=O)$ band was detected in the spectra of aldehydes of the type $[N-C=CH-CHO]$[117]. Strong hydrogen bonding may modify beyond recognition the absorption frequencies and intensities of the groups involved. Thus the $(O-H)$ band in chelated hydroxyquinones was claimed to be missing[59], but was eventually detected[118] using the special precautions which were necessary because the band was extremely broad and of low peak absorption.

In many instances the regions in which different specific bands appear overlap partially or completely. The choice of groups which the band in such circumstances may represent can be restricted by preliminary chemical analysis. If the compound contains only C, H, and O a strong band in the region 3000–3670 cm⁻¹ is possibly evidence of the presence of an (O–H) group. From the spectrum of the pure solid or liquid sample nothing more about the nature of this group can be said, particularly if the compound is of mixed aromatic and aliphatic nature. The influence of hydrogen bonding in pure hydroxylic compounds blurs the differences between, say, alcoholic and phenolic (O–H) bands. The frequency alone, even if obtained for the free (O–H) group, may not suffice to differentiate between these two types of hydroxylic group since the regions strongly overlap, but a determination of the specific intensity should be decisive. Carboxylic hydroxyls are easily recognized in the condensed phase by the characteristic broad absorptions having several submaxima[119].

The situation may become more complicated if besides C, H and O, N is also present. A band near 3300 cm⁻¹ can then be due either to (O–H) or (N–H) unless the nitrogen belongs to a nitro group or group other than (N–H). An (NH₂) group should not present difficulties because it has two stretching bands due to the symmetric and asymmetric vibrations, respectively. Often the single band of a secondary (N–H) group can immediately be differentiated from an (O–H) band, because the former bands are weaker and narrower. However, with aromatic amines or with hydrogen bonding, these differences may become unreliable: if hydrogen bonding persists in solution, the differentiation between an (O–H) and an (N–H) stretching band may even be impossible. In such cases other spectral regions may be explored for discriminating features. For instance, if the oxygen content can be accounted for in terms of (C=O) bands, then the band in the 3300 cm⁻¹ region is likely to be due to an (N–H) group: in that case other bands such as (C–N) stretching, (N–H) bending, etc. should be found. Unfortunately these are not really characteristic bands and moreover they fall in a crowded region of the spectrum.

The (C=O) band is not readily identified if its frequency and intensity are much altered by conjugation and hydrogen bonding of the chelate type, such as in enolized β-diketones, tropolones and similar structures. An example of such difficulties arises in the structure of the o-quinonehydrazones[120]. These compounds are tautomeric with the hydroxyphenylazobenzenes:

and they give reactions typical of both classes of compound.

Considering the formulae, the differentiation should be straightforward from the presence of (C=O) and (N–H) bands in the case of I, and the absence of these but presence of (O–H) bands in the case of structure II. In both structures strong hydrogen bonding is present which will persist in solution. The spectrum contains a weak and broad band near 3300 cm^{-1} which could be due to an (N–H) or to an (O–H) group. Thus the (C=O) band is a key factor in deciding the structure. When Bz is a phenyl group, no such band is present and therefore it may be concluded that the azo structure is the correct one. When Bz is naphthyl there is no typical (C=O) band but an incompletely resolved peak near 1612 cm^{-1}, partly overlapped by a stronger band at 1600 cm^{-1}. This peak might just as well be due to a skeletal mode of the aromatic framework as to an atypical (C=O) group. Since this band is missing in the spectrum of the o-methoxyazobenzene-naphthalenes, which are not tautomeric, its assignment to the (C=O) group of the o-naphthoquinone phenylhydrazone structure appears likely. This preference is further corroborated by the observations made with the spectrum of the deuterated compounds where the acidic hydrogen was exchanged for deuterium. The band shift from about 1560 to 1500 cm^{-1} is particularly important in suggesting a structural analogy with the amides (the amide–II band shifts in a similar way), which would be

This example was of a structural problem with circumstances un-favourable to the application of characteristic bands; it involved strong electronic interactions between functional groups and the framework, and the formation of strong chelate-type hydrogen bonds, resulting in the appearance of atypical bands. Circumstances are far more favourable in molecules containing typical functional groups on a more or less "inert" framework, localizing the polar influences of the functional groups to the immediate environment. Such compounds exhibit spectra with some prominent bands which reflect very precisely the character of the functional groups and the structure of their immediate environment, besides a number of less pronounced bands which can be accounted for by the vibrations of the less perturbed parts of the skeleton and the corresponding (C–H) groups. For the first of these types of band the term "characteristic zone absorption" has been proposed by JONES[121]. Systematic work with large series of compounds containing identical structural zones and the appli-cation of isotopic substitution has led to an almost complete assignment of the spectra of such complex compounds as the steroids[122]. The empirical assignment of the bands in the spectrum of methyl laurate by Jones may illustrate the process. (Fig. VII, 15 and Table VII, 2).

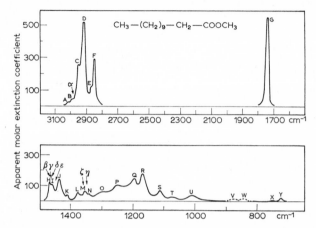

Fig. VII, 15. The infra-red spectrum of methyl laurate. Letters refer to the assignments of bands in Table VII, 2. *(Reproduced by courtesy of Dr. R. N. Jones and the Editor of the Canadian Journal of Chemistry).*

A very important application of infra-red spectra should at least be briefly mentioned, although it is in fact not directly connected with the characteristic features in the sense employed in the foregoing paragraphs. This is the identification of substances by comparison with the available spectra. For this purpose the entire spectrum has to be considered, as it is very characteristic of a compound. Many reference spectra are available in various collections. The most useful are collected on punched-cards[123, 124] and the number of individual spectra is of the order of 10,000 or more. There are also smaller but more specialized collections such as the A.P.I. cata-logue[125] containing mainly hydrocarbon spectra, or the collections of steroid spectra[126], narcotics[127], plastics and resins[128], etc. Many spectra are scattered through the literature, but the existing bibliographies[129, 130] are a great help if this kind of search has to be made. In systematic searching for a reference spectrum in a punched-card collection, the best procedure probably consists of dividing the spectrum into small intervals of say 200 cm^{-1} or less, noting the strong bands in particular intervals and searching the appropriately coded cards for the corresponding spectra. If this kind of work has to be done frequently, card handling machines may be used[131]. Alternatively, the class of the unknown compound may first be determined from characteristic bands and then the search made amongst the spectra of that class. This much more time-consuming procedure will be necessary if the reference spectrum is not available in a coded form.

Eventually, the spectrum of the unknown substance has to be compared

TABLE VII, 2

SUMMARY OF BAND ASSIGNMENTS FOR METHYL LAURATE

Points of inflection are designated by square brackets

Band	v_{max} (cm^{-1})	ε_{max}		Group	Mode
			Assignment		
A	[3020]	16		–COOCH$_3$	asym. (C–H) stretch (a')
B	2995	40		–COOCH$_3$	asym. (C–H) stretch (a'')
α	2955	—		–COOCH$_3$	sym. (C–H) stretch
C	2950	260		CH$_3$–	asym. (C–H) stretch
D	2922	520		–(CH$_2$)$_9$–	asym. (C–H) stretch
E	[2870]	120		CH$_3$–	sym. (C–H) stretch
F	2852	290		–(CH$_2$)$_9$–	sym. (C–H) stretch
G	1742	550		–COOCH$_3$	(C=O) stretch
H	1467	113 band β	–(CH$_2$)$_9$–	(C–H) scissor
		band γ	CH$_3$–	asym. (C–H) bend
I	1458	107 band δ	–COOCH$_3$	asym. (C–H) bend (a'')
ε	1440	—		–(CH$_2$)$_9$–	(C–H) scissor or wag
J	1436	135		–COOCH$_3$	sym. (C–H) bend
K	1419	36		α-CH$_2$–	(C–H) scissor
L	1378	51		CH$_3$–	sym. (C–H) bend
ζ	1368	—		–(CH$_2$)$_9$–	(C–H) wag or twist
M	1362	62		α-CH$_2$–	(C–H) wag
η	1352	—		–(CH$_2$)$_9$–	(C–H) wag or twist
N	[1340]	40		–(CH$_2$)$_9$–	(C–H) wag or twist
O	[1305]	50		–(CH$_2$)$_9$–	(C–H) twist (or wag?)
P	1245	97		–CH$_2$–COOCH$_3$	(C–O) skeletal coupled with (α-CH$_2$) deformation
Q	1196	137		–CH$_2$–COOCH$_3$	(C–O) skeletal coupled with (α-CH$_2$) deformation
R	1169	162		–CH$_2$–COOCH$_3$	(C–O) skeletal coupled with (α-CH$_2$) deformation
S	1112	64		–(CH$_2$)$_9$–	(C–C) skeletal coupled with end groups
T	1074	25		–(CH$_2$)$_9$–	(C–C) skeletal
U	1016	30		–CH$_2$–COOCH$_3$	(C–O) skeletal coupled with (α-CH$_2$) deformation
V	875	—		–COOCH$_3$	methyl rock?
W	845	—		–COOCH$_3$	methyl rock?
X	755	8		–(CH$_2$)$_9$–	(C–H) rock
Y	721	27		–(CH$_2$)$_9$–	(C–H) rock

with one of several spectra selected in the search. The weaker bands will now be of importance and one must not confuse the bands of possible impurities with bands which are structurally significant. The identification at this stage should not present difficulties, but some pitfalls may exist. With substances in the solid state, polymorphism may cause very considerable differences in the spectra[132]. On the other hand, different compounds may have very similar spectra; for example, hexa(α-chloro)- and hexa(α-bromo)-hexaethylbenzene[133]. The spectra of these two compounds are practically identical down to 700 cm⁻¹; below that frequency, marked differences appear.

Identification by infra-red spectra is by no means restricted to well-defined compounds, but may be applied to very complex materials of

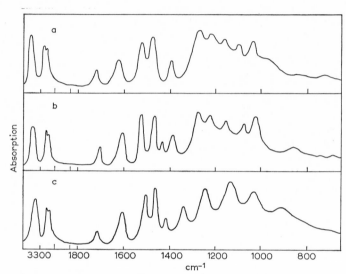

Fig. VII, 16. Infra-red spectra of lignin from (a) a lignite, (b) spruce wood, and (c) oak wood.

mineralogical or biological origin. For instance, it was possible to show that a lignite was of softwood origin by demonstrating the similarity between the spectrum of lignin isolated from this lignite and that from spruce, which is significantly different from the spectrum of hardwood lignin (Fig. VII, 16)[134].

REFERENCES

[1] M. V. VOLKENSTEIN, M. A. ELYASHEVITCH AND B. I. STEPANOV, *Kolebanya Molekul II*, Moscow, 1949, p. 360.

[2] M. V. VOLKENSTEIN, M. A. ELYASHEVITCH AND B. I. STEPANOV, *Kolebanya Molekul II*, Moscow, 1949, p. 364.

[3] W. T. KING AND B. CRAWFORD, *J. Mol. Spectry.*, 5 (1961) 421.

[4] J. O. HALFORD, *J. Chem. Phys.*, 24 (1956) 830.

[5] S. BRATOŽ AND S. BESNAINOU, *J. Chim. Phys.*, 56 (1959) 555.

[6] P. MIRONE AND P. CHIORBOLI, *Atti Accad. Nazl. Lincei, Mem. Classe Sci. Fis., Mat. Nat., Sez. IIa*, 8 (1961) 215.

[7] G. DIJKSTRA, *Thesis*, Amsterdam, 1957.

[8] O. BURKHARD, *Proc. Indian Acad. Sci. Sect. A*, 8 (1938) 365.

[9] M. FALK AND E. W. WHALLEY, *J. Chem. Phys.*, 34 (1961) 1554.

[10] G. C. PIMENTEL AND W. A. KLEMPERER, *J. Chem. Phys.*, 23 (1955) 376.

[11] G. HERZBERG, *Molecular Spectra and Molecular Structure II. Infrared and Raman Spectra of Polyatomic Molecules*, G. Van Nostrand, New York, 1945, p. 180.

[12] R. C. LORD AND F. A. MILLER, *Appl. Spectry.*, 10 (1956) 115.

[13] C. TANAKA, K. KURATANI, AND S. MIZUSHIMA, *Spectrochim. Acta*, 9 (1957) 265.

14 A. V. STUART AND G. B. B. M. SUTHERLAND, *J. Chem. Phys.*, 24 (1956) 559.
15 D. HADŽI AND M. PINTAR, *Spectrochim. Acta*, 12 (1958) 162.
16 R. BLINC AND D. HADŽI, *Spectrochim. Acta*, 15 (1959) 82.
17 D. HADŽI AND N. SHEPPARD, *Proc. Roy. Soc. (London), Ser. A.* 216 (1953) 247.
18 R. MECKE AND G. ROSSMY, *Z. Electrochem.*, 59 (1955) 866.
19 R. D. B. FRAZER AND W. C. PRICE, *Proc. Roy. Soc. (London), Ser. B*, 141 (1953) 66.
20 T. MIYAZAWA, T. SHIMANOUCHI AND S. MIZUSHIMA, *J. Chem. Phys.*, 29 (1958) 611.
21 D. M. SIMPSON AND G. B. B. M. SUTHERLAND, *Proc. Roy. Soc. (London) Ser. A*, 197 (1949) 169.
22 L. P. HAMMETT, *Physical Organic Chemistry*, McGraw-Hill Book Co., New York, 1940.
23 R. W. TAFT, in M. S. NEWMAN (Editor), *Steric Effects in Organic Chemistry*, John Wiley & Sons, New York, 1956, p. 556.
24 P. J. STONE AND H. W. THOMPSON, *Spectrochim. Acta*, 10 (1957) 17.
25 A. CABANA, J. L. PATENAUDE, C. SANDORFY AND P. M. G. BAVIN, *J. Phys. Chem.*, 64 (1960) 1941.
26 T. L. BROWN, *J. Phys. Chem.*, 61 (1957) 820.
27 M. ST. C. FLETT, *Spectrochim. Acta*, 10 (1957) 21.
28 M. ST. C. FLETT, *Trans. Faraday Soc.*, 44 (1948) 767.
29 R. A. RUSSELL AND H. W. THOMPSON, *Proc. Roy. Soc. (London), Ser. A*, 234 (1956) 318.
30 P. J. KRUEGER AND H. W. THOMPSON, *Proc. Roy. Soc. (London), Ser. A*, 243 (1957) 143.
31 S. CALIFANO AND R. MOCCIA, *Gazz. Chim. Ital.*, 86 (1956) 1014.
32 S. F. MASON, *J. Chem. Soc.*, (1958) 3619.
33 H. W. THOMPSON AND D. A. JAMESON, *Spectrochim. Acta*, 13 (1958) 236.
34 D. HADŽI AND J. JAN, unpublished.
35 J. JAN, D. HADŽI, AND G. MODENA, *Ric. Sci. Suppl.*, 30 (1960) 1065.
36 W. GORDY AND W. J. ORVILLE-THOMAS, *J. Chem. Phys.*, 24 (1956) 439.
37 A. L. SMITH AND N. C. ANGELOTTI, *Spectrochim. Acta*, 15 (1959) 412.
38 W. GORDY, *J. Chem. Phys,.* 14 (1946) 305.
39 H. W. THOMPSON, *Spectrochim. Acta*, 16 (1960) 238.
40 H. J. BERNSTEIN, *Spectrochim. Acta*, 18 (1962) 161.
41 L. J. BELLAMY AND R. L. WILLIAMS, *J. Chem. Soc.*, (1956) 2753.
42 J. M. LEBAS AND M. L. JOSIEN, *Bull. Soc. Chim. France*, (1956) 62.
43 E. D. SCHMIDT, *Z. Electrochem.*, 66 (1862) 53.
44 N. SHEPPARD, *Trans. Faraday Soc.*, 51 (1955) 1465.
45 J. K. WILMSHURST, *J. Chem. Soc.*, (1955) 2818.
46 L. J. BELLAMY, *J. Chem. Soc.*, (1955) 2818.
47 S. BRATOŽ, *Calcul des Fonctions d'Onde Moléculaires*, C. N. R. S., Paris, 1958, p. 287.
48 R. R. GATTY AND J. C. POLANYI, *Trans. Faraday Soc.*, 57 (1961) 2099.
49 A. D. WALSH, *Proc. Roy. Soc. (London), Ser. A*, 207 (1951) 13.
50 C. A. COULSON, *Valence*, Oxford University Press, 1952, p. 200.
51 C. A. COULSON, *Valence*, Oxford University Press, 1952, p. 207.
52 J. BENT, *J. Chem. Phys.*, 33 (1960) 1259.
53 E. M. ARNETT AND Ch. J. WU, *J. Am. Chem. Soc.*, 82 (1960) 4999.
54 C. P. SMYTH, *Dielectric Behaviour and Structure*, McGraw-Hill Book Co., New York, 1955.
55 R. WEST AND R. H. BANEY, *J. Phys. Chem.*, 64 (1960) 822.
56 R. E. KAGARISE, *J. Am. Chem. Soc.*, 77 (1955) 1371.
57 H. W. THOMPSON AND D. JAMESON, *Spectrochim. Acta*, 13 (1959) 236; R. N. JONES, W. F. FORBES, AND W. A. MUELLER, *Can. J. Chem.*, 35 (1957) 504.
58 N. FUSON, M. L. JOSIEN, AND E. M. SHELTON, *J. Am. Chem. Soc.*, 76 (1954) 2526.
59 H. W. THOMPSON, R. W. NEEDHAM AND D. JAMESON, *Spectrochim. Acta*, 9 (1957) 208.
60 W. H. T. DAVISON, *J. Chem. Soc.*, (1951) 2456.
61 B. PULLMAN AND A. PULLMAN, *Les Théories Electroniques de la Chimie Organique*, Masson et Cie., Paris, 1952, p. 588.
62 M. L. JOSIEN, N. FUSON, J. M. LEBAS AND T. M. GREGORY, *J. Chem. Phys.*, 21 (1953) 331.
63 J. TANAKA, S. NAGAKURA AND M. KOBAYASHI, *J. Chem. Phys.*, 24 (1956) 311.
44 S. BRATOŽ AND S. BESNAINOU, *J. Chem. Phys.*, 34 (1961) 1142.

[65] C. E. GRIFFIN, *Chem. Ind. (London)*, (1960) 1058.
[66] J. F. BROWN, *J. Am. Chem. Soc.*, 77 (1955) 6341.
[67] R. D. CROSS AND V. A. FASSEL, *J. Am. Chem. Soc.*, 78 (1956) 4225.
[68] H. W. THOMPSON AND M. R. MANDER, *Trans. Faraday Soc.*, 53 (1957) 1402.
[69] J. P. JESSON AND H. W. THOMPSON, *Spectrochim. Acta*, 13 (1958) 217.
[70] R. P. SMITH, *J. Phys. Chem.*, 60 (1956) 1293.
[71] E. M. LAYTON, R. D. KROSS, AND V. A. FASSEL, *J. Chem. Phys.*, 25 (1956) 138.
[72] J. D. S. GOULDEN, *Spectrochim. Acta*, 6 (1954) 129.
[73] M. L. JOSIEN, D. PELTIER AND A. PICHEVIN, *Compt. Rend.*, 250 (1960) 1643.
[74] D. COOK, *J. Am. Chem. Soc.*, 80 (1958) 49.
[75] L. J. BELLAMY AND R. L. WILLIAMS, *J. Chem. Soc.*, (1957) 4294.
[76] T. L. BROWN, *J. Phys. Chem.*, 64 (1960) 1798.
[77] C. N. R. RAO AND R. VENKATARAGHAVAN, *Can. J. Chem.*, 39 (1961) 1757.
[78] P. J. KRUEGER, in E. THORNTON AND H. W. THOMPSON (Editors), *Molecular Spectroscopy*, Pergamon Press, London, 1959, p. 181.
[79] T. L. BROWN, *J. Am. Chem. Soc.*, 80 (1958) 794.
[80] G. M. BARROW, *J. Chem. Phys.*, 21 (1953) 2008.
[81] T. L. BROWN AND M. T. ROGERS, *J. Am. Chem. Soc.*, 79 (1957) 577.
[82] S. CALIFANO AND R. MOCCIA, *Gazz. Chim. Ital.*, 87 (1957) 58.
[83] J. J. ELLIOT AND S. F. MASON, *J. Chem. Soc.*, (1959) 1275.
[84] E. D. SCHMIDT AND J. BELLANATO, *Z. Electrochem.*, 65 (1961) 362.
[85] S. A. FRANCIS, *J. Chem. Phys.*, 19 (1951) 942.
[86] M. ST. C. FLETT, *J. Phys. Radium*, 15 (1954) 388.
[87] C. A. COULSON, in E. THORNTON AND H. W. THOMPSON (Editors), *Molecular Spectroscopy*, Pergamon Press, London 1959, p. 183.
[88] C. A. COULSON, *Valence*, Oxford University Press, 1952, p. 147.
[89] W. J. ORVILLE-THOMAS, *Chem. Rev.*, 57 (1957) 1179.
[90] H. C. BROWN, D. H. McDANIEL AND O. HÄFLIGER, in E. A. BRAUDE AND F. C. NACHOD (Editors), *Determination of Organic Structures by Physical Methods*, Academic Press, New York, 1955, p. 567.
[91] D. HADŽI, I. PETROV AND M. ŽITKO, *Advances in Molecular Spectroscopy*, Pergamon Press, London, 1961, p. 794.
[92] T. L. BROWN, *Chem. Rev.*, 58 (1958) 581.
[93] J. WENOGRAD AND R. H. SPURR, *J. Am. Chem. Soc.*, 79 (1957) 5844.
[94] S. BESNAINOU, R. PRAT AND S. BRATOŽ, *Compt. Rend.*, 253 (1961) 2874.
[95] N. SHEPPARD, *Advan. Spectry.*, 1 (1959) 288.
[96] R. N. JONES, D. A. RAMSAY, F. HERLING AND K. DOBRINER, *J. Am. Chem. Soc.*, 74 (1952) 2828.
[97] R. N. JONES AND E. SPINNER, *Can. J. Chem.*, 36 (1958) 1020.
[98] H. GÖTZ, E. HEILBRONNER, A. R. KATRITZKY AND R. N. JONES, *Helv. Chim. Acta*, 44 (1961) 387.
[99] R. MECKE AND K. NOACK, *Chem. Ber.*, 93 (1960) 210.
[100] K. NOACK AND R. N. JONES, *Can. J. Chem.*, 39 (1961) 2225.
[101] E. J. COREY, M. G. HOWELL, A. BOSTON, R. C. YOUNG AND R. A. SNEER, *J. Am. Chem. Soc.*, 78 (1956) 5036.
[102] A. R. H. COLE, R. N. JONES AND K. DOBRINER, *J. Am. Chem. Soc.*, 74 (1952) 5571.
[103] D. H. R. BARTON, *J. Chem. Soc.*, (1956) 331.
[104] J. E. PAGE, *Chem. Ind. (London)*, (1958) 58.
[105] A. R. H. COLE, G. T. A. MÜLLER, D. W. THORNTON AND R. L. S. WILLIX, *J. Chem. Soc.*, (1959) 1218.
[106] A. R. H. COLE, P. R. JEFFERIES, AND G. T. A. MÜLLER, *J. Chem. Soc.*, (1959) 1222.
[107] J. S. COOK AND I. H. REECE, *Australian J. Chem.*, 14 (1961) 211.
[108] K. U. INGOLD, *Can. J. Chem.*, 38 (1960) 1092.
[109] D. KIVELSON, S. WINSTEIN, P. BUCK AND R. L. HANSEN, *J. Am. Chem. Soc.*, 83 (1961) 2938.
[110] M. DAVIES, *J. Chem. Phys.*, 8 (1940) 577; M. OKI AND H. IWAMURA, *Bull. Chem. Soc. Japan*, 32 (1959) 950.

[111] M. OKI, H. HOSOYA AND H. IWAMURA, *Bull. Chem. Soc. Japan*, 34 (1961) 1391.

[112] A. R. H. COLE AND G. T. A. MÜLLER, *J. Chem. Soc.*, (1959) 1224.

[113] L. J. BELLAMY, *The Infrared Spectra of Complex Molecules*, Methuen, London, 1958.

[114] R. N. JONES AND C. SANDORFY, in W. WEST (Editor), *Chemical Applications of Spectroscopy*, Interscience, New York, 1956, p. 247.

[115] A. D. CROSS, *An Introduction to Practical Infrared Spectroscopy*, Butterworths Sci. Publ., London, 1960.

[116] H. J. HEDIGER (Ed)., KIRBA-Kartei, Büllach, Switzerland, 1961.

[117] H. H. BOSSHARD, E. JENNY AND H. ZOLLINGER, *Helv. Chim. Acta*, 44 (1961) 1203.

[118] D. HADŽI AND N. SHEPPARD, *Trans. Faraday Soc.*, 50 (1954) 911.

[119] G. B. B. M. SUTHERLAND AND M. DAVIES, *J. Chem. Phys.*, 6 (1938) 755, 767; S. BRATOŽ, D. HADŽI AND N. SHEPPARD, *Spectrochim. Acta*, 8 (1956) 249.

[120] D. HADŽI, *J. Chem. Soc.*, (1956) 2143.

[121] R. N. JONES, *Can. J. Chem.*, 40 (1962) 301.

[122] R. N. JONES, *Trans. Roy. Soc. Can. Sect. III*, 52 (1958) 9.

[123] *Documentation of Molecular Spectroscopy*, Butterworths Sci. Publ., London.

[124] *Sadtler Catalogue*, Samuel P. Sadtler and Son, Philadelphia.

[125] *Infrared Spectral Data*, American Petroleum Institute, Pittsburgh.

[126] G. ROBERTS, B. S. GALLAGHER AND R. N. JONES, *Infrared Absorption Spectra of Steroids — an Atlas*, Interscience, New York, 1958.

[127] C. E. HUBLEY AND L. LEVI, *Bull. Narcotics, U.N. Dept. Social Affairs*, 7 (1955).

[128] D. HUMMEL, *Kunststoff- Lack- und Gummi Analyse*, Carl Hanser, München, 1958.

[129] H. M. HERSHENSON, *Infrared Absorption Spectra*, Academic Press, New York, 1959.

[130] *Bibliography of Published Information on Infrared Spectroscopy*, H. M. S. O., London, 1955, and later volumes.

[131] A. W. BAKER, N. WRIGHT AND A. OPLER, *Anal. Chem.*, 25 (1953) 1457.

[132] D. HADŽI AND L. PREMRU, *Boll. Sci. Fac. Chim. Ind. Bologna*, 18 (1960) 148.

[133] H. HOPFF AND A. K. WICK, *Helv. Chim. Acta*, 44 (1961) 19.

[134] D. HADŽI AND A. NOVAK, *Vestn. Sloven. Kem. Drustva*, 3 (1956) 113.

Chapter VIII

Infra-red Spectra of Solids: Dichroism and Polymers

S. KRIMM

Department of Physics, University of Michigan, Ann Arbor, Michigan

The vibrational spectrum of a molecule is determined by the potential energy associated with its particular configuration of nuclei (see Chapters IV and V). A molecule in the vapour phase will generally have vanishingly small interactions with other molecules. The potential energy can then be expressed entirely in terms of internal parameters, *viz.*, the displacement of interatomic distances from their equilibrium values. When, however, molecules interact with each other, as in a condensed phase, the potential energy of the nuclei depends not only on the internal force field in the molecule but also on the configuration of other molecules relative to the given one. Such extramolecular terms produce changes in the vibrational spectrum, and the interpretation of the infra-red spectra of solids requires

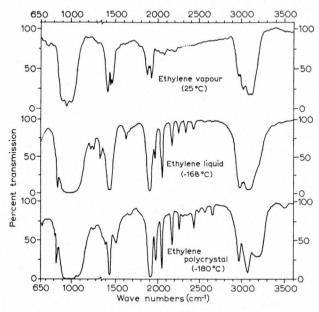

Fig. VIII, 1. Infra-red spectra of equivalent absorbing paths of ethylene in the vapour, liquid, and crystalline states.[1]

an understanding of the effects which such additional potential energy terms can produce. The added complexity in the spectrum resulting from such terms is more than balanced by the acquisition of a sensitive probe of the environment of a molecule in the liquid or solid state.

The general effects of condensation on a molecular spectrum can be illustrated[1] by Fig. VIII, 1. This shows the infra-red spectra of equivalent absorbing paths of ethylene in the vapour, liquid, and polycrystalline states. Several effects of the change in state may be noted: (i) More bands appear in the spectrum of the liquid than in that of the vapour. This is generally true. In this case there are also more bands in the spectrum of the crystal than in the spectrum of the liquid. This is not always the case, although the number of bands in the spectrum of the solid will generally exceed that in the spectrum of the vapour. (ii) Bands in the spectrum of the liquid and solid which are also present in the spectrum of the vapour are generally only slightly shifted in frequency, in the above case less than 1 per cent, and in general not more than about 2 per cent. (iii) Significant changes in band shapes occur, often accompanied by changes in intensities. Bands in the spectrum of the vapour show the typical PQR branch structure due to rotational energy transitions (see Chapter IV); under high resolving power the branches would consist of very many closely spaced narrow lines. The bands in the spectrum of the liquid are broad, and inherently so, for no increase in instrumental resolving power will sharpen them. On the other hand, the bands in the spectrum of the solid are very narrow, often narrower than the spectral slit width of the spectrometer, so that their true shapes are not even reproduced completely accurately. (iv) Although not evident in the spectra shown in Fig. VIII, 1, the solid state spectrum in general possesses new bands in the very low frequency region, from ~ 400 cm^{-1} down, not exhibited by the vapour.

The general origins of the above effects are well understood. The low frequency bands arise from hindered translations and rotations of the molecules in the lattice, and are therefore characteristic of the solid state. The change in band shapes when a molecule passes from the vapour to the liquid phase is also a consequence of the inability of the molecules to undergo unimpeded rotation. As a result, the quantized rotational energy levels in the free molecule disappear, and with them the associated rotational fine structure. Collisions and other interactions between molecules have a relatively much smaller effect on the vibrational energy levels, and therefore absorption bands of vibrational origin remain in the spectrum of the liquid. The breadth usually observed for such bands reflects in a general way the diffuse spectrum of perturbations to which on the average a molecule is subjected. Passing to the solid state, these intermolecular interactions become highly specific as a consequence of the long range order between molecules, and this results in a marked sharpening of absorption bands. The second effect noted above, namely that only a small shift in frequency of absorption bands accompanies condensation, is a consequence of the relatively minor influence which intermolecular interactions in either the liquid or solid states have on the internal force field of a molecule. In essence this indicates that the molecule retains its basic identity throughout the changes in phase. This means that the information about the molecule which was obtained from detailed studies in the vapour or liquid phase can be carried over into the study of the spectrum in the liquid or solid phase. Of course, the above comments assume that no significant structural change in the molecule accompanies the change of phase.

The first effect noted above, namely the appearance and disappearance of absorption bands concomitant with the phase change, requires special comment. It has been shown (see Chapter IV) that the ($3N$–6) internal vibrational modes of a molecule of N atoms do not all give rise in general to infra-red absorption. The vibration must be accompanied by an oscillating dipole moment, *i.e.*, a transition moment, in the molecule. Molecular symmetry ensures that some vibrational modes will not give dipole moment variations and therefore will be inactive in infra-red absorption. Selection rules govern the infra-red (and Raman) activity of the various modes. For example, if a molecule has a centre of symmetry the mutual exclusion rule will be obeyed, *viz.*, modes which are symmetric with respect to the centre will be Raman active and infra-red inactive, while modes which are antisymmetric will be Raman inactive and infra-red active. (See Chapter IV). One of the most important effects of a phase change can be to change the symmetry of the potential energy function, thereby altering the restrictions imposed by the selection rules. For a liquid, no selection rules are in general operative because, as a result of the essentially random intermolecular interactions, the potential field experienced by any one molecule has lost all characteristic symmetry. Thus, modes which were previously inactive in the infra-red absorption of the free molecule can become active in the liquid state, and so the liquid spectrum usually contains more bands than that of the vapour. A similar effect operates in the solid state, although in this case the reduction in symmetry is usually not as drastic as in the liquid. Other factors often operate, however, to increase the number of bands in the solid state spectrum. If the unit cell of the crystal contains more than one chemically equivalent molecule then interaction between these molecules can give rise to a splitting in the absorption band associated with a vibrational mode. Often combination and overtone bands can appear with significant intensity in the solid state spectrum. Establishing the detailed origin of such band changes can give information on the nature of interactions in the solid state.

Our aims in this chapter will be threefold. First, to discuss in a little more detail the characteristic alterations in the vibrational spectrum associated with a change in state. Second, to investigate one of the new experimental techniques which become possible in the study of solids, *viz.*, the interaction of oriented molecules with polarized infra-red radiation. From the dichroic characteristics of a particular absorption band we will see that it becomes possible to learn something about the orientation of the transition moment of the associated vibrational mode. Our third aim will be to illustrate the application of these concepts to the analysis of the spectra of solids. Examples will be chosen from the class of solids known as high polymers. Their spectra not only demonstrate the effects indicated above, but, in addition, indicate the possibilities and difficulties associated with the spectroscopic study of complex molecules, and in particular with sub-stances which we are essentially constrained to analyze in the solid state.

(1) Infra-red Spectra of Solids

(1A) Molecular crystals

The effects on the spectrum of a molecule when it is transferred, without change in structure, from the vapour to an infinitely large crystal are considered first. Subsequently departures from these conditions, *viz.*, the consequences of structural changes on condensation and the spectra of finite crystals, both of which are characteristic of polymers, will be dis-cussed. Only the main results of the theory are given; for more detailed dis-cussions the reader is referred to original references[2–5] and review articles[6].

Suppose that V^0 is the potential energy function of the free molecule. The associated force constants determine the vibrational frequencies of the molecule, and the symmetry of this function determines which modes will be infra-red or Raman active. Let such molecules now be condensed into an infinitely large crystal; this has an infinite number of vibrational modes comprising lattice as well as intramolecular vibrations. These crystal normal modes can be thought of as consisting of identical vibrational modes in each unit cell, the constant phase difference between the motions in adjacent cells, however, varying from one crystal mode to another. Only those vibrations of the crystal can be active in the infra-red or Raman spectrum in which the molecular motions in any unit cell are *in phase* with similar vibrational modes in all other unit cells. (The unit cell is the smallest volume of the crystal from which the entire crystal can be generated by translations alone.) Modes in which the phase difference between unit cell vibrations is other than zero give rise effectively to a vanishing transition moment when summed over the crystal. Therefore, in the discussion of fundamental frequencies we need be concerned only with the analysis of the vibrational modes of molecules within one unit cell of the crystal.

The potential energy associated with the unit cell can be written, in the harmonic approximation, as

$$V = \sum_j (V_j^0 + V_j') + \sum_j \sum_k V_{jk} + V_L + V_{Lj} \tag{1}$$

where the summations extend over all of the molecules in the unit cell. The various terms are:

V_j^0, the potential energy function of the free jth molecule.

V_j', the perturbation to V_j^0 due to the equilibrium field of the crystal at the site of the jth molecule.

V_{jk} represents terms involving displacement coordinates in the jth and kth molecules, that is, it encompasses interactions between vibrations in different molecules.

V_L contains terms which involve the relative displacement and rotational orientation of molecules with respect to each other, and thus represents the lattice potential.

V_{Lj} denotes those terms involving interaction between lattice coordinates and the internal coordinates of the jth molecule.

The V_{Lj} term is generally very small (about 0.1 cm^{-1} in 3000 cm^{-1}), and we will neglect it in the subsequent discussion. The lattice frequencies, associated with the coordinates in the V_L term, are usually small in comparison with the internal frequencies of the molecule, less than 100 cm^{-1} compared to say about 1000 cm^{-1}. If equation (1) contained only the V_L and V_j^0 terms it would be possible to separate the vibrational problem, by means of a Born–Oppenheimer type of approximation, into the vibrations of the free molecules and the vibrations of the lattice. The former have already been treated (see Chapters IV and V), and the lattice vibrations are in principle readily determinable[7]. (It might be noted that the above approximation is probably no longer satisfactorily valid when we are dealing with internal molecular modes of low frequency, say of the order of 100–200 cm^{-1}). In this approximation, therefore, the vibrational spectrum of the molecule in the crystal is the same as that of the free molecule. The changes in the spectrum which appear on condensation obviously must result from the perturbation terms in equation (1), and we must now consider their effect.

If the V_j' term is included, the separability of the molecular and lattice vibrations is still retained. The effect of this term on the spectrum can be twofold. First, the alteration of the potential field of the molecule can cause shifts in the fundamental frequencies. Second, the alteration in the symmetry of the potential field can cause changes in the selection rules. Let us consider these factors in turn. In the case of ethylene (Fig. VIII, 1), the vapour exhibits a band at 949 cm^{-1}, originating from a (CH$_2$) wagging mode. In the crystal this band has shifted to 970 cm^{-1}. A (C–H) stretching mode occurs at 3105 cm^{-1} in the vapour and at 3075 cm^{-1} in the crystal. Comparable shifts are observed for other bands. Such shifts are due to the first of the above factors, the so-called static field effect. The potential field of a molecule at its site in a crystal, and due in part to the equilibrium arrangement of its neighbours, is not the same as the field of a free molecule. The environment has caused slight changes in force constants and this is reflected in small frequency shifts in the absorption bands. Detailed normal vibration analyses of molecules in crystals should thus permit us to build up a knowledge of the effect of crystalline forces upon the electronic structure of molecules.

Consider now the spectrum of cyclopropane in the vapour and crystalline phases[8]. The A_1' symmetry species (CH_2) deformation mode at 1454 cm^{-1} is permitted in the Raman spectrum of the free molecule but is forbidden in the infra-red spectrum by the selection rules. Yet in the infra-red spectrum of the crystal this band is present. The $E'(CH_2)$ deformation mode is infra-red active in the free molecule, and is found in its spectrum at 1442 cm^{-1}. This is a degenerate mode in the free molecule, but in the spectrum of the crystal it is split into two components, at 1424 and 1434 cm^{-1}, which arise in part from the removal of this degeneracy by the lower symmetry of the molecular site in the crystal. This splitting arises from the second factor mentioned above, and is referred to as site group or static field splitting. Both of the above effects in cyclopropane are attributable to the altered symmetry of the potential function of the molecule, with an attendant change in selection rules. The free cyclopropane molecule has D_{3h} symmetry, which means that it possesses the following symmetry elements (see Chapter IV): a 3-fold rotation axis, a mirror plane perpendicular to this axis, three 2-fold rotation axes perpendicular to the 3-fold axis, three reflection planes containing the 3-fold axis, and the identity operation. In the crystal the evidence suggests that the cyclopropane molecule possesses a site symmetry of C_s, that is, its only symmetry elements are one reflection plane (containing the previous 3-fold axis) and the identity operation. This lowered symmetry has resulted from the manner in which the molecules have packed together to form the crystal. As we see, it has permitted activity in previously inactive modes and allowed a splitting of degenerate modes of the free molecule.

While an analysis of the crystal spectrum based on the site group symmetry in the crystal is certainly more correct than one based on the symmetry of the free molecule, it is nevertheless deficient in some important respects because of the neglect of the V_{jk} term in equation (1). This term has now to be considered. Its inclusion in the potential energy function implies the coupling of vibrations in different molecules. Since the coupling term is usually quite small, its effect on the frequencies can be obtained from a perturbation calculation. The result is that, if the unit cell contains N molecules, the N-fold degeneracy present without the V_{jk} term can be removed, so that in general a molecular mode of a single molecule will give rise to N crystal modes.

To appreciate this point more fully, consider a hypothetical crystal containing two molecules per unit cell, related to each other by a 2-fold screw axis (see Fig. VIII, 2), — i.e., a rotation of 180° followed by a translation of half the identity distance. The normal modes of such a vibrating system will be those shown in Fig. VIII, 2(a) and 2(b): in (a) the vibrations

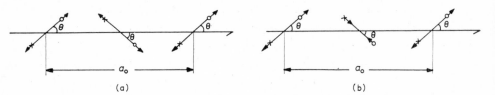

Fig. VIII, 2. Hypothetical linear crystal with two diatomic molecules per unit cell related to each other by a twofold screw axis. (a) symmetric, (b) antisymmetric, stretching vibration.

are symmetric with respect to the screw axis, while in (b) they are anti-symmetric with respect to this axis. If $V_{jk} = 0$, the frequencies of these two modes will be the same: the stretching vibration of the molecules in such a crystal is therefore doubly degenerate. When $V_{jk} \neq 0$, the frequencies of these two modes will be different, i.e., the degeneracy will have been removed. The magnitude of the splitting will be a function of the magnitude of V_{jk}. The action of the V_{jk} term is therefore to introduce the possibility of additional splitting in bands, up to N components per non-degenerate mode of the molecule. This splitting is called the factor group or correlation field splitting. The mean value of these components, in this approximation, will be the frequency which results from the static field effect alone. As we shall see, it is experimentally possible to distinguish between static field and correlation field splitting, even though the experimentally observed splittings of each type are of the same order of magnitude. The inclusion of the V_{jk} term thus implies an analysis based on the symmetry of the entire unit cell rather than just the symmetry of a molecular site.

It should be pointed out that the molecular symmetry, the site symmetry, and the unit cell, or factor group, symmetry are significantly related to each other, and this has important consequences with respect to the selection rules predicted from each. The essential symmetry relationship is that the site group must be a subgroup both of the molecular point group and of the crystal factor group. This condition often permits the use of crystal spectra in obtaining detailed information on the structure of the crystal[8], since, if the molecular symmetry of the free molecule is known (as it usually is), the site symmetry can often be inferred from the site selection rules seen to be operative in the crystal, and the unit cell group will then be restricted by the condition that it must have the site group as a subgroup. This symmetry restriction also leads to some general relationships between site group and factor group selection rules. Thus: (i) a molecular mode cannot be active in the crystal if it is forbidden by the site symmetry; (ii) if a mode is active according to the site group symmetry it will give rise to at least one active component under the factor group selection rules; and (iii) a vibration which is degenerate under the site group retains this degeneracy when analyzed according to the factor group. It should of course be remembered that because activity is permitted to a vibration this does not imply anything about the intensity of the corresponding band. In general, those modes which possess large intrinsic transition moments in the free molecule will appear with comparable intensity in the crystal spectrum. Those modes which are inactive in the free molecule are likely to appear weakly in the crystal spectrum, since their activity results from dipole moments induced in the molecule by the equilibrium symmetry of the crystal. Often, however, such inactive modes appear with moderate intensity in the crystal spectrum, so this should not be taken as a rigorous statement.

The previous discussion has been based on a harmonic potential function, that is, one containing only quadratic terms. Experimental evidence on the number and breadth of bands in the spectra of crystals indicates that this assumption, which predicts the appearance of a limited number of sharp fundamental frequencies, is inadequate. We therefore conclude that the potential function must contain anharmonic terms. The effect of these, as in the case of the free molecule, is to introduce the possibility of combination and overtone frequencies appearing in the spectrum. Several characteristics of such combinations and overtones in the spectra of crystals are of importance. In the first place, it can be shown[4, 6] that combination frequencies involving non-unit cell fundamentals can be active in the infra-red spectrum, whereas we have seen that the fundamentals themselves are never active. The requirement for this to occur is that the sum of the phase differences for the combining non-factor group fundamentals shall be zero. Such combinations seem not to be commonly observed; rather, most combination bands can be interpreted satisfactorily on the basis of the site or factor group fundamentals. The existence of the above type of combination band may nevertheless be partially responsible for the relatively broad bands which are often observed in crystal spectra.

If we consider only the combinations allowed by the factor group analysis, the most important spectral difference in comparison with the free molecule is that which results from combinations between internal molecular vibrations and lattice modes. Because many of the latter are found at low frequencies, the result of such combinations can be to broaden the appearance of the fundamental absorption and possibly to shift its peak position slightly. In some cases, these combination bands will be well resolved, and in such instances their identification is aided by studying the effect of temperature on the spectrum: the difference bands are expected, as usual, to decrease in intensity as the temperature is lowered. Another effect of combination with lattice modes is the apparent appearance of a forbidden fundamental. This could occur if combinations between the fundamental and lattice modes were allowed, in which case a band would appear in the spectrum in the vicinity of the fundamental frequency. The operation of these factors in general results in the appearance of more overtone and combination bands in the spectrum of the crystal than in that of the free molecule.

The experimental study of the infra-red spectra of solids differs in certain important respects from the study of gases, and it is worthwhile indicating the nature of these differences. Perhaps the most important new phenomenon in solids is the presence of oriented molecules and their resulting specific interaction with polarized radiation. This characteristic, namely dichroism, will be treated in detail in Section 2. A problem which often arises in obtaining spectra of solids is the preparation of suitably thin samples. With solids such as polymers the thickness of a film can be controlled by varying the concentration of the solutions from which the film is made. Or, if the film is made by pressing a powdered sample, the thickness can be controlled by varying the weight of material used. In cases of very intractable materials, thin sections can be obtained by microtoming. For molecular crystals the problem may be more severe. Such crystals are most commonly obtained by growing from solution or by condensation from the vapour phase. While crystals of $50-100\mu$ thickness are relatively easy to prepare in this manner, thicknesses in the range of $5-10\mu$ (which may be needed for examining very intense bands) are more difficult to obtain. In addition, it is often not feasible to obtain more than one crystal orientation by these techniques. As a result, reflection spectra and their interpretation are being increasingly studied (see Chapters II and VII). It has been shown in several ways[9-11] that the reflection spectrum as a function of frequency can be converted mathematically into an absorption spectrum. The obvious advantages of such a technique are that it is possible to use thick samples and to examine specifically cut crystal orientations. It has even been possible[12] to make absolute intensity measurements on bands by use of this reflection technique. It has been demonstrated recently[13] that the measurement of a spectrum under conditions where total internal reflection occurs produces a result which closely resembles an ordinary transmission spectrum.

This method is likely to become widely used in future spectral studies of solids.

An important experimental technique involves the study of solid solutions in which the molecule under examination is in dilute solid solution with an isotopic species. The effect, assuming that the crystal structure is unchanged, is to uncouple the motions of neighbouring molecules, thus eliminating the interaction which gives rise to correlation field splitting[14, 15]. This technique thus makes it possible to identify correlation field splitting and to distinguish it from static field splitting.

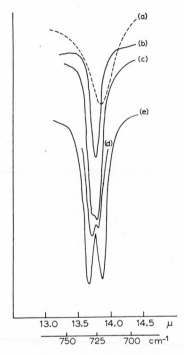

Fig. VIII, 3. Infra-red spectra of solid solutions of n-$C_{64}H_{130}$ in n-$C_{100}D_{202}$. Weight ratio for (b) 1:20, (c) 1:3, (d) 1:1, (e) 1:0. Curve (a) is for the melt[16].

As an illustration, consider the doublet at 720 and 731 cm^{-1} found in the spectrum of n-paraffins and polyethylene[16] (Fig. VIII, 3). Various considerations suggest that these two components arise from coupled (CH_2) rocking vibrations in the two molecules in the unit cell (Fig. VIII, 4). By isolating normal molecules in a lattice of deuterated paraffin molecules we expect no change in the lattice parameters nor in the crystal forces between molecules. Since the frequency of the (CD_2) rocking mode, however, differs greatly from that of the (CH_2) rocking mode, any interaction between neighbouring molecules of differing isotopic composition should be very small. Therefore, if the splitting does arise from intermolecular interactions we would expect it to disappear as the dilution increases. As seen from Fig. VIII, 3, this is the case, and it therefore substantiates the correlation field origin of the observed splitting. The single band remaining in the dilute

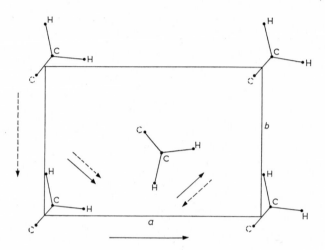

Fig. VIII, 4. Cross-section of the unit cell of polyethylene, showing the two chains per unit cell and the net transition moments for the in-phase and out-of-phase (CH_2) rocking modes.

solution, *viz.*, at 725 cm^{-1}, must represent the frequency as determined by the static field of the crystal. It is interesting to note that it is close to the mean value of the components, as expected, and also that it differs significantly from the frequency in the melt, *viz.*, 720 cm^{-1}. This 5 cm^{-1} shift measures essentially the static field effect. It is also pertinent to observe that the splitting depends on the dilution ratio. This can be understood on the basis of interaction not only between pairs but between larger clusters of molecules. It has been shown[17] that, if molecules are related to each other by a zig-zag chain structure, the splitting of the 1:1 mixture should be one-half that of the pure crystal. This is the case here, *viz.*, 6 cm^{-1} splitting for 1:1, and reflects the known zig-zag structure formed by neighbouring chains in the crystals of *n*-paraffins (Fig. VIII, 4).

The study of interactions between small groups of molecules can also be fruitfully pursued by the matrix isolation technique[18]. In this method the molecule of interest is isolated in a dilute solid solution with an inert molecule, such as the rare gases or nitrogen. In this way it has been possible to infer the presence, and possible structure, of dimers, trimers and higher multimers of interacting molecules[19, 20]. Again we see that the study of the spectra of solids can provide a key to unlocking the details of intermolecular interactions in condensed phases.

(1B) High polymers

A high polymer molecule in the context used here is a molecule which is built up of a linear chain of identical units covalently bonded to each other. The simplest example is polyethylene, which can be designated chemically as $(CH_2)_n$, where n may be 10,000. The chemically repeating unit can of course be more complicated than a (CH_2) group. Such molecules are capable of crystallizing in the solid state, and we would expect that most aspects of their spectra would be understandable in terms of the principles already discussed. This is in fact the case, yet in several respects polymer spectra differ significantly from those of simple molecular crystals. This arises from the possibility of the simultaneous presence in a specimen of both crystalline and non-crystalline components. This feature is important in understanding the spectra of such complex solids.

The crystallization of a single high polymer molecule in the solid state forms a one-dimensional crystal, i.e., the linear chain possesses translational symmetry. Such chains pack together to form a three-dimensional crystal. The vibrations of such infinite linear chains can be treated in the manner indicated in the previous section, and it has been shown [21-23] that similar results are obtained. Thus, only those modes can exhibit infra-red or Raman activity in which motions within each repeat unit along the chain are in phase with each other; and if this repeat unit contains more than one chemical group (for example, there are two (CH_2) groups in the repeat unit along the polyethylene chain, it being a planar zig-zag structure) then interaction between their identical modes is to be expected, with a consequent splitting of the fundamental frequency. An analysis based on the single chain approach is often quite useful, since the three-dimensional crystal structure may contain only one chain per unit cell or, if more than one, interactions between chains may be very small. When there is more than one chain per unit cell, however, the analysis should always start out with the more complete structure since interchain interaction effects may be important. Such is the case, for instance, for polyethylene.

The spectra of high polymers nevertheless contain features beyond those predicted from an analysis of linear or three-dimensional crystals, and for an understanding of these we must recognize the contribution to the spectrum of non-crystalline portions of polymer chains. For many reasons (imperfect order along the chain, entanglements between the long chains, rapid cooling which inhibits complete crystallization) a solid polymer specimen is never one hundred per cent crystalline and is often far less. A detailed picture of the solid state structure and morphology of high polymers is only now becoming available, but we know that there appear to be portions of molecules which are not incorporated in regions of relatively long range three-dimensional periodicity. There are several implications with respect to the spectral contributions of such segments of molecules.

First, we may expect in general a complete absence of selection rules governing the spectrum of the non-crystalline portions of chains. This results from the amorphous or liquid-like environment of such regions, with its consequent absence of symmetry. It is therefore possible that frequencies of the repeat unit which are inactive in the crystalline structure could be active when this unit is part of a non-crystalline region.

Second, such non-crystalline regions can contain rotationally isomeric forms of the chain. Since these represent essentially new structures, entirely new frequencies can be introduced into the spectrum. In this respect polymers differ from the molecular crystals considered in Section 1A, since in that case no change in internal structure of the molecule was considered to be associated with a change of phase. In molecules which contain carbon–carbon single bonds, however, we know[24, 25] that with respect to rotation about this bond there are three spectroscopically stable

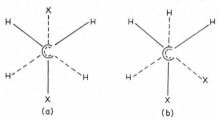

Fig. VIII, 5. Rotational isomers of XCH_2-CH_2X. (a) *trans*, (b) *gauche*.

orientations. Thus, for molecules of the form XCH_2-CH_2X, where X is a single atom or a continuation of a linear chain, so-called *trans* and *gauche* isomeric structures are possible (see Fig. VIII, 5). These are spectroscopically different structures, and should give rise to different fundamental frequencies. There is much evidence to substantiate this for small molecules[24, 25], and, as we shall see, for polymers as well. In the latter case we often deal with structures of the form $(-CH_2-CHY-)_n$, and this allows three different isomeric structures to exist. The spectrum of a polymer can thus be complicated by the presence of frequencies which arise from structures other than that in the crystal phase. These structures are not always completely distinguishable at first sight because their frequencies may be close together, but careful analysis has usually permitted their identification.

The third effect which departure from perfect crystallization can produce is the activation of non-factor group modes. We have seen that these are inactive for infinite chains or crystals. However, if finite portions of linear chains are present, such modes can be active[23]. This arises from the requirement that the finite chain encompass an integral number of half wavelengths of the phase variation between modes in adjacent units. When this number is odd, the entire chain can exhibit a net oscillating dipole moment. Such modes are of course weaker than the one in which the phase difference is zero. They may be present, however, and could in part be responsible for the broad absorption bands found in the spectra of polymers.

A factor which can strongly influence the spectra of solids, as also liquids and sometimes gases, deserves brief mention here, namely hydrogen bonding. The origin of such bonding is considered in more detail in Chapter XII and in other references[26, 27]. Its spectroscopic significance lies in its effects upon the molecular frequencies. First, hydrogen bonding lowers the (X–H) stretching frequency and raises the (X–H) deformation frequency — the changes in ν(X–H) can be 100 cm^{-1} or more. Second, hydrogen bonding gives rise to increased band widths for the above modes, even in the solid state. Third, the stretching of the hydrogen bond itself, $i.e.$, (H ... Y), contributes low frequencies to the spectrum. These are not as yet well characterized, but they appear in the 50–250 cm^{-1} region. Fourth, and in many cases of great importance, the hydrogen bond can permit coupling between similar vibrational modes in different molecules or in different parts of the same molecule. This can lead to additional shifts and splittings in the observed frequencies. As will be seen in Section 3D, this phenomenon plays an important rôle in explaining the spectra of proteins and in permitting the identification of several of the possible polypeptide chain conformations.

(2) Dichroism

As was mentioned in Section 1A, one of the important new experimental phenomena that arise in the investigation of the spectra of solids is the interaction of crystals and other oriented solids with polarized infra-red radiation. From the dichroism observed for a band, $viz.$, the difference in absorption for two different characteristic orientations of the electric vector, significant information can often be obtained about transition moment directions and factor group symmetries. Let us first discuss briefly the means of obtaining polarized infra-red radiation.

(2A) Production and use of polarized radiation

Polarized infra-red radiation is most conveniently produced by a transmission polarizer. The simplest such type is shown in Fig. VIII, 6. It consists of a number of sheets of a dielectric material, transparent in the region of interest and set so that the incident beam strikes the surface at Brewster's angle, $i.e.$, at $\tan^{-1} n$, where n is the refractive index of the dielectric. Under these conditions the reflected beam contains only the component with

electric vector perpendicular to the plane of incidence. Thus, the transmitted beam will be enriched in the component with electric vector parallel
to the plane of incidence. If the intensities of these two components in the

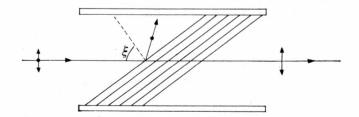

Fig. VIII, 6. Transmission polarizer. ξ = Brewster's angle = $\tan^{-1}n\,(\cong 60°)$.

emerging beam are indicated by I_σ and I_π respectively, then the degree of
polarization P for a polarizer of m sheets is given theoretically by[28]

$$P = \frac{I_\pi - I_\sigma}{I_\pi + I_\sigma} = \frac{1 - \left(\dfrac{2n^2}{n^4+1}\right)^m}{1 + \left(\dfrac{2n^2}{n^4+1}\right)^m} \qquad (2)$$

This formula is derived on the reasonable assumption that multiple reflections do not occur in the sheets. Polarizers for the near infra-red have
been made using selenium[28, 29] $(n \cong 2.5)$ and silver chloride[30] $(n \cong 2.1)$
sheets, and for the far infra-red with polyethylene[31] $(n \cong 1.5?)$ sheets. The
predicted values of P from equation (2), for $m = 6$ (a typical value), are
99.8 %, 98.7 %, and 71.5 % respectively for the materials above. A twelve
sheet polyethylene polarizer would have a value of P of 94.5 %. Polarizers
such as those illustrated in Fig. VIII, 6 will cause some displacement of the
beam by refraction, which can be serious if the sheets are thick. Several
designs have been suggested[32, 33] to eliminate this difficulty. In all cases the
plane of the electric vector is varied by rotating the polarizer about the light
beam as axis.

The spectrometer itself will have a polarizing effect on the radiation
passing through it. This is a consequence of the many reflections from the
prism faces in a prism spectrometer and of the polarization concomitant
with diffraction from a grating in a grating spectrometer[33]. The usual
method of taking this factor into account is to record background curves for
the two polarizer settings, which are usually with the electric vector parallel
and perpendicular to the spectrometer slit, and to refer the corresponding
sample absorptions to these curves. It is also possible to eliminate the effect
of the instrument polarization by setting the two planes of polarization,
which are usually 90° apart, such that each makes an angle of 45° with the

spectrometer slit. In this way, assuming that the polarizer precedes the mono-chromator, the spectrometer transmits the same relative intensity for each polarizer setting. The limiting factor on true intensity measurements for each setting will then be the degree of polarization obtainable with the polarizer[34].

The orientation of the sample with respect to the plane of polarization is also an important factor in dichroism measurements. Since all oriented solids which exhibit dichroism would also be expected to be birefringent, a plane polarized beam of light would in general not maintain its plane of polarization in traversing the material. An anisotropic solid, even if non-absorbing, is characterized by a refractive index ellipsoid, oriented charac-teristically with respect to the structure, whose axial lengths are a measure of the refractive indices for light propagating with electric vector parallel to the corresponding axial directions. Consider a section of such an ellipsoid which contains two of the principal axes, and imagine that linearly polarized light is propagating in a direction normal to this section. If the electric vector is parallel to either principal axis, then the radiation traverses the specimen *without* change in the orientation of its plane of polarization and emerges as linearly polarized light. On the other hand, if the electric vector makes an angle other than zero with a principal axis, the vector will be resolved inside the crystal into components along each axis, these will travel through the crystal at different velocities, and the resulting phase difference will give rise to elliptical polarization in the emerging beam. To avoid complications associated with this situation, measurements are always made with the electric vector parallel to a principal axis of the specimen. For substances of higher than monoclinic symmetry (where only one axis is defined) the principal axes are fixed by symmetry along crystallographic axes, and so can be located by visible light measurements (since they will be independent of the frequency of the radiation). A satisfactory measuring arrangement, assuming the monochromator to be immediately before the detector, is therefore to set a principal axis of the specimen at 45° to the spectrometer slit and to orient the electric vector in turn parallel and perpendicular to this direction by rotation of the polarizer.

(2B) Origin of dichroism

The potential energy of interaction of an electric dipole with an external electric field is proportional to $\boldsymbol{\mu} \cdot \boldsymbol{E}$, where $\boldsymbol{\mu}$ is the dipole moment and $\boldsymbol{E}$ is the electric field strength. The effect of such a perturbation term in the Hamiltonian is to permit, in an electromagnetic field, induced transitions between the ground state and the first excited state for a normal vibration of the molecule. The energy absorbed by the molecule is found (see Chapter X) to be proportional to $[(\partial\boldsymbol{\mu}/\partial Q) \cdot \boldsymbol{E}]^2$, where $\partial\boldsymbol{\mu}/\partial Q$ is the change in dipole moment with respect to the normal coordinate Q, and is thus proportional to the transition moment for this vibration. The important feature of this relationship in the present context is the scalar product: radiation with electric vector parallel to the transition moment can be absorbed, radiation with electric vector perpendicular to the transition moment will not be absorbed. In a crystal such moments are uniquely oriented in space so that the possibility exists of specific interaction with polarized radiation.

The anisotropic absorption of such an oriented transition moment is characterized by the dichroic ratio of the absorption band, defined as

$$R_0 = \frac{\int_0^\infty \varepsilon_\pi(\nu)\mathrm{d}\nu}{\int_0^\infty \varepsilon_\sigma(\nu)\mathrm{d}\nu} \tag{3}$$

where $\varepsilon_\pi(\nu)$ and $\varepsilon_\sigma(\nu)$ are extinction coefficients for plane polarized radiation incident normal to the transition moment and with the electric vector oriented respectively parallel and perpendicular to this direction. The extinction coefficient $\varepsilon(\nu)$ at a frequency ν is defined by Beer's law

$$I(\nu) = I_0(\nu) \exp\left[-\varepsilon(\nu)l\right] \tag{4}$$

where I_0 and I are the incident and transmitted intensities respectively and l is the specimen thickness. If the absorption band can be represented by a Lorentz type equation, viz.,

$$\varepsilon(\nu) = \frac{a^2}{(\nu - \nu_0)^2 + b^2} \tag{5}$$

where ν_0 is the frequency at maximum absorption and a and b are constants, then substitution of (5) into (4) gives

$$R_0 = \frac{\varepsilon_\pi(\nu_0)}{\varepsilon_\sigma(\nu_0)} \tag{6}$$

The experimentally determined dichroic ratio is

$$R = \frac{D_\pi(\nu_0)}{D_\sigma(\nu_0)} \tag{7}$$

where D is the measured optical density, viz., $\log_{10}(I_0/I)$. Various factors can cause R to be different from R_0. Besides the difficulty of measuring D if there are overlapping bands, perhaps the most important problem is associated with the imperfect polarization of the polarizer. This can, under certain circumstances, give rise to errors of the order of a factor of two[34]. Another source of error lies in the fact that the beam is usually convergent rather than parallel when it passes through the sample. This can lead to major errors when the transition moment is parallel to the incident beam direction[35]. The other factors will in general operate to make R less than R_0, but should not change its qualitative characteristic, viz., whether absorption is greater with the electric vector parallel or perpendicular to the unique axis of the specimen.

   The above discussion has dealt with a single oriented molecule. It is
necessary now to consider the effects of aggregation upon dichroic behaviour.
In the simplest approximation, corresponding to the influence of only the
static field, the specimen is considered as an oriented gas of molecules[36, 37].
That is, interactions between similar molecules in the unit cell are neglected,
and the observed dichroic ratio is interpreted as a sum of contributions from
independent fixed molecular transition moments. This is a very useful approximation since interactions between molecules (and often between
identical units of a single long chain molecule) are often weak enough to be
neglected. However, for detailed study this approximation is inadequate.
We must then include the factor group symmetry and take account of
correlation field effects. Neglect of the former could result in the prediction
of inactivity for modes which become active under the factor group symmetry. Neglect of the latter can lead to a complete misconception as to the
dichroic nature of the spectrum. Consider the crystal illustrated in Fig. VIII, 2.
On the basis of the oriented gas model we would predict one band in the
spectrum associated with the stretching mode, of dichroic ratio (referred to
the two-fold screw axis) $R_0 = \cos^2\theta / \sin^2\theta = \cot^2\theta$. On the other hand,
cognizance of the correlation field splitting leads to the prediction of two
bands, that associated with mode (a) being completely polarized along the
screw axis and that associated with mode (b) being completely polarized
perpendicular to the screw axis. Clearly the oriented gas model can be used
only after it has been established that effects due to the crystalline field are
negligible. Illustrations of these two cases will be considered later.
   It must be kept clearly in mind that what we measure by means of dichroism is related to the transition moment direction. This may or may not
be simply related to a bond direction in the molecule. For simple separable
group frequencies, such as (NH) and (CH$_2$) stretching for example, it may
be reasonable to correlate the transition moment with the bond direction or
the symmetry axis of the group. However, with more complicated normal
modes this is often not possible. Thus what appears to be a simple separable
bond stretching vibration, the (C=O) stretching mode of the peptide group,
has been shown experimentally[38] and theoretically[39] to have a transition
moment making an angle of about 20° with the axis of the (C=O) bond.
Clearly caution must be exercised in making structural deductions from
measured dichroic ratios. The directions and amplitudes of the atomic
motions in a normal mode must be known before the dichroism of the band
is used to prescribe the exact orientation of a molecule or a group therein.

(2C) Uses of dichroism

The polarization of band components with respect to the axes of a
crystal can provide important information on the crystal symmetry and on

the correctness of the structure assumed in the analysis. We will consider two examples in this connection. In the previously mentioned study of cyclopropane[8] the following interesting situation was observed. A band, absent in the spectrum of the gas, appears in the spectrum of the liquid at 741 cm^{-1}; in the spectrum of the crystal it is observed as a triplet, with components at 742, 747, and 756 cm^{-1}. The appearance of absorption at about 750 cm^{-1} in the crystal spectrum but not in that of the gas is evidence that the site symmetry is different from that of the free molecule. The appearance of the triplet is evidence of a correlation field splitting, and this is corroborated by the observation that each component is polarized entirely along only one of three mutually perpendicular characteristic axes of the crystal established by visible light examination. The latter point is of major importance, since it permitted the deduction that the cyclopropane crystal, whose structure was as yet unknown, must belong to the ortho-rhombic system. This knowledge delimits the factor group symmetry which is possible, and with the molecular symmetry of the free molecule known, and the condition that the site group must be a subgroup of the molecular group as well as of the factor group, it became possible to specify the site group and in fact to infer a reasonable space group. Thus, the polarization properties of the bands assisted in a determination of the crystal structure.

As another example, consider the polyethylene crystal (see Fig. VIII, 4). We noted earlier that the 720, 731 cm^{-1} doublet in the spectrum was thought to be due to interacting (CH$_2$) rocking modes on neighbouring molecules, and that this was substantiated by the spectra of isotopic solid solutions. Examining the nature of the interacting rocking modes shows

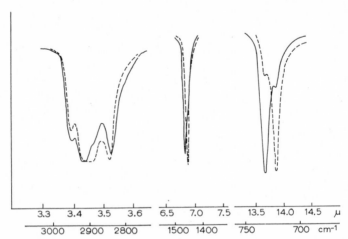

Fig. VIII, 7. Infra-red spectrum of a single crystal of monoclinic n-C$_{36}$H$_{74}$. ——— radiation with electric vector polarized along a-axis, - - - - - radiation with electric vector polarized along b-axis[16].

that we should expect each of the components of this doublet to be polarized along only one of the two axes perpendicular to the chain axis. A study
of the polarized spectrum of a single crystal of an *n*-paraffin with radiation
propagating along the chain axis in fact shows[16] that the 720 cm^{-1} component absorbs only with the electric vector polarized along the *b*-axis of the
crystal, whereas the 731 cm^{-1} component absorbs only when the electric
vector is polarized along the *a*-axis (see Fig. VIII, 7). The dichroic results
thus confirm our predictions, thereby giving us confidence in the assumptions which were originally made.

Studies of dichrosm are also of prime importance in the analysis of the
spectra of high polymers. In order to study the dichroic properties of a
polymer specimen it is necessary that the long chain molecules be suitably
oriented in space, since in the typical semi-crystalline polymer the crystalline
regions are oriented at random. In synthetic polymers this is usually
achieved by applying a simple mechanical strain to the unoriented sample.
The result is that crystallites become oriented with respect to this stretching
direction, usually with the long chain axis of the molecule more or less
parallel to this direction. In natural polymers, *e.g.* cellulose and the fibrous
proteins, there is usually a macroscopically definable fibre axis and again the
molecules have their chain axes aligned essentially parallel to this direction.
In both cases, however, the overall alignment of chains is not perfect,
certainly not nearly as regular as the alignment of molecules in a single
crystal. This means that we usually must deal with a distribution of orientations of individual crystalline regions, probably interspersed among a
partially oriented non-crystalline matrix. In the above cases of what are
called uniaxial orientation, that is, alignment with respect to an axis but
random orientation azimuthally about this axis, we are justified in treating
the polymer as an oriented gas of crystallites, and all calculations of dichroism thus far have been based on this assumption. Implicit also is the belief
that the regions determining the dichroism are small compared to the wavelength of the radiation, so that it is justifiable to sum the contributions of all
crystallites first before considering their interaction with the radiation.
(Otherwise we would have a situation where the electric vector is not
parallel to the principal axes of the crystallites, with the complications
arising from the resolution into components considered in Section 2A). It is
particularly necessary therefore to keep this orientation distribution in
mind in evaluating quantitative deductions of structure from dichroic ratio
measurements on high polymers.

The qualitative dichroisms of bands in high polymer spectra are of great
importance. They identify the symmetry species with which a normal mode
is associated, and in many cases they are useful in determining aspects of the
molecular structure. Thus, the symmetry analysis of the spectrum of

polyethylene predicts two infra-red active modes, (CH_2) wagging and (CH_2) twisting, which should exhibit polarization along the long chain axis. The detection of two such parallel bands in crystalline polyethylene would therefore serve to identify the two possible frequencies involved. Infra-red dichroism was of structural importance in distinguishing between two different polypeptide chain conformations in fibrous proteins, the folded and the extended forms, and provided a guide to the determination of the detailed structures of these molecules[40]. Many other applications of this aspect of infra-red dichroism have been used in the study of the spectra of high polymers[41].

Efforts have also been made to exploit the quantitative aspects of dichroism. These have fallen into two categories: the prediction of the dichroism associated with a given orientation distribution of transition moments, and the attempt to use the observed dichroic data to obtain direct information on the structure. The first approach is dictated by the fact that from the dichroic ratio of a single band it is not possible to infer uniquely the nature of the distribution of transition moments. Recourse must then be had to postulating reasonable models for this distribution function, calculating the dichroic ratio in terms of the parameters of the

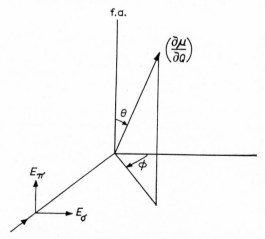

Fig. VIII, 8. Uniaxially oriented transition moments, $\partial\mu/\partial Q$, at an angle θ to the fibre axis (f.a.).

distribution, and characterizing oriented polymers in terms of these parameters.

As a simple illustration, consider the case of a uniaxially oriented set of transition moments as defined above, all making an angle θ with the fibre axis (see Fig. VIII, 8). The extinction coefficient for parallel radiation is given by

$$\varepsilon_\pi(\nu_0) \propto \int_0^{2\pi} \left(\frac{\partial \mu}{\partial Q}\right)^2 \cos^2 \theta \, \frac{m}{2\pi} \, d\phi \tag{8}$$

where m is the total number of transition moments; the extinction coefficient for perpendicular radiation is given by

$$\varepsilon_\sigma(\nu_0) \propto \int_0^{2\pi} \left(\frac{\partial \mu}{\partial Q}\right)^2 \sin^2 \theta \cos^2 \phi \, \frac{m}{2\pi} \, d\phi \tag{9}$$

The dichroic ratio is then

$$R_0 = \frac{\varepsilon_\pi(\nu_0)}{\varepsilon_\sigma(\nu_0)} = 2 \cot^2 \theta \tag{10}$$

(It is interesting to note that equation (10) also gives the dichroic ratio for a normal vibration of a unit in an infinitely long helix, where the transition moment in the unit makes an angle θ with the helix axis and the units can be considered as weakly coupled[42]). If the molecular chain axes make an angle θ with the fibre axis, the transition moments being distributed uniformly at an angle α to the chain axis, then it can be shown[43] that

$$R_0 = \frac{2 \cot^2 \alpha \cos^2 \theta + \sin^2 \theta}{\cot^2 \alpha \sin^2 \theta + (1 + \cos^2 \theta)/2} \tag{11}$$

Similarly, more complex distribution functions can be assumed and their dichroic properties evaluated[44]. There is, however, little to be gained from this approach since it depends upon the assumption of a specific orientation distribution, which cannot be verified from the dichroic data alone.

An alternative approach has been to specify the conditions under which it becomes possible to make exact structural statements from observed dichroic data (assuming, of course, that errors due to imperfect polarization of the radiation have been eliminated[34]). It has been shown[45] that under certain conditions, which are always satisfied in a uniaxially oriented polymer, it is permissible to consider the specimen as made up of a fraction f of chains aligned with their axes perfectly parallel to the macroscopic fibre axis and a fraction $(1-f)$ of chains which are completely randomly oriented. If now it is possible to identify three bands in the spectrum associated with three independent transition moment directions of the repeat unit, then determinations of the dichroic ratios of these bands permit the elimination of the parameter f and the evaluation of the two angles which specify the orientation of the repeat unit with respect to the chain axis. It also becomes possible to test the correctness of proposed chain structures by application of this method.

Another illustration of this general approach is concerned with instances in which it becomes possible to identify mutually perpendicular transition moments associated with the normal vibrations of a chemical group, as for example the symmetric stretching, antisymmetric stretching, and wagging modes of the (CH_2) group. For three such modes only certain combinations of dichroism are permitted to the three absorption bands[46], *viz.*, $\pi\pi\sigma$, $\sigma\sigma\pi$, $\pi\sigma u$, and *uuu* (where *u* signifies that a band is unpolarized, *i.e.*, shows no dichroism). If two of the bands are easily identified, as for example the two (CH_2) stretching modes, then the dichroism of the third band can be specified, and this could be of assistance in identifying it in a complex spectrum. In another instance[47], if two perpendicular transition moments are identifiable it is possible to determine their orientation under certain circumstances without making any assumptions as to the chain orientation distribution or the fraction of disordered material. The quantitative study of dichroism in the infra-red spectra of high polymers is therefore capable, in certain cases, of yielding specific structural parameters.

(3) Infra-red Spectra of High Polymers

In this section the methods used to analyze the spectra of high polymers will be discussed and examples given of their application. For a more detailed treatment a review article[41] should be consulted.

(3A) Methods of analysis of high polymer spectra

Since the use of infra-red spectroscopy in the study of various properties of polymers must ultimately hinge on the depth of analysis of the spectrum, the importance of such analyses is obvious. The methods of analysis are basically the same as those used for the study of smaller molecules, but because of the complexity of high polymers, only recently have such techniques been applied in depth. Here we shall indicate briefly the methods which lead to detailed spectral assignments.

The theoretical methods of analysis are concerned with the prediction of the spectrum on the basis of the structure and force field of the molecule. Two such methods are of importance: symmetry analysis and normal coordinate analysis. The first seeks to provide general statements concerning the nature of the spectrum on the basis of the symmetry of the molecular structure. This includes derivation of the selection rules and possible inference of the symmetry modes of vibration. The second attempts to calculate, on the basis of the structure and an assumed potential energy function, the normal frequencies and normal modes of vibration of the molecule.

To illustrate the symmetry analysis, consider a single infinitely long planar zig-zag polyethylene chain. Its structure is defined by a set of symmetry elements (see Fig. VIII, 9). These are: C_2 — a two-fold rotation axis, C_2^s — a two-fold screw axis, i — a centre of inversion, σ — a mirror plane, and σ_g — a glide plane. In addition there are the identity operation, E, and the infinite number of translations by multiples of the unit cell repeat distance. All of these leave the configuration of the molecule unchanged. This set of symmetry elements, in which the translations are

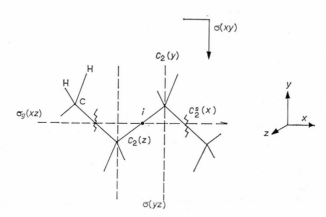

Fig. VIII, 9. Structure and symmetry elements of single, infinitely long, planar zig-zag, polyethylene chain[16].

considered as equivalent to the identity operation, form the factor, or unit cell, group. They constitute a group in the mathematical sense, and when we examine their multiplication table, *i.e.*, the set of all pairs of products of symmetry operations, we find that it is isomorphic with the point group D_{2h}. In other words, a one-to-one correspondence can be made between the symmetry elements of the two groups such that their multiplication tables are the same.

For each of the point groups, character tables have been worked out[48]. That for D_{2h} is given in the upper left-hand portion of Table VIII, 1. The character table designates the symmetry species (denoted by A_g, B_{1g}, etc.) into which the vibrations divide. Each symmetry species consists of characters, $+1$ or -1 in the present case, which describe the behaviour of the normal mode with respect to the various symmetry operations, *viz.*, whether it is symmetric or antisymmetric respectively. From such a character table it is possible to determine the number of normal modes of various types which are to be found in each species and their activity in the infra-red and Raman spectrum. We will only quote here the formulae relevant to such calculations[48, 49]. The total number of normal modes under a symmetry species i is given by

$$n_i = \frac{1}{N} \sum_R U_R(\pm 1 + 2 \cos \phi_R)\chi_i(R) \qquad (12)$$

where N is the order of the group (the number of symmetry elements it contains); U_R is the number of atoms that remain invariant under the operation R; the plus or minus sign is to be used according as R is a pure rotation through ϕ or a rotation through ϕ followed by a reflection in a plane perpendicular to the axis; $\chi_i(R)$ is the character of the symmetry element in the ith species; and the summation extends over all of the symmetry elements. The number of pure translations under a symmetry species is given by

$$n_i(T) = \frac{1}{N} \sum_R (\pm 1 + 2 \cos \phi_R) \chi_i(R) \tag{13}$$

The difference between n_i and $n_i(T)$ represents the number of internal vibrational modes, except for the one rotation about the chain axis. These can in turn be subdivided into internal modes within chemical groups (*e.g.*, the (CH_2) group in the present case) and translatory and rotatory types of oscillations between groups. The numbers of the latter modes can be determined from the following equations

$$n_i(T') = \frac{1}{N} \sum_R [U_R(s) - 1](\pm 1 + 2 \cos \phi_R) \chi_i(R) \tag{14}$$

and

$$n_i(R') = \frac{1}{N} \sum_R [U_R(s - v)](1 \pm 2 \cos \phi_R) \chi_i(R) \tag{15}$$

In these equations $U_R(s)$ is the number of chemical groups which remain invariant under the symmetry operation R, v represents the number of chemical groups which consist of a single atom only, and $U_R(s-v)$ is the number of chemical groups other than single atoms which are invariant to the symmetry operation R. The difference between n_i and $n_i(T) + n_i(T') + n_i(R')$ is n_i', the number of modes internal to the chemical group. These various quantities have been calculated and are shown in Table VIII, 1.

It might be remarked that this information, *viz.*, the numbers of normal modes in each symmetry species, their symmetry character, and their vibrational types, permits us to infer the general nature of the modes. Such inferences provide what we may call symmetry modes; the true normal modes may be combinations of symmetry modes within a given species. Nevertheless, these symmetry modes do provide some insight into the vibrations of the molecule and are often quite close to the true normal modes. Such a set of symmetry modes for the polyethylene chain is shown in Fig. VIII, 10.

The selection rules for infra-red and Raman activity are obtained as follows. Modes under a given species can be infra-red active only if the quantity

$$n_i(\mu) = \frac{1}{N} \sum_R (\pm 1 + 2 \cos \phi_R) \chi_i(R) \tag{16}$$

TABLE VIII, 1

CHARACTER TABLE AND SELECTION RULES FOR POLYETHYLENE CHAIN

D_{2h}	E	$C_2(z)$	$C_2(y)$	$C_2^s(x)$	i	$\sigma(xy)$	$\sigma_g(xz)$	$\sigma(yz)$	n_i	T	T'	R'	n_i'	IR	R
A_g	1	1	1	1	1	1	1	1	3	0	1	0	2	f	P
B_{1g}	1	1	−1	−1	1	1	−1	−1	2	0	1	1	0	f	D
B_{2g}	1	−1	1	−1	1	−1	1	−1	1	0	0	1	0	f	D
B_{3g}	1	−1	−1	1	1	−1	−1	1	3	0	R_x	1	1	f	D
A_u	1	1	1	1	−1	−1	−1	−1	1	0	0	1	0	f	f
B_{1u}	1	1	−1	−1	−1	−1	1	1	3	T_z	0	1	1	a	f
B_{2u}	1	−1	1	−1	−1	1	−1	1	3	T_y	0	0	2	a	f
B_{3u}	1	−1	−1	1	−1	1	1	−1	2	T_x	0	1	0	a	f

	E	$C_2(z)$	$C_2(y)$	$C_2^s(x)$	i	$\sigma(xy)$	$\sigma_g(xz)$	$\sigma(yz)$
U_R	6	0	2	0	0	2	0	6
ϕ	0°	180°	180°	180°	180°	0°	0°	0°
$\pm 1 + 2\cos\phi$	3	−1	−1	−1	−3	1	1	1
$U_R(\pm 1 + 2\cos\phi)$	18	0	−2	0	0	2	0	6
$U_R(s)$	2	0	2	0	0	2	0	2
$(U_R(s)-1)(\pm 1 + 2\cos\phi)$	3	1	−1	1	3	1	−1	1
$U_R(s-v)$	2	0	2	0	0	2	0	2
$(U_R(s-v))(1 \pm 2\cos\phi)$	6	0	−2	0	0	−2	0	−2
$2\cos\phi(\pm 1 + 2\cos\phi)$	6	2	2	2	6	2	2	2

f = forbidden, a = active, P = polarized, D = depolarized.

is different from zero. This is the same as equation (13), and indicates that the polarization properties of the modes will be the same as the translation direction associated with that particular species. Modes under a given

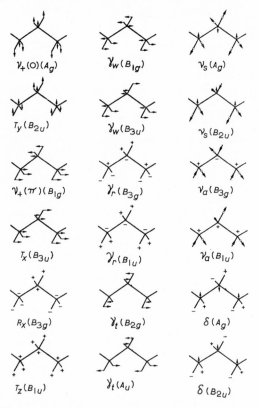

$\nu_+(0)(A_g)$ $\gamma_w(B_{1g})$ $\nu_s(A_g)$

$T_y(B_{2u})$ $\gamma_w(B_{3u})$ $\nu_s(B_{2u})$

$\nu_+(\pi)(B_{1g})$ $\gamma_r(B_{3g})$ $\nu_a(B_{3g})$

$T_x(B_{3u})$ $\gamma_r(B_{1u})$ $\nu_a(B_{1u})$

$R_x(B_{3g})$ $\gamma_t(B_{2g})$ $\delta(A_g)$

$T_z(B_{1u})$ $\gamma_t(A_u)$ $\delta(B_{2u})$

Fig. VIII, 10. Symmetry modes of a single polyethylene chain[16].

species can be Raman active if the following quantity, associated with the polarizability α, is different from zero.

$$n_i(\alpha) = \frac{1}{N} \sum_R 2 \cos \phi_R(\pm 1 + 2 \cos \phi_R) \chi_i(R) \tag{17}$$

The results of applying these equations are shown in Table VIII, 1. We see therefore that a symmetry analysis provides an important starting point in establishing the general characteristics of the spectrum to be expected from a given structure. If its predictions can be verified, we gain a measure of confidence in the assumed structure. Often the number of possible structures is small and the spectral predictions quite different for each, so that it may be possible to choose the correct structure on the basis of a spectroscopic analysis.

The other theoretical method, namely a normal coordinate analysis, seeks to go further than the general approach given above. It attempts to determine, from an assumed potential energy function for the molecule, the frequencies and forms of the normal vibrations. If the predictions as to frequencies can be substantiated, then the assumed potential function gains credence. The general methods used in such calculations have already been considered (see Chapter V). Their application to high polymers, however, has lagged behind their use in the study of small molecules, primarily because of the greater complexity of the larger molecular systems. With the advent of computers, however, more efforts are being made to extend normal coordinate calculations to polymers, and the initial successes[50, 51] indicate that this will be a fruitful field. The normal vibrations of poly-ethylene have been studied extensively[41], primarily because of the relative simplicity of its structure. Even in this case, however, a completely satis-factory calculation is only now emerging[52], and it still leaves one question somewhat unsettled — the correct assignment of the skeletal stretching frequencies. The difficulty resides in our, as yet, incomplete knowledge of force fields in molecules, especially large ones, and emphasizes the necessity of securing experimental evidence for assignments of bands in the spectrum.

We turn now to the experimental aspects of the analysis of high polymer spectra. Of these, one of the most important, and as yet least investigated, is the low frequency region of the spectrum. Until recently infra-red spectro-scopic studies were almost entirely limited to the region above about 400 cm^{-1}. Yet preliminary studies[41] indicate that polymers exhibit sig-nificant absorptions at frequencies below 400 cm^{-1}. These are primarily deformation modes, but torsion and lattice frequencies are also expected to occur in this region. The importance of studying this region is not only to assign such fundamental frequencies but also to be able thereby to identify with greater confidence some of the weaker bands in the fun-damental region as combinations and overtones. Raman spectra could of course supply some of these low frequency bands, as well as important fundamentals in those cases where selection rules prohibit their appearance in the infra-red spectrum. Unfortunately, experimental difficulties have limited the satisfactory Raman study of polymers. With the advent of improved instrumentation for studies in the far infra-red (see Chapter III), however, data will soon be provided in this low frequency region.

Another experimental technique of great importance is the study of oriented samples with polarized radiation. This has been discussed in Section 2, and it only needs to be noted here that extension of such methods into the far infra-red region is of prime importance.

In a complex spectrum it is necessary to be able to correlate bands with particular normal modes. One of the most important techniques for doing this is isotopic substitution. Because of the prevalence of hydrogen in high polymers, its substitution by deuterium is of great value in identifying hydrogen modes. Deuterium is readily available and its specific insertion in a molecule can usually be accomplished without very great difficulty. In a general way, the substitution of a heavier isotope does not change the forces between atoms, so that modes which involve the motion of the substituted atom will have their frequencies decreased by the mass effect alone. In the case of hydrogen–deuterium substitution the maximum decrease would be by $\sqrt{2}$. If the molecule can be selectively deuterated, then it is often possible to identify different kinds of hydrogen modes (*e.g.*, (OH)*vs.*(CH), (CH$_2$)*vs.*(CH$_3$), aromatic *vs.* aliphatic), and in this way to simplify the process of analyzing a spectrum. Very often normal modes are mixed vibrations, *i.e.*, they involve contributions from more than one type of vibration of a chemical group. Selective deuteration can usually reveal the contribution made by component group vibrations to such mixed modes[41].

The utility of isotopic substitution is enhanced by quantitative treatment, that is, by predicting the frequency shift to be associated with a given mass change. An exact rule for doing this is the Teller–Redlich product rule, and of course normal coordinate calculations enable such frequency shifts to be determined (see Chapters IV and V). The difficulty with the product rule is that it is a relationship involving the product of all modes in a given symmetry species. If a polymer molecule has low symmetry, and therefore few species each containing many modes, this rule is not of much help. Similarly, normal coordinate calculations are not available for many polymers. In this situation an approximate isotopic frequency rule[53] has been found to be helpful. On the assumption that a chemical group (*e.g.*, (CH$_2$)) can be considered to have separable vibrations, the frequency

TABLE VIII, 2

FREQUENCY SHIFT RATIOS FOR ISOTOPIC SUBSTITUTIONS

CH_2—CD_2		CH_3—CD_3	
Mode*	ν/ν^i	Mode	ν/ν^i
ν_s	1.379	ν_s	1.398
ν_a	1.349	ν_a	1.349
δ	1.349	δ_s	1.300
γ_w	1.323	δ_a	1.384
γ_t	1.414	γ_r	1.292
γ_r	1.379		

* ν = stretching, δ = bending, γ_w = wagging, γ_t = twisting, γ_r = rocking, s = symmetric, a = antisymmetric

shifts for individual modes can be computed. These are shown in Table VIII, 2 for (CH$_2$) and (CH$_3$) modes. The rule is useful in providing relative frequency shift ratios for different vibrations, and in indicating by the deviation from these ratios departures of modes from the separability criterion.

One important procedure in high polymer studies is the comparison of a variety of specimens and related compounds. In order to identify those bands associated with the crystalline structure upon which the analysis is based, specimens of varying crystallinity must be prepared, either chemically or physically, and the variation of band intensities studied. Another useful method is the study of low molecular weight analogues of the polymer, since these can usually be obtained as single crystals. The n-paraffins represent such analogues of polyethylene, and a great deal of important information relative to the analysis of the polyethylene spectrum has been obtained by studying these compounds[16, 52, 54, 55]. Sometimes the physical properties of the specimen can be made use of in the spectroscopic study. Thus, as a polymer specimen is stretched it often happens that the crystalline regions orient in such a way that one crystal axis first becomes preferentially oriented along the stretching direction and then perpendicular to it[55]. By following dichroism changes with elongation it then becomes possible to correlate bands with symmetry species in a more detailed manner. Finally, it may be necessary to study the spectra of small molecules which contain groups present in the polymer molecule in order to help interpret spectral complexities in the latter. This was very important in the study of the spectrum of polyvinyl chloride.

The concerted application of the techniques discussed in this section has made it possible to untangle the details of the spectra of many high polymers[41].

(3B) Polyethylene

The infra-red spectrum of a not too highly crystalline polyethylene is shown in Fig. VIII, 11. Spectra of more highly crystalline samples have also been obtained[57]. The symmetry analysis of a single polyethylene chain was con-

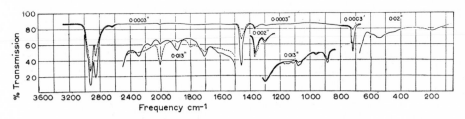

Fig. VIII, 11. Infra-red spectrum of polyethylene, $(CH_2)_n$[16].

sidered in the previous section. In extending this analysis to the two chain unit cell structure (Fig. VIII, 4), whose symmetry is isomorphic to point group $\boldsymbol{D}_{2h}$, the following additional predictions result[16]: infra-red active σ modes of the single chain should be split into two components, one polarized along the a-axis and the other along the b-axis of the crystal; π modes should not be split; a $\gamma_t(CH_2)$ mode, inactive in the single chain, should be infra-red active in the crystal, of π polarization; two lattice modes should be infra-red active.

By comparison with the spectra of small molecules, the major features in polyethylene are understandable: bands in the 2900 cm^{-1} region are associated with (CH_2) stretching modes, bands near 1450 cm^{-1} are due to (CH_2) deformation modes, and the bands near 725 cm^{-1} are correlated with (CH_2) rocking vibrations. The splittings in some bands were thought to be due to interaction between chains, and we have seen from earlier discussions that this appears to be substantiated by the experimental evidence. More recent investigations have revolved about several specific assignment problems which were not easily resolved at first: the identification of the crystalline bands in the spectrum, the assignment of the $\gamma_w(CH_2)$ and $\gamma_t(CH_2)$ modes of the crystal, a detailed explanation of the correlation field splitting, and a satisfactory normal coordinate calculation.

The study of n-paraffins as well as the availability of very highly crystalline polyethylene has helped to distinguish between the crystalline and non-crystalline bands in the spectrum[41, 57, 58]. The detailed analysis of the latter is still uncertain, but the identification of the former has permitted a more secure assignment to be made of the $\gamma_w(CH_2)$ and $\gamma_t(CH_2)$ modes[41, 58]. This new analysis is in better agreement with the assignment of combinations and overtones[41], with data on a series of n-paraffins[54], and with calculations of normal frequencies[52]. (Calculations are now in substantial agreement with all of these assignments except for one point: whereas the two skeletal chain stretching modes are assigned to Raman bands at 1061 and 1131 cm^{-1}, there is disagreement[41, 52] as to which of the two modes ($\nu_+(0)$ and $\nu_+(\pi)$ of Fig. VIII, 10) is associated with which band). These assignments[41] are shown in Table VIII, 3. It will be noted that whereas the correlation field splitting is observed in the infra-red spectrum it has not been seen in the Raman spectrum. It seems likely[41] that this is a result of a relatively smaller polarizability change in one of the modes as compared to the other, with a consequent weaker intensity expected for the corresponding Raman line. A detailed study has been made[54] of the correlation field splitting, and the magnitude appears to be satisfactorily accounted for by short range repulsive forces between closest hydrogen atoms of (CH_2) groups on neighbouring chains. Thus, it has been possible to achieve a detailed and essentially complete understanding of the spectrum of crystalline polyethylene. This is not yet true of the non-crystalline component.

The spectrum of polyethylene provides a good example of the types of interactions which are encountered in the spectra of solids, and particularly high polymers. The correlation field splitting, due to interactions between

TABLE VIII, 3

ASSIGNMENTS OF FUNDAMENTAL FREQUENCIES OF CRYSTALLINE POLYETHYLENE

| Mode | Symmetry species | Frequency* | |
		Infra-red	Raman
$\nu_a(CH_2)$	B_{1u}	2924	f
	B_{2u}	2899	f
	A_g	f	2883
	B_{3g}	f	?
$\nu_s(CH_2)$	B_{1u}	2850	f
	B_{2u}	2857	f
	A_g	f	2848
	B_{3g}	f	?
$\delta(CH_2)$	B_{1u}	1473	f
	B_{2u}	1463	f
	A_g	f	1440
	B_{3g}	f	?
$\gamma_w(CH_2)$	B_{3u}	1176	f
	A_u	f	f
	B_{1g}	f	?
	B_{2g}	f	1415
$\gamma_t(CH_2)$	B_{3u}	1050	f
	A_u	f	f
	B_{1g}	f	?
	B_{2g}	f	1295
$\gamma_r(CH_2)$	B_{1u}	731	f
	B_{2u}	720	f
	A_g	f	1168
	B_{3g}	f	?
$\nu_+(0)$	A_g	f	1061
	B_{3g}	f	?
$\nu_+(\pi)$	B_{1g}	f	?
	B_{2g}	f	1131

* f = forbidden

chains, has already been considered. It is of the order of 10 cm^{-1} throughout the spectrum. The interaction which occurs within the chain between the (CH$_2$) groups of the zig-zag repeat is, expectedly, much larger. It is also more variable in magnitude, ranging from about 5–30 cm^{-1} for the internal modes (ν_a, ν_s, δ) to about 240–440 cm^{-1} for the external modes (γ_w, γ_t, γ_r). The skeletal stretching modes interact less strongly: the splitting between symmetric and antisymmetric vibrations is 70 cm^{-1}. This type of inter-action splitting is to be looked for generally in the spectra of high polymers, and can serve as an indication of structural characteristics of the chain.

(3C) Polyvinyl chloride

The spectrum of polyvinyl chloride (PVC), (CH$_2$.CHCl)$_n$, has also been the subject of much study[41]. The spectrum demonstrates several interesting features: it provides evidence on the chain structure which could not be determined with certainty from X-ray diffraction studies; it indicates the presence of relatively long range intramolecular interactions; and it has permitted the determination of the non-crystalline structures which are present in the polymer specimen.

Early X-ray diffraction studies of oriented PVC showed that it had a fibre axis identity period of about 5.1 Å. Since the polyethylene repeat distance is about half of this, it was inferred that the repeat unit of PVC contained two monomer units. The Cl atoms were presumed to be oriented alternately on either side of the planar zig-zag carbon chain (Fig. VIII, 12),

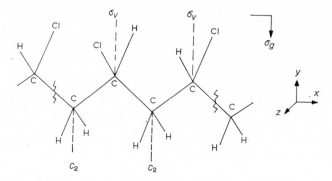

Fig. VIII, 12. Structure and symmetry elements of a single, infinitely long, syndiotactic polyvinyl chloride chain.

to form what we presently call a syndiotactic chain structure. This structure has been the basis of the spectral analysis[41], and it appears to account quite satisfactorily for the observations. Because of certain particular characteristics of the spectrum, it is possible to have confidence in the relative correctness of the assumed structure. Here is an instance, therefore, in which the infra-red spectrum has provided important evidence, complementary to that of X-ray diffraction, in establishing a polymer chain structure.

The results of the symmetry analysis of a single syndiotactic PVC chain (which is a satisfactory restriction at present) are shown in Table VIII, 4. Polarized infra-red spectra of PVC have been obtained for various degrees of specimen crystallinity and on various deuterated species[59]. Spectra of the less crystalline PVC and its deuterated analogues are shown in Fig. VIII, 13. The band positions, polarizations, phase of origin, and assignments are shown in Table VIII, 5. The σ bands marked with an asterisk show the interesting property, referred to earlier, of changing their dichroism with elongation[56]. They must therefore belong to the same symmetry species, which is different from that for bands which retain σ character during elongation. A pre-

TABLE VIII, 4

SYMMETRY SPECIES, NUMBER OF NORMAL MODES, SELECTION RULES, AND MODE CHARACTERISTICS FOR SYNDIOTACTIC POLYVINYL CHLORIDE

C_{2v}	E	C_2	σ_v	σ_g	n_i	IR	R	Mode characterization
A_1	1	1	1	1	10	σ	a	ν(CH), δ(CH), ν_s(CH$_2$), δ(CH$_2$), γ_t(CH$_2$), ν(CCl), δ(CCl), $\nu_+(0)$, $\nu(\pi/2)$, T_y
A_2	1	1	-1	-1	7	f	a	γ_w(CH), ν_s(CH$_2$), δ(CH$_2$), γ_t(CH$_2$), γ_w(CCl), $\nu_+(\pi/2)$, $\nu_-(\pi/2)$
B_1	1	-1	1	-1	11	σ	a	ν(CH), δ(CH), ν_a(CH$_2$), γ_w(CH$_2$), γ_r(CH$_2$), ν(CCl), δ(CCl), $\nu_+(\pi/2)$, $\nu_-(\pi/2)$, T_z, R_x
B_2	1	-1	-1	1	8	π	a	γ_w(CH), ν_a(CH$_2$), γ_w(CH$_2$), γ_r(CH$_2$), γ_w(CCl), $\nu_+(\pi)$, $\nu(\pi/2)$, T_x

σ = perpendicular, π = parallel, f = forbidden, a = active.
ν = stretching, δ = bending, γ_w = wagging, γ_t = twisting, γ_r = rocking, s = symmetric, a = antisymmetric.

liminary normal coordinate analysis has been carried out[51], and confirms most of the assignments suggested in Table VIII, 5.

If the PVC structure is syndiotactic, as assumed, then we can see from Table VIII, 4 that two ν(C–Cl) modes are predicted. If the interaction

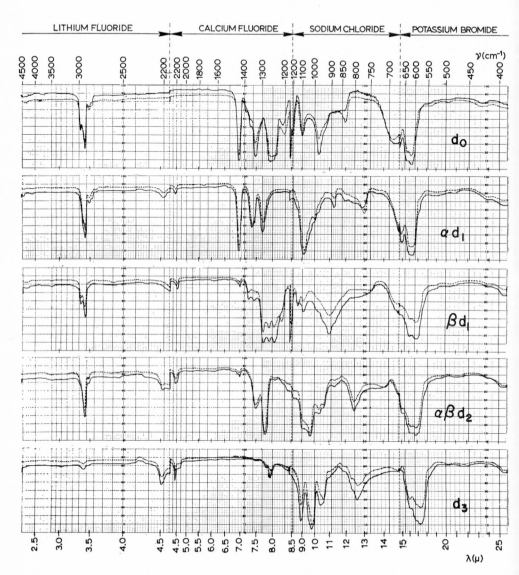

Fig. VIII, 13. Infra-red spectra of PVC and its deuterated analogues: d_0, ordinary PVC; αd_1, $(CH_2-CDCl)_n$; βd_1, $(CHD-CHCl)_n$; $\alpha\beta d_2$, $(CHD-CDCl)_n$; d_3, $(CD_2-CDCl)_n$.
———— radiation with electric vector perpendicular to the stretching direction.
- - - - - - radiation with electric vector parallel to the stretching direction.[59]

TABLE VIII, 5

INFRA-RED SPECTRUM AND ASSIGNMENTS FOR POLYVINYL CHLORIDE

Frequency cm^{-1}	Polarization	Relative intensity	Phase	Assignment
418		vw	C	
~427	π?	vw	A	
492	π	vw	C	
540	π	vw	A	ν(CCl) T_{HHH}
570		vw(sh)	C	
588	σ	vw(sh)	A	ν(CCl) T_{HHC}
604	σ*	s	C	ν(CCl) B_1
615	σ	s	A	ν(CCl) S_{HH} (A)
~638	σ	ms	A	ν(CCl) S'_{HH} (A)
640	σ	ms	C	ν(CCl) A_1
{685	$\underline{\sigma}^\dagger$	m	A	ν(CCl) S_{HC} (A)
{693	π			
~710		vvw(sh)	A	ν(CCl) S'_{HC} (A)
768		vw	A	ν(CCl) S_{CC} (A)
{835	$\underline{\pi}^\dagger$	mw	C	γ_r(CH$_2$) B_2
{840	σ			
~880	π	vw	A	
~925	σ	w(sh)	A	
960	σ*	ms	C	γ_r(CH$_2$) B_1
970	σ	ms	A	γ_r(CH$_2$) (A)
~1030		vvw	C	
1090	σ(*?)	mw(sh)	C	$\nu_+(\pi/2)$ B_1
1105	σ	m	C, A	$\nu_+(0)$ A_1; $\nu_+(0)$ (A)
1122	π	w	A	$\nu_+(\pi)$ (A)
1170	σ	vw(sh)	A	
1195	π	w	C	$\nu_+(\pi)$ B_2
{1203	$\underline{\pi}^\dagger$	w	A	γ_w(CH) (A)
{1210	σ			
1230	π	mw	C	γ_w(CH) B_2
1245	σ	m(sh)	A	δ(CH) (A)
1258	σ*	s	C	δ(CH) B_1
1310	σ	vw(sh)	A	γ_t(CH$_2$) (A)
1338	σ	ms	C	δ(CH) $A_1(+\gamma_t$(CH$_2$) A_1?)
1355	σ*	w	C	γ_w(CH$_2$) B_1
1365	σ	w	A	γ_w(CH$_2$) (A)
1387	π	w	C	γ_w(CH$_2$) B_2
1428	σ	s	C	δ(CH$_2$) A_1
1438	σ	m	A	δ(CH$_2$) (A)
~1780		vvw		
2810	π?	vw	C	δ(CH$_2$)$A_1+\gamma_w$(CH$_2$)$B_2 = 2815$ B_2
2820	σ?	vw	C	
2850	σ	vw	A	ν_s(CH$_2$) (A)?
2910	σ	s	C, A	ν_s(CH$_2$) A_1
2930	σ?	w	C, A	ν_a(CH$_2$) B_1
2970	σ	mw	C, A	ν(CH) A_1 and B_1

* Bands show π dichroism at low draw ratios.

† Underlined component is stronger.

ν = stretching, δ = bending, γ_w = wagging, γ_t = twisting, γ_r = rocking.

s = strong, m = medium, w = weak, v = very, sh = shoulder.

A = amorphous, C = crystalline.

between chlorine atom motions is large enough, we would predict two identifiable frequencies for these modes. The ν(C–Cl) modes occur in the 600–700 cm^{-1} region of the spectrum, and as can be seen from Fig. VIII, 13 there are many bands located here. The situation was clarified only after the preparation and study of a very highly crystalline polymer (prepared by radiation polymerization of a urea–vinyl chloride complex)[59]. The spectrum of this polymer shows only two sharp bands in this region, at 604 and 640 cm^{-1}. These are thought to correspond to the two predicted ν(C–Cl) modes of the syndiotactic chain structure. Their polarization behaviour is consistent with this assignment. A similar splitting is predicted for the δ(C–H) modes, and various arguments[41, 59] indicate that bands at 1258 and 1338 cm^{-1} are assignable to these modes. That such assignments can be satisfactorily made is strong evidence for the assumed syndiotactic chain structure. It is interesting to note that such large splittings occur even though the (CHCl) groups are separated by (CH$_2$) groups. This demonstrates the inadequacy of using the group frequency approach alone, *i.e.*, assuming that normal vibrations are localized within chemical groups. Such vibrations are characteristic of the entire molecule, or repeat unit in the present case, and are only approximately described by a group frequency notation.

The assignment of other modes has been assisted by the availability of the spectra of the various deuterated PVC's. For the details, the original reference should be consulted[59]. The presence of non-crystalline structures was indicated by the additional strong bands which appear in the ν(C–Cl) region in the partly crystalline polymer, *viz.*, at 615, 638, 685, and 693 cm^{-1}. (The presence of a non-crystalline band at 638 cm^{-1} was established with the help of the deuterated PVC spectra[59].) Many previous studies on small molecules indicate that these bands are associated most probably with rotational isomers involving the (C–Cl) bond. This was confirmed by a detailed study of many small chlorine-containing molecules[60]. The result that emerged for secondary chlorides was the following: the frequency range in which the ν(C–Cl) mode is found is a function of the *two* substituents which are *trans* to the Cl atom across the two neighbouring (C–C) bonds. These structures can be designated S_{HH}, S_{HC}, and S_{CC}, the S referring to a secondary Cl frequency and the H and C to hydrogen or carbon atoms *trans* to the Cl atom. It was also observed that the S_{HH} frequency range depended on whether the carbon skeleton was planar (S_{HH}) or was bent out of a plane at the second carbon atom from (C–Cl) (S'_{HH}). The ranges found were: S_{HH}, 608–615 cm^{-1}; S'_{HH}, 627–637 cm^{-1}; S_{HC}, 655–674 cm^{-1}; S_{CC}, $\sim$ 760 cm^{-1}. This information, making allowance for a small frequency shift which seems to occur in the polymer, can now be used to assign structures to the PVC bands noted above.

The lower crystallinity of some PVC polymers is thought to be due to the lack of long-range syndiotactic order in the chain. Thus, instead of the regular alternation of Cl atoms shown in Fig. VIII, 12, in some regions the Cl atoms are randomly situated with respect to the plane of the carbon chain. In such regions the regular interaction giving rise to the 604, 640 cm^{-1} doublet will be absent, and the ν(C–Cl) frequency will be a function of the rotationally isomeric structure assumed by the chain. We can think of this in terms of the pair configurations: syndiotactic, if neighbouring Cl atoms are on opposite sides of the plane, and isotactic, if neighbouring Cl atoms are on the same side of the plane. Of the three relatively stable orientations for rotation about the (C–C) bond (see Section 1B) we find that one is highly unfavoured energetically, $viz.$, that which places two Cl atoms adjacent to each other as in the planar isotactic structure. By looking at molecular models we now observe the following. For a syndiotactic pair the most stable conformation is the planar zig-zag, giving rise to an S_{HH} mode; the next most stable conformation gives rise to an S_{HC} mode. That which would give an S'_{HH} mode places Cl atoms next to each other, and as we have seen is very unlikely to occur. For an isotactic pair the planar structure is unfavoured; the most favoured structure gives rise to an S_{HC} mode, the next to an S'_{HH} mode. The following assignments of bands to structures in the non-crystalline regions can now be made: 615, S_{HH} of syndiotactic pairs; 638, S'_{HH} of isotactic pairs; 685, S_{HC} of isotactic pairs; 693, S_{HC} of syndiotactic pairs. The distinction between the latter two modes is based on the behaviour observed on heating PVC, $viz.$, the 638 cm^{-1} band weakens and a shift takes place from 693 cm^{-1} to 685 cm^{-1}. Presumably the release of chain restrictions by heating increases the proportion of more favoured conformations. Analysis of the infra-red spectrum has thus yielded a fairly detailed picture of the structures of crystalline and non-crystalline chains in polyvinyl chloride.

(3D) Proteins

The spectrum of a protein is quite complex, and a complete analysis is far from being achieved. Certain characteristic bands, however, have been studied in sufficient detail to permit their use in the identification of different chain conformations. The results also indicate the types of interactions which are permitted via hydrogen bonded groups.

Polypeptide chains are known to exist in several conformations, some extended and one folded[40]. One such extended conformation, the anti-parallel-chain pleated sheet, is shown in Fig. VIII, 14. Because of interaction between peptide groups (–NHCO–) within each chain and (across the hydrogen bonds) between chains, it is expected that several vibrational modes of the repeating unit involving a particular normal mode of the peptide group will be possible[61] (Fig. VIII, 14). The frequencies of these modes have been shown[62] to be given by

$$\nu(\delta,\ \delta') = \nu_0 + \sum_s D_s \cos (s\delta) + \sum_{s'} D'_s \cos (s'\delta') \qquad (18)$$

where ν_0 is the unperturbed frequency, D_s and D'_s are the constants determining intrachain and interchain peptide group interactions between sth

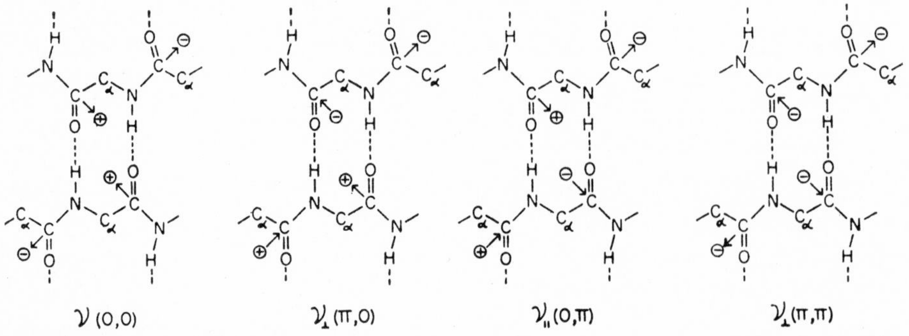

ν (0,0) $\nu_\perp$ (π,0) $\nu_\parallel$ (0,π) $\nu_\perp$ (π,π)

INFRA—RED INACTIVE

Fig. VIII, 14. Vibrational modes of the anti-parallel chain pleated sheet. The arrows and plus or minus signs show the transition moment components of the peptide group vibrations[61].

neighbours respectively, and δ and δ' are the phase angles between intrachain and interchain peptide group motions respectively. This relationship has been applied[61, 63] to the amide I and II bands (essentially (C=O) stretching and (N–H) deformation modes) of various polypeptide chain structures. By choosing three bands of a known structure which can be

TABLE VIII, 6

CALCULATED AMIDE I AND AMIDE II FREQUENCIES FOR VARIOUS POLYPEPTIDE CHAIN CONFORMATIONS

Conformation	Mode	Amide I, cm^{-1}	Amide II, cm^{-1}
Unordered	ν_0	1658	1520*
Nylon 66	ν_N	1640*	1540*
Antiparallel-chain pleated sheet	$\nu_\parallel(0, \pi)_A$	1685* (w)	1530* (s)
	$\nu_\perp(\pi, 0)_A$	1632* (s)	1510 (w)
	$\nu_\perp(\pi, \pi)_A$	1668 (vw)	1550 (w)
Parallel-chain pleated sheet	$\nu_\parallel(0, 0)_P$	1648 (w)	1530 (s)
	$\nu_\perp(\pi, 0)_P$	1632 (s)	1550 (w)
Parallel-chain polar sheet	$\nu(0, 0)_{pol}$	1648 (s) ($\perp$)	1550 (s) ($\parallel$)
	$\nu_\perp(\pi, 0)_{pol}$	1632 (vw)	1530 (w)
α-Helix	$\nu_\parallel(0)_\alpha$	1650* (s)	1516* (w)
	$\nu_\perp(2\pi/3.6)_\alpha$	1646 (w)	1546 (s)
Polyglycine II	$\nu_\parallel(0)_{PG}$	1624 (vw)	1558* (s)
	$\nu_\perp(2\pi/3)_{PG}$	1648* (s)	1531 (w)

* Assumed frequencies of modes.

s = strong, w = weak, vw = very weak.

$\parallel$ = parallel band, $\perp$ = perpendicular band.

assigned without ambiguity, it is possible to determine v_0, D_s, and D'_s and then to apply these to the calculation of the modes of other structures. The results of such calculations[63] are shown in Table VIII, 6. A comparison[63] with observed bands in various proteins shows quite good agreement with the results of the above calculation. This analysis thus provides a means of structure identification even for a macromolecule as complex as a protein. It and the other studies of the spectra of solids and high polymers also demonstrate that the basic principles of spectra in condensed phases are well understood.

REFERENCES

[1] C. Brecher and R. S. Halford, *J. Chem. Phys.*, 35 (1961) 1109.

[2] R. S. Halford, *J. Chem. Phys.*, 14 (1946) 8.

[3] D. F. Hornig, *J. Chem. Phys.*, 16 (1948) 1063.

[4] H. Winston and R. S. Halford, *J. Chem. Phys.*, 17 (1949) 607.

[5] T. H. Walnut, *J. Chem. Phys.*, 20 (1952) 58.

[6] W. Vedder and D. F. Hornig, *Advan. Spectry.*, 2 (1961) 189; S. S. Mitra, *Solid State Physics*, Academic Press, New York, 13 (1962) 1.

[7] M. Born and K. Huang, *Dynamical Theory of Crystal Lattices*, Oxford University Press, London, 1954.

[8] C. Brecher, E. Krikorian, J. Blanc and R. S. Halford, *J. Chem. Phys.*, 35 (1961) 1097.

[9] I. Simon, *J. Opt. Soc. Am.*, 41 (1951) 336.

[10] T. S. Robinson, *Proc. Phys. Soc.* (London), B65 (1952) 910.

[11] T. S. Robinson and W. C. Price, *Proc. Phys. Soc.* (London), B66 (1953) 969.

[12] G. R. Anderson and W. R. Person, *J. Chem. Phys.*, 36 (1962) 62.

[13] J. Fahrenfort, *Spectrochim. Acta*, 17 (1961) 698.

[14] H. J. Hrostowski and G. C. Pimentel, *J. Chem. Phys.*, 19 (1951) 661.

[15] G. L. Hiebert and D. F. Hornig, *J. Chem. Phys.*, 20 (1952) 918.

[16] S. Krimm, C. Y. Liang, and G. B. B. M. Sutherland, *J. Chem. Phys.*, 25 (1956) 549.

[17] D. F. Hornig and G. L. Hiebert, *J. Chem. Phys.*, 27 (1957) 752.

[18] E. Whittle, D. A. Dows and G. C. Pimentel. *J. Chem. Phys.*, 22 (1954) 1943.

[19] E. D. Becker and G. C. Pimentel, *J. Chem. Phys.*, 25 (1956) 224.

[20] M. Van Thiel, E. D. Becker and G. C. Pimentel, *J. Chem. Phys.*, 27 (1957) 95.

[21] M. C. Tobin, *J. Chem. Phys.*, 23 (1955) 891.

[22] C. Y. Liang, S. Krimm and G. B. B. M. Sutherland, *J. Chem. Phys.*, 25 (1956) 543.

[23] C. Y. Liang, *J. Mol. Spectry.*, 1 (1957) 61.

[24] S. Mizushima, *Structure of Molecules and Internal Rotation*, Academic Press, New York, 1954.

[25] N. Sheppard, *Advan. Spectry.*, 1 (1959) 288.

[26] C. G. Cannon, *Spectrochim. Acta*, 10 (1958) 341.

[27] G. C. Pimentel and A. L. McClellan, *The Hydrogen Bond*, W. H. Freeman and Company, San Francisco, 1960.

[28] G. K. T. Conn and G. K. Eaton, *J. Opt. Soc. Am.*, 44 (1954) 553.

[29] A. Elliott, E. J. Ambrose and R. B. Temple, *J. Opt. Soc. Am.*, 38 (1948) 212.

[30] R. Newman and R. S. Halford, *Rev. Sci. Instr.*, 19 (1948) 270.

[31] T. Shimanouchi and M. Kawano, *Bull. Chem. Soc. Japan*, 32 (1959) 894.

[32] A. S. Makas and W. A. Shurcliff, *J. Opt. Soc. Am.*, 45 (1955) 998.

[33] A. Yamaguchi, I. Ichishima and S. Mizushima, *Spectrochim. Acta*, 12 (1958) 294.

[34] E. Charney, *J. Opt. Soc. Am.*, 45 (1955) 980.

[35] D. L. Wood and S. S. Mitra, *J. Opt. Soc. Am.*, 48 (1958) 537.

[36] E. J. Ambrose, A. Elliott and R. B. Temple, *Proc. Roy. Soc.* (*London*), A206 (1951) 192.

[37] G. C. PIMENTEL and A. L. McCLELLAN, *J. Chem. Phys.*, 20 (1952) 270.

[38] I. SANDEMAN, *Proc. Roy. Soc. (London)*, A232 (1955) 105.

[39] T. MIYAZAWA, T. SHIMANOUCHI and S. MIZUSHIMA, *J. Chem. Phys.*, 29 (1958) 611.

[40] C. H. BAMFORD, A. ELLIOTT and W. E. HANBY, *Synthetic Polypeptides*, Academic Press, New York, 1956.

[41] S. KRIMM, *Fortschr. Hochpolymer. Forsch.*, 2 (1960) 51.

[42] P. W. HIGGS, *Proc. Roy. Soc. (London)*, A220 (1953) 472.

[43] R. D. B. FRASER, *J. Chem. Phys.*, 21 (1953) 1511.

[44] R. D. B. FRASER, *J. Chem. Phys.*, 28 (1958) 1113.

[45] M. BEER, *Proc. Roy. Soc. (London)* A236 (1956) 136.

[46] C. Y. LIANG and S. KRIMM, *J. Chem. Phys.*, 27 (1957) 1437.

[47] S. KRIMM, *J. Chem. Phys.*, 32 (1960) 313.

[48] E. B. WILSON, J. C. DECIUS and P. C. CROSS, *Molecular Vibrations*, McGraw-Hill, New York, 1955.

[49] S. BHAGAVANTAM and T. VENKATARAYUDU, *Theory of Groups and its Application to Physical Problems*, Waltair, Andhra University, 1951.

[50] H. TADOKORO, *J. Chem. Phys.*, 33 (1960) 1558.

[51] T. SHIMANOUCHI and M. TASUMI, *Bull. Chem. Soc. Japan*, 34 (1961) 359.

[52] J. H. SCHACHTSCHNEIDER and R. G. SNYDER, *Spectrochim. Acta*, in press; T. P. LIN and J. L. KOENIG, *J Mol. Spectry.*, 9 (1962) 228; M. TASUMI, T. SHIMANOUCHI and T. MIYAZAWA, *J. Mol. Spectry.*, 9 (1962) 261.

[53] S. KRIMM, *J. Chem. Phys.*, 32 (1960) 1780.

[54] R. G. SNYDER, *J. Mol. Spectry.*, 4 (1960) 411; 7 (1961) 116.

[55] R. F. HOLLAND and J. R. NIELSEN, *J. Mol. Spectry.*, 8 (1962) 383.

[56] M. TASUMI and T. SHIMANOUCHI, *Spectrochim. Acta*, 17 (1961) 731.

[57] J. R. NIELSEN and R. F. HOLLAND, *J. Mol. Spectry.*, 6 (1961) 394.

[58] J. R. NIELSEN and R. F. HOLLAND, *J. Mol. Spectry.*, 4 (1960) 488.

[59] S. KRIMM, V. L. FOLT, J. J. SHIPMAN, and A. R. BERENS, *J. Polymer Sci.*, in press.

[60] J. J. SHIPMAN, V. L. FOLT and S. KRIMM, *Spectrochim. Acta*, 18 (1962) 1603.

[61] T. MIYAZAWA and E. R. BLOUT, *J. Am. Chem. Soc.*, 83 (1961) 712.

[62] T. MIYAZAWA, *J. Chem. Phys.*, 32 (1960) 1647.

[63] S. KRIMM, *J. Mol. Biol.*, 4 (1962) 528.

Chapter IX

Inorganic Applications of Infra-red Spectroscopy

E. A. V. EBSWORTH

University Chemical Laboratory, Cambridge

Since 1945, infra-red spectroscopy has had a great influence upon the development of inorganic chemistry. In the first place, the identification of compounds, both old and new, has been made much easier by the application of infra-red spectroscopy to qualitative and structural analysis. Much recent research would have been impossible without its aid and few inorganic research laboratories are now without an infra-red spectrometer. Many studies of molecular symmetry have made use of vibrational spectra, while attempts have been made to obtain information about the electronic structures of molecules from their vibrational frequencies and from the force constants that can be calculated from the observed spectra. These are three ways in which infra-red spectroscopy has impinged upon inorganic chemistry, and though they are by no means unrelated, they form convenient divisions for the discussion that follows. The second and third aspects are of great importance to anyone who is interested in molecular structure, but the qualitative applications have had by far the greatest influence upon inorganic chemistry as a whole, and are therefore considered first.

(1) Qualitative Analysis

The infra-red spectrum of a compound is as much a characteristic property as its refractive index or boiling point, and as such can be most useful in qualitative analysis. An infra-red band has three characteristic features: its frequency, its intensity and the shape of its envelope, and all three may be of use in identifying a compound spectroscopically. Comparison of the spectrum of an unknown with that of the compound it is suspected of being is often enough to establish or reject the identification. The vapour-phase spectra of molecules whose moments of inertia are relatively small or in appropriate ratio (see the following Section) may show characteristic band contours, or even rotational detail, and these band contours may be most helpful in qualitative analysis (see p. 336). Even in the spectra of liquids or solids the observed band-widths may help. It is important to remember, though, that the spectrum of a solid may depend on the state in which the material has been studied. If, for example, the compound is mulled with some inert dispersing-agent such as nujol, the band-widths may be partly a function of the state of division of the solid, while the spectra obtained from mulls and from potassium bromide discs are not always identical (see Chapter II, pp. 79, 80).

Such comparisons of spectra may well be less significant than their analysis in terms of group frequencies. As with organic systems (see Chapter VII), extensive empirical studies have identified infra-red bands whose presence is correlated with that of particular molecular groupings. Where such a correlation has been firmly established, the observation of a characteristic band is often strong evidence for the presence of a particular group; the absence of the characteristic band implies the contrary conclusion.

Such analysis depends largely on the certainty of the frequency–structure correlation. This in its turn depends on the number of compounds containing the particular group whose spectra have been studied. Since bond moments are likely to be more variable for inorganic than for organic systems, band intensities are also likely to be much more variable, and a semiquantitative study of band intensities should form a part of all basic correlation-studies. Certain vibrations, such as (C–F) stretching modes, give strong infra-red absorptions, but others, such as (S–H) stretching modes, can be weaker, and may not readily be detected spectroscopically. This difficulty may lead to the apparent absence of a band from a spectrum in which, on the basis of a rigid frequency–structure correlation, it should be present; bands may also be observed which on the same basis should not be there. A combination or overtone vibration may have roughly the same frequency as the fundamental of some group which is not present in the molecule being studied; the second-order band may be mistaken for the fundamental, and the presence of the group associated with the fundamental be wrongly deduced. The usually weak overtone and combination bands may be intensified relative to a fundamental by a process of intensity borrowing called Fermi resonance (see p. 132), and a confusing multiplicity of strong bands can appear, as in the spectra of isothiocyanates[1, 2] at about 2100 cm^{-1}. Such second-order bands may even be used as characteristic frequencies in the same way as fundamentals. Where the spectra of solids are concerned, however, the appearance of additional bands may be caused by differences between molecular symmetry and site symmetry, or by coupling with lattice modes; the infra-red spectra of solids should always be interpreted with caution.

Simple frequencies may also be displaced by coupling. The (M–X) stretching modes in species of the form (MX$_n$) do not always appear close to the isolated (M–X) stretching frequency. In the *pseudo*-linear disiloxane[3] the two (Si–O) stretching modes are separated by about 500 cm^{-1}, though in disilyl sulphide, where a non-linear configuration of (Si–S–Si) bonds reduces the coupling, the separation is only 35 cm^{-1} [4]. In tetrahedral MX$_4$ species there are two (M–X) stretching vibrations, the one totally symmetric and infra-red forbidden, the other triply degenerate and infra-red active. Neither is strictly comparable with the stretching frequency of a single (M–X) bond; for such a comparison, the weighted mean, or one-quarter of the sum of the totally symmetric and three times the degenerate frequencies may be used. Similarly, in (MX$_2$) species, the mean of the symmetric and antisymmetric frequencies can be taken. Coupling of this kind often means that it is impossible to describe a molecular vibration as the stretching of a particular bond or the bending of a particular angle, and in many cases such descriptions are useful only as labels, having limited physical meaning. In a molecule like PF$_5$, for example, there is only one mode that is purely a bond stretching vibration, and it is difficult to pick out (P–F) stretching frequencies from the spectrum of such a molecule.

Despite these difficulties, qualitative infra-red spectroscopy is extremely useful to the experimental inorganic chemist. Characteristic inorganic frequencies are not yet systematically collected in a single source but BELLAMY's account[5] of organic compounds has many useful data; other reviews or papers give the vibrational frequencies of crystalline salts (including many oxyanions)[6, 7], and of compounds of transition metals[8–10], boron[11, 12], aluminium[13], silicon[14–15], germanium[16], tin[17] and phosphorus[18–20]. In many cases the compounds studied were organometallic. It is not possible to discuss all of these correlations here, but some representative frequencies are given in the Tables that follow, and are discussed below.

(1A) (M–H) Stretching frequencies (Table IX, 1)

These usually appear in a region of the spectrum that is relatively free from other vibrations, and so are little affected by coupling. They can be sensitive to the other groups bound to M, and to environmental effects. (N–H) and (O–H) stretching modes are substantially lowered by hydrogen bonding, which also broadens the absorption bands (see Chapter XII). There are two regions associated with (B–H) stretching modes: the higher (2630 – 2250 cm^{-1}) is characteristic of terminal (B–H) bonds, and the lower (2200 – 1540 cm^{-1}) of bridging (B–H) groups, which are usually broad bands.* Absorptions between 2200 and 1500 cm^{-1} in the spectra of aluminium and beryllium borohydrides imply the presence of bridging hydrogen atoms in these molecules[30].

---

* In alkyldiboranes the strongest absorption associated with bridging (B–H) groups appears between 1610 and 1540 cm^{-1}.[12]

TABLE IX, 1

(M–H) STRETCHING FREQUENCIES

Approximate ranges for (M–H) stretching frequencies (cm^{-1}), with some indication of intensities. The ranges do not allow for hydrogen bonding. (The numbers in brackets are the appropriate references)

B(11)	bridging 2200–1540 s	C(5) 3300–2850 s-w	N(5) 3500–3300 s-w	O(5) 3700–3500 s-w
	terminal 2630–2350 s			

Al(13) 1900–1700 s

Si(14) 2300–2100 s   P(5) 2450–2350 m   S(5) 2600–2500 w

Ge(21, 22) 2150–2050 s   As(23) 2120(AsH$_3$)   Se(24) 2350(SeH$_2$)

Sn(25, 26) 1900–1850 s   Sb(27) 1890(SbH$_3$)   Te(28) ~2000(TeH$_2$)

Transition metal(29) 2250–1750 s-w

s = strong, m = medium, w = weak, s-w = strong to weak.

(1B) (M–H) Deformation frequencies

These appear over a wide range, from 1700 to 700 cm^{-1} (or even lower if rocking modes are included). They are liable to be affected by coupling with stretching vibrations of single bonds between heavy atoms; thus in [(CH$_3$)$_3$NH]$^+$, several bands between 1600 and 1000 cm^{-1} were found to be sensitive to deuteration at nitrogen.[31] In compounds of the form MH$_3$X, the (MH$_3$) deformation frequencies (excluding rocking modes) are between 1500 and 1000 cm^{-1} if M is C[32], 1000 and 800 cm^{-1} if M is Si[33–34], and 900 and 750 cm^{-1} if M is Ge[21, 22]; the frequencies are influenced by the nature of X. Transition metal hydrides give bands at about 700 cm^{-1} that are shifted by deuteration and have been assigned to (M–H) deformation modes[35]. The deformation frequencies of (N–H) and (O–H) bonds are usually increased by hydrogen bonding (see Chapter XII) and are modified when the O or N atom is part of a donor–acceptor complex (see p. 321).

(1C) Further single bond stretching frequencies

These are so liable to be affected by coupling that it is not possible to give reliable ranges, though particular systems may have quite characteristic spectra; derivatives of the CF$_3$S group, for instance, give bands at about 760 and 400 cm^{-1} that are due to the (C–S) stretching and the symmetrical (CF$_3$) deformation modes, which are rather strongly coupled together[36]. Some typical (M–C) and (M F) stretching frequencies in simple alkyls and fluorides are given in Tables IX, 2 and IX, 3, as weighted mean values (see p. 313); except when M is nitrogen or oxygen, the (M–F) frequency is higher than the (M–C). Certain other representative frequencies are given in Table IX, 4; by interpolation these values could provide approximate estimates of the stretching frequencies of other (M–X) bonds.

TABLE IX, 2

WEIGHTED MEAN VALUES FOR (M–C) STRETCHING FREQUENCIES (CM⁻¹) IN SIMPLE
METHYLS, $M(CH_3)_n$

(The numbers in brackets are the appropriate references)

$n = 3$	$n = 4$	$n = 3$	$n = 2$	$n = 1$
B(37) 1002	C(38) 1120	N(39) 972	O(39) 1030	F(40) 1048
Al*(41) 780—550	Si(42) 672	P(39) 689	S(39) 716	Cl(40) 732
Ga(43) 574	Ge(42) 589	As(39) 580	Se(39) 595	Br(40) 611
In(43) 489	Sn(42) 520	Sb(39) 513	Te(39) —	I(40) 533
	Pb(44) 470	Bi(39) 460		

* These frequencies are for the dimer, $Al_2(CH_3)_6$.

TABLE IX, 3

WEIGHTED MEAN VALUES FOR (M–F) STRETCHING FREQUENCIES (CM⁻¹) IN SIMPLE
FLUORIDES, MF_n

$n = 3$	$n = 4$	$n = 3$	$n = 2$
B(45) 1277	C(46) 1188	N(47) 947	O(48) 872
	Si(49) 973	P(47) 871	
	Ge(50) 785	As(51) 665	

TABLE IX, 4

SOME TYPICAL (M–X) STRETCHING FREQUENCIES (CM⁻¹)

(Weighted mean values are given for MX_n)

(B–Cl) in BCl_3(52)	807	(B–Br) in BBr_3(53)	651	(B–I) in BI_3(53)	544
(Si–Cl) in $SiCl_4$(54)	562	(Si–Br) in $SiBr_4$(55)	429	(Si–I) in SiI_4(55)	346
(Ge–Cl) in $GeCl_4$(54)	439	(Ge–Br) in $GeBr_4$(56)	305	(Ge–I) in GeI_4(57)	238
(Sn–Cl) in $SnCl_4$(54)	394	(Sn–Br) in $SnBr_4$(54)	264	(Sn–I) in SnI_4(57)	199
(Si–Si) in Si_2H_6(33)	434	(Ge–Ge) in Ge_2H_6(21)	229 or 265	(Sn–Sn) in Sn_2Me_6(58)	190

(M–N) in transition metal ammines (59, 60) 350—550 (approx.)
(M–C) in transition metal carbonyls (61, 62) 300—500 (approx.)

Bands at about 300 cm⁻¹ in cobaltammines have recently been assigned to skeletal bending
modes (60).

(1D) Multiple bond stretching frequencies

The so-called "double bond" and "triple bond" regions of the organic
correlation charts have some relevance to the spectra of inorganic molecules
containing multiple bonds between elements of the first row of the Periodic
Table. The stretching frequencies of the isoelectronic (C≡O) and (C≡N)
groups are about 2100 cm⁻¹, though both are sensitive to their electronic
environments. Systems that contain adjacent double bonds, such as the

References pp. 340–344

cyanate ion $(N=C=O)^-$, usually give one infra-red band at a frequency greater than 2000 cm^{-1}, (i.e. in what is conventionally the "triple-bond" region) because of coupling between the two double bond stretching vibrations (see Table IX, 5).

TABLE IX, 5

FUNDAMENTAL FREQUENCIES (CM^{-1}) OF SOME LINEAR TRIATOMIC SYSTEMS

(Modes formally forbidden in the infra-red are in italics)

System	Frequencies			Phase	Reference
CO_2	1337*	667	2349	vapour	63
N_2O	1285	589	2223	vapour	64
CNO$^-$	1057	471	2052		182
NO_2^+	1400	537	2390		65
N_3^-	1344	645	2041	solid (K salt)	66
CN_2^{2-}	1234	598	2120	,, (Na salt)	67
NCO$^-$	1207	632†	2165	,, (K salt)	68
NCS$^-$	743	470	2066	solution	69
NCSe$^-$	558	420†	2070	solid (K salt)	70

* Mean of Fermi resonance doublet.
† Mean of doublet due to crystal splitting.

Where an element from the second or some later row of the Periodic Table is involved in a multiple bond, the stretching frequency is considerably lower than when two first-row elements are multiply bound together. In the unusual molecule HCP, for example, the stretching frequency of the $(C\equiv P)$ bond is only 1265 cm^{-1} [71]. The stretching frequencies of double bonds between first-row elements are usually between 1500 and 1800 cm^{-1}, but double bonds between a first-row and a second-row element usually absorb between 1150 and 1500 cm^{-1} (see Table IX, 6). Oxidation of

TABLE IX, 6

SOME TYPICAL DOUBLE-BOND STRETCHING FREQUENCIES (CM^{-1})

System	(M=O Stretching) frequency	Reference	System	(M=X) Stretching frequency	Reference
$POCl_3$	1295	72	$>$P=O†	1350–1175	76
$VOCl_3$	1035	73	M=O*	1100– 800	77–8
$SOCl_2$	1229	74	$>$S=O†	1215–1020	79
$SeOCl_2$	955	74			
SOF_2	1308	74			
$SeOF_2$	1046	75			
SO_2Cl_2	{ 1414 / 1182	74	$>$S$<$O† / O	1440–1300 / 1230–1140	79
SO_2F_2	{ 1502 / 1269	74	$K_2[Cl_5OsN]$	1023	80

* M is a transition metal.
† The highest frequencies are observed when the other substituents are light electronegative elements like oxygen or fluorine.

the second-row element leads to a slight increase in stretching frequency: the (S=O) stretching frequency in thionyl fluoride is 1308 cm^{-1} [74], as against 1386 cm^{-1} (mean) in sulphuryl fluoride[74] and about 1370 cm^{-1} in SF_4O[81]. The stretching frequencies of the formal double bonds between oxygen or nitrogen and many transition elements are between 800 and 1100 cm^{-1}, depending to some extent upon the overall charge on the species in question.

(1E) Polyatomic anions

The vibrational frequencies of some common oxyanions taken mostly from solution spectra and sometimes solely from Raman data are given in Table IX, 7.

TABLE IX, 7

VIBRATIONAL FREQUENCIES (CM^{-1}) OF SOME SIMPLE OXYANIONS

(Taken from solution spectra unless otherwise stated; frequencies of infra-red forbidden modes are in italics and appropriate references in brackets)

General formula, point group and symmetry classes of vibrations		Ions and frequencies				
MO$_2$	a_1	NO_2^- (82)		ClO_2^- (83)		
		1335, 816		797, 396		
C_{2v}(bent)	e	1240		860		
MO$_3$	a_1	CO_3^{2-} (84)		NO_3^- (84)		
		1063		*1050*		
D_{3h}(planar)	a_2	879		831		
	e	1415, 680		1390, 720		
		SO_3^{2-} (85)	ClO_3^- (86)	SeO_3^{2-} (87)	BrO_3^- (86)	IO_3^- (86)
	a_1	966, 612	932, 613	806, ?598	805, 418	790, 360
C_{3v}(pyr)	e	925, 471	982, 479	862, 375	830, 356	820, 326
MO$_4$		PO_4^{3-} (88)	SO_4^{2-} (88)	CrO_4^{2-} (89)	ClO_4^- (88)	*MnO$_4^-$ (6, 7)
	a_1	*937*	*981*	*847*	*935*	?
T_d(tetr)	e	*420*	*451*	*348*	*462*	?
	f_2	1022, 562	1104, 613	884, 368	1102, 628	~900, ~400
		AsO_4^{3-} (88)	SeO_4^{2-} (88)	MoO_4^{2-} (88)		
	a_1	*810*	*834*	*944*		
	e	*342*	*339*	*218*		
	f_2	? , 398	875, 416	896, 360		
				WO_4^{2-} (185)		ReO_4^- (90)
	a_1			*931*		*971*
	e			*324*		*332*
	f_2			832, 324		916, 332

* IR only.

References pp. 340–344

TABLE IX, 8

CHARACTERISTIC FREQUENCIES OF SOME COMMON POLYATOMIC IONS IN THE
SOLID STATE

(In some cases only two or three compounds have been studied, so the ranges given must be
regarded as approximate, as are the indications of intensities)
(Adapted from Ferraro, ref. 9)

Ion	300–400	400–500	500–600	600–700	700–800	800–900	900–1000	1000–1100	1100–1200	1200–1300	1300–1400	1400–1500
BO_2^-											M-VS	
$B_4O_7^{2-}$							S	W-S			M-VS	
CO_3^{2-}			(a)			W-S						S
HCO_3^-				W-M S		S		S				S
*SCN^-		DOUBLET			W-S							
SiO_3^{2-}		S			VW-S			S				
NO_2^-						W-S				S	M-S	
NO_3^-						W-S						S
**NH_4^+												M-S
PO_4^{3-}			(a)					S				
HPO_4^{2-}			W-VS			M-S	S	S				
$H_2PO_4^-$						W-S		M-S				
SO_3^{2-}				S			W-S					
SO_4^{2-}				W-S					S			
HSO_4^-				S		M-S		M-S	M-S			
$S_2O_3^{2-}$			W-S	S				S	S			
$S_2O_5^{2-}$				S			M-S	M-S	VS			
$S_2O_8^{2-}$					S				S	S		
SeO_3^{2-}					S M-S							
SeO_4^{2-}						S						
ClO_3^-			S	S				S				
ClO_4^-				S					S			
BrO_3^-	S	S				S						
IO_3^-	M-S					S S-W						
VO_3^-					S	S	S					
CrO_4^{2-}		W-S				S	W-S(a)					
$Cr_2O_7^{2-}$		W-S			W-S	(a)M-S S	S					
MoO_4^{2-}	M-S					S	M					
WO_4^{2-}						S						
MnO_4^-	(a)						S					

Legend:

S Strong
M Medium intensity
W Weak
V Very
(a) Not reliable

Frequency cm⁻¹: 300, 400, 500, 600, 700, 800, 900, 1000, 1100, 1200, 1300, 1400, 1500

* Bands are also found near 2100 cm⁻¹.
** In NH_4F the infra-red active vibrations are at about 1490 and 2800 cm⁻¹;[184] other ammonium salts give bands at 3050—3300 cm⁻¹.

Some symmetric modes of symmetrical polyatomic ions are forbidden in the infra-red for the free ions, but are sometimes observed in the spectra of crystalline solids because of reduced site symmetry. The symmetrical stretching vibration of the free $(CO_3)^{2-}$ ion, although infra-red inactive, is observed as a weak absorption in carbonates having the aragonite structure[91]; similarly, the totally symmetric stretching mode of $(ClO_4)^-$ is observed in crystalline perchlorates[92]. Splitting of degenerate modes, as with the bending vibration[68] of the $(NCO)^-$ ion, is another effect of reduced site symmetry.

A change in environment from the liquid to the solid state may cause changes not only in number and activity of vibrational modes, but also in their frequency. The Raman frequencies of the sulphite ion in solid sodium sulphite, 983, 632 (a_1); 947, 494 cm^{-1} (e),[85] differ markedly from the solution values (see Table IX, 7). Such changes must be borne in mind when comparing spectra from different phases. Characteristic infra-red frequencies for a large number of polynuclear anions are given in Table IX, 8 in the form of a frequency-diagram. Frequencies from crystalline solids in this Table may be compared with the analogous frequencies for some free ions (Table IX, 7). Frequencies of certain other polyatomic anions are given in Tables IX, 5 (pseudohalides), IX, 9 (fluoroanions) and IX, 13.

TABLE IX, 9

INFRA-RED FREQUENCIES (CM^{-1}) OF SOME FLUOROANIONS IN THE SOLID STATE

(see reference 93)

MF_4		Be 773[a] 819	B 1100, ~530[b]	Au 585, 477
MF_6	M^{II}	407—489	M = Cr, Mn, Fe, Co, Ni, Cu, Zn.	
	M^{III}	446—617	M = Sc, Ti, V, Cr, Mn, Fe, Co, Ga, In.	
	M^{IV}	502—654[c]	M = Ti, V, Cr, Mn, Fe, Co, Ni, Ru, Rh, Pd, Re, Os, Ir, Pt, Ge, Sn, Pb.	
	M^{V}	594—715[d]	M = V, Nb, Mo, Ru, Ta, W, Re, Os, Ir, As, Sb.	

[a] Lattice doublet
[b] See also ref. 94
[c] SiF_6^{2-} gives infra-red bands at 726 and 480 cm^{-1}
[d] PF_6^- gives infra-red bands at 845 and 559 cm^{-1}; AsF_6^- has an additional band at 400 cm^{-1}

(1F) Complex species

When a molecule combines with some other species to form a complex, its vibrational spectrum is likely to change in a number of ways. The changes can usually be related to changes in molecular symmetry, or to changes in individual frequencies, or to both.

(i) Changes in molecular symmetry

The change from the ammonia molecule to the ammonium ion brings a change in shape from pyramidal (point group C_{3v}) to tetrahedral (point group T_d); all four frequencies of the former are infra-red active, but only two of the latter. There are similar changes in symmetry when a molecular fluoride such as BF_3 accepts F^- to form a fluoroanion; the frequencies of BF_3 and $(BF_4)^-$, and of SiF_4 and $(SiF_6)^{2-}$ are given in Table IX, 13. These changes are in the coordination at the central atom. Molecular interactions, however, may also involve peripheral atoms or groups, as when the ammonia molecule or the ammonium ion forms hydrogen bonds; again, the overall group symmetry may be affected. The free nitrate ion has three equivalent planar (N–O) bonds; it belongs to the point group D_{3h}. Only three of its four modes are infra-red active; the symmetrical stretching frequency, $\nu_1 (1050 \text{ cm}^{-1})$ is infra-red forbidden, while the degenerate stretching mode (ν_3, 1390 cm^{-1}) is active[84]. When bound to some other species through one or two of its oxygen atoms, the three-fold symmetry is destroyed; if still planar and with two equivalent oxygen atoms, the point group becomes C_{2v} (II or III below)[95]:

I. Free nitrate ion.   II. Monodentate nitrate.   III. Bidentate nitrate.

The three distinct (N–O) stretching modes are then active in the infra-red. The appearance of ν_1, together with the splitting of ν_3, is illustrated in Table IX, 10 which includes the (N–O) stretching frequencies of methyl nitrate to represent the extreme case of (II). The spectra of various other

TABLE IX, 10

INFRA-RED FREQUENCIES (CM^{-1}) ASSOCIATED WITH (N–O) STRETCHING MODES OF SOME NITRATES

System	Frequencies			Reference
(NO_3^-) free	1390		1051 (IR forbidden)	84
$NaNO_3$ (solid)	1381			96
KNO_3 (solid)	1383		1052 vvw	96
Complex nitrates (solid)	1531—1481	1290—1253	1034—970	95
$Cu(NO_3)_2$ anhydrous (solid)*	1592—1504	1289—1264	1021	97
CH_3NO_3 vapour	1672	1287	854	95

* The spectrum of the vapour is similar, though the band systems are simpler, save for an additional band at 1088 cm^{-1}.

anions, such as sulphate[98], oxalate[99] and carbonate[91] have been studied in this way; differences in the spectra of monodentate and bidentate carbonate ions[100] are reported. Some ions, such as sulphate or nitrite, can act as bridges between two metal atoms in binuclear complexes, causing yet other characteristic differences in their infra-red spectra. It is not, however, easy to distinguish between the effects of complex formation and the effects of low site symmetry (see Section 1E and Chapter VIII).

(ii) Changes in frequency

When coordination takes place to a central atom (as in BF_3) or from it (as with adducts of ammonia), the stretching frequencies of the original bonds are usually lowered. Table IX, 11 shows this, together with the

TABLE IX, 11

INFRA-RED FREQUENCIES (CM^{-1}) OF (NH_3) IN METAL AMMINES

(see references 10 and 101)

Mode	In NH_3 vapour[186]	In metal ammines
(N–H) stretching	3336	3300—3200*
NH_3 deformation (antisym.)	1628	1650—1560
NH_3 deformation (sym.)	950($\pm$ 18)	1350—1150
NH_3 rock	—	950—650

* May be substantially lowered by hydrogen bonding.

characteristic deformation and rocking frequencies of coordinated ammonia. The stretching frequency in gaseous CO is higher than in metal carbonyls[102], while the (C≡N) stretching frequencies of complex cyanides depend on the metal atom and on such factors as its oxidation-state and coordination number*[103]. The thiocyanate ion, (NCS)⁻, can coordinate through N or through S: the high-frequency [(C≡N) stretching] mode is raised from 2055 cm^{-1} for the free ion to 2085—2095 cm^{-1} in N–metal complexes and to 2100—2125 cm^{-1} in S–metal complexes; the low-frequency skeletal stretching mode, however, is raised from 749 cm^{-1} in the free ion to 780—860 cm^{-1} in N–metal complexes, but is lowered by coordination through sulphur to 690—720 cm^{-1} [104, 183]. On this basis it has been suggested that the complex ions $[Pd(SCN)_4]^{2-}$ and $[Pt(SCN)_4]^{2-}$ contain S–metal bonds, but that the tertiary phosphine complexes $[(R_3P)_2Pd(NCS)_2]$ and $[(R_3P)_2Pt[(NCS)_2]$ are coordinated through nitrogen[183]. It is also possible to distinguish nitro-complexes, in which the NO_2-group is coordinated to a metal atom through nitrogen, from nitrito-complexes (oxygen coordination), by their infra-red spectra.[105]

* The (C≡O) stretching frequencies in transition metal carbonyls are very sensitive to the nature of the other substituents at the metal atom, and there seems to be a direct correlation between the (C≡O) stretching frequency and the ability of the other substituent to accept π-electrons from the metal[102, 187, 188].

When the carbonyl group acts as a bridge between two metal atoms, the (C≡O) stretching frequency is usually between 1750 and 1900 cm⁻¹, while for singly-coordinated or terminal (C≡O) groups it is between 1900 and 2250 cm⁻¹. The absence of bands in the former range for $Mn_2(CO)_{10}$ suggested that the metal atoms were directly linked, without (C≡O) bridges[106]; this has since been confirmed[107]. However, stretching frequencies of terminal (C≡O) groups have been observed as low as 1735 cm⁻¹ [102], so that the presence of bridging (C≡O) groups cannot be established with certainty from infra-red spectra alone. When the thiocyanate ion acts as a bridge, the (C≡N) stretching frequency is higher than for the singly-coordinated ion[104], and the same is true of bridging as against singly-coordinated (C≡N)[103]; in the infra-red spectrum of $K_4[Ni(CN)_3]_2$, the absence of bands in the (C≡N) stretching region at frequencies higher than 2135 cm⁻¹, the value in monomeric cyanide complexes of nickel, has led to the conclusion that the polymeric ion does not contain (C≡N) bridges[108]. The (C≡N) stretching frequencies of alkyl cyanides[109] and isocyanides[110] increase when the (C≡N) group coordinates to a metal atom, though in adducts of trialkylsilyl cyanides (or isocyanides — the structures are uncertain) the reverse is true[111]. In olefin complexes of transition metals the (C=C) stretching frequency is usually found between 1500 and 1530 cm⁻¹ [112, 113], some 100—150 cm⁻¹ lower than in the free olefins.

Pairs of geometric isomers can often be distinguished by their infra-red spectra. Many *trans*-dinitro complexes give bands at 1415, 1330 and 822 cm⁻¹;

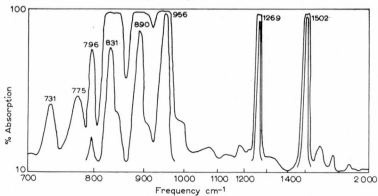

Fig. IX, 1. Vapour-phase spectrum for worked example (1).
(100-mm cell; pressures of *ca.* 10 mm and *ca.* 1 mm).

the analogous *cis*-isomers give three bands at somewhat lower frequencies, the 822 cm⁻¹ analogue being split into several components, while there is an additional band at 1350 cm⁻¹. As symmetry considerations predict, the spectra of the *trans*-isomers are the simpler[114].

Worked examples (1) Fig. IX, 1 shows the infra-red spectrum of a single substance, molecular weight 215, obtained by the irradiation of a mixture of S_2F_{10} and SO_2. What can be deduced about its structure? (For the infra-red spectrum of S_2F_{10}, see ref. 115).

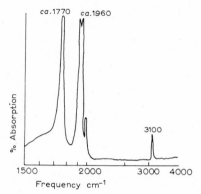

Fig. IX, 2. Nujol mull spectrum of worked example (2): (the nujol band is not shown)

(2) When the compound $\pi C_5H_5Fe(CO)_2H$ decomposes at room temperature, the brown homogeneous crystalline product gives the infra-red spectrum shown in part in Fig. IX, 2. What does the spectrum suggest about the nature of the product?

(These examples are discussed on pp. 338, 339).

(2) Determination of Molecular Symmetry

The number and activity of the vibrations of a polyatomic molecule depend on the molecular symmetry (see Chapter IV). The more symmetrical the molecule, the fewer are the distinct vibrational modes, and the fewer the coincidences between infra-red and Raman spectra. Accordingly, vibrational spectra can help to determine molecular configurations. At the lowest level, the number of infra-red bands may indicate whether or not the molecule is highly symmetrical; more useful and decisive is the *principle of mutual exclusion*, according to which there should be no fundamental frequencies common to the infra-red and Raman spectra of a molecule with a centre of symmetry. For complex molecules a full vibrational analysis may be unattainable, and it is often possible to do no more than test the consistency of the spectra with a proposed structure. The complete analysis of the vibrational spectra of a relatively simple molecule, however, may go far towards establishing the molecular configuration.

In making such an analysis, it is usually necessary to obtain both infra-red and Raman spectra, infra-red evidence alone has very much less force. Various possible molecular structures are assigned to their point groups (HERZBERG[40], Chapter IV), and the numbers and activities of their vibrational modes are determined using tables (HERZBERG[40], pp. 105–130, 252–3). The number of distinct infra-red and Raman modes, with the polarized Raman lines and coincidences in the two spectra predicted for each model are noted; where vapour-phase infra-red spectra may be available any predictable band contours are also noted. Comparison is made with the observed spectra, whose frequencies must be assigned with further reference to similar molecules and to characteristic group frequencies. Isotopic substitution is often invaluable in distinguishing vibrations involving the motion of the substituted atoms, and may thus clarify a particular structural question; where molecules of the type $(H_m X)_n M$ are concerned, for instance, it is sometimes possible to decide the geometry at M by determining the number and activity of the (M–X) vibrations, which are the modes the least affected by deuteration.

Deductions about molecular symmetry from vibrational spectra can rarely be regarded as conclusive, particularly where more complex molecules are concerned. The selection rules refer to the free (*i.e.* isolated) molecule in its vibrational groundstate; they may break down in condensed phases, and even in the gas phase at high pressures[116, 117]. In the solid state, (see p. 320, and Chapter VIII), the vibrational modes are affected by the site symmetry; such molecular symmetry deductions must therefore be regarded with caution. Again, selection rules do not predict the intensities of bands that are formally allowed; the failure to observe a weak band that is nonetheless present may suggest that it is forbidden, and so lead to an incorrect structure. Similarly, an overtone or combination band may be mistaken for a forbidden fundamental; this is more common in infra-red than in Raman spectra, where second-order bands are less often observed. Absorptions forbidden in the vibrational ground-state may be allowed in some vibrationally excited state; if this is sufficiently populated at room temperature, weak bands may be observed. Such "hot" bands differ from fundamentals in the temperature dependence of their intensities. Finally, the vibrational spectrum of a molecule like disiloxane, $(SiH_3)_2O$, in which the heavy atom skeleton is non-linear in its ground-state but has a low and flat potential barrier to inversion, may show some confusing features (see p. 334).

Even with complete infra-red and Raman spectra, the deduction of molecular symmetry is not always either easy or conclusive; the partial analysis of an infra-red spectrum is much less decisive. In transition metal carbonyls and complex cyanides, the (C≡O) and (C≡N) stretching modes are usually easy to identify, and appear in a region of the spectrum that is relatively free from other fundamental absorptions. It has become common practice to make deductions about the overall molecular symmetry from the number of infra-red bands observed in this region. Conclusions drawn from this sort of study must be regarded as tentative at best, even when the spectrum has been obtained under high resolution in the liquid or vapour phase. The analysis of the spectra of solids in this way is quite unreliable unless the crystal structure of the solid is known.

(2A) The use of band contours

Vapour phase band contours are helpful not only in making vibrational assignments but also in indicating the symmetry of the species present. For a symmetric top molecule, vibrations involve dipole changes either parallel or perpendicular to the top axis, giving "parallel" and "perpendicular" bands, respectively. These often have characteristic contours[120] depending on the moments of inertia and their ratio* (see p. 154 Chapter IV).

Band contours in the spectra of asymmetric top molecules depend not only on the three moments of inertia, but also on how far the vibrational dipole changes coincide in direction with the principal axes of the molecule. The three moments of inertia are conventionally labelled I_A, I_B and I_C in ascending order; vibrations involving dipole changes parallel to the corresponding axes give A, B and C type bands (see p. 157). Envelopes for these band types were calculated by BADGER and ZUMWALT[121]; since the $P–R$ separation depends on the moments of inertia, it is possible to estimate the expected $P–R$ separation for a molecule of assumed geometry.

As a straightforward illustration of band contour types for a molecule whose symmetry is not in doubt, we may quote the spectra of $COCl_2$.

TABLE IX, 12

VIBRATIONS OF CARBONYL CHLORIDE (POINT GROUP C_{2v})

Approximate description of mode	Symmetry class			
	a_1	a_2	b_1	b_2
(C=O) stretching	ν_1			
(CCl$_2$) stretching	ν_2		ν_4	
(CCl$_2$) bending	ν_3			
(CCl$_2$) rocking			ν_5	
Out-of-plane bending				ν_6
Expected band contour	B	(inactive)	A	C

For the convention as to numbering the frequencies, see Chapter IV.

Carbonyl chloride belongs to the point group C_{2v}, for which the principal axes and the directions of the vibrational dipole changes coincide. A brief study of the molecule makes it clear that the A axis lies in the molecular

---

* The structure of perchloryl fluoride, ClO_3F, was shown to involve tetrahedrally-coordinated chlorine (point group C_{3v}) by a high-resolution study of the parallel and perpendicular bands[118], as well as by analysis of the vibrational spectrum under low resolution[119].

References pp. 340–344

plane but perpendicular to the (C=O) bond; the *B*-axis lies along the (C=O) bond, while the *C*-axis is perpendicular to the molecular plane. The vibrations, with their symmetry classes, are given in Table IX, 12; those of symmetry class a_1 give dipole changes parallel to the *B*-axis, those of symmetry class b_1 give dipole changes parallel to the *A*-axis, while those of symmetry class b_2 give dipole changes parallel to the *C*-axis, so the expected band contours are as given in the Table (see also Fig. IX,3). In the observed

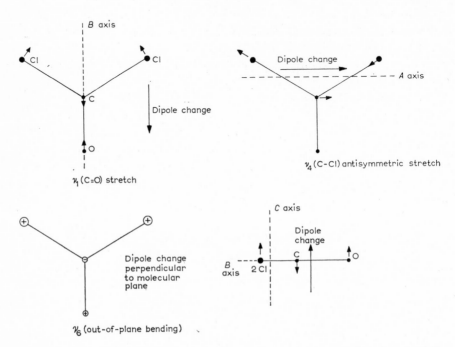

Fig. IX, 3. Very approximate representations of some of the normal modes of $COCl_2$.

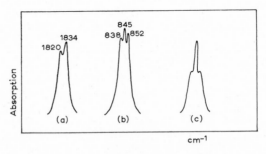

Fig. IX, 4. Contours of some of the bands in the vapour phase spectrum of $COCl_2$: (a) type-*B* band at 1827 cm⁻¹ (100-mm cell, 10 mm pressure); (b) type-*A* band at 849 cm⁻¹ (100-mm cell, 5 mm pressure, correction +4 cm⁻¹); (c) very approximate shape expected for type-*C* band (derived using reference 121).

spectrum (Fig. IX, 4) the type-B bands at 1827, 567 and 285 cm^{-1} are assigned to ν_1, ν_2 and ν_3 respectively; the type-A bands at 849 and 440 cm^{-1}, to ν_4 and ν_5, while the type-C band at 440 cm^{-1} represents ν_6 (the two overlapping bands near 570 cm^{-1}, ν_2 and ν_6, can be resolved under high resolution, and the different contours can be distinguished quite clearly[122]). Thus the fundamentals can be assigned almost entirely on the basis of their band contours. The observed contours depend significantly on the slit-widths used in recording the spectra, and the type-A band of one molecule might look like the type-C band of another, although in any given spectrum it is usually quite easy to distinguish type-A- and type-C-bands.

Where the dipole axes do not coincide with the principal axes of the molecule, the band contours are not so helpful. In $\boldsymbol{C_s}$-type molecules (having a single plane of symmetry) in which the heavy atoms lie in the plane of symmetry, the out-of-plane vibrations necessarily give type-C bands. The in-plane band contours are usually A/B hybrids, only by chance are pure A or B type bands observed. If the angles between the direction of dipole change and the principal axes are known, some approximate prediction of the band contours may be attempted. Band contours are of little help in the spectra of molecules of lower symmetry, or in the study of condensed phases.

(3) Structural Assessments

The examples presented in the remainder of this chapter illustrate aspects of molecular spectra discussed above. They have been chosen to give a realistic impression of structural diagnoses in that a number of the conclusions are of a tentative nature. The results of vibrational studies of some simple systems are summarized in Table IX, 13, which is followed by more detailed discussion of more complicated and perhaps more interesting cases.

(3A) Dinitrogen difluoride, N_2F_2

This compound exists in two isomeric forms, one of which is much more reactive than the other. The vapour infra-red spectrum of the inactive form is relatively simple, showing only one very strong band [132] (see Tables IX, 14 and 15), and so implies a relatively high symmetry; the planar *trans* structure is suggested[132] for this isomer (structure I below):

This has a centre of symmetry, a plane of symmetry and a two-fold axis perpendicular to the molecular plane, (point group $\boldsymbol{C_{2h}}$); the vibrations are

TABLE IX, 13

VIBRATIONAL FREQUENCIES AND SYMMETRY OF SOME SIMPLE SYSTEMS

v, l and s refer to vapour, liquid and solid phase spectra respectively. (p) and (dp) signify polarized and depolarized. *n.o.*, forbidden mode, not observed; *n.o.*, not observed; *n.s.*, forbidden mode, not studied in this range. Frequencies from combination modes are in square brackets. The italic numbers are the appropriate references.

MX_2		$HgCl_2$				SCl_2	
		$IR(v,\ 123)$	$R(v,\ 124)$			$IR(v,\ 125)$	$R(l,\ 126)$
$\boldsymbol{D_{\infty h}}$(linear)	σ_g^+	n.o.	355	$\boldsymbol{C_{2v}}$(bent)	a_1	[509]	514(p)
	σ_u^+	413	n.o.			[199]	208(p)
	π_u	n.s.	n.o.		b_1	525	535

MX_3		BF_3				$AsCl_3$	
		$IR(v,\ 127)$	$R(v,\ 128)$			$IR(l,\ 129)$	$R(l,\ 55)$
$\boldsymbol{D_{3h}}$(planar)	a_1'	n.o.	888	$\boldsymbol{C_{3v}}$(pyramidal)	a_1	412	405(p)
	a_2''*	691.5, 720	723			194	195(p)
	e'*	1446, 1497	1448, 1501		e	307(?)	370(dp)
		480.5, 482	439—513			155	158(dp)

MX_4		BF_4^-			SiF_4	
		$IR(s,\ 94)$	$R(l,\ 130)$		$IR(v,\ 49)$	$R(l,49)$
$\boldsymbol{T_d}$(tetrahedral)	a_1	n.o.	786		n.o.	800
	e	n.s.	369		n.o.	268
	f_2	~1100	1100		1031	1010
		~ 530	541		391	390

MX_6		OsF_6			$[SiF_6]^{2-}$	
		$IR(v,\ 131)$	$R(l,\ 131)$		$IR(s,\ 93)$	$R(l,\ 54)$
$\boldsymbol{O_h}$(octahedral)	a_{1g}	n.o.	733		n.o.	656
	e_g	n.o.	n.o. [632]		n.o.	510
	f_{1u}	720	n.o.		726	n.o.
		268			480	
	f_{2g}	n.o.	252		n.o.	n.o.
	f_{2u}	n.o.	n.o. [230]		n.o.	n.o.

* The pairs of frequencies for the a_2'' and e' modes arise because there are two isotopes of boron in appreciable concentration; the observation that the a_1 mode is single implies that the boron atom does not move in this vibration, affording strong support for the planar structure.

therefore of symmetry classes a_g, a_u, b_g and b_u (Herzberg, p. 106), and of these only the a_u and b_u modes are infra-red active, the others being Raman active but forbidden in the infra-red (the "mutual exclusion principle"). Only the out-of-plane mode should have a clear band contour; it should give a type-C band. Table IX, 15 shows that only three of the six fundamentals should be infra-red active; since, however, by the rule ($g \times u = u$), the only second order bands allowed are combinations of an infra-red and a Raman active fundamental, possible values for all the fundamental frequencies have

TABLE IX, 14

EXPECTED MODES OF *trans* N_2F_2

Approximate description of mode	Symmetry class			
	a_g	a_u	b_g	b_u
(N=N) stretching	ν_1			
(N–F) stretching	ν_2			ν_5
(NNF) bending	ν_3			ν_6
Torsion (out-of-plane)		ν_4		
Activity and band contour	R	IR	R	IR
	(p)	C	(dp)	A/B

TABLE IX, 15

OBSERVED SPECTRUM AND ASSIGNMENTS OF INACTIVE ISOMER N_2F_2[132]

Frequency (cm^{-1})	Assignment	Frequency (cm^{-1})	Assignment
360 m	ν_4	1581 m	$\nu_3+\nu_5$
421 m	ν_6	1996 m	$\nu_1+\nu_4$
989 vs	ν_5	2159 m	$\nu_2+\nu_6+2\nu_4$
1097 w	?	2871 vw	$\nu_2+\nu_6+4\nu_4$
1366 m	$\nu_2+\nu_4$	2975 vw	$2\nu_2+\nu_3+\nu_4$
1434 m	$\nu_2+\nu_6$		

been deduced from the combination bands. This tentative analysis needs to be supported by Raman data.

The infra-red spectrum of the active isomer is much richer in bands[132], implying that the structure has lower symmetry; moreover, the presence of bands with typical A-type and B-type contours suggests that the principal axes of the molecule may coincide with the directions of the vibrational dipole changes. The first possibility is that the active isomer is the planar *cis*-form (see II above). This structure would have two perpendicular planes of symmetry, with a two-fold axis along the junction of the planes (point group C_{2v}). The A axis is parallel to the (N=N) bond; the B axis is perpendicular to it and in the plane of the molecule, while the C axis is perpendicular to the molecular plane. The vibrations may be of symmetry classes a_1, a_2, b_1 or b_2, of which only the a_2 modes are forbidden in the infra-red*; the modes, with their symmetry classes, are given in Table IX, 16. The a_1 modes are associated with dipole changes parallel to the B axis, as is obvious for the symmetrical (N–F) stretching mode, ν_2 (see Fig. IX, 5); the b_1 modes are associated with dipole changes parallel to the A axis, as is clear for the antisymmetric (N–F) stretching mode, ν_5, while there are

---

* The letters a_1, a_2, b_1, etc, designate the symmetry species of the vibrations, and have no necessary connection with the A, B, or C axes.

TABLE IX, 16

VIBRATIONS OF *cis*-PLANAR N_2F_2 (POINT GROUP C_{2v})

Approximate description of mode	Symmetry class			
	a_1	a_2	b_1	b_2
(N=N) stretching	ν_1			
(N–F) stretching	ν_2		ν_5	
(NNF) bending	ν_3		ν_6	
twisting		ν_4		
Expected band contour	B	inactive	A	(C)

TABLE IX, 17

OBSERVED SPECTRUM OF ACTIVE ISOMER N_2F_2 (VAPOUR PHASE),[132] 400—1600 CM^{-1}

Frequency	Contour	Assignment
552 w	B	ν_3
573 vw	A?	$\nu_1-\nu_5$?
737 vs	A	ν_6
896 vs	B	ν_2
952 vs	A	ν_5
1096 vw	B	$2\nu_3$
1524 s	B	ν_1

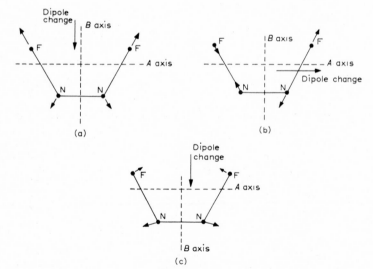

Fig. IX, 5. Very approximate representation of some of the normal modes of *cis*-N_2F_2.

(a) ν_2, (N–F) symmetrical stretching. (b) ν_5, (N–F) antisymmetrical stretching.
(c) ν_1, (N=N) stretching.

no b_2 modes. It is particularly important to notice that the (N=N) stretching mode, ν_1, gives a dipole change perpendicular to the (N=N) bond, and so is associated with a type-B band[133], despite the fact that the most obvious internuclear motion is parallel to the (N=N) bond and so to the A axis; this follows from the totally symmetric character of the vibration, which must therefore give rise to a dipole change in the same direction as for the other a_1 modes (See Fig. IX, 5).

Most of the assignments in Table IX, 17 follow from the observed band contours. The band at 737 cm^{-1} is here assigned to ν_6, in accordance with its type-A contour; the band at 573 cm^{-1}, which is weak, is assigned to a difference tone. Thus the observed spectrum can be accounted for satisfactorily on the basis of the proposed planar *cis*-structure.

It has been suggested [132] that the active isomer might have the unusual structure described as 1,1-difluorodiazene (formula III p. 327). Such a molecule would also belong to the point group $\boldsymbol{C_{2v}}$, and the expected vibrational modes are very much as for the planar *cis*-form. The main difference is that the out-of-plane bending mode, which is forbidden for the *cis*-compound, is in this case infra-red active, and should give a type-C band. The published spectrum shows no type-C contour, and this mode (*cf*. COF$_2$) would be expected at a frequency higher than 500 cm^{-1}. The *cis*-structure provides rather the better account of the infra-red absorptions but the third structure is not finally eliminated. Detection of the a_2 mode of the *cis*-compound in the Raman spectrum would reinforce the above evidence.

(3B) Sulphur tetrafluoride, SF_4[134]

Several structures are possible for this molecule. If all four fluorines are equivalent, then tetrahedral (a), square-planar (b) and square-pyramidal (c)

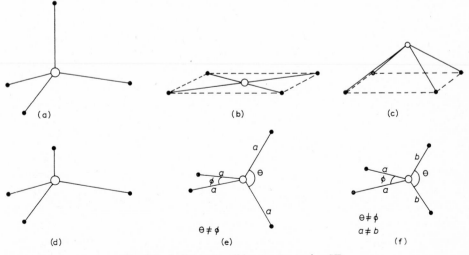

Fig. IX, 6. Some possible structures for SF$_4$.

structures (see Fig. IX, 6) must be considered. If only three fluorines are equivalent, the fourth being symmetrically placed with respect to them, the point group would be C_{3v}(d). With equal (S–F) bond lengths, but two different FSF angles, the point group would be D_{2d} if the two FSF planes were perpendicular to one another (e); if the (S–F) bonds in one plane differed in length from those in the perpendicular plane (f) the point group would be C_{2v} and not D_{2d}, while less symmetrical structures, such as that with four different (S–F) bond lengths (point group C_1) might occur. Of these possibilities the most likely is perhaps the C_{2v} model, because the analogous TeCl$_4$ has this structure[135]. Since the various structures differ in the number and activity of their vibrational modes, a study of the vibrational spectra might at least eliminate some of them.

TABLE IX, 18

POINT GROUPS, AND ANALYSIS OF NUMBER AND ACTIVITY OF MODES, FOR THE VARIOUS POSSIBLE STRUCTURES FOR SF$_4$[134]

Point group	n_i	n_R	n_c	n_p
C_1	9	9	9	9
C_{2v}	8	9	8	4
C_{3v}	6	6	6	3
C_{4v}	4	7	4	2
D_{2d}	4	7	4	2
D_{4h}	3	3	0	1
T_d	2	4	2	1

n_i, number of infra-red active modes.
n_R, number of Raman active modes.
n_c, number of coincidences between infra-red and Raman.
n_p, number of polarized Raman lines.

Table IX, 18 shows the number of distinct fundamentals expected in the infra-red and Raman for the different models. A preliminary study showed that at least six frequencies in the two spectra (taken together) were of sufficient intensity for fundamental modes, and many other features could be accounted for as combinations of these. As the infra-red spectrum was recorded only for frequencies higher than 400 cm^{-1}, a complete count of coincidences was not possible; nonetheless, in the range for which both spectra were available at least four coincidences occurred. In the Raman spectrum, at least one line was polarized and at least three were depolarized. These observations alone exclude all the models except those belonging to the point groups C_{2v} and C_{3v}; a decision between these was reached by studying the vapour phase infra-red band contours. They were not at all like those expected of a symmetric top molecule, but could be interpreted as types A, B and C-bands of an asymmetric top with moments of inertia roughly equal to those expected of the C_{2v} model. Doubts remain about the assignments of two of the nine fundamentals, but the vibrational spectra afford significant evidence in favour of the C_{2v} model[134]. This structure is supported by the n.m.r. spectrum of the compound[135, 136].

(3C) Halogen fluorides

Chlorine trifluoride has a T-shaped structure, in which the central ClF bond is shorter than the other two[137]. Its infra-red spectrum has been analysed in terms of the required point group (C_{2v}), making use of band contours[138]. The infra-red[139] and Raman[140] spectra of BrF_5 have been interpreted in terms of a square-pyramid structure (point group C_{4v}), while the vibrational spectra of IF_7 imply a pentagonal bipyramid structure (point group D_{5h})[141]. The assignments are summarized in Table IX, 19.

TABLE IX, 19

FUNDAMENTAL FREQUENCIES AND STRUCTURES OF SOME HALOGEN FLUORIDES

v and l refer to vapour and liquid phase spectra respectively. (p) and (dp) signify polarized and depolarized. *n.o.*, forbidden mode, not observed; n.o., not observed; n.s., not studied in this range. Modes in square brackets are derived from combination bands. The italic numbers are the appropriate references.

		IR(v, 138)	R(l, 138,142)			IR(v, 139)	R(l, 140)
ClF_3	a_1	751(type B)	753	BrF_5	a_1	690	683(p)
		527(type B)	529			583	572(p)
C_{2v}		326(type B)	321	C_{4v}		n.s.	365(p)
(T-shaped)	b_1	703(type A)		(square pyramid)	b_1	*n.o.*	536(dp)
		434 ?	424		b_2	*n.o.*	481(dp)
	b_2	364 ?	n.o.			n.s.	315(dp)
					e	645	626(dp)
						418	415(dp)
						n.s.	244(dp)

IF_7	D_{5h} (pentagonal bipyramid, *141*)					
	a_1'	a_2''	e_1'	e_1''	e_2'	e_2''
IR(v)	*n.o.*	670, 368	547, 426, [250]	*n.o.*	*n.o.*	*n.o.*
R(l)	678, 635	*n.o.*	*n.o.*	360	511, 313	*n.o.*

(3D) Diboron tetrachloride, B_2Cl_4

Electron diffraction of the vapour of this compound indicated that the two (Cl_2B) groups were rotated about the (B–B) bond at 90° to one another (point group V_d)[143]; an X-ray study of the solid, however, showed that the whole molecule is planar in this phase (point group V_h)[144]. The main difference between the two structures is that the planar model has a centre of symmetry, so that there should be no coincidences between the infra-red and Raman spectra. For the non-planar model, though the a_1 and b_1 modes are allowed only in the Raman, the b_2 and e modes are active in both spectra, so that there should be a number of coincidences (see Table IX, 20).

TABLE IX, 20

PREDICTIONS AND OBSERVED SPECTRA FOR B_2Cl_4

(see Tables IX, 18 and 19 for meaning of abbreviations)

Predicted for	n_i	n_R	n_c	$n_{(p)}$
V_h	5	6	0	3
V_d	5	9	5	3
Observed	4	7	3	2

Symmetry class	Observed frequencies (cm^{-1}) (145)	
	Raman	Infra-red
a_1	1131 (p)	n.o.
	401 (p)	n.o.
	225	n.o.
b_2	729 (vvw)	730 (vvs)
	291 (m)	291 (m)
e	917 (m)	917 (vvs)
	n.o.	617
	180	n.s.

Though the Raman spectrum was only obtained in the liquid phase and the infra-red spectrum in the vapour phase, the vibrational spectra taken together clearly indicate the non-planar model[145]. There are three coincidences between infra-red and Raman spectra, though in one the Raman line is admittedly very weak; of the predicted coincidences for the V_d model, one could not be checked because the Raman line (180 cm^{-1}) was at a frequency below the infra-red range studied, while only one coincidence expected on the basis of the V_d structure was not observed (the Raman line was missing).

(3E) Disiloxane, $(SiH_3)_2O$

The planar arrangement of the heavy atoms of trisilylamine[146], in contrast to the pyramidal trimethylamine[147], makes the question of the (SiOSi) angle in disiloxane of considerable interest. The skeleton is effectively a triatomic system, and all three skeletal modes should be active in both infra-red and Raman for a bent configuration (point group C_{2v}). For a linear configuration there is a centre of symmetry; the antisymmetric stretching and the bending modes are infra-red active but Raman forbidden, while the symmetrical stretching mode is Raman active but forbidden in the infra-red. The Raman spectrum of the liquid[3] showed no line that could reasonably be assigned to a skeletal bending mode, while a strong and polarized line at 606 cm^{-1} was clearly due to the symmetrical skeletal stretching mode. This was missing from the infra-red spectrum of the vapour³ even at high pressure in a long-path cell[148]. At the same time, the very strong infra-red band at 1107 cm⁻¹ that was missing from the Raman spectrum was relatively unaffected by deuteration, and so was assigned to the antisymmetric skeletal stretching mode³. All this strongly suggests that the skeleton is linear and not bent, an interpretation that was reinforced by the observation of two skeletal stretching modes in the infra-red and Raman spectra of disilyl sulphide[4, 149]; moreover, the skeletal bending vibration was Raman active for disilyl sulphide and disilyl selenide[149]. The very large splitting of the stretching modes in the oxygen derivative (ca. 500 cm⁻¹), which drops to ca. 35 cm⁻¹ in the bent sulphide, is more what would be expected of a linear than of a bent molecule.

A study of the bands due to the SiH_3-rocking modes in the infra-red spectrum of disiloxane frozen in an argon matrix showed that under these conditions two bands could be resolved[148]; for a molecule with a linear skeleton the rocking mode should be doubly degenerate, and only one band should appear. Finally, a very elegant piece of Raman spectroscopy showed that the molecule is almost certainly bent[150]. A sample was prepared enriched with ¹⁸O, and the Raman line due to the symmetrical skeletal stretching mode of the enriched sample showed a new shoulder on the low-frequency side. This means that this frequency is sensitive to the mass of the oxygen atom, and that the oxygen atom must move in the vibration; this would not happen for a symmetrical linear system, indicating that the skeleton is probably bent. A later electron diffraction study[151] indicates that the (SiOSi) angle is about 145°. The low frequency infra-red absorptions[152] and a theoretical study of the system[153], have led to a reinterpretation of the vibrational spectra in terms of a *pseudo*-linear model — that is, a model whose configuration of minimum potential energy is at a bond angle of appreciably less than 180°, but whose potential well for the bending mode is broad and flat. These calculations show that the selection rules followed at room temperature are those of the linear system, though there are some modifications of the spectrum that are not expected for a truly linear skeleton.

(3F) Nitric acid monohydrate

The infra-red spectrum of nitric acid monohydrate in the liquid phase does not differ significantly from the spectra of other aqueous nitric acid solutions. In the solid state, however, a new and very strong absorption appears at about 1130 cm⁻¹. This has been assigned to the deformation mode of $(H_3O)^+$, by analogy with the isoelectronic NH_3[154]. The spectra of crystalline monohydrates of the hydrogen halides confirmed that this assignment was correct[155], and established that the solid nitrate is $(H_3O)^+NO_3^-$. A similar study has shown that the monohydrate of perchloric acid is ionized as $(H_3O)^+ClO_4^-$ in both solid and liquid phases[154].

(3G) Nitrogen pentoxide, N_2O_5

The infra-red spectrum of the vapour is the same as that of the rapidly-condensed solid, and can be interpreted in terms of the vibrations of two nitro groups linked through a non-linear (NON) bridge, the relative orientations of the (NON) plane and the two nitro groups being uncertain[156]. The vibrational spectra of the stable crystalline solid are quite different; they consist of a superposition of the spectra of the $(NO_2)^+$ and $(NO_3)^-$ ions, showing that these are the structural units in the crystal[157, 158]. This is in agreement with an X-ray analysis[159].

Brief mention should be made of an interesting study of the vibrational spectra of the oxides of nitrogen in matrices at low temperatures. The existence of isomeric dimers is suggested to explain the spectra of NO, N_2O_3 and N_2O_4[156].

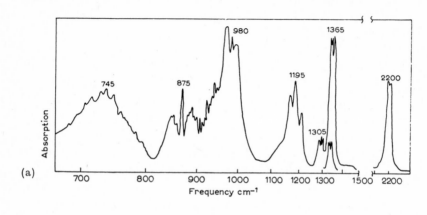

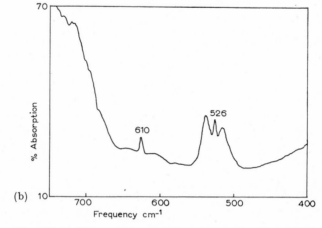

Fig. IX, 7. Vapour phase spectrum for worked example (3).
(a) 2300—650 cm⁻¹ (pressure *ca.* 10 mm and *ca.* 1 mm in 100-mm cell).
(b) 750—400 cm⁻¹ (pressure *ca.* 30 mm, 100-mm cell).

Worked example (3) Figs. IX, 7(a) and 7(b) show the spectrum of volatile material formed when SiH_3SCF_3 decomposes at room temperature. What can be deduced from this spectrum about the nature of the decomposition products? (This example is discussed on p. 339).

(4) Electronic Interpretation of Vibrational Spectra

Numerous attempts have been made to deduce information about the electronic structures of molecules from their vibrational spectra. The commonest approach is to use vibrational frequencies or force constants as indices of bond character. Vibrational frequencies, however, depend not only on the nature of the bond or bonds concerned, but also on the masses of the bonded atoms and the vibrations of neighbouring groups; force constants are more directly related to the properties of particular bonds, and should always be used in preference to vibrational frequencies in discussions of this kind. In COF_2, for example, the (C=O) stretching frequency is about 100 cm^{-1} higher than in $COBr_2$[122, 160] or $COCl_2$[122], which has been ascribed to the higher electronegativity of fluorine; the (C=O) stretching force constants, however, are very similar in all three molecules[160], so that the change in frequency is apparently a mass effect. The same may well be true of the effect of fluorine substitution on the (S=O) stretching frequency in sulphur(IV) compounds[74, 79]. The calculated force constants themselves will depend on the type of force field assumed (see Chapter V), while the relationship between force constants and electronic structures of bonds is imperfectly understood. Thus there is an element of uncertainty in all these studies, of which some typical examples are outlined in the following paragraphs.

Several scales of electronegativity have been based on the force constants found for diatomic and polyatomic molecules[161-163]; there is a roughly linear relationship[163] between the (M–H) force constant and the square of the Pauling electronegativity of M.

In the isoelectronic series MH_4^n (M is B, C or N; Al, Si or P), MX_4^{n-} (M is Zn, Ga or Ge; Cd, In or Sn, and X is Cl, Br or I), the force constant changes inversely with the interatomic distance; in the oxides MO_4^{n-} (M is P, S or Cl; W, Re or Os) this is not true, and it has been concluded that π-bonding is important only in the oxides[164]. Formulae have been devised for predicting the force constants of ideal, single bonds between two elements from fundamental atomic parameters[165, 166]: predicted force constants are then compared with those obtained from the observed spectra, the low observed values being put down to ionic character and the high observed values to π-bonding[39, 54, 165, 166]. The significance of these formulae is distinctly limited, since their validity for ideal, single bonds cannot be properly tested, but unusually high force constants and vibrational frequencies are often ascribed to π-bonding. In Me_2NBCl_2 the (B–N) stretching mode is at the abnormally high frequency for a single bond of 1526 cm^{-1}, which leads to the large force constant of 7 mdyne/Å: this has been explained in terms of $(p \to p)$ π-bonding from nitrogen to boron[167].

The lowering of the (C=O) stretching frequency of carbon monoxide on coordination to a transition metal is associated with a decrease in the force constant from *ca.* 19 mdyne/Å in the gas[168] to 16—17.5 mdyne/Å in nickel carbonyl (the exact value depending on the type of force field assumed[168,169]), though in BH_3CO the (C≡O) stretching force constant may be much the same as in carbon monoxide[170]. The decrease in the metal carbonyls is believed to be due to electron donation from filled d-orbitals of π-symmetry on the metal atom to the anti-bonding π-orbitals of the (C≡O) group. Changes in (C≡O) stretching force constant in a number of metal carbonyl derivatives have been correlated with the π-electron acceptor properties of the other ligands[102,168]*. A similar type of deduction has been made from the increase in (C≡N) stretching frequency in complex cyanides for bridging as against terminal groups, but this has also been explained in terms of vibrational interactions using an unchanged (C≡N) force constant[103].

The relationships between vibrational frequencies and bond energies or reactivity in transition metal compounds have been extensively studied. In ammines the (N–H) stretching force constant drops as the (M–N) force constant increases[60]; there is a very rough correlation between the (NH_3) symmetrical deformation and rocking frequencies and the stability constants, and there is a closer relationship between the frequencies of bands believed to represent (M–N) stretching modes in hydrazine complexes and the solution heats of formation of the analogous ethylenediamine complexes[171]. It must be borne in mind, however, that stability constants and solution heats of formation refer to exchange reactions in aqueous solution. In complex hydrides of platinum the (Pt–H) stretching frequency varies inversely with the activating effect of the *"trans"*-ligand[172], and studies have been made of the influence of *trans*-ligands on the (Pt–N)[173], (N–H)[174,175] and (Pt–C)[176] stretching frequencies. Studies of the (N–H) modes may be confused by hydrogen bonding, which must be eliminated by recording spectra in inert solvents[174].

(5) Worked Examples

(1) p. 322. The bands at 1502 cm^{-1} and 1269 cm^{-1} strongly suggest the presence of $\displaystyle >S\big<{}^O_O$ with O or F bound to the sulphur atom. The complex

---

* Two particularly interesting discussions of the spectra of substituted mononuclear metal carbonyls in these terms have recently appeared[187,188].

pattern of bands between 700 and 1000 cm^{-1} is like that in SF$_5$derivatives such as S$_2$F$_{10}$ or SF$_5$Cl, so a plausible structure on the infra-red evidence would be F$_5$SOSF. An analysis of the n.m.r spectrum confirmed this[177].

(The structure is drawn with an O double-bonded above and below the central S atoms: F_5SOSF with O atoms above and below.)

(2) p. 323. The single peak at about 3100 cm^{-1} implies the presence of a π–C$_5$H$_5$ group; the other two strong bands shown are in the regions associated with terminal and bridging carbonyl groups respectively. This suggests that the compound may be polymeric, with both terminal and bridging (CO) groups; from the molecular weight, 354, the dimeric structure:

$$\text{(C}_5\text{H}_5\text{)Fe} \underset{\diagdown(CO)\diagup}{\overset{\diagup(CO)\diagdown}{\quad}} \text{Fe(C}_5\text{H}_5\text{)}$$

(with terminal C≡O groups on each Fe pointing downward)

might seem plausible[178], and this has been confirmed by X-ray analysis[179] (though the arrangement of (C$_5$H$_5$) and terminal (CO) groups is not as shown). The absence of (Fe–H) could be established by deuteration.

(3) p. 337. The bands at 2200 and 970 cm^{-1} show that one component contains (Si–H) bonds; the "strong, weak, weak, strong" rotational detail apparent in the bands at about 970 and 750 cm^{-1}, together with the wide separation of the PQR branches of the band at 875 cm^{-1}, indicate the presence of a symmetric top molecule with small moments of inertia. The most probable species is SiH$_3$F, and a glance at the spectrum of this compound shows beyond doubt that SiH$_3$F is a major constituent of the mixture. This leaves the moderate to strong bands at 1368, $\sim$1200, and 526 cm^{-1} unaccounted for. The band at about 1200 cm^{-1} is of the frequency and intensity of a (C–F) stretching mode; the band contours at 1360, 1310 and 526 cm^{-1} resemble the type-A bands of an asymmetric top molecule with small moments of inertia; the band at 610 cm^{-1} appears to be a rather weak type C band, possibly of the same molecule, while the complex envelope at about 1200 cm^{-1} might well include at least one type-B band. If fluorosilane is one component of the original material, then by simple stoichiometry the other should be thiocarbonyl fluoride, SCF$_2$, which belongs to the point group $\mathcal{C}_{2v}$:

$$\text{SiH}_3\text{SCF}_3 = \text{SiH}_3\text{F} + \text{SCF}_2$$

Attempts to separate the two components were partly successful, and another type-A band was found at about 788 cm^{-1}. On the basis of the observed band contours, the vibrational assignments of Table IX, 21 were made, which compare well with the analogous frequencies of carbonyl fluoride. The value of ν_5 was deduced from a combination band. Taking

TABLE IX, 21

FREQUENCIES (CM^{-1}) AND ASSIGNMENTS FOR SCF$_2$, WITH COMPARABLE VALUES FOR OCF$_2$

Frequency and contour		Assignment for SCF$_2$	Value in OCF$_2$
1368 vs	type A	(S=C) stretch, ν_1	1942
1312 w	type A	$788+526$, $\nu_2+\nu_3$	
1212 s	overlapping type B bands?	$788+422$, $\nu_2+\nu_5$	
1188 s		(CF$_2$) stretch (asym.), ν_4	1249
788 m	type A	(CF$_2$) stretch (sym.), ν_2	965
622 w	type C	out-of-plane bend, ν_6	774
526 m	type A	(CF$_2$) scissors, ν_3	626
422 w	type B	(CF$_2$) rock, ν_5*	584

* Originally deduced from 1212 combination frequency; since observed as a weak band in the spectrum of the pure compound.

reasonable values for the molecular dimensions, the Badger and Zumwalt parameters were calculated to be $S = -\frac{1}{2}$ and $\rho = \frac{5}{4}$, leading to predicted PR-separations of 18, 14 and 22 cm^{-1} for type A, B and C bands respectively; the observed values were 18, 14 and 20 cm^{-1}. Thus although thiocarbonyl fluoride had not been isolated or characterized, its presence was established in the material and a vibrational assignment made. This assignment has since been confirmed[180].

FURTHER READING

FERRARO's article[9] gives an interesting general account of the inorganic applications of infra-red spectroscopy, while that by COTTON[8], though limited to the spectra of transition metals, is most valuable and stimulating. LAWSON's book[181], though it has some faults, is very useful as a compilation of references.

REFERENCES

[1] N. S. HAM AND J. B. WILLIS, Spectrochim. Acta, 16 (1960) 279.

[2] F. A. MILLER AND W. B. WHITE, Z. Elektrochem., 64 (1960) 701.

[3] R. C. LORD, D. W. ROBINSON AND W. C. SCHUMB, J. Am. Chem. Soc., 78 (1956) 1327.

[4] H. R. LINTON AND E. R. NIXON, J. Chem. Phys., 29 (1958) 921.

[5] L. J. BELLAMY, The Infrared Spectra of Complex Molecules, 2nd. Ed., Methuen, London, 1958.

[6] F. A. MILLER AND C. H. WILKINS, Anal. Chem., 24 (1952) 1253.

[7] F. A. MILLER, G. L. CARLSON, F. F. BENTLEY AND W. H. JONES, Spectrochim. Acta, 16 (1961) 135.

[8] F. A. COTTON, in Modern Coordination Chemistry, J. LEWIS AND R. G. WILKINS (Editors), Interscience, New York, 1960, p. 301.

[9] Examples given by J. R. FERRARO, J. Chem. Educ., 38 (1961) 201.

[10] G. F. SVATOS, D. M. SWEENY, S. MITZUSHIMA, C. CURRAN AND J. V. QUAGLIANO, J. Am. Chem. Soc., 79 (1957) 3313.

[11] L. J. BELLAMY, W. GERRARD, M. F. LAPPERT AND R. L. WILLIAMS, J. Chem. Soc., (1958) 2412.

[12] W. J. LEHMANN AND I. SHAPIRO, *Spectrochim. Acta*, 17 (1961) 396.

[13] G. SCHOMBURG AND E. G. HOFMANN, *Z. Elektrochem.*, 61 (1957) 1111.

[14] A. L. SMITH AND N. C. ANGELOTTI, *Spectrochim. Acta*, 15 (1959) 412.

[15] G. J. JANZ AND Y. MIKAWA, *Bull. Chem. Soc. Japan*, 34 (1961) 1495.

[16] M. P. BROWN, R. OKAWARA AND E. G. ROCHOW, *Spectrochim. Acta*, 16 (1960) 595.

[17] V. S. GRIFFITHS AND G. A. W. DERWISH, *J. Mol. Spectry.*, 5 (1960) 148.

[18] D. E. C. CORBRIDGE AND E. J. LOWE, *J. Chem. Soc.*, (1954) 493, 4555.

[19] L. J. BELLAMY AND L. BEECHER, *J. Chem. Soc.*, (1953) 728.

[20] D. F. PEPPARD, J. R. FERRARO AND G. W. MASON, *J. Inorg. Nucl. Chem.*, 12 (1959) 60.

[21] D. A. DOWS AND R. M. HEXTER, *J. Chem. Phys.*, 24 (1956) 1029.

[22] R. C. LORD AND C. M. STEESE, *J. Chem. Phys.*, 22 (1954) 542.

[23] V. M. McCONAGHIE AND H. H. NIELSEN, *Proc. Natl. Acad. Sci. U.S.*, 34 (1948) 455.

[24] D. M. CAMERON, W. C. SEARS AND H. H. NIELSEN, *J. Chem. Phys.*, 7 (1939) 994.

[25] D. R. LIDE, *J. Chem. Phys.*, 19 (1951) 1605.

[26] H. J. EMELÉUS AND S. F. A. KETTLE, *J. Chem. Soc.*, (1958) 2444.

[27] W. H. HAYNIE AND H. H. NIELSEN, *J. Chem. Phys.*, 21 (1953) 1839.

[28] K. ROSSMAN AND J. W. STRALEY, *J. Chem. Phys.*, 24 (1956) 1276.

[29] M. L. H. GREEN, *Angew. Chem.*, 72 (1960) 719.

[30] W. C. PRICE, H. C. LONGUET-HIGGINS, B. RICE AND T. F. YOUNG, *J. Chem. Phys.*, 17 (1949) 217.

[31] E. A. V. EBSWORTH AND N. SHEPPARD, *Spectrochim. Acta*, 13 (1959) 261.

[32] N. SHEPPARD, *Trans. Faraday Soc.*, 51 (1955) 1465.

[33] G. BETHKE AND M. K. WILSON, *J. Chem. Phys.*, 26 (1957) 1107.

[34] C. NEWMAN, J. K. O'LOANE, S. R. POLO AND M. K. WILSON, *J. Chem. Phys.*, 25 (1956) 855.

[35] W. P. EDGELL, G. ASATO, W. WILSON AND C. ANGELL, *J. Am. Chem. Soc.*, 81 (1959) 2022; W. P. EDGELL AND R. SUMMIT, *J. Am. Chem. Soc.*, 83 (1961) 1772.

[36] S. N. NABI AND N. SHEPPARD, *J. Chem. Soc.*, (1959) 3439.

[37] J. R. HALL, N. SHEPPARD AND L. A. WOODWARD, *Spectrochim. Acta*, 15 (1959) 249.

[38] N. SHEPPARD AND D. M. SIMPSON, *Quart. Rev. (London)*, 7 (1953) 19.

[39] H. SIEBERT, *Z. Anorg. Allgem. Chem.*, 273 (1953) 161; 271 (1952) 65.

[40] G. HERZBERG, *Infrared and Raman Spectra of Polyatomic Molecules*, Van Nostrand, New York, 1945, p. 315.

[41] K. S. PITZER AND R. K. SHELINE, *J. Chem. Phys.*, 16 (1948) 552.

[42] H. SIEBERT, *Z. Anorg. Allgem. Chem.*, 268 (1951) 177.

[43] J. R. HALL AND L. A. WOODWARD, unpublished observations (personal communication).

[44] R. K. SHELINE AND K. S. PITZER, *J. Chem. Phys.*, 18 (1950) 595.

[45] G. HERZBERG, *Infrared and Raman Spectra of Polyatomic Molecules*, Van Nostrand, New York, 1945, p. 299.

[46] P. J. H. WOLTZ AND A. H. NIELSEN, *J. Chem. Phys.*, 20 (1952) 307.

[47] M. K. WILSON AND S. R. POLO, *J. Chem. Phys.*, 20 (1952) 1716.

[48] H. J. BERNSTEIN AND J. POWLING, *J. Chem. Phys.*, 18 (1950) 685.

[49] E. A. JONES, J. S. KIRBY-SMITH, P. J. H. WOLTZ AND A. H. NIELSEN, *J. Chem. Phys.*, 19 (1951) 242.

[50] A. D. GAUNT, L. N. SHORT AND L. A. WOODWARD, *Trans. Faraday Soc.*, 48 (1952) 873.

[51] D. M. YOST AND J. E. SHERBORNE, *J. Chem. Phys.*, 2 (1934) 125.

[52] R. E. SCRUBY, J. R. LACHER AND J. D. PARK, *J. Chem. Phys.*, 19 (1951) 386.

[53] T. WENTINK AND V. H. TIENSUU, *J. Chem. Phys.*, 28 (1958) 826.

[54] H. SIEBERT, *Z. Anorg. Allgem. Chem.*, 274 (1953) 34.

[55] M. L. DELWAULLE, *J. Phys. Chem.*, 56 (1952) 355.

[56] D. F. HEATH AND J. W. LINNETT, *Trans. Faraday Soc.*, 44 (1948) 561.

[57] H. STAMMREICH, R. FORNERIS AND Y. TAVAREZ, *J. Chem. Phys.*, 25 (1956) 1279.

[58] M. P. BROWN, E. CARTMELL AND G. W. A. FOWLES, *J. Chem. Soc.*, (1960) 506.

[59] D. B. POWELL AND N. SHEPPARD, *J. Chem. Soc.*, (1956) 3108.

[60] T. SHIMANOUCHI AND I. NAKAGAWA, *Spectrochim. Acta*, 18 (1962) 89.

[61] L. H. JONES, *J. Chem. Phys.*, 28 (1958) 1215.

[62] H. MURATA AND K. KAWAI, *J. Chem. Phys.*, 27 (1957) 605.

[63] G. HERZBERG, *Infrared and Raman Spectra of Polyatomic Molecules*, Van Nostrand, New York, 1945, p. 272.

[64] G. HERZBERG, *Infrared and Raman Spectra of Polyatomic Molecules*, Van Nostrand, New York, 1945, p. 277.

[65] P. GRAY AND A. D. YOFFE, *Chem. Rev.*, 55 (1955) 1069.

[66] P. GRAY AND T. C. WADDINGTON, *Trans. Faraday Soc.*, 53 (1957) 901.

[67] S. K. DEB AND A. D. YOFFE, *Trans. Faraday Soc.*, 55 (1959) 106.

[68] A. MAKI AND J. C. DECIUS, *J. Chem. Phys.*, 31 (1959) 772.

[69] L. H. JONES, *J. Chem. Phys.*, 25 (1956) 1069.

[70] H. W. MORGAN, *J. Inorg. Nucl. Chem.*, 16 (1960) 367.

[71] T. E. GIER, *J. Am. Chem. Soc.*, 83 (1961) 1769.

[72] M. L. DELWAULLE AND F. FRANCOIS, *Compt. Rend.*, 220 (1945) 817.

[73] F. A. MILLER AND L. R. COUSINS, *J. Chem. Phys.*, 26 (1957) 329.

[74] R. J. GILLESPIE AND E. A. ROBINSON, *Can. J. Chem.*, 39 (1961) 2171.

[75] M. F. A. DOVE, *Ph.D. Thesis*, Cambridge (England) 1961.

[76] L. J. BELLAMY, *The Infrared Spectra of Complex Molecules*, 2nd Ed., Methuen, London, 1958, p. 350.

[77] C. G. BARRACLOUGH, J. LEWIS AND R. S. NYHOLM, *J. Chem. Soc.*, (1959) 3552.

[78] L. H. JONES, *J. Chem. Phys.*, 23 (1955) 2105.

[79] L. J. BELLAMY, *The Infrared Spectra of Complex Molecules*, 2nd Ed., Methuen, London, 1958, p. 311.

[80] J. LEWIS AND G. WILKINSON, *J. Inorg. Nucl. Chem.*, 6 (1958) 12.

[81] P. L. GOGGIN, H. L. ROBERTS AND L. A. WOODWARD, *Trans. Faraday Soc.*, 57 (1961) 1877.

[82] R. E. WESTON AND T. F. BRODASKY, *J. Chem. Phys.*, 27 (1957) 683.

[83] J. P. MATTHIEU, *Compt. Rend.*, 234 (1953) 2272.

[84] G. HERZBERG, *Infrared and Raman Spectra of Polyatomic Molecules*, Van Nostrand, New York, 1945, p. 178.

[85] A. SIMON AND K. WALDEMANN, *Z. Physik. Chem. (Leipzig)*, 204 (1955) 235.

[86] K. W. F. KOHLRAUSCH, *Ramanspektren*, Becher and Eisler, Leipzig, 1943, p. 135.

[87] K. W. F. KOHLRAUSCH, *Ramanspektren*, Becher and Eisler, Leipzig, 1943, p. 412.

[88] K. W. F. KOHLRAUSCH, *Ramanspektren*, Becher and Eisler, Leipzig, 1943, p. 151.

[89] H. STAMMREICH, D. BASSI AND O. SALA, *Spectrochim. Acta*, 12 (1958) 403.

[90] H. H. CLAASEN AND A. J. ZEILEN, *J. Chem. Phys.*, 22 (1954) 707.

[91] B. M. GATEHOUSE, S. E. LIVINGSTONE AND R. S. NYHOLM, *J. Chem. Soc.*, (1958) 3137.

[92] S. D. ROSS, *Spectrochim. Acta*, 18 (1962) 225.

[93] R. D. PEACOCK AND D. W. A. SHARP, *J. Chem. Soc.*, (1959) 2762.

[94] G. L. COTÉ AND H. W. THOMPSON, *Proc. Roy. Soc. (London)*, Ser. A., 210 (1951) 217.

[95] B. M. GATEHOUSE, S. E. LIVINGSTONE AND R. S. NYHOLM, *J. Chem. Soc.*, (1957) 4222.

[96] K. BUJIS AND C. J. H. SCHUTTE, *Spectrochim. Acta*, 18 (1962) 307.

[97] C. C. ADDISON AND B. M. GATEHOUSE, *Chem. Ind. (London)*, (1958) 464.

[98] K. NAKAMOTO, J. FUJITA, S. TANAKA AND M. KOBAYASHI, *J. Am. Chem. Soc.*, 79 (1957) 4904.

[99] J. FUJITA, K. NAKAMOTO AND M. KOBAYASHI, *J. Phys. Chem.*, 61 (1957) 1014.

[100] E. P. BERTIN, R. B. PENLAND, S. MITZUSHIMA, C. CURRAN AND J. V. QUAGLIANO, *J. Am. Chem. Soc.*, 81 (1959) 3818.

[101] G. F. SVATOS, C. CURRAN AND J. V. QUAGLIANO, *J. Am. Chem. Soc.*, 77 (1955) 6159.

[102] F. A. COTTON, in J. LEWIS AND R. G. WILKINS (Editors), *Modern Coordination Chemistry*, Interscience, New York, 1960, p. 344-6.

[103] D. A. DOWS, A. HAIM AND W. K. WILMARTH, *J. Inorg. Nucl. Chem.*, 21 (1961) 33.

[104] A. TRAMER, *J. Chim. Phys.*, 59 (1962) 232.

[105] R. B. PENLAND, T. J. LANE AND J. V. QUAGLIANO, *J. Am. Chem. Soc.*, 78 (1956) 887.

[106] E. O. BRIMM, M. A. LYNCH AND W. J. SESNY, *J. Am. Chem. Soc.*, 76 (1954) 3831.

[107] L. DAHL, E. ISHISHI AND R. RUNDLE, *J. Chem. Phys.*, 26 (1957) 1750.

[108] W. P. GRIFFITH AND G. WILKINSON, *J. Inorg. Nucl. Chem.*, 7 (1958) 295.

[109] H. A. BRUNE AND W. ZEIL, *Z. Naturforsch.*, 16a (1961) 1251.

[110] F. A. COTTON AND R. V. PARISH, *J. Chem. Soc.*, (1960) 1440.

[111] D. M. SEYFERTH AND N. KAHLEN, *J. Am. Chem. Soc.*, **82** (1960) 1080.

[112] D. B. POWELL AND N. SHEPPARD, *Spectrochim. Acta*, **13** (1958) 69.

[113] H. B. JONASSEN AND W. B. KIRSCH, *J. Am. Chem. Soc.*, **79** (1957) 1279.

[114] J. CHATT, L. A. DUNCANSON, B. M. GATEHOUSE, J. LEWIS, R. S. NYHOLM, M. L. TOBE, P. F. TODD AND L. M. VENANZI, *J. Chem. Soc.*, (1959) 4073.

[115] R. E. DODD, L. A. WOODWARD AND H. L. ROBERTS, *Trans. Faraday Soc.*, **53** (1957) 1545.

[116] J. A. A. KETELAAR, *Spectrochim. Acta*, **14** (1959) 237.

[117] J. C. EVANS AND H. J. BERNSTEIN, *Can. J. Chem.*, **34** (1956) 1127.

[118] R. P. MADDEN AND W. S. BENEDICT, *J. Chem. Phys.*, **25** (1956) 594.

[119] D. R. LIDE AND D. E. MANN, *J. Chem. Phys.*, **25** (1956) 1128.

[120] S. L. GERHARD AND D. M. DENNISON, *Phys. Rev.*, **43** (1932) 197.

[121] R. M. BADGER AND L. R. ZUMWALT, *J. Chem. Phys.*, **6** (1938) 711.

[122] J. OVEREND AND J. C. EVANS, *Trans. Faraday Soc.*, **55** (1959) 1817.

[123] W. KLEMPERER AND L. LINDEMANN, *J. Chem. Phys.*, **25** (1956) 397.

[124] H. BRAUNE AND G. ENGLEBRECHT, *Z. Physik. Chem.*, B19 (1932) 303.

[125] J. A. HENDON AND A. H. NEILSEN, *Phys. Rev.*, **99** (1955) 1624; J. A. HENDON, *M. Sc. Thesis*, Univ. of Tennessee, 1954.

[126] H. STAMMREICH, R. FORNERIS AND K. SONE, *J. Chem. Phys.*, **25** (1955) 972.

[127] D. M. GAGE AND E. F. BARKER, *J. Chem. Phys.*, **7** (1939) 455.

[128] D. M. YOST, D. DEVAULT, T. F. ANDERSON AND E. N. LASSTERRE, *J. Chem. Phys.*, **6** (1938) 424.

[129] P. W. DAVIS AND R. A. OETJEN, *J. Mol. Spectry.*, **2** (1958) 253.

[130] J. O. EDWARDS, G. C. MASON, V. F. ROSE AND J. W. SCHULTZ, *J. Am. Chem. Soc.*, **77** (1955) 266.

[131] B. WEINSTOCK, H. H. CLAASEN AND J. G. MALM, *J. Chem. Phys.*, **32** (1960) 181.

[132] R. H. SANBORN, *J. Chem. Phys.*, **33** (1960) 1855.

[133] R. ETTINGER, F. A. JOHNSON AND C. B. COLBURN, *J. Chem. Phys.*, **34** (1961) 2187.

[134] R. E. DODD, L. A. WOODWARD AND H. L. ROBERTS, *Trans. Faraday Soc.*, **52** (1956) 1052.

[135] F. A. COTTON, J. W. GEORGE AND J. S. WAUGH, *J. Chem. Phys.*, **28** (1958) 994.

[136] E. L. MUETTERTIES AND W. D. PHILLIPS, *J. Am. Chem. Soc.*, **81** (1959) 1084.

[137] D. F. SMITH, *J. Chem. Phys.*, **21** (1953) 609.

[138] H. H. CLAASEN, B. WEINSTOCK AND J. G. MALM, *J. Chem. Phys.*, **28** (1958) 285.

[139] T. G. BURKE AND E. A. JONES, *J. Chem. Phys.*, **19** (1951) 1611.

[140] C. V. STEVENSON AND E. A. JONES, *J. Chem. Phys.*, **20** (1952) 1830.

[141] R. C. LORD, M. A. LYNCH, W. C. SCHUMB AND E. J. SLOWINSKII, *J. Am. Chem. Soc.*, **72** (1950) 522.

[142] E. A. JONES, T. F. PARKINSON AND R. B. MURRAY, *J. Chem. Phys.*, **17** (1949) 501.

[143] K. HEDBURG, quoted in ref. 145.

[144] M. AJOTI, P. J. WHEATLY AND W. N. LIPSCOMB, *J. Chem. Phys.*, **27** (1957) 196.

[145] D. E. MANN AND L. FANO, *J. Chem. Phys.*, **26** (1957) 1665.

[146] K. HEDBURG, *J. Am. Chem. Soc.*, **77** (1955) 6555.

[147] L. O. BROCKWAY AND H. O. JENKINS, *J. Am. Chem. Soc.*, **58** (1936) 2036.

[148] R. F. CURL AND K. S. PITZER, *J. Am. Chem. Soc.*, **80** (1958) 2371.

[149] E. A. V. EBSWORTH, R. TAYLOR AND L. A. WOODWARD, *Trans. Faraday Soc.*, **55** (1959) 211.

[150] D. C. McKEAN, R. TAYLOR AND L. A. WOODWARD, *Proc. Chem. Soc.*, (1959) 321.

[151] O. BASTIANSEN, quoted in ref. 152.

[152] J. R. ARONSON, R. C. LORD AND D. W. ROBINSON, *J. Chem. Phys.*, **33** (1960) 1004. D. W. ROBINSON, W. J. LAFFERTY, J. R. ARONSON, J. R. DUROG AND R. C. LORD, *J. Chem. Phys.*, **35** (1961) 2245.

[153] W. R. THORSON AND I. NAKAGAWA, *J. Chem. Phys.*, **33** (1960) 994.

[154] D. E. BETHELL AND N. SHEPPARD, *J. Chem. Phys.*, **21** (1953) 1421.

[155] C. C. FERRISO AND D. F. HORNIG, *J. Am. Chem. Soc.*, **75** (1953) 4113.

[156] W. G. FATELEY, H. A. BENT AND B. CRAWFORD, *J. Chem. Phys.*, **31** (1959) 204.

[157] R. TERANISHI AND J. C. DECIUS, *J. Chem. Phys.*, **22** (1954) 896.

[158] D. J. MILLEN, *J. Chem. Soc.*, (1950) 2606.

[159] E. GRISON, K. ERIKS AND J. L. DE VRIES, *Acta Cryst.*, **3** (1950) 290.
[160] J. OVEREND AND J. R. SCHERER, *J. Chem. Phys.*, **32** (1960) 1296.
[161] A. D. WALSH, *Proc. Roy. Soc. (London), Ser. A*, **207** (1951) 13.
[162] W. GORDY, *J. Chem. Phys.*, **14** (1946) 305.
[163] J. K. WILMSHURST, *J. Chem. Phys.*, **28** (1958) 733.
[164] L. A. WOODWARD, *Trans. Faraday Soc.*, **54** (1958) 1271.
[165] J. GOUBEAU, *Angew. Chem.*, **69** (1957) 77; **73** (1961) 305.
[166] H. KRIEGSMANN, *Z. Anorg. Allgem. Chem.*, **299** (1959) 138.
[167] J. GOUBEAU, M. RAHTZ AND H. J. BECHER, *Z. Anorg. Allgem. Chem.*, **275** (1954) 161.
[168] M. BIGORGNE AND A. ZELWER, *Bull. Soc. Chim. France*, (1960) 1986.
[169] L. H. JONES, *J. Mol. Spectry.*, **5** (1960) 133.
[170] L. A. WOODWARD AND J. R. HALL, *Spectrochim. Acta*, **16** (1960) 654.
[171] L. SACCONI AND A. SABATINI, *Nature*, **186** (1960) 549.
[172] J. CHATT, L. A. DUNCANSON AND B. L. SHAW, *Chem. Ind. (London)*, (1958) 859.
[173] D. B. POWELL, *J. Chem. Soc.*, (1956) 4495.
[174] J. CHATT, L. A. DUNCANSON AND L. M. VENANZI, *J. Chem. Soc.*, (1955) 4461.
[175] J. CHATT, L. A. DUNCANSON, B. L. SHAW AND L. M. VENANZI, *Discussions Faraday Soc.*, **26** (1958) 131.
[176] D. M. ADAMS, J. CHATT AND B. L. SHAW, *J. Chem. Soc.*, (1960) 2047.
[177] K. PACKER AND R. K. HARRIS, *J. Chem. Soc.*, (1961) 4736.
[178] F. A. COTTON, A. D. LIEHR AND G. WILKINSON, *J. Inorg. Nucl. Chem.*, **1** (1955) 175.
[179] O. S. MILLS, *Acta Cryst.*, **11** (1958) 620.
[180] A. J. DOWNS AND E. A. V. EBSWORTH, *J. Chem. Soc.*, (1960) 3516; and A. J. DOWNS, *Spectrochim. Acta* (in the press).
[181] K. E. LAWSON, *Infrared Absorption of Inorganic Substances*, Reinhold, New York, 1961.
[182] W. BECK, *Chem. Ber.*, **95** (1962) 341.
[183] A. TURCO AND C. PECILE, *Nature*, **191** (1961) 66.
[184] R. C. PLUMB AND D. F. HORNIG, *J. Chem. Phys.*, **23** (1955) 947.
[185] G. HERZBERG, *Infrared and Raman Spectra of Polyatomic Molecules*, Van Nostrand, New York, 1945, p. 294.
[186] L. A. WOODWARD AND H. L. ROBERTS, *Trans. Faraday Soc.*, **52** (1956) 615.
[187] L. E. ORGEL, *Inorg. Chem.*, **1** (1962) 25.
[188] F. A. COTTON AND C. S. KRAIHANZEL, *J. Am. Chem. Soc.*, **83** (1962) 4432.

Chapter X

Quantitative Intensity Studies and Dipole Moment Derivatives

JOHN OVEREND

Department of Chemistry University of Minnesota, Minneapolis

Most of this chapter deals with the absolute intensities of vibrational–rotational transitions in dilute gases. There are two underlying reasons for this choice.

First, in the theoretical treatment of gas phase intensities it is a very good approximation to neglect molecular interactions and to interpret the intensity results in terms of intramolecular parameters. In a few very simple cases (*e.g.* methane[1]) serious attempts at *a priori* calculations of intensities have been made through solving the quantum-mechanical Hamiltonian. In these, the Hamiltonian for an individual molecule has been considered and the results should properly be compared with the observed gas phase intensities. But, even in the majority of cases, where rigorous *a priori* calculations of intensities have not been made, gas phase intensity data may be transformed, to a very good approximation, into derivatives of the molecular dipole moment with respect to defined symmetry coordinates. Intensity data have frequently been further interpreted in terms of bond moments and effective charges, although unfortunately there are distinct limits to the validity of such interpretations.

The present state of theory for intensities in condensed phases presents greater complications. It is well known that condensed phase intensities are frequently markedly different from gas phase ones, which is attributable in part to intermolecular interactions. Some progress has been made towards understanding the differences in intensity between gas and crystal, but there still remain many apparent anomalies. The present state of the theory of pure liquid and solution intensities is even less satisfactory. Thus, from a theoretical viewpoint, it seems appropriate to concentrate on the isolated molecule, as in this case the available data already yield significant conclusions.

The second reason is experimental. The determination of gas phase intensities is now reduced to a fairly routine, though hardly trivial, procedure. The many experimental difficulties encountered in gas phase measurements, to be described later, must also be considered when making measurements in condensed phases. But there, additional difficulties in determining the sample thickness and the band-shape function to be used for the wing corrections arise, and although these latter difficulties are now receiving serious attention, there are few reliable data presently available for substances in condensed phases.

(1) Basic Theory

(1A) Absorption of radiation

An understanding of infra-red intensities requires a closer look at the mechanism by which light interacts with matter. In the presence of a radiation field there is a probability that a molecule will exchange energy with the field and appear in a quantum state other than its original one. This process is responsible for the appearance of spectra; if the molecule gains energy we observe absorption of radiation, if it loses energy, emission occurs. The probability of a randomly oriented molecule, e.g., in the gas or liquid phase, being promoted from a state n'' to a state n' is

$$\frac{8\pi^3}{3h^2} \langle n''|\boldsymbol{p}|n'\rangle^2 \rho(\nu_{n'',n'}) \tag{1}$$

where $\langle n''|\boldsymbol{p}|n'\rangle$ is the quantum-mechanical matrix element of the dipole moment, and $\rho(\nu_{n''n'})$ is the density of the radiation of the particular frequency matching the quantum jump. The probability that a molecule in an excited state will drop to a lower state is also given by (1) and thus if there are N'' molecules in the lower state and N' in the upper, the net absorption probability is given by

$$\frac{8\pi^3}{3h^2} \langle n''|\boldsymbol{p}|n'\rangle^2 \rho(\nu_{n'', n'})(N''-N') \tag{2}$$

Consider a differential element of absorbing material of length $\mathrm{d}l$ and of unit cross-section: it will exchange energy with the radiation field according to (2). At each exchange the energy of the field will change by $(\boldsymbol{h}\nu_{n''n'})$ and the net loss of energy will be

$$-\mathrm{d}I = \nu_{n'',n'} \frac{8\pi^3}{3h} \langle n''|\boldsymbol{p}|n'\rangle^2 \rho(\nu_{n''n'})(N''-N')\,\mathrm{d}l \tag{3}$$

The radiation flux and density are related by

$$I = c\rho \tag{4}$$

and hence ρ can be eliminated from (3) to give

$$-\mathrm{d}\ln I = \nu_{n'',n'} \frac{8\pi^3}{3hc} \langle n''|\boldsymbol{p}|n'\rangle^2 (N''-N')\,\mathrm{d}l \tag{5}$$

which may be integrated immediately to

$$\ln(I_0/I) = \nu_{n'',\,n'} \frac{8\pi^3 l}{3hc} \langle n''|\boldsymbol{p}|n'\rangle^2 (N''-N') \tag{6}$$

At equilibrium, the populations of the states n'' and n' follow the Boltzmann distribution and

$$(N''-N') = n\boldsymbol{N}Q_v^{-1}[\exp(-E_{n''}/\boldsymbol{k}T) - \exp(-E_{n'}/\boldsymbol{k}T)] \tag{7}$$

where

$$Q_v = \sum_i \exp(-E_i/\boldsymbol{k}T)$$

$\boldsymbol{N}$ is Avogadro's number and n is the molar concentration.

Although this discussion is primarily concerned with vibrational transitions, in the gas phase there are, of course, also transitions in which not only the vibrational quantum numbers, but also the rotational quantum numbers change. Now, under moderate resolution, the vibrational spectra of simple molecules usually appear as a series of absorption bands which may be assigned to transitions between different vibrational states. Although each band usually corresponds to a single vibrational transition, it has many unresolved components corresponding to the various possibilities for accompanying rotational transitions. Therefore, in the case of any but the simplest polyatomic molecule (where the rotational fine structure is clearly resolved), it is not possible to determine an experimental quantity which may be compared directly with (6). Rather, the transition probabilities for all the rotational components must be summed and this quantity compared with the total integrated intensity of the vibrational transition. First, however, it is necessary to recognize that although these components have the same vibrational matrix elements, they have slightly different frequencies, and, consequently, it is more convenient to take the transition frequency in (6) over to the left side of the equation[2]. The summation over the rotational fine structure can then be carried out exactly[2] to yield

$$\Gamma_{n'',\,n'} = \frac{1}{nl} \int_{\text{Band}} \ln(I_0/I)\,\mathrm{d}\ln\nu = \frac{8\pi^3 \boldsymbol{N}}{3hc} \langle n''|\boldsymbol{p}|n'\rangle^2 Q_v^{-1}$$
$$\times [\exp(-E_{n''}/\boldsymbol{k}T) - \exp(-E_{n'}/\boldsymbol{k}T)] \tag{8}$$

Equation (8) is applicable as it stands to a fundamental transition (*i.e.* from n'' as the ground vibrational state $v = 0$, to n', having vibrational quantum number $v = 1$). The factor $Q_v^{-1}[\exp(-E_{n''}/\boldsymbol{k}T) - \exp(-E_{n'}/\boldsymbol{k}T)]$ is usually close to unity and may often be ignored; the contributions of the hot bands to the absorption in the fundamental region will also be ignored. Thus, one arrives at the relatively simple expression

$$\Gamma_{n'',\,n'} = \frac{1}{nl} \int_{\text{Band}} \ln(I_0/I)\,\mathrm{d}\ln\nu = \frac{8\pi^3 \boldsymbol{N}}{3hc} \langle 0|\boldsymbol{p}|1\rangle^2 \tag{9}$$

References p. 376

for the integrated intensity of a vibrational fundamental.

The matrix element of the dipole moment

$$\langle 0|\boldsymbol{p}|1\rangle = \int \psi_0^*(Q^i)\,\boldsymbol{p}\,\psi_1(Q^i)\,\mathrm{d}Q^i \qquad (10)$$

may be simplified by developing the components of $\boldsymbol{p}$ in a Taylor series in the normal coordinate Q^i, e.g.,

$$p^\xi(Q) = p_0^\xi + \sum_i \frac{\partial p^\xi}{\partial Q^i} Q^i + \tfrac{1}{2}\sum_{i,j} \frac{\partial^2 p^\xi}{\partial Q^i\,\partial Q^j} Q^i Q^j + \cdots \qquad (11)$$

where ξ stands for the Cartesian directions x, y and z.

It is common practice to consider only the constant and linear terms in (11), and so, in the harmonic oscillator approximation, for a transition between the ground state and the first excited state of the ith normal mode,

$$\langle 0|p^\xi|1\rangle = \frac{\partial p^\xi}{\partial Q^i} \int \psi_0^* Q^i \psi_1 \,\mathrm{d}Q^i = \left(\frac{h}{8\pi^2 c\omega_i}\right)^{\frac{1}{2}} \frac{\partial p^\xi}{\partial Q^i} \qquad (12)$$

where ω_i is the harmonic frequency of the ith mode. On substituting this result in (9), the explicit relationship

$$\Gamma_i = \frac{N\pi}{3c^2\omega_i}\left(\frac{\partial \boldsymbol{p}}{\partial Q^i}\right)^2, \qquad (13)$$

where

$$\left(\frac{\partial \boldsymbol{p}}{\partial Q^i}\right)^2 = \left(\frac{\partial p^x}{\partial Q^i}\right)^2 + \left(\frac{\partial p^y}{\partial Q^i}\right)^2 + \left(\frac{\partial p^z}{\partial Q^i}\right)^2$$

between the integrated intensity of a fundamental absorption band and the derivative of the molecular dipole moment with respect to a normal co-ordinate results. It is the latter quantity which is usually sought in quantitative intensity studies. It goes without saying that, in many cases, the integral in (10) vanishes because of symmetry restrictions, in which case the transition is forbidden by selection rules (cf. Chapter IV).

Further, if the molecule has fairly high symmetry, the integral in (12) will often vanish except for one component of $\boldsymbol{p}$ for vibrations of a particular symmetry class, i.e., the change in dipole moment will be oriented along a fixed direction in the molecule for all vibrations of that symmetry class. Even so, it is useful to carry the vector concept of the dipole moment and its derivatives and to keep in mind its directional nature. A molecule of lower symmetry may have two or even three non-vanishing components of $\langle 0|\boldsymbol{p}|1\rangle$ in the same symmetry class and in such a case, the vector notation must be used. It is then important to remember that the direction of $\partial p/\partial Q$ is completely arbitrary and there is no reason to expect the dipole moment slopes to be similarly oriented for all vibrations of the same symmetry.

(1B) Summation over hot bands

Equation (7) is exact for a single transition between two levels n' and n''. However, such a transition can seldom be studied in practice, for most spectral bands consist of a main band with a number of overlapping hot bands. In the case of a diatomic molecule, for example, there are hot bands due to $2 \leftarrow 1$, $3 \leftarrow 2$, etc., which all fall at about the same frequency as the $1 \leftarrow 0$ transition. Vibration bands of polyatomic molecules are even more complicated, as any transition from a state n_1, n_2, n_3, ... to one (n_1+1), n_2, n_3, ... falls at about the same frequency as the fundamental $(1, 0, 0, \ldots)$ $\leftarrow (0, 0, 0, \ldots)$ and contributes a hot band.

For obvious reasons, the experimental intensity is usually determined by integrating over a fundamental and all the associated hot bands, and for comparison with this quantity, (7) should be summed over all the corresponding transitions[3, 4]. For a diatomic fundamental this yields a quantity

$$\Gamma_{(obs)} = \frac{8\pi^3 N}{3hc} \sum_{v=0}^{\infty} \langle v|p|v+1\rangle^2 Q_v^{-1} \{\exp[-vh\beta\omega] - \exp[-(v+1)h\beta\omega]\} \quad (15)$$

where $\beta = 1/kT$. In the harmonic-oscillator approximation,

$$\langle v|p|v+1\rangle^2 = \frac{h}{8\pi^2\omega}(v+1)\left(\frac{dp}{dQ}\right)^2 \quad (16)$$

and hence,

$$\Gamma_{(obs)} = \frac{N\pi}{3c^2\omega}\left(\frac{dp}{dQ}\right)^2 Q_v^{-1} \sum_{v=0}^{\infty}(v+1)\{\exp[-vh\beta\omega] - \exp[-(v+1)h\beta\omega]\} \quad (17)$$

The summation in (17) may be carried out exactly to yield

$$\Gamma_{(obs)} = \frac{N\pi}{3c^2\omega}\left(\frac{dp}{dQ}\right)^2 \quad (18)$$

which is the same as (13). Thus, in the harmonic approximation, the intensity of a fundamental band of a diatomic molecule is independent of temperature: the increase in induced emission exactly cancels the higher absorption probability as the temperature is raised and excited states become populated. This result is most useful, for integrated fundamental intensities can be treated exactly as though all the molecules in the sample were in the ground state.

In the case of a polyatomic molecule, a similar expression holds. Q_v is the molecular vibrational partition function and may be written as a product of harmonic oscillator partition functions, one for each normal mode. The summation in (17) then extends over all possible vibrational states and when this is evaluated, it is found that (18) is generally true for all polyatomic fundamentals.

References p. 376

(1C) Overtones and combination bands

The assumptions leading to equation (13) forbid overtone and combination bands in the absorption spectrum. The reason for the appearance of overtones is illustrated most simply for a diatomic molecule. If the quadratic term in the dipole moment expansion is retained, the matrix element may be expressed as

$$\langle n''|p|n'\rangle = \frac{\mathrm{d}p}{\mathrm{d}Q}\int \psi_{n''}^* Q\psi_{n'}\,\mathrm{d}\tau + \frac{\mathrm{d}^2p}{\mathrm{d}Q^2}\int \psi_{n''}^* Q^2\psi_{n'}\,\mathrm{d}\tau + \ldots \qquad (19)$$

It is important to recognize that the actual molecule is not strictly harmonic, and that, for the $2 \leftarrow 0$ transition, the first integral has a finite (though small) value, whereas the second integral has a value close to that for a harmonic oscillator, i.e., $h/4\sqrt{2}\,\pi^2\omega$. If $\mathrm{d}p/\mathrm{d}Q$ is first order and $\mathrm{d}^2p/\mathrm{d}Q^2$ second order, both terms will contribute in second order to the first overtone; i.e., the intensity depends on both the mechanical and electrical anharmonicities.

If intensity data are available for both the fundamental and first overtone of a diatomic molecule, both $\mathrm{d}p/\mathrm{d}r$ and $\mathrm{d}^2p/\mathrm{d}r^2$ may be evaluated. For example, PENNER and WEBER[5] determined the intensity of the carbon monoxide fundamental and first overtone to be 2700 cm²/mole and 9.5 cm²/mole respectively, and taking these data with HERMAN and SHULER's[6] matrix elements, one can obtain two relations between p_1 and p_2, which may be solved to give $p_1 = \pm 3.08$ D/Å; $p_2 = \pm 1.18$ D/Å² or, $p_1 = \pm 2.98$ D/Å; $p_2 = \pm 14.09$ D/Å². The alternative results arise because the matrix element of the dipole moment is related to the square root of the observed intensity and both sign alternatives must be considered. It is important to note that the coefficient controlling the contribution of $\mathrm{d}^2p/\mathrm{d}Q^2$ to the intensity of the fundamental is small, and in the double harmonic approximation, i.e., treating the molecule as a harmonic oscillator with a linear dipole moment function, the value found for p_1 from the fundamental is 3.09 D/Å which does not differ very much from the two previously-quoted values. Similar results have been found for other diatomic molecules where overtone data have been analyzed. Thus, it has appeared reasonable to extend the double harmonic approximation to polyatomic molecules and to approximate the intensities of fundamental transitions by (18).

(1D) Perturbations

Up to this point, it has been tacitly assumed that the normal vibrations of a polyatomic molecule are independent and that in each normal mode, the vibrational states are well represented by the harmonic-oscillator wave functions. It is well known, however, that even in simple molecules, higher order terms in the Hamiltonian lead to significant perturbations which invalidate the simple intensity expressions. The most common perturbations are Fermi resonance and Coriolis interaction which can couple two or more states (see Chapter IV, pp. 132 and 151); the former is frequently encountered in polyatomic molecules and is important in gas, liquid, solution and solid spectra.

In dealing with these perturbations, it is useful to retain the formalism of equation (13) and to express the true intensities in terms of transitions to unperturbed states. The logarithmic integration of optical density offers a very real advantage where the bands are perturbed by resonance, for, as Crawford has shown, the value of Γ obtained by integrating over the observed bands involving the resonating states, is exactly equal to the sum of the Γ's corresponding to the hypothetical transitions to the unperturbed states.

It is informative to examine the effect of Fermi resonance on vibrational intensities. Consider specifically transitions from the ground state to a pair of levels described by vibrational wave functions ψ_n and ψ_m. Let these be expressed as orthogonal combinations of the unperturbed functions, ψ_n^0 and ψ_m^0, i.e.,

$$\psi_n = a\psi_n^0 + b\psi_m^0 \tag{20}$$

$$\psi_m = b\psi_n^0 - a\psi_m^0 \tag{21}$$

where $a^2 + b^2 = 1$. Then the matrix elements for the actual transitions may be written

$$\langle 0|\boldsymbol{p}|n\rangle = a\langle 0|\boldsymbol{p}|n^0\rangle + b\langle 0|\boldsymbol{p}|m^0\rangle \tag{22}$$

$$\langle 0|\boldsymbol{p}|m\rangle = b\langle 0|\boldsymbol{p}|n^0\rangle - a\langle 0|\boldsymbol{p}|m^0\rangle \tag{23}$$

Usually n^0 is a fundamental and m^0 an overtone or combination which may be assumed to have negligible intrinsic intensity* — it is forbidden in the double harmonic approximation — and $\langle 0|\boldsymbol{p}|m^0\rangle$ may be taken to be zero. If the two levels n and m are in complete resonance, $a \simeq b$ and $\Gamma_n \simeq \Gamma_m$; i.e., the absorption will be a doublet with components of roughly equal intensity. However, irrespective of the values of a and b, the entire integrated intensity of the doublet is attributable to the "unperturbed fundamental transition"; this approximation has usually been made in the interpretation of resonant multiplets in the spectra of all but the simplest molecules.

Again, on the assumption that only one unperturbed transition has intrinsic intensity, it is possible to use the observed intensity ratio to determine the unperturbed energy levels in a resonance doublet. The secular equation for the perturbation[7] may be solved to yield the energy relationship

$$\Delta E = (4|W_{nm}|^2 + \Delta E^0)^{\frac{1}{2}} \tag{24}$$

---

* It should be remarked that for reasons discussed in the preceding, this is not such a good approximation as the assumption that higher terms do not contribute to the fundamental.

and the ratio of the coefficients a and b in (22), (23)

$$\frac{a^2}{b^2} = \frac{(4|W_{nm}|^2+\Delta E^0)^{\frac{1}{2}}+\Delta E^0}{(4|W_{nm}|^2+\Delta E^0)^{\frac{1}{2}}-\Delta E^0} \tag{25}$$

where ΔE is the observed separation of states, ΔE^0 the separation of the unperturbed states, and W_{nm} the matrix element of the perturbation operator. Substitution of (22) and (23) in (10) gives

$$\frac{a^2}{b^2} = \frac{\Gamma_n}{\Gamma_m} = \rho \tag{26}$$

and this result, together with (24) and (25) yields

$$\Delta E^0 = \Delta E(\rho-1)/(\rho+1)$$

Finally, because of the symmetric nature of the perturbation, the unperturbed energy levels are given by

$$E_n^0 = \tfrac{1}{2}(E_n+E_m+\Delta E^0), \quad E_m^0 = \tfrac{1}{2}(E_n+E_m-\Delta E^0) \tag{27}$$

Thus, ΔE^0 may be estimated from the observed intensity ratio and taken with (27) to yield values for the unperturbed energies.

But, if $\langle 0|\boldsymbol{p}|m^0\rangle$ is of similar magnitude to $\langle 0|\boldsymbol{p}|n^0\rangle$ and $a \cong b$, $\Gamma_m \cong 0$ and most of the intensity appears in Γ_n. Thus, it is possible to have complete Fermi resonance between two adjacent levels and yet have just one single intense band in the spectrum.

Coriolis interaction between two upper states also results in a transfer of intensity. Usually two non-degenerate levels are coupled, in which case the intensity transfer is from one branch to the other within each band; Γ for each band is invariant under this type of perturbation. A particularly useful fact is that the direction of intensity transfer depends on the relative signs of $d\boldsymbol{p}/dQ$ for the two coupled vibrations, and can be used to determine this quantity[8]. The effect of Coriolis interaction between two degenerate levels is more complicated and intensity is transferred from one band to the other[9].

(1E) Units and dimensions

It follows immediately from equation (9) that the units of Γ are (concentration $\times$ length)$^{-1}$. CRAWFORD[2] has suggested that the most appropriate units are cm^2/mole, which give convenient magnitudes for Γ; ca. 100–10,000 for fundamentals and ca. 1–100 for overtones. An additional advantage is that Γ expressed in these units has the dimensions of a true absorption cross-section.

Many authors have expressed vibrational intensities in terms of another quantity

$$A = \frac{1}{cl} \int \ln(I_0/I)\mathrm{d}\nu \qquad (28)$$

which has units of (frequency/concentration × length). Some authors have used cycles/sec for the units of the frequency, others cycles/cm. The path length is usually expressed in cm and the concentration (c) in moles/cc, millimoles/cc or in atmospheres; in the latter case it is particularly important to specify the temperature. The most commonly used intensity units are compared in Table X, 1[10].

TABLE X, 1

UNITS OF ABSORPTION INTENSITY

(Taken from I. M. Mills, Ann. Rep. Progr. Chem. (Chem. Soc. London), LV (1958) 56).

Quantity	Units	Equivalent value of A (cm/mole)
Γ	cm²/mole	$= (\nu_0/\text{cm}^{-1})$ (cm/mole)
A	cm/mole	$= 1$ cm/mole
	"dark" $= 1$ cm/millimole	$= 10^3$ cm/mole
	"intensity unit"	$= 10^7$ cm/mole
	cm^{-2} atm^{-1}, 273° K	$= 22{,}415$ cm/mole
	cm^{-2} atm^{-1}, 298° K	$= 24{,}468$ cm/mole
	sec^{-1} cm^{-1} atm^{-1}, 273° K	$= \dfrac{22{,}415}{2.9979 \cdot 10^{10}} = 7.4769 \cdot 10^{-7}$ cm/mole

From the definitions of Γ and A, it follows that they are related by the approximate expression,

$$A = \Gamma\nu_0 \qquad (29)$$

where ν_0 is the frequency of the band origin in cm^{-1}. This relationship has been used throughout this chapter to convert from A to Γ, where the original integration was not performed on a logarithmic frequency scale.*

From (9) and (13), it immediately follows that the units for $\partial p/\partial Q$ are cm$^{3/2}$ sec^{-1}. The normal coordinates have dimensions of length × (mass)$^{1/2}$, *cf.* eqn. 10, p. 170, giving the dipole moment dimensions of g$^{1/2}$ cm$^{5/2}$ sec^{-1}, (*i.e.*, e.s.u. cm). However, it is more usual to express the dipole moment in Debye units; 1D $= 10^{-18}$ g$^{1/2}$ cm$^{5/2}$ sec^{-1}, and to use D/Å for derivatives of the dipole moment with respect to interatomic distances.

---

* When the integrated intensity is expressed in terms of A, the frequency ν in (6) is assumed to be constant. Many authors have equated this to the frequency ω in (13), and have used the expression

$$A_i = \frac{N\pi}{3c^2}\left(\frac{\partial p}{\mathrm{d}Q^i}\right)^2$$

However, it is clear from the derivation that ν refers to the absorption frequency whereas ω refers to the harmonic frequency, and the proper relationship is

$$A_i = \left(\frac{\nu_i}{\omega}\right)\frac{N\pi}{3c^2}\left(\frac{\partial p}{\partial Q^i}\right)^2.$$

References p. 376

(2) **Experimental Methods**

(2A) The Wilson-Wells theorem

The first attempts to determine experimental values of vibrational inten-sities of gas phase molecules produced confusing results; the intensity of the HCl fundamental reported by BARTHOLOMÉ [11] differed from an earlier measurement by BOURGIN [12] by a factor of four. KEMBLE [13], who recognized that the resolving power of the spectrometer was an important factor, ascribed the discrepancy to inadequate resolution by Bartholomé, but at that time there was no real evidence that Bourgin's value was correct.

A decade later, WILSON and WELLS [14] reviewed the problems of measuring infra-red intensities and published a method for their experimental deter-mination based on a theorem relating the apparent value of the intensity to the true value, $A cl = \int \ln(I_0/I) \mathrm{d}\nu$. The principal experimental difficulty arises from the fact that a monochromator, when set on a particular fre-quency ν', does not transmit radiation of just that frequency, but rather a band of frequencies described by a slit function $g(\nu, \nu')$. In general, $g(\nu, \nu')$ is zero except in a rather narrow range close to ν'; the width of this range is of the order of the resolving power of the monochromator. Consequently, the apparent intensity of radiation, $T(\nu')$, at a frequency ν' is not equal to the true intensity $I(\nu')$, but is given by

$$T(\nu') = \int_0^\infty I(\nu) g(\nu, \nu') \, \mathrm{d}\nu \tag{30}$$

and thus the apparent integrated area of an absorption band is not equal to the theoretical quantity A, but rather to a quantity

$$B = \frac{1}{cl} \int_{\text{Band}} \ln(T_0/T) \, \mathrm{d}\nu' = \frac{1}{cl} \int_{\text{Band}} \ln \left\{ \frac{\int_0^\infty I_0(\nu) \, g(\nu, \nu') \, \mathrm{d}\nu}{\int_0^\infty I(\nu) \, g(\nu, \nu') \, \mathrm{d}\nu} \right\} \, \mathrm{d}\nu' \tag{31}$$

WILSON and WELLS [14] showed that

$$\lim_{cl \to 0} B = A \tag{32}$$

Therefore, if the apparent integrated absorption (Bcl) is plotted against cl as in Fig. X, 1, the value of A is determined by the slope of the tangent at the origin. It may also be shown [15] that at higher values of cl, the apparent intensity is less than the true value. The Wilson–Wells theorem also applies to logarithmic integration; *i.e.*,

$$\lim_{cl \to 0} \Gamma_{\text{(apparent)}} = \Gamma_{\text{(true)}}$$

Although the Wilson–Wells extrapolation theorem overcomes the problems of finite slit widths, it does not lead to an entirely satisfactory method for the determination of intensities, for there is often considerable ambiguity in fixing the tangent at the origin and one must rely most heavily on data taken at low absorption which are subject to the largest relative errors in concentration and apparent absorption.

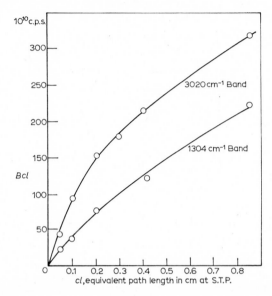

Fig. X, 1. Typical plot of integrated absorption against cl. This example shows the two infra-red active fundamentals of methane and the curvature is quite apparent.

If the experimental conditions are chosen so that neither I_0 nor I vary appreciably over the range in which the slit function is finite, equation (31) reduces to

$$B = \frac{1}{cl} \int_{\text{Band}} \ln \ (I_0/I) \, \mathrm{d}v' = A \qquad (33)$$

and the true value of the integrated intensity may be determined directly. It is relatively easy to ensure that I_0 does not change rapidly if care is taken to exclude atmospheric water vapour and carbon dioxide from the absorbing path. If the molecules are studied in the gas phase, the vibrational absorption band will contain many rotational lines. Even though these lines may not be resolved by the spectrometer, they nevertheless give rise to rapid fluctuations in I and invalidate the approximations leading to (33).

(2B) Pressure broadening

The true width of a single line increases as the total pressure in the absorption cell is raised[16], and at sufficiently high pressure the rotational fine structure becomes completely smeared out to give the band a smooth contour. Therefore, by pressure broadening the absorbing sample, either by using very high pressures of the sample itself, or, more usually, by adding an infra-red transparent gas, it is possible to meet the requirement that I is roughly constant over the slit function. In many intensity studies there has been an attempt to satisfy the above criteria for I_0 and I so that A can be determined from the spectral curve by direct integration, but frequently the total pressure was limited to a few atmospheres by cell design, and in some cases the results were in serious error. The effect of pressure broadening is demonstrated for the ν_3 fundamental of methane in Fig. X, 2, whilst Fig X, 3

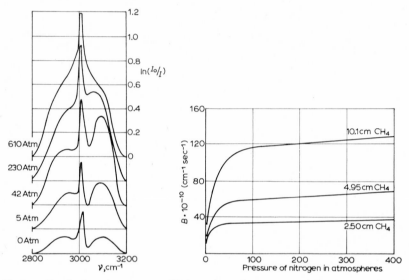

Fig. X, 2. ν_3 Band of methane at *ca.* 3000 cm^{-1} at the same partial pressure of methane but under different pressures of nitrogen. Note the apparent increase in intensity.

Fig. X, 3. Apparent integrated absorption of the ν_3 band of methane as a function of pressure of added nitrogen.

(Figs. X, 2 and X, 3 are from Welsh, Pashler and Dunn, J. Chem. Phys., 19 (1951) 340).

shows the apparent intensity varying as a function of the density of added nitrogen. The initial steep rise in Fig. X, 3 is the effect of pressure broadening and at about 100 atmospheres of nitrogen the broadening is essentially complete.

Pressure-induced absorption, due to intermolecular interactions (see Chapter IV), is responsible for the slight rise as the pressure of nitrogen is further increased, and this should be discounted if the intensity of an isolated molecule is sought, *i.e.*, the linear portion of the curve should be extrapolated to zero density of nitrogen. Most workers have not considered it necessary to correct for pressure-induced absorption and the intensity has been measured directly under conditions of complete broadening.

The pressure necessary for complete broadening depends on the individual spectrometer, on the nature of the rotational fine structure and on the effectiveness of the broadening gas. PENNER and WEBER[5] suggested a relatively simple and important test to ensure that adequate pressures are used, namely; *the Beer's law plot must be a straight line through the origin,* with the experimental points randomly scattered. The linear Beer's law plot offers the additional advantage of a determinable slope with a statistically-estimated dispersion. In some cases broadening may be complete at a pressure of only one atmosphere (*e.g.,* in a parallel band of a heavy, linear molecule where the rotational fine structure is quite closely spaced and the band envelope has a smooth contour with no sharp peaks). In other cases, particularly with very light molecules, or bands having strong Q branches, complete broadening may require 100 atmospheres, *c.f.* Fig. X, 3.

The difficulties obtaining in the application of the Wilson–Wells method are clearly demonstrated by the 670 cm^{-1} band of CO_2, which has about half its intensity in a strong, line-like Q branch. Table X, 2 lists the values

TABLE X, 2

EXPERIMENTAL VALUES OF THE INTENSITY OF THE 670 CM^{-1} BAND OF CO_2

Ref.	A cm^{-1}/cm atmos at S.T.P.	Units of integration	Method	Broadening gas	Pressure (p.s.i.)
19	187	Not stated	WW	N_2	56
20	161	Not stated	WW	N_2	28
21	170	Not stated	WW	He	700
17	235* / 241*	14–16 μ / Total band	WW	A	1000
15	233 / 240	14–16 μ / Total band	Curve of growth		
18	242	Total band	Curve of growth on individual rotational lines		

* Measured as Γ and reduced to A by equation 29.

obtained by the Wilson–Wells method for intensity of this band by several investigators using successively refined experimental techniques[17]. Also included are two independent values[15, 18] determined by curve-of-growth methods which are inherently more reliable. It is seen that the pressures used by the early investigators were inadequate — a consequence of the fact that the narrow Q branch must be considered as a single rotational line, which should be broadened so that its half-width is about equal to the spectrometer slit width if there is to be negligible error in the intensity. Most of the measurements in Table X, 2 were made with prism spectrometers using slit widths of *ca.* 2 cm^{-1}; the pressure necessary to broaden a single rotational line to this half-width is about 1000 p.s.i. of argon or of nitrogen.

(2C) Experimental determination of gas phase intensities

Single beam spectrometers have frequently been employed for intensity studies, for the more primitive instrument has certain very real advantages which outweigh its inconvenience. Absorption by atmospheric CO_2 and water-vapour give rise to rapid fluctuations in I and I_0, and invalidate the basic relationship, eqn. (33). Scattered light is also objectionable in that it introduces errors into I_0 and I. Scattered light is virtually eliminated in a double monochromator or a double-pass, single monochromator. With other instruments it can be estimated by using a crystal shutter that is opaque to radiation of the frequency at which the monochromator is set, but transparent at higher frequencies. Atmospheric absorption, scattered light and irreproducibility are readily detected in a single beam instrument, so clearly, in fact, that it is largely for this reason that single beam instruments enjoy their status in the intensity field.

The high pressures required for gas phase intensity studies demand absorption cells which are usually of metal with NaCl or KBr crystal

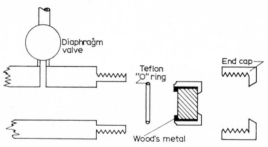

Fig. X, 4. Typical design of a high-pressure cell for gas phase intensity studies.

windows about an inch thick. A typical cell is shown in Fig. X, 4. (Needless to say, it is extremely important to determine the purity of the absorbing gas — this was not always done in the past).

In the standard technique of the Wilson–Wells method the transmission curve (I) for the cell containing a pressurized sample is first measured, and, immediately afterwards, the curve of the same cell containing only pressurizing gas (I_0). This technique requires a high degree of reproducibility in the instrument which should be checked on every measurement.

The sample gas is introduced into the evacuated cell, and its pressure and temperature recorded. The molecular concentration can be determined from the equation of state. The cell is transferred to a metal line capable of withstanding high pressures and the line evacuated. The line is then connected through a reducing valve to a cylinder of transparent gas (*e.g.*, argon, nitrogen or helium), and the valve to the cell opened for about two seconds to admit the pressurizing gas. This is found to give reproducible results and it appears that back diffusion of sample is negligible. The pressurized cell is allowed to stand until the gases become completely mixed — the larger cells may require an hour or more. It is possible to speed up this process by admitting the gases tangentially to the cell body[17], or by introducing a few "teflon" chips which act as stirrers when the cell is shaken.

Cells are usually 1—10 cm long and the length is measured to 0.01 mm. Very weak bands are usually measured in multiple reflection cells and very intense ones at extremely low partial pressures of absorbing gas. In the latter case the sample is usually prepared by taking a determinable pressure of absorbing gas and diluting several times with the transparent pressurizing gas.

I and I_0 are measured from the spectral traces and $\ln[I_0/I]$ is plotted against ν (or $\ln \nu$) and the area under the absorption band taken as Bcl. From repeated measurements at a series of values of cl a Beer's law plot is constructed. In the graphical integration two very real difficulties are encountered. Most absorption bands have fairly extensive wings, often stretching 50 cm^{-1} or more from the absorption maximum and although these have low optical density, they make a considerable contribution to the intensity. Moreover, the very fact that the optical density is low makes the intensity difficult to determine. Some workers have restricted the graphical integration to the main part of the band and have applied a wing correction calculated from an assumed Lorentzian shape. However, the accumulated evidence[18] is that the Lorentzian shape function does not obtain in the extreme wings of rotational lines, and such a correction may give erroneously high intensities. It seems that the safest approach in the measurement of gas phase intensities, is to carry the graphical integration as far as the absorption is measurable and to interpret this as the total band intensity.

The other complication is that frequently two or more absorption bands overlap, and although the total intensity can be measured quite accurately, the separation into band intensities tends to be more subjective. Where the overlap is small, the usual procedure has been to separate the region of absorption into two approximately symmetrical bands. This procedure is arbitrary, as an absorption band may be unsymmetrical for a variety of reasons. Where overlapping is serious and the bands cannot be separated graphically, it is still possible to determine useful intensity data, as was shown by DICKSON, MILLS and CRAWFORD in their study of the methyl halides[22].

(2D) Curves of growth

Many of the difficulties encountered in intensity measurements stem from the dependence of the apparent intensity on the spectrometer slit width. In the curve-of-growth method as applied to isolated rotational–vibrational lines, the intensity is not measured directly, but rather the *equivalent width*, which, for a single spectral line, is defined as

$$W = \int_{\text{line}} \left(\frac{I_0 - I}{I_0}\right) d\nu \tag{34}$$

This is essentially the integral of the fraction of incident radiation removed from the beam by the sample, and is independent of the spectrometer slit function as long as the spectrum is scanned slowly enough for the detector to follow faithfully. If the line has the Lorentzian shape, the equivalent width is related to the quantity A by the equation[23],

$$W = 2\pi\gamma_L \mathrm{f}(x)$$
where
$$\mathrm{f}(x) = xe^{-x}[J_0(ix) - iJ_1(ix)] \tag{35}$$
$$x = Sl/2\pi\gamma_L$$

γ_L is the half-width of the Lorentzian line, $J_0(ix)$ and $J_1(ix)$ are Bessel functions of order zero and one, and S is the true vibrational intensity for unit path of absorbing gas at any particular pressure, *i.e.*, $S/c = A$. At low values of x, *i.e.*, at very short path lengths, $\mathrm{f}(x) = (2x/\pi)^{1/2}$ and at quite high values of x, $\mathrm{f}(x) = x$. Accordingly, as γ_L is determined by the collision frequency and is a constant for a gas at constant pressure, measurements with the same pressure at two path lengths (one in the linear and the other in the square root region) allow the determination of both S and γ_L. It should be stressed that the curve-of-growth method can be applied to individual rotational–vibrational lines only when they are completely resolved. With present-day instruments, this technique is thus limited to simple molecules, *e.g.*, HCl, HF, CO_2, etc.

The curve-of-growth method is also applicable under conditions of low resolution where the vibrational band shows no rotational fine structure. But, even though the individual rotational lines are unresolved, it is necessary to know the frequency of each line, its relative strength and its relative half-width in order to calculate the curve of growth. This requirement limits the method to relatively simple molecules whose dynamic constants are well known.

The greatest advantage of the curve-of-growth method lies in the fact that pressure broadening of the spectra is not required. It is in fact the only reliable way to determine the intensity of a weak band which is overlapped by the wing of a much more intense one. The method does, however, require an embarrassingly intimate knowledge of the details of the rotational fine structure and is presently applicable only to fairly simple molecules.

The Wilson–Wells method is the only generally applicable technique for the measurement of gas phase intensities in moderately sized molecules of real chemical interest, and it has certainly been shown to be capable of yielding precise estimates of the intensity when proper precautions are taken.

(2E) Intensities in condensed phases

The basic Wilson–Wells method is applicable to intensity determination in condensed phases. In such cases, there is normally no rotational fine structure and the absorption spectrum consists of a series of bands; the half-widths of these vary considerably, from 50 cm⁻¹ down to fractions of a wavenumber. If the ratio of spectrometer slit width to half-band width is favourable, the true intensity may be measured directly at a series of absorbing concentrations, a Beer's law plot constructed, and the value of Γ or A determined from the slope. If the band is relatively narrow, the intensity cannot be determined so clearly, and furthermore, there is no possibility of broadening the absorption band to obtain more favourable conditions for intensity measurement.

If this situation obtains, rather than determine the slope of the tangent at the origin, it is preferable to plot Γ (obs)/cl or B/cl against cl. The intercept at $cl = 0$ is the true intensity. An objection to this procedure is that the value of the intercept depends critically on intensity measurements at low cl where experimental errors are large. Furthermore, the experimental plots often tend to curve upwards rather sharply in this region.

In principle, one could determine the true vibrational intensity from a single measurement at one concentration if the slit correction were known, although even then it would appear preferable to make several determinations to obtain an estimate of the probable statistical error. RAMSAY[24] has given correction factors based on a triangular slit function and a Lorentzian band shape, and KOSTKOWSKI and BASS[25] have given similar correction factors based on a Gaussian slit function and both Lorentzian and Gaussian band shapes. To apply meaningful corrections, it is necessary to know the true band-shape function and the spectrometer slit width, and although these can often be estimated fairly accurately, they do lead to an additional error which cannot readily be estimated. For this reason, it seems preferable to rely on the basic Wilson–Wells method, which has the advantage of yielding a linear Beer's law plot if sufficiently narrow slit widths are attainable. Commercial grating spectrometers are becoming increasingly available and with these, slit widths of *ca.* 0.3 cm⁻¹ can be employed throughout most of the fundamental region of the infra-red spectrum. With these it should be possible to measure most bands without appreciable slit errors.

Absorption bands in condensed phases are also found to have wings where the optical density is too small to measure reliably, but which extend over a fairly considerable frequency range and possibly contribute significantly to the band intensity. One approach to this problem is to measure the optical density as far from the band centre as possible and to add to this quantity a correction factor calculated by assuming a shape function for the band, and integrating analytically over the remainder of the wing. Some workers have taken this approach a stage further and have assumed a simple shape function for the entire band, characterized by a few parameters such as peak optical density, half-width, etc. which can be quickly estimated from the spectral curve. The band intensity is then determined by substituting these parameters into the integrated shape-function. A fuller account of these approximate methods is given by JONES and SANDORFY[26].

There are other serious difficulties associated with the determination of I_0 for substances in condensed phases. With gases, I_0 is given reasonably accurately by the transmission of the empty cell. With liquids, the empty cell does not give an effective I_0; the marked difference in refractive index between sample and air gives rise to higher reflective losses in the empty cell and to the appearance of interference fringes. Thus, the I_0 curve is usually crudely estimated by linear interpolation between areas of no apparent absorption on either side of the band.

The accurate determination of intensities in pure liquids and solids is also hampered by the difficulty of measuring the thickness of the very thin sample films. Even for relatively weak bands, the sample thickness is typically less than 50 μ. Some workers have measured the thickness interferometrically, although there are difficulties in this procedure, particularly with solid samples.

There have been recent efforts to circumvent all these difficulties by using alternative spectroscopic techniques such as measuring dispersion curves or reflection spectra, which lead to the same dipole moment derivatives. These alternative procedures are described in Chapter XI.

(3) Reduction of Experimental Gas Phase Data

(3A) The normal-coordinate transformation

The fundamental vibrational intensities of a polyatomic molecule lead to values of $|\partial p/\partial Q^i|$, i.e., the magnitude of derivative of the molecular dipole with respect to the normal coordinate. To proceed further, it is necessary to determine the derivative of the dipole moment with respect to a defined molecular coordinate which is usually taken as a symmetry coordinate, S; (cf. Chapter V). The transformation relating these two sets of coordinates is

$$S^j = \sum_i L_i^j Q^i \tag{36}$$

where the coefficients L_i^j are the elements of the L matrix discussed in

Chapter V, (see eqn. 8, p. 170). The derivatives transform tensorially and are covariant; *i.e.*,

$$p_j^\xi = \frac{\partial p^\xi}{\partial S^j} = \sum_i \frac{\partial p^\xi}{\partial Q^i} \frac{\partial Q^i}{\partial S^j} \tag{37}$$

and for this transformation, the coefficients $\partial Q^i / \partial S^j$ are required. These are readily calculated from the inverse of (36).

$$Q^i = \sum_j \frac{\partial Q^i}{\partial S^j} S^j = \sum_j (L^{-1})_j^i S^j$$

and thus,

$$p_j^\xi = \sum_i (L^{-1})_j^i \frac{\partial p^\xi}{\partial Q^i} \tag{38}$$

$$\boldsymbol{p}_j = \sum_i (L^{-1})_j^i \frac{\partial \boldsymbol{p}}{\partial Q^i} \tag{39}$$

note the sum over i.

It is immediately apparent that, to calculate any particular $\boldsymbol{p}_j$, all $\partial \boldsymbol{p}/\partial Q^i$ with nonvanishing $(L^{-1})_j^i$ are required. Happily, if the molecule has symmetry, the $\boldsymbol{L}^{-1}$ matrix factors into diagonal blocks and $(L^{-1})_j^i$ vanishes unless S^j and Q^i belong to the same irreducible representation. Therefore, to obtain $\boldsymbol{p}_j$ for a symmetry coordinate belonging to a particular symmetry species, all $\partial \boldsymbol{p}/\partial Q^i$ of that species must be included in the summation in (39).

There are, unfortunately, many intensity data in the literature which cannot be transformed to $\boldsymbol{p}_j$'s as the measurements did not include all the bands in any single symmetry species. Even though a transition occurs in the long wavelength region of the spectrum, it must be included in the summation in (39). In many polyatomic molecules, there are fundamentals which are extremely weak and cannot be assigned with certainty, for example $\nu(C\equiv N)$ in HCN, and it is reasonable to estimate their intensity as zero.

The vector nature of the dipole moment places restrictions on the transformation in (38) and (39). It is possible, in principle, to transform each component of the $\partial \boldsymbol{p}/\partial Q$'s into the corresponding component of $\boldsymbol{p}_j$, but there is no way of knowing the components of $\partial \boldsymbol{p}/\partial Q$; the intensity measurement yields the magnitude, but not the direction. Only in those cases where the molecular symmetry is sufficiently high that all components of $\partial \boldsymbol{p}/\partial Q$ save one vanish for a particular symmetry species can the transformation be made, for then the simple algebraic equation (38) may be used. The vanishing of the components of $\partial \boldsymbol{p}/\partial Q$ is readily determined from the character table by the usual selection rules.

The $(L^{-1})_j^i$ coefficients are in practice calculated by inversion of the $\boldsymbol{L}$ matrices obtained by solution of the secular equation ((15), p. 171), but they may also be calculated from the force constants F_{jk} through the expression

$$(L^{-1})^i_j = \sum_k \frac{1}{\lambda_i} L^k_i F_{jk} \qquad (40)$$

if the L^k_i elements are normalized to equation 15, p. 171.

As has already been discussed in Chapter V, the normal coordinates cannot be observed directly; they are calculated from the vibrational secular equation which includes the molecular force constants. Reliable values of $\mathbf{p}_j$, therefore, can be obtained only for those molecules which have previously been the subject of a careful force constant calculation.

(3B) Intensities of isotopic molecules

The derivatives of the dipole moment with respect to defined coordinates depend (in the Born–Oppenheimer approximation) on the charge distributions, *but not on the nuclear masses*. Therefore, the values of $\mathbf{p}_j$ are the same for isotopically substituted molecules if the symmetry coordinate S_j is defined in the same way. The normal coordinates and the vibrational frequencies do, however, depend on the atomic masses, and in general $\partial \mathbf{p}/\partial Q^i$ will change under isotopic substitution.

Now, the fact that the sign of each $\partial \mathbf{p}/\partial Q^i$ is indeterminate, as is also the sign of each $(L^{-1})^i_j$, means that (38) does not lead to a unique value of

TABLE X, 3

VALUES OF $\partial \mathbf{p}/\partial S^j$ FOR ETHANE, E_u CLASS

(Taken from ref. 27)

Molecule	Combination $\partial \mathbf{p}/\partial Q^{(7,8,9)}$	$(\partial \mathbf{p}/\partial S^7)$ Debyes/Å	$(\partial \mathbf{p}/\partial S^8)$ Debyes/Å	$(\partial \mathbf{p}/\partial S^9)$ Debyes/Å
	$(+++)$	$+1.114$	$+0.203$	$+0.414$
	$(++-)$	$+1.135$	$+0.297$	-0.140
C_2H_6	$(+-+)$	$+1.211$	-0.291	$+0.412$
	$(+--)$	$+1.232$	-0.197	-0.142
	Error	±0.0020	±0.020	±0.005
	$(+++)$	$+1.044$	$+0.263$	$+0.399$
	$(++-)$	$+1.038$	$+0.337$	-0.170
C_2D_6	$(+-+)$	$+1.232$	-0.298	$+0.432$
	$(+--)$	$+1.226$	-0.223	-0.146
	Error	±0.033	±0.020	±0.013
Mean value of preferred combination		$+1.221$	-0.295	$+0.418$

$|\mathbf{p}_j|$, but in general gives $2^{(n-1)}$ different solutions, where n is the number of normal vibrations in the particular symmetry species; only one of these solutions is physically correct. If isotopic intensity data are available, a second set of $2^{(n-1)}$ values of the $|\mathbf{p}_j|$ may be obtained; the correct solution must necessarily have the same values for corresponding $\mathbf{p}_j$'s calculated from both isotopic molecules. Additional isotopic data may be used to supply further sets of solutions and in this way a unique set of p_j's can sometimes be determined. Table X, 3 shows all possible values of p_j calculated for the E_u class of ethane and ethane-d_6[27]. Clearly many possible solutions are unacceptable. There is, of course, no necessity for the relative signs of $\partial p/\partial Q^i$ to be the same for isotopic molecules.

Isotopic substitution frequently lowers the symmetry of a molecule, and it is frequently not possible to determine the p_j's. The most useful recourse in this case is to determine all possible sets of p_j from the first molecule and to use these with the relationship

$$\frac{\partial p^\xi}{\partial Q^i} = \sum_j L_i^j p_j^\xi$$

$$(\partial p/\partial Q^i)^2 = \sum_\xi (\partial p^\xi/\partial Q^i)^2 \qquad (41)$$

to calculate alternative possible sets of intensities, which are then compared with the experimental results[28].

An unique set of p_j's cannot always be chosen, as the calculated values do not agree exactly, being subject to uncertainties in the experimental intensities, the harmonic approximation, and in the normal coordinates.

(3C) Correction of p_j for molecular rotation

The symmetry coordinates in which the p_j's are expressed are usually taken as linear combinations of $(3N-6)$ internal valence coordinates (cf. Chapter V) and although these satisfy the momentum conservation conditions, which must obtain for all internal vibrations, they do not describe translations and rotations; these are just ignored. Thus, the actual molecular motion in a normal mode of vibration is described by the normal coordinates plus a compensating amount of translation and rotation such that there is no angular or linear momentum change. Neither translation nor rotation contributes to the vibrational frequency if the molecule resides in field-free space, but molecular rotation does contribute to the absorption intensity if the molecule has a permanent dipole moment, as is evidenced by the appearance of pure rotational spectra. The compensating rotation accompanying a vibration occurs with the same frequency as the vibration and contributes intensity to the vibrational spectrum. This contribution must be subtracted from the value of p_j determined by (39) before this quantity may be treated as an intramolecular parameter; that is to say, before p_j's from two isotopic molecules may be compared. CRAWFORD[22, 29] has given a method of calculation of this rotational correction which is straightforward though somewhat complicated, and which involves only geometrical parameters, atomic masses, and the permanent molecular dipole moment. This correction arises whenever p_j falls in a symmetry species which includes a molecular rotation and the molecule has a permanent dipole moment.

The magnitude of the correction can often be quite large, as, for example, in the case of $CH_2:CF_2$. Here, the correction must be applied to p_j's in the B_1 and B_2 classes; the results for the B_1 class vibrations taking $p_0 = 1.37$ D, are shown in Table X, 4.

TABLE X, 4

$C_2H_2F_2$, B_1 SPECIES

p_j's (D/Å) before removal of rotational contribution

Sign combination	$S_1(C-F)$	$S_2(C-H)$	$S_3(\phi\text{FCC})$	$S_4(\phi\text{HCC})$
(i) $++++$	5.743	0.760	0.220	-0.172
(ii) $+++-$	5.245	0.721	-0.220	-0.0600
(iii) $++-+$	3.221	0.478	-0.043	-1.325
(iv) $+-++$	-2.736	1.126	-0.466	1.157
(v) $-+++$	5.756	-0.807	0.238	-0.117
(vi) $--++$	-2.723	-0.440	0.484	1.213
(vii) $-+-+$	3.234	-1.088	-0.026	-1.269
(viii) $-++-$	5.258	-0.845	-0.202	-0.004
Rotational correction to p_j	∓ 0.0945	± 0.0523	∓ 0.964	∓ 0.0757

The correction terms are all quite small except for that to p_3, which corresponds to the symmetry coordinate

$$S_3 = 1/\sqrt{2}[\Delta(\phi_1\text{FCC}) - \Delta(\phi_2\text{FCC})]$$

Note that this correction term is larger than the uncorrected value of p_3. The physical origin of this large correction is in the fact that the centre of mass of the molecule lies close to the carbon atom of the relatively heavy (CF_2) group and consequently the real motion of the molecule is not a rocking of the (CF_2) group, as implied in the definition of the symmetry coordinate, but rather a rocking of the rest of the molecule.

(3D) Isotope rules

Just as the Teller–Redlich product rule arises because of the invariance of the potential energy under isotopic substitution, the invariance of the dipole moment function leads to relationships between the intensities of isotopic molecules. Two such relationships have been discovered by CRAWFORD[28]; both follow from the relationship, which is really a restatement of (39),

$$\left(\frac{\partial p}{\partial Q^i}\right)^2 = \sum_{j,k}\sum_{\xi} p_j^{\xi} \cdot p_k^{\xi} L_i^j L_i^k \tag{42}$$

The summation over all components of p_j and p_k must be included for completeness; in the case of a molecule with fairly high symmetry there may be only one non-vanishing component of $\boldsymbol{p}$. The coefficients $(L)_i{}^j$ may be expressed in terms of the elements of the inverse $\boldsymbol{F}$ matrix, $(F^{-1})^{kj}$, leading to the "F sum rule",

$$\frac{3c^2}{N\pi}\sum_i \Gamma_i = \sum_i \frac{1}{\omega_i}\left(\frac{\partial \boldsymbol{p}}{\partial Q^i}\right)^2 = 4\pi^2 \sum_\xi p_j^\xi \cdot p_k^\xi (F^{-1})^{kj} \tag{43}$$

The inverse force constants, like the force constants, are invariant under isotopic substitution and so the left hand side will be the same for all isotopic species. ω_i should properly be the true harmonic frequency.

The other sum rule is derived by expressing the $(L)_i^j$ in terms of the elements of the inverse kinetic energy matrix (*cf.* Chapter V), and is known as the "G sum rule";

$$\frac{3c^2}{N\pi}\sum_i \omega_i \Gamma_i = \sum_i \left(\frac{\partial \boldsymbol{p}}{\partial Q^i}\right)^2 = \sum_{j,k}\sum_\xi p_j^\xi p_k^\xi G^{jk} \tag{44}$$

As was discussed in Chapter V, the elements of the $\boldsymbol{G}$ matrix depend on molecular geometry and atomic masses and will naturally differ for different isotopic molecules; they can, however, be readily calculated.

If the molecule has symmetry, the elements of $\boldsymbol{F}^{-1}$ and $\boldsymbol{G}$ will vanish unless i and j belong to the same symmetry species and (43) and (44) hold for each separate symmetry block. It must be stressed that the F sum rule is invariant under isotopic substitution *only* for $\boldsymbol{p}_j$'s which have been corrected for the compensating rotation of the molecule as described in the preceding section.

These sum rules have several useful applications; the F sum rule is a convenient check on the raw experimental intensity data when isotopic molecules are studied; it can also be used to check vibrational assignments in much the same way as the Teller–Redlich product rule. The G sum rule provides a relationship between the derived quantities and serves as a useful check on the validity of the normal coordinate transformation used in calculating the $\boldsymbol{p}_j$'s.

(4) Dipole Moment Derivatives – Experimental Results

Gas phase intensity measurements have been made on many simple molecules; often the same molecules have been independently measured more than once. At first, many workers neglected the requirements discussed in the preceding sections and some early studies yielded intensities of the same band which differed by a factor of two. However, with the advent of improved techniques, different laboratories reported intensities varying by little more than the estimated probable errors, *i.e.* $\pm$ 1 to 2 per cent with careful work in favourable cases, and there is now general agreement on the

References p. 376

vibrational intensities of quite a few simple molecules; *e.g.*, CO_2, SO_2, HCN, SiF_4, SF_6, CH_4, CH_3CH_3, $CH_2=CH_2$, $HC\equiv CH$, C_6H_6, CH_3X, and CH_2O, etc. An extensive list of references to experimental results is given by MILLS[10], and no attempt will be made here to report all established values for infra-red intensities; instead a few typical results will be considered in some detail.

(4A) Benzene

The infra-red intensities of benzene and some of its deuterated analogues have been reported by SPEDDING and WHIFFEN[30]. They used the Wilson–Wells method, with nitrogen at one atmosphere as the broadening gas, and obtained satisfactorily linear Beer's law plots for the in-plane fundamentals. The out-of-plane vibrational bands have sharp Q branches and, with only one atmosphere of broadening gas, give slightly curved Beer's law plots; accordingly the values of Γ for these modes are not as well determined. The benzene fundamentals have also been measured under conditions of complete pressure broadening[41]; both sets of results are compared in Table X, 5. The

TABLE X, 5

INFRA-RED INTENSITIES OF BENZENE

		Γ, $cm^2/mole$	
Mode	Frequency, cm^{-1}	Spedding and Whiffen[30]	Overend and Youngquist[41]
ν_{11} (A_{2u})	673	13100	12570 ± 300
ν_{18} (E_{1u})	1038	852	817 ± 9
ν_{19} (E_{1u})	1486	1000	1083 ± 15
ν_{20} (E_{1u})	3080	$\begin{cases} 2470^a \\ 1950^b \end{cases}$	2230 ± 40

a Total intensity in region of 3000 cm^{-1} including all combination bands.
b Estimated unperturbed intensity of combination band subtracted out.

agreement is satisfactory, and it seems reasonably certain that the intensities are essentially correct.

Spedding and Whiffen also measured the fundamental intensities of C_6H_5D and $p\text{-}C_6H_4D_2$. Beer's law plots were drawn for the stronger bands; the weaker ones were measured at only one sample pressure and are indicated by parentheses in Table X, 6.

The spectrum of C_6H_6 is complicated by Fermi resonance between the fundamental ν_{20} and the two E_{1u} species combinations at 3081 and 3084 cm^{-1}. Spedding and Whiffen, by comparing the spectrum with that of $C_6H_4D_2$ where there is apparently little or no Fermi resonance, inferred that the unperturbed intensity of these combination bands is 520 $cm^2/mole$ and this has been subtracted from the total absorption in the (C–H)stretching region of benzene. The band at 1528 cm^{-1} in benzene is assigned to the E_{1u} combination (673+849 cm^{-1}) and is assumed to derive all its intensity from ν_{19} through Fermi resonance. Its intensity has, accordingly, been included with that of ν_{19} in Table X, 5.

TABLE X, 6

INFRA-RED INTENSITIES OF C_6D_5H AND $p\text{-}C_6H_4D_2$[30]

	Frequency cm^{-1}	Symmetry	Γ, cm^2/mole obs.	calc.	Frequency, cm^{-1}	Symmetry	Γ, cm^2/mole obs.	calc.
C_6D_5H	607	B_2	9400	8900	1032	A_1	410	410
	698	B_2	1960	1900	1078	B_1	190	190
	778	B_2	2090	2140	1462	B_1 }	790	790
	926	B_2	(170)	170	1475	A_1 }		
	859	B_1	(230)	260	1590	$(B+A_1)$	(a)	10
	973	A_1	(a)	20	2277	A_1	230	230
	1000	A_1	(a)	20	3070	A_1	1540	1560
$p\text{-}C_6H_4D_2$	597	B_{1u}	10700	11100	1107	B_{3u}	90	90
	874	B_{1u}	1700	1540	1414	B_{3u}	310	260
	823	B_{3u}	370	370	1475	B_{2u}	420	420
	992	B_{2u}	(a)	60	2278	B_{2u}	480	480
	1034	B_{2u}	410	370	3080	$(B_{2u}+B_{3u})$	1200	1220

[a] Observed but too weak to measure.

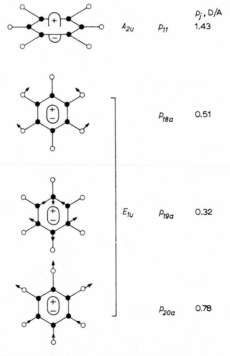

		p_j, D/A
A_{2u}	P_{11}	1.43
	P_{18a}	0.51
E_{1u}	P_{19a}	0.32
	P_{20a}	0.78

Fig. X, 5. Dipole moment derivatives for benzene.

The transformation of the C_6H_6 intensities to p_j's was carried out with normal coordinates calculated by WHIFFEN[31]. Four alternative sets of p_j's result from the E_{1u} species and the isotopic data were used by Spedding and Whiffen to determine the correct set, by calculating from each set of p_j's, the intensities of the bands in C_6H_5D and p-$C_6H_4D_2$ and comparing with the observed intensities. The final choice of p_j's is displayed pictorially in Fig. X, 5. The distortion of the molecule in the symmetry coordinate S^{11} is indicated by arrows, the sign of the dipole moment change is not known, and the $+$ and $-$ signs for p_{11} could be reversed, as could those for all the E_{1u} vibrations. However, in the latter case, the relative signs of the p_j's do follow from the normal coordinate analysis and, if p_{18_a} is changed, p_{19_a} and p_{20_a} must also be changed.

(4B) Ethylene

Intensity measurements on ethylene were made by GOLIKE, MILLS, PERSON and CRAWFORD[28] using the Wilson–Wells technique with pressures of 700 p.s.i. of nitrogen to broaden the spectrum. Their results are shown in

TABLE X, 7

INFRA-RED INTENSITIES OF ETHYLENE C_2H_4[28]

| Mode | Frequency, cm^{-1} | Γ, $cm^2/mole$ | | | $\partial p/\partial Q^i$ |
		Thorndike	Dispersion	Golike, et al.	$cm^{3/2}\ sec^{-1}$
ν_7 (B_{1u})	949.2	10900	7300	8400	106.6
ν_9 (B_{2u})	3105.5	1372	947	802	62.4
ν_{10} (B_{2u})	810.3	—	—	(65)	8.7
ν_{11} (B_{3u})	2989.5	676	441	452	45.9
ν_{12} (B_{3u})	1443.5	1088	790	676	37.3

Table X, 7 together with the similar earlier ones of THORNDIKE, WELLS and WILSON[32], and those of HAMMER[33] obtained from dispersion studies. The agreement between Golike's and Hammer's results is disappointing, but currently it seems reasonable to take the results of Golike, et al. as correct. The weak band due to ν_{10} is partially obscured by ν_7 and its intensity is somewhat uncertain; the value given in Table X, 7 is the estimate of Golike, et al. who were able to measure one branch which they assumed to be half the total band intensity.

The observed (C–H) and (C–D) stretching frequencies were adjusted until all the frequencies fitted the isotopic product rule. The harmonic frequencies so obtained, rather than the observed frequencies, were used in the evaluation of the $\partial p/\partial Q^i$.

Golike, et al. extended their study to C_2D_4 and cis and trans $C_2H_2D_2$, and these results are shown in Table X, 8. The normal coordinates used in the analysis were calculated from the potential function given by CRAW-FORD, LANCASTER and INSKEEP[34] which was fitted to the "harmonic" frequencies of ethylene and five deuteroisomers.

TABLE X, 8

INFRA-RED INTENSITIES OF C_2D_4, $trans$-$C_2H_2D_2$ AND cis-$C_2H_2D_2$[28]

	Mode		Frequency, cm^{-1}	Γ, $cm^2/mole$	$\partial p/\partial Q_i$, $cm^{3/2}$ sec^{-1}
C_2D_4	ν_7	(B_{1u})	720	5794.0	77.1
	ν_9	(B_{2u})	2345	520.7	43.1
	ν_{10}	(B_{2u})	589	(7.3)	2.5
	ν_{11}	(B_{3u})	2200	346.4	34.1
	ν_{12}	(B_{3u})	1078	481.4	27.2
$trans$-$C_2H_2D_2$	ν_4	(A_u)	988	3740	72.5 ± 1.0
	ν_7	(A_u)	727	3406	59.4 ± 1.0
	ν_9	(B_u)	3065	640.8	55.4 ± 0.5
	ν_{10}	(B_u)	660	(6.5)	2.2 ± 6
	ν_{11}	(B_u)	2271	410.4	27.7 ± 0.4
	ν_{12}	(B_u)	1300	592.3	33.2 ± 0.3
	$(\nu_8+\nu_9)$	(A_u)	1848	108.2	
	$(\nu_7+\nu_8)$	(B_u)	1590	65.4	
cis-$C_2H_2D_2$	ν_7	(B_2)	843	8531	101.1 ± 2.0
	ν_1	(A_1)	2349	212	27.5 ± 1.0
	ν_2	(A_1)	1558 (a)	—	0
	ν_3	(A_1)	1213 (a)	—	0
	ν_9	(A_1)	3043 (a)	418.7	44.7 (b)
	ν_{10}	(A_1)	656 (a)	—	0
	ν_{11}	(B_1)	2254	278	30.9 ± 1.0
	ν_{12}	(B_1)	1344	511	31.3 ± 0.2
	ν_5	(B_1)	3056	219.7	32.4 (b)
	ν_6	(B_1)	1035	(38)	7.5 ± 5.0
	$(\nu_2+\nu_{12})$	(B_1)	2903	(2.5)	
	$(\nu_4+\nu_7)$	(B_1)	1818	116	
	$(\nu_7+\nu_8)$	(B_1)	1598	77.0	

a These frequencies were not observed but were calculated by CRAWFORD, et al., ref. 4.
b The bands due to ν_5 and ν_9 overlap and it was not possible to determine the separate areas experimentally. The values of $\partial p/\partial Q_5$ and $\partial p/\partial Q_9$ shown in the table were obtained by dividing the observed area of 638.4 $cm^2/mole$ in proportion to the intensities of ν_5 and ν_9 calculated from the $\partial p/\partial S$ values previously determined from C_2H_4 and C_2D_4.

The value of p_7 was calculated from the $\partial p/\partial Q_i$ values of the out-of-plane vibrations in C_2H_4, C_2D_4, cis-$C_2H_2D_2$ and $trans$-$C_2H_2D_2$, and reasonably good agreement was obtained among the different isotopes. The value of p_7 shown in Fig. X, 6 is the average of these independent determinations. The p_j's for the in-plane vibrations were calculated from the C_2H_4 and C_2D_4 data. Although a comparison of the p_j values corresponding to the alternative sign choices indicated a preference for the $(++)$ combination in the B_{2u} class and the $(+-)$ combination in the B_{3u} class, it was, un-

fortunately, not conclusive. In order to utilize the data from the other
isotopic molecules, all possible sets of p_j values were used to calculate the
$\partial p/\partial Q_i$'s and these were then compared with the experimental values. This
lent additional support to the choice indicated above which is shown
pictorially in Fig. X, 6 column (I). The other results, which are not un-

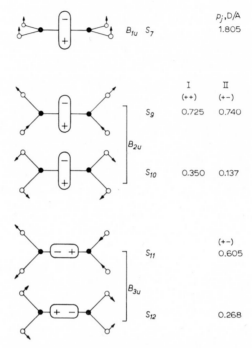

Fig. X, 6. Dipole moment derivatives for ethylene.

reasonable, are shown in column (II). This alternative leads to the same
relative signs of the p_j as those established by the first choice.

The relative signs of p_j within each symmetry species are fixed by the
calculation, but again all the signs in any species may be arbitrarily reversed.
As drawn in Fig. X, 6 the dipole moments developed on extension of the
(C–H) bonds have similar sign, but anomalously, those developed on bending
the (C–H) bonds in the same direction have opposite signs. This anomaly
in the bending motion could be eliminated by reversing the signs of all the
p_j's in either the B_{2u} or B_{3u} species, but this would merely throw the sign
anomaly into the stretching motion. These results bring out another interesting feature. The p_j values for the (C–H) stretching coordinates are
easily transformed into $\partial p/\partial r_{CH}$ through the original symmetry-coordinate
transformation[28]. There are two contributions, one from p_9 perpendicular
to the (C=C) bond and one from p_{11} along the (C=C) bond.

These give the components and hence the orientation of $\partial p / \partial r_{CH}$, which is found to be oriented at the angle shown in Fig. X, 7, rather than along the (C–H) bond.

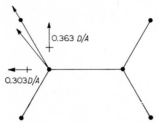

0.363 D/A

0.303 D/A

Fig. X, 7. Sketch showing orientation of $\partial p / \partial r$ for a carbon hydrogen bond in ethylene.

(4C) HCN and DCN

HYDE and HORNIG[35] used the Wilson–Wells method for all the fundamentals of HCN and DCN with nitrogen at 63 p.s.i. to broaden the spectrum. Their value of Γ_2 for HCN (cf. Table X, 9) is checked within 20 per cent by the

TABLE X, 9

HCN AND DCN[35]

Mode		Frequency, cm^{-1}	Γ, $cm^2/mole$	$\partial p / \partial Q$, $cm^{3/2} sec^{-1}$
HCN	ν_1	2089	6.9	4.5
	ν_2	712	6420	57
	ν_3	3312	1630	88
DCN	ν_1	1921	140	20
	ν_2	569	2403	31
	ν_3	2629	1159	66

work of FOLEY[36] who measured the intensity of individual rotational lines in the ν_2 band and obtained a value of $\Gamma_2 = 5420$ $cm^2/mole$. In the case of the ν_1 and ν_3 bands of both HCN and DCN, they measured the absorption areas, $\int ((I_0-I)/I_0)d\nu$ directly from the spectrometer trace rather than the quantity B, and the Beer's law plots are curved. The one corresponding to ν_1 in HCN shows a curious upward curvature which is attributed to formation of the dimer at higher pressures. The quantity B was measured for the ν_2 bands and the Beer's law plot for HCN was satisfactorily linear, but that for DCN failed to pass through the origin. This discrepancy was attributed to errors in the background. All in all, the quality of their data is such that the uncertainty in the $\partial p / \partial Q$ values is about 10 per cent.

The observed vibrational frequencies of HCN and DCN do not fit the product rule exactly and two alternative sets of quadratic force constants were obtained. The normal-coordinate transformation, used to calculate the p_j values shown in Fig. X, 8 was based on the averaged values of these force constants. On comparing the p_j values of HCN with those for DCN, it is immediately obvious that the correct set of p_j's is that corresponding to $\partial p/\partial Q_1$ and $\partial p/\partial Q_2$ taken with the same sign and this choice is shown in Fig. X, 8.

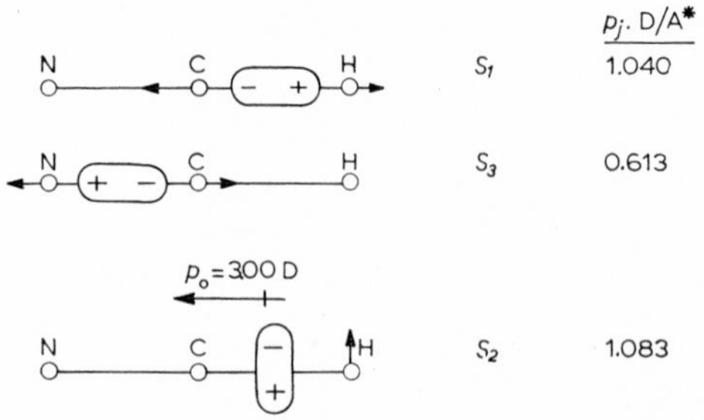

Fig. X, 8. HCN and DCN, dipole moment slopes.

*Average of values from HCN and DCN.

There is some compensating rotation accompanying the bending vibration, and as the molecule has a permanent dipole moment, there is a contribution to p_2 from this rotation which must be subtracted from the observed p_2 before the data are compared with those for other molecules (Table X, 10). This rotational correction is implicit in Hyde and Hornig's

TABLE X, 10

HCN AND DCN, ROTATIONAL CORRECTION

HCN		D/Å	
p_2 (observed)	$=$	0.626	
$V_{(01)}$	$=$	-0.431	(a)
$p_{(0)2} = p_{(1)2} - V_{(01)2}$	$=$	1.057	(b)
	$=$	-0.195	(c)
DCN			
p_2 (observed)	$=$	0.431	
$V_{(02)}$	$=$	-0.678	(a)
$p_{(0)2} = p_{(2)2} - V_{(02)2}$	$=$	1.109	(b)
	$=$	0.247	(c)

a Taking value of p_0 for HCN to be 3.00 D, see ref. 16.
b $(\partial p/\partial Q)/p_0$ positive.
c $(\partial p/\partial Q)/p_0$ negative.

equations relating the moments of the (C–H) and (C≡N) bonds to $\partial p/\partial Q_2$. However, CRAWFORD's method[28] brings out the physical significance more clearly. Two alternative solutions arise because the sign of p_2 may be the same as or opposite to the sign of the permanent moment, but the only one which gives the same value of p_2 for both HCN and DCN is that in which p_2 is taken with the same sign as the permanent moment. This result establishes the relative signs of p_0 and p_2.

(4D) The bond moment hypothesis

All the quantities discussed in the preceding sections are derived exactly, in the double harmonic approximation, from the measured intensities. It is, however, desirable to reduce these data further to chemical bond parameters which might be chemically more meaningful and which might eventually be systematized in much the same way as bond energies, bond lengths and force constants. The customary simple reduction to *bond moments* and *effective charges* requires three further assumptions. (i) When a bond is stretched through a distance dr, an additional contribution to the moment, $(\partial\mu/\partial r)dr$ is developed in the direction of the bond. (ii) When a bond is bent through an angle $d\alpha$, the change in dipole moment is $\mu_0\, d\alpha$ where μ_0 is the effective bond moment. (iii) When any bond is bent or stretched, the only change in dipole moment is in that particular bond. These assumptions have been used in most intensity studies to derive bond moments μ_0 and effective charges $\partial\mu/\partial r$. A large number of bond moments and effective charges have been tabulated by HORNIG and McKEAN[37] in an excellent critical review of the bond moment hypothesis and the interested reader is referred to that article. Suffice it to say that there are some very real objections to the bond moment model. If the experimental intensities of ethylene are accepted as correct, and there is no reason why they should not be, it is definitely established that the dipole moment change when a (C–H) bond is stretched is not oriented along the (C–H) bond, and further, that the p_j's for the bending vibrations cannot be understood in terms of bond moments. Thus, in the particular case of ethylene, the simple assumptions of the bond moment hypothesis appear to be invalid. Similar results have been found for other molecules and it now seems that additional features must be introduced into a model to provide a realistic description of infra-red intensities. Steps are presently being taken in this direction; for example, transverse components are sometimes included in bond moments, and the double harmonic approximation is being scrutinized more closely, but insufficient work has been done to lead to firm conclusions.

(4E) Intensities in condensed phases

There is not sufficient space in this chapter to discuss the many measurements of infra-red intensities in condensed phases. Many data have been obtained on single characteristic group frequencies, *e.g.*, the carbonyl stretching vibration, and these have been correlated with the electrical properties of substituents, with observed vibrational frequencies and with reactivity parameters. The reader is referred to Chapter VI and a review by BROWN[38].

All too frequently the intensity has been interpreted in terms of the change in dipole moment with an internal coordinate rather than with a normal coordinate. Sometimes this approximation is permissible, but the true relationship described in eqn. (39) should always be kept in mind.

Some progress has been made towards understanding infra-red intensities in condensed phases in terms of intermolecular interactions[39, 40], but as this work is still at a tentative level, it will not be described here.

REFERENCES

[1] I. M. MILLS, *Mol. Phys.*, 1 (1958) 99.
[2] B. CRAWFORD, JR., *J. Chem. Phys.*, 29 (1958) 1042.
[3] E. B. WILSON, J. C. DECIUS AND P. C. CROSS, *Molecular Vibrations*, McGraw-Hill, New York, 1955.
[4] I. M. MILLS AND D. H. WHIFFEN, *J. Chem. Phys.*, 30 (1959) 1619.
[5] S. S. PENNER AND D. WEBER, *J. Chem. Phys.*, 19 (1951) 807.
[6] R. C. HERMAN AND K. E. SHULER, *J. Chem. Phys.*, 22 (1954) 481.
[7] G. HERZBERG, *Infra-red and Raman Spectra*, Van Nostrand, New York, 1945.
[8] I. C. HISATSUNE AND D. F. EGGERS, JR., *J. Chem. Phys.*, 23 (1955) 487.
[9] J. OVEREND AND B. CRAWFORD, JR., *J. Chem. Phys.*, 29 (1958) 1002.
[10] I. M. MILLS, *Ann. Rept. Progr. Chem.* (*Chem. Soc. London*), LV (1958) 56.
[11] E. BARTHOLOMÉ, *Z. Physik. Chem.* (*Leipzig*), B23 (1933) 131.
[12] D. G. BOURGIN, *Phys. Rev.*, 29 (1927) 794.
[13] E. C. KEMBLE, *J. Chem. Phys.*, 3 (1935) 316.
[14] E. B. WILSON, JR., AND A. J. WELLS, *J. Chem. Phys.*, 14 (1946) 578.
[15] L. D. KAPLAN AND D. F. EGGERS, JR., *J. Chem. Phys.*, 25 (1956) 876.
[16] C. H. TOWNES AND A. L. SCHAWLOW, *Microwave Spectroscopy*, McGraw-Hill, New York, 1955.
[17] J. OVEREND, M. J. YOUNGQUIST, E. C. CURTIS AND B. CRAWFORD, JR., *J. Chem. Phys.*, 30 (1959) 532.
[18] R. P. MADDEN, *J. Chem. Phys.*, 35 (1961) 2083.
[19] A. M. THORNDIKE, *J. Chem. Phys.*, 15 (1947) 868.
[20] D. F. EGGERS, JR., AND B. L. CRAWFORD, JR., *J. Chem. Phys.*, 19 (1951) 1554.
[21] D. WEBER, R. J. HOLM AND S. S. PENNER, *J. Chem. Phys.*, 20 (1952) 1820.
[22] A. D. DICKSON, I. M. MILLS AND B. CRAWFORD, JR., *J. Chem. Phys.*, 27 (1957) 445.
[23] R. LADENBURG AND F. REICHE, *Ann. Physik*, 42 (1913) 181.
[24] D. A. RAMSAY, *J. Am. Chem. Soc.*, 74 (1952) 72.
[25] H. J. KOSTKOWSKI AND A. M. BASS, *J. Opt. Soc. Am.*, 46 (1956) 1060.
[26] R. N. JONES AND C. SANDORFY, in A. WEISSBERGER, (Editor), *Technique of Organic Chemistry*, Vol. IX, Chapter IV, Interscience, New York, 1956.
[27] I. M. NYQUIST, I. M. MILLS, W. B. PERSON AND B. CRAWFORD, JR., *J. Chem. Phys.*, 26 (1957) 552.
[28] R. C. GOLIKE, I. M. MILLS, W. B. PERSON AND B. CRAWFORD, JR., *J. Chem. Phys.*, 25 (1956) 1266.
[29] B. CRAWFORD, JR., *J. Chem. Phys.*, 20 (1952) 977.
[30] H. SPEDDING AND D. H. WHIFFEN, *Proc. Roy. Soc.* (*London*), Ser. *A*, 238 (1956) 245.
[31] D. H. WHIFFEN, *Phil. Trans. Roy. Soc. London*, Ser. *A*, 248 (1955) 131.
[32] A. M. THORNDIKE, A. J. WELLS AND E. B. WILSON, JR., *J. Chem. Phys.*, 15 (1947) 157.
[33] C. F. HAMMER, *Dissertation*, University of Wisconsin, 1951.
[34] B. CRAWFORD, J. E. LANCASTER AND R. G. INSKEEP, *J. Chem. Phys.*, 21 (1953) 678.
[35] G. E. HYDE AND D. F. HORNIG, *J. Chem. Phys.*, 20 (1952) 647.
[36] H. M. FOLEY, *Phys. Rev.*, 69 (1946) 628.
[37] D. F. HORNIG AND D. C. MCKEAN, *J. Phys. Chem.*, 59 (1955) 1133.
[38] T. L. BROWN, *Chem. Rev.*, 58 (1958) 581.
[39] W. B. PERSON, *J. Chem. Phys.*, 28 (1958) 319.
[40] A. D. BUCKINGHAM, *Proc. Roy. Soc.* (*London*), Ser. *A*, 248 (1958) 169.
[41] J. OVEREND AND M. J. YOUNGQUIST, unpublished work.

Chapter XI

The Methods and Results of Dispersion Studies

J. FAHRENFORT

Spectroscopy Department, Koninklijke/Shell-Laboratorium, Amsterdam
(Shell Internationale Research Maatschappij N.V.)

It is generally known that in regions of the frequency spectrum where a material absorbs radiation, the refractive index shows variations, known as anomalous dispersion.

The theory of the propagation of light waves in a material medium tells us that absorption and dispersion are closely related and are in fact the result of a single cause, the excitation of the oscillators in the medium by the light wave, the frequency of which approximates to the eigen frequency of the oscillators.

In order to study the properties of these oscillators one can, by virtue of this fundamental relation, just as well determine the dispersion spectrum of the material as the absorption spectrum. It will depend on experimental circumstances whether one will choose one way or the other, or possibly both.

In the following sections we will review the methods of dispersion studies and the results obtained by them.

(1) The Complex Refractive Index [1]

In an isotropic, non-magnetic material, in which no energy is dissipated, Maxwell's relations provide a wave equation which holds for each component of the field E. For one of the components we may write

$$E_y = E_0 e^{i\omega(t-x/v)} \tag{1}$$

where t is time, $\omega(= 2\pi\nu)$ is the angular frequency of the wave, and x is the direction of propagation. Equation (1) requires that $1/v^2 = \varepsilon/c^2$, which means that v is the velocity of the wave in the medium, ε being a dimensionless quantity, the dielectric constant. The ratio of v to the velocity c in a vacuum is normally written as n, the refractive index, whence we have:

$$n^2 = \frac{c^2}{v^2} = \varepsilon \tag{2}$$

In absorbing media the energy dissipation from the electromagnetic field is usually represented by attributing a conductivity σ to the medium. Again (1) can be written as the solution of the conditions, this time with the proviso that

$$\frac{c^2}{v^2} = n'^2 = \varepsilon - \frac{i4\pi\sigma}{\omega} \tag{3}$$

where n' now is a complex refractive index, which is usually written in the form

$$n' = n(1-i\kappa) \tag{4}$$

Substitution of (4) into (3) yields

$$n^2 - n^2\kappa^2 - 2in^2\kappa = \varepsilon - \frac{4\pi\sigma i}{\omega} = \varepsilon'$$

whence

$$n^2(1-\kappa^2) = \varepsilon$$

and

$$n^2\kappa = \frac{2\pi\sigma}{\omega} = \frac{\sigma}{v}$$

If $\sigma = 0$ we have again $\kappa = 0$ and $n^2 = \varepsilon$.
If we substitute (4) in the expression (1) for the plane wave, we obtain

$$E_y = E_0 e^{i\omega(t - nx/c)} e^{-\omega n\kappa x/c} \tag{5}$$

On comparing this equation with the solution for the transparent medium, we find an additional factor, which describes the damping of the wave traveling in the x-direction. The energy carried by the wave is proportional to the mean square $\overline{E_y^2} = I$, which means that it diminishes according to

$$I = I_0 e^{-2\omega\kappa nx/c} = I_0 e^{-\pi n\kappa vx/c} = I_0 e^{-\alpha x} \tag{6}$$

which is an expression of Lambert's law, defining an absorption coefficient:

$$\alpha = \frac{4\pi n\kappa v}{c}, \text{ or, if } v \text{ is expressed in cm}^{-1}$$

$$\alpha = 4\pi n\kappa v \tag{7}$$

(2) Dispersion Theory

In the previous section we have seen that the behaviour of electromagnetic waves in isotropic media can be described by one parameter, the complex refractive index n'. In its derivation we have taken a macroscopic point of view, assuming a homogeneous distribution of matter and leaving the molecular structure out of consideration. The relation which must ultimately exist between the macroscopic properties, such as the refractive index, and the characteristics of the individual molecules of which our object is composed is given by dispersion theory.

We suppose that our medium consists of damped harmonic oscillators, which will on irradiation be polarized by the electromagnetic field. The forces working on an oscillator of mass m, carrying a charge e, subjected to an electric field:

$$E'_Q = E'_{Q0} e^{i\omega t} \tag{8}$$

will be:

$$eE'_Q - aQ - b\frac{\mathrm{d}Q}{\mathrm{d}t} = m\frac{\mathrm{d}^2Q}{\mathrm{d}t^2} \tag{9}$$

where Q is the coordinate of vibration, a the force constant of the oscillator and b a constant describing its damping.

The solution of (9) is given by

$$Q = Q_0 e^{i\omega t} \tag{10}$$

Substituting (10) in (9) and dividing by m, we find an expression for Q, which in turn yields the electric moment of a medium containing N identical oscillators per unit volume

$$\boldsymbol{P} = NeQ = \frac{Ne^2/m}{\omega_0^2 - \omega^2 + i\gamma\omega} \boldsymbol{E}' = \beta\boldsymbol{E}' \tag{11}$$

Here a/m has been replaced by the square of the eigen-frequency ω_0; γ replaces b/m and is called the damping constant, while β evidently represents the polarizability of the medium.

The field $\boldsymbol{E}'$ which actually polarizes the molecules is not simply the field of the electromagnetic wave, but has an additional component due to the induced dipoles of the surrounding polarized molecules, which becomes apparent if the distances between the particles are small, as is the case in condensed phases. Calculation of this additional field is particularly difficult but leads to a simple form for macroscopically isotropic media such as compressed gases, liquids and amorphous solids, as well as for isotropic crystals consisting of isotropic molecules. For these cases the general theory[1] gives the same results as the much simpler, though less convincing, argument treated below.

In this argument the field $\boldsymbol{E}'$ is found by the consideration of a small spherical surface around a given central molecule, which forms the boundary between a region in which the molecular structure is still apparent for the central molecule, and a region for which it is equivalent to a homogeneously polarized medium. The fields of the molecules within the sphere are assumed to cancel, resulting in a zero contribution, and the remaining field is given by that of the free charges on the surface of the sphere, which equals $\frac{4}{3}\pi \boldsymbol{P}$.

Thus we have

$$\boldsymbol{E'} = \boldsymbol{E} + \tfrac{4}{3}\pi \boldsymbol{P} \tag{12}$$

if $\boldsymbol{E}$ is the electromagnetic field in the dielectric.

Substitution of (12) in (11) yields

$$\boldsymbol{P} = \frac{\beta}{1 - \frac{4}{3}\pi\beta} \boldsymbol{E} \tag{13}$$

A correlation between the refractive index and the polarizability is found from the expression for the dielectric displacement $\boldsymbol{D}$, which consists of one part which, as in vacuum, is equal to the electric field, and another part $4\pi\boldsymbol{P}$ due to the induced moment. Thus

$$\boldsymbol{D} = \boldsymbol{E} + 4\pi\boldsymbol{P} = \varepsilon'\boldsymbol{E} = n'^2\boldsymbol{E} \tag{14}$$

On substituting (13) in (14), solving for β and combining with (11) we have

$$\frac{n'^2 - 1}{n'^2 + 2} = \frac{4\pi}{3} \frac{Ne^2}{m(\omega_0^2 - \omega^2 + i\gamma\omega)} \tag{15}$$

Equation (15) is known as the Lorentz–Lorenz dispersion formula, and is valid only for a medium consisting of one type of oscillator. The formula can be expanded to include dispersion of media containing sets of different oscillators:

$$\frac{n'^2 - 1}{n'^2 + 2} = \sum_j \frac{4}{3}\pi^2 \frac{\rho_j}{(\omega_{j0}^2 - \omega^2 - i\gamma_j\omega)} \tag{16}$$

with

$$\rho_j = \frac{Ne_j^2}{\pi m_j} \tag{17}$$

When considering the jth eigenfrequency, well-isolated in the spectrum, we can assume that the contribution of all other oscillators in the region of the jth may be represented by the constant real value n_0 of the refractive index. Then, (16) takes the form:

$$\frac{n'^2 - 1}{n'^2 + 2} = \frac{n_0^2 - 1}{n_0^2 + 2} + \frac{4}{3}\pi^2 \frac{\rho_j}{(\omega_{j0}^2 - \omega^2 + i\gamma_j\omega)} \tag{18}$$

Making use of the relation $n^2 - 1 = 3b/(1-b)$, valid if $b = (n^2-1)/(n^2+2)$, it is easily shown that (18) can be written as

$$n'^2 = n_0^2 + \frac{4\pi^2\rho_j'}{(\omega_{j0}'^2 - \omega^2 + i\gamma_j\omega)} \tag{19}$$

where

$$\rho_j' = \rho_j \left(\frac{n_0^2 + 2}{3} \right)^2$$

$$\omega_{j0}'^2 = \omega_{j0}^2 - 4\pi^2 \rho_j' \frac{1}{(n_0^2 + 2)} \Biggr\}$$

(20)

A quantum-mechanical treatment of dispersion leads to a dispersion formula of exactly the same form as (19), but for the replacement of the squared variable charge e_j^2 of the oscillator in (17) by $e^2 f_j$, where e is the elementary charge and f_j is a weight factor called the oscillator strength. It is common usage to call ρ the effective oscillator strength. f_j is related to the quantum-mechanical transition probability by the expression:

$$\frac{e^2 f_j}{m} = \frac{4}{3} \frac{\pi}{h} \omega_j |R_j|^2,$$

(21)

where $|R_j|$ is the matrix element of the dipole moment μ associated with the normal mode Q_j. For a purely harmonic mode

$$|R_j|^2 = \frac{h}{8\pi^2 \nu} \left(\frac{\partial \mu}{\partial Q_j} \right)^2$$

The damping constant γ is related to the quantum mechanical lifetime τ of the excited state by $\gamma \smile 1/\tau$.

If we split equation (19) into its real and imaginary components we obtain the equations from which the constants of the dispersion formula may be calculated:

$$n^2(1 - \kappa^2) = n_0^2 + \frac{\rho_j'(\nu_j'^2 - \nu^2)}{[(\nu_{j0}')^2 - \nu^2]^2 + g^2 \nu^2}$$

(22)

$$2n^2\kappa = \frac{\rho_j' g \nu}{[(\nu_{j0}')^2 - \nu^2]^2 + g^2 \nu^2}$$

(23)

where ω has been replaced by $2\pi\nu$ and γ by $2\pi g$. It can be shown that the resonant frequency ν_{j0}' is found at the maximum of the plot of $2n^2\kappa\nu$ versus ν. At $2n^2\kappa\nu = \frac{1}{2}(2n^2\kappa\nu)_{max}$ we have

$$g = \frac{(\nu_{j0}')^2 - \nu^2}{\nu} \simeq 2(\nu_{j0}' - \nu)$$

Furthermore the effective oscillator strength is given by $\rho_j' = g(2n^2\kappa\nu)_{max}$. ρ_j' of course is also found by integrating $2n^2\kappa\nu d\nu$:

$$\int_0^\infty 2n^2\kappa\nu d\nu = \int_0^\infty \frac{\rho_j' \nu^2 g \, d\nu}{[(\nu_{j0}')^2 - \nu^2]^2 + g^2 \nu^2} = \frac{\pi}{2} \rho_j'$$

(24)

In practice the integration is carried out only in the region where $2n^2\kappa\nu$ has measurable values.

We have thus demonstrated that knowledge of the optical constants n and κ will allow us to determine values for ν_{j0}', g and ρ_j', which are constants for the jth band of the medium in question. Reduction of these constants to properties of the molecules still involves the effective field factor, which unfortunately has a simple form only for isotropic systems. In that case, however, we can immediately calculate it from the refractive index (see (20)), and therefore it is more advantageous to measure the dispersion than the absorption of dense media.

As the absorption coefficient (7) can easily be calculated from n and κ, a direct comparison with absorption data can be made.

It seems proper to mention here that dispersion studies, important though they may be, are only an experimental alternative to absorption measurements, with their own advantages but also complications, as fundamentally the complete complex refractive index gives no other information than the absorption coefficient alone. This statement becomes clear if we look at the integral transforms given by KRAMERS and KRONIG[2]

$$n_c - 1 = \frac{2}{\pi} \int_0^\infty \frac{n\kappa\omega - (n\kappa\omega)_c}{\omega^2 - \omega_c^2} \, d\omega \tag{25a}$$

and

$$(n\kappa)_c = -\frac{2\omega_c}{\pi} \int_0^\infty \frac{(n-1) - (n-1)_c}{\omega^2 - \omega_c^2} \, d\omega \tag{25b}$$

where c denotes one selected frequency.

Equations (25a and b) form one pair out of a whole family of relations known as the Kramers–Kronig relations, which can be shown to exist between physical variables connected causally[3]. They show that the real part of the refractive index may be calculated at a selected frequency if the imaginary part is known over the whole spectrum, so that the information contained in the spectrum of $n\kappa$ (or of the absorption coefficient) is also contained in the spectrum of n and *vice versa*. In Section 4 we shall encounter some other relations of the same type.

(3) **Refraction and Reflection at a Boundary**

(3A) General formulation

To use the equations derived in the preceding section, we shall need information on the optical constants n and κ. This can be obtained only by studying the behaviour of light waves in their interaction with the medium under investigation.

From experience we know that a light wave meeting a boundary between two media will split into two parts, one part being reflected into the first medium, the other propagating as a refracted beam into the second. The laws governing these phenomena were given long ago by Snellius and Fresnel. They can also be rigorously derived from electromagnetic theory[1].

From the boundary condition that in the interface the sum of the components of the electro-magnetic field must be equal for the two media follow Fresnel's formulae for the reflected beam:

$$\frac{r_p}{a_p} = \frac{tg(\theta - \theta_1)}{tg(\theta + \theta_1)} \tag{26a}$$

and

$$\frac{r_s}{a_s} = -\frac{\sin(\theta - \theta_1)}{\sin(\theta + \theta_1)} \tag{26b}$$

where a and r are the amplitudes of the incident and the reflected wave, and the subscripts p and s refer to polarization in and perpendicular to the plane of incidence (*i.e.* the plane defined by the directional vector of the incident beam and the normal to the interface). θ is the angle of incidence, θ_1 the angle of refraction.

Snellius' law follows from the condition that in the interface the phase of both the reflected and the refracted wave must equal that of the incident wave. This leads to the conclusion that

$$\frac{\sin \theta}{v_1} = \frac{\sin \theta'}{v_1} = \frac{\sin \theta_1}{v_2}$$

where θ' is the angle of reflection[1] and v_1 and v_2 are the velocities of light in the two media. Hence

$$\pi - \theta = \theta'$$

and

$$\sin \theta = \frac{v_1}{v_2} \sin \theta_1 = n \sin \theta_1 \tag{27}$$

(3B) Incidence on a non-absorbing medium

Combination of (26) and (27) yields a number of important expressions. First we remark that for non-absorbing media the expressions (26) are real and that the intensity of the reflected radiation is found simply by squaring the amplitudes.

On inspection of (26a) it will also be clear that for $\theta + \theta_1 = \pi/2$ the intensity $R_p = r_p^2 = 0$. Because then $\sin \theta_1 = \cos \theta$, we have $n = tg\theta_B$. This angle θ_B at which evidently the refracted and reflected beams are perpendicular to each other, is called the Brewster angle. Its determination provides a simple means of finding the refractive index of non-absorbing media.

If we write (26b) for unit amplitude of the incident light as

$$r_s = -\frac{\sin \theta \cos \theta_1 - \cos \theta \sin \theta_1}{\sin \theta \cos \theta_1 + \cos \theta \sin \theta_1}$$

replace $\cos \theta_1$ by $\sqrt{1 - \sin^2 \theta / n^2}$, and multiply by $n/\sin \theta$, we obtain:

$$r_s = -\frac{\sqrt{n^2 - \sin^2 \theta} - \cos \theta}{\sqrt{n^2 - \sin^2 \theta} + \cos \theta} \tag{28}$$

and similarly

$$r_p = -r_s \frac{\sqrt{n^2 - \sin^2 \theta} - \sin \theta \, tg\theta}{\sqrt{n^2 - \sin^2 \theta} + \sin \theta \, tg\theta} \tag{29}$$

For normal incidence we have $\theta = 0°$ and hence:

$$-r_p = r_s = \frac{1 - n}{1 + n} \tag{30}$$

When the incidence on the interface is from an optically denser to a less dense medium, we have a special case if $n < \sin \theta$. We then write (28) in the form

$$r_s = \frac{\cos \theta - i\sqrt{\sin^2 \theta - n^2}}{\cos \theta + i\sqrt{\sin^2 \theta - n^2}} \tag{31}$$

The amplitude has become complex, and the intensity of the reflected beam will be obtained by squaring the absolute value of the amplitude. Thus

$$|r_s|^2 = \frac{\sqrt{\cos^2 \theta + \sin^2 \theta - n^2}}{\sqrt{\cos^2 \theta + \sin^2 \theta - n^2}} = 1$$

with a similar relation for r_p.

The intensity of the reflected beam is equal to that of the incident beam; in other words, we have total reflection. This phenomenon will be used below, and, though it is fully contained in the formulae (28) and (29), Fig. XI, 1 better illustrates its true nature[4] for the case of the s

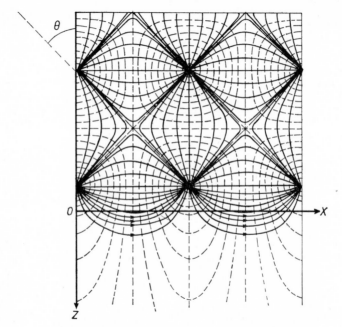

Fig. XI, 1. The energy stream for total reflection.

component. In this Fig. the plane of incidence is the plane of the paper, and the lines of force of the electric field are perpendicular to it. The dotted lines are the calculated magnetic lines of force which are seen to be distorted by the presence of the second medium lying under the boundary OX.

The drawn lines, which are perpendicular to both the electric and magnetic lines of force, give the energy stream at a given instant. It is seen that the energy stream is at certain places directed from the first into the second medium, and at other places in the opposite direction, the energy returning completely into the first medium. As the energy stream passes through the second medium over a small distance, this picture suggests that the reflected beam should be slightly displaced along the OX direction, which was demonstrated experimentally by Goos and HÄNCHEN[5].

(3C) Incidence on an absorbing medium

If the reflecting medium is an absorbing one, we shall have to introduce the complex refractive index $n' = n(1-i\kappa)$ into (28), (29) and (30). This will result in complex reflected amplitudes. Substituting

$$\sqrt{n'^2 - \sin^2\theta} = a - ib \tag{32}$$

we obtain for oblique incidence

$$r_s = -\frac{a - ib - \cos\theta}{a - ib + \cos\theta} = |r_s| e^{i\Delta_s}, \tag{33}$$

$$r_p = -r_s \frac{a - ib - \sin\theta\, tg\theta}{a - ib + \sin\theta\, tg\theta} = |r_p| e^{i\Delta_p} \tag{34}$$

and for normal incidence

$$r_s = -r_p = \frac{1 - n'}{1 + n'} \tag{35}$$

We see that the absorptive properties of the medium cause characteristic phase changes in the reflected light, and that the phase of the s component is in general different from that of the p component. If the incident light is linearly polarized in such a way that the amplitudes of s and p component are equal, the reflected light will in general be elliptically polarized.

The reflected intensities will again be given by the squared absolute values of the amplitudes, whence

$$R_s = |r_s|^2 = \frac{(a - \cos\theta)^2 + b^2}{(a + \cos\theta)^2 + b^2} = \frac{a^2 + b^2 - 2a\cos\theta + \cos^2\theta}{a^2 + b^2 + 2a\cos\theta + \cos^2\theta} \tag{36}$$

$$R_p = |r_p|^2 = |r_s|^2 \frac{(a - \sin\theta\, tg\theta)^2 + b^2}{(a + \sin\theta\, tg\theta)^2 + b^2} = |r_s|^2 \frac{a^2 + b^2 - 2a\sin\theta\, tg\theta + \sin^2\theta\, tg^2\theta}{a^2 + b^2 + 2a\sin\theta\, tg\theta + \sin^2\theta\, tg^2\theta} \tag{37}$$

and for normal incidence

$$R = |r_s|^2 = |r_p|^2 = \frac{(1-n)^2 + n^2\kappa^2}{(1+n)^2 + n^2\kappa^2} \tag{38}$$

In (36) and (37) we have

$$a^2 + b^2 = \{[n^2(1-\kappa^2) - \sin^2\theta]^2 + 4n^4\kappa^2\}^{\frac{1}{2}} \tag{39}$$

$$a = [\tfrac{1}{2}[n^2(1-\kappa^2) - \sin^2\theta] + \tfrac{1}{2}\{[n^2(1-\kappa^2) - \sin^2\theta]^2 + 4n^4\kappa^2\}^{\frac{1}{2}}]^{\frac{1}{2}} \tag{40}$$

By differentiation of (37) with respect to θ it can be shown[6] that R_p reaches a minimum, which for small κ is approximated by the condition

$$x^4 \cot^4\theta_B - x^2 - 2x^2 \cos^2\theta_B + 2x \sin^2\theta_B = 0 \tag{41}$$

where $x = n^2(1+\kappa^2)$.

θ_B replaces the Brewster angle for an absorbing medium; reflectivity reaches a minimum value instead of zero. It is easily shown that $tg^2\theta = n^2(1+\kappa^2)$ is a root of (41).

(4) The Methods Used for Dispersion Studies

In the previous section we have given an outline of the theoretical background of dispersion studies, and we have seen that

(i) The propagation of an electromagnetic wave in an absorbing medium is ruled by the complex refractive index.

(ii) This complex refractive index is directly related to molecular properties, such as dipole moment, eigenfrequency and life-time of excited states.

(iii) The intensity as well as the phase of the radiation refracted or reflected at an interface can be described by formulae in which apart from the angle of incidence, the complex refractive index is the only parameter.

The methods used in dispersion studies can roughly be classified into two types, one in which either the real or the imaginary component of n' is determined, the other in which the two components are determined simultaneously.

(4A) The determination of only one component of the complex refractive index

(i) Determination of the real refractive index

In this class we find three methods, which essentially are extensions of the methods used in visible optics. Their usefulness depends on the fulfilment of certain simplifying conditions such as weak absorption and a negligible damping constant.

(a) The prism method   The index n is determined in an instrument consisting essentially of two coupled monochromators. The first of these is used to produce a beam of monochromatic light, which is concentrated on the slit of the second. In this a hollow prism, to be filled with the substance under investigation, serves as the dispersing element. Either by moving the exit slit of the second monochromator or somehow deflecting the beam until it is focussed on the exit slit, the deviation of the beam on passing the prism may be determined. With the prism at minimum deviation the relation between n and the deviation δ can be written as

$$\sin \frac{A+\delta}{2} = n \sin \frac{A}{2},$$

if A is the refracting angle of the prism.

The angle readings are very critical as a δ of one arc second corresponds to about 10^{-5} index units. With carefully built apparatus, however, this is quite feasible and on some instruments, *e.g.* the large spectrometer–refractometer of the Weizman Institute in Rehovoth, deflections can be read with an accuracy of about $3 \cdot 10^{-3}$ arc second. A schematic diagram of this instrument is given in Fig. XI, 2.

The method is well suited for dispersion measurements on gases and non-absorbing liquids. Very weak absorption bands may be studied throughout, but usually the comparatively thick layers in the prism will cause such a strong absorption in the middle of a band that measurements are only possible in the band wings. If absorption changes rapidly with frequency,

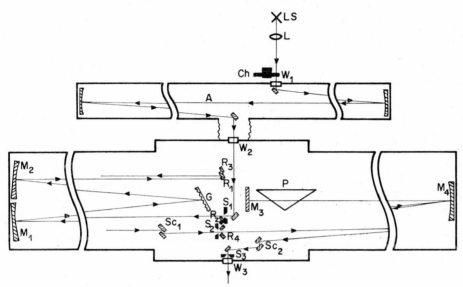

Fig. XI, 2. Schematic diagram of the optical system of the Rehovoth spectrometer – refracto-meter (after refs. 25 and 26). Sc_1 is the scanning device to choose the wavelength emerging from the first monochromator. Sc_2 is used to deflect the beam onto the exit slit S_3.

the intensity distribution of the transmitted beam will differ from normal, and tend to falsify results slightly by "*pseudo*dispersion".

(b) Interferometry If a plane parallel layer of the material under in-vestigation is illuminated with a parallel beam giving an angle of refrac-tion θ (Fig. XI, 3)

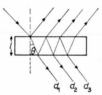

Fig. XI, 3. Interference in a plane parallel layer.

the refracted part of the beam will be partly reflected at the second face and partly transmitted as d_1. The reflected part will travel backward and forward through the layer and lose part of its energy as a transmitted beam at each encounter with the second face. Hence the transmitted beam will consist of several superimposed waves each of different phase, causing an interference phenomenon which becomes apparent on changing the wave-length of the incident beam.

References pp. 403–404

The change of phase resulting from each passage through the layer will be, according to (1)

$$\partial = 2\pi l \cos \theta_1 \frac{n}{\lambda} \qquad (42)$$

l being the thickness of the layer and λ the wavelength in a vacuum. The transmitted intensity is found to be (where R is reflecting power of the faces for natural light)

$$D_t = \frac{(1-R)^2}{1+R^2-2R \cos 2\partial} \qquad (43)$$

The extrema of transmission

$$D_{t_{max}} = \frac{(1-R)^2}{(1-R)^2} = 1 \qquad (44)$$

and

$$D_{t_{min}} = \frac{(1-R)^2}{(1+R)^2} \qquad (45)$$

are reached for $\cos 2\partial = 1$ and $\cos 2\partial = -1$ respectively.

Thus we see that a good contrast is obtained only if R reaches appreciable values, and that for two consecutive maxima according to (42) we have:

$$\frac{2ln_1 \cos \theta}{\lambda_1} = N \quad \text{and} \quad \frac{2ln_2 \cos \theta}{\lambda_2} = N+1 \qquad (46)$$

where N is an integer, the order of the interference. If the refractive index does not change appreciably over the interval $\lambda_1 - \lambda_2$, we find, eliminating N

$$2ln \cos \theta = \frac{\lambda_1 \lambda_2}{\lambda_1 - \lambda_2} \qquad (47)$$

from which n can be calculated if l is known. In order to fulfil the condition of constant n, the two maxima should always be close together, which means that N and hence l should be fairly large. If the condition is not fulfilled even then, the order of the interference must be known. This is a severe complication, which may be solved by the use of a variable-spacing interferometer[7], or by following the gradual change in the position of the fringes when, starting from a pure solvent, solutions of increasing concentration are measured[8]. The order of the fringes of the pure solvent, having a constant n in the relevant wavelength region can be determined by successive application of (47) and (46). This procedure, however, makes the method rather elaborate, especially if the visibility of the fringes becomes obscured by absorption. If absorption exceeds 50 per cent, the observation of fringes becomes impossible.

(c) Critical-angle refractometry   The use of the Abbé refractometer in the infra-red is quite feasible, provided that the prisms are made of a transparent material of high refractive index, such as arsenic trisulphide, AsS_3. Measurements can be made in transmission[9, 10] as well as in reflection[11].

Transmission   The critical angle of total reflection is found by observing the sudden fall of transmitted intensity at that angle, where $\sin \theta = n_l/n_p$, n_l and n_p being the indices of the liquid sample and the prism. If $\sin \theta < n_l/n_p$, there will be a refracted beam which travels a distance $d/\cos \theta_1$, d being the thickness of the sample layer between the prisms, through the sample. If θ_1 approximates to $90°$ this distance may become considerable, which means that even a small specific absorption will flatten the contrast between regions of total reflection and transmission.

JAFFE *et al.*[10] give some figures concerning the indeterminacy of n due to absorption, for a spacing between the prisms of 50μ. From their table we quote:

$n\kappa$	Δn
0.001	0.00035
0.01	0.0087

Reflection   In reflection the absorption becomes manifest in another way. In the absence of absorption the curves of reflected energy versus θ show a strong increase in the region just below θ_{crit}, and reach unity at θ_{crit}. If $\kappa \neq 0$, there is no longer such a sudden increase but a gradual one. For low κ the position of the critical angle may still be approximated by the position of the inflection point in the curves, but for values of $n\kappa > 0.01$ this can no longer be indicated.

The three methods treated above yield values of the real part of the refractive index only. In order to gain a full knowledge of n', the data may be completed by measurements of absorption or, if n is known throughout the band, by application of the Kramers-Kronig relation (25b). Another procedure stems from the observation that (22) approximates its asymptotic value more slowly than (23), so that far from v_0, (22) can be written as

$$n^2 = n_0^2 + \frac{\rho'}{(v_0')^2 - v^2} \tag{48}$$

This means that in this region the real part alone carries the information on ρ', which may be determined by fitting the refractive index from (48) to the experimental values on the far wings of the band.

Starting from (24), some authors[12] relate ρ' to the integrated absorption coefficient A_i, by the equation

$$\rho' = \frac{1}{\pi^2} \bar{n} A_i \tag{49}$$

where $\bar{n}$ represents the refractive index averaged over the band.

References pp. 403–404

(ii) Determination of the imaginary part of the refractive index

Another method that might be applied for dispersion studies starts with the determination of the imaginary part of n', *i.e.* of $n\kappa$. This is of course equivalent to the measurement of the absorption coefficient. With the help of the Kramers–Kronig relation (25a) the complete n' could then be calculated.

No such determinations have yet been reported.

(4B) Simultaneous determination of n and κ

As we have seen, knowledge of n and κ simultaneously through the spectrum gives us complete information on the optical behaviour, and allows us to assess the properties of the molecules involved. Reflection spectroscopy* offers several ways of determining n and κ simultaneously from comparatively simple experiments, and, although handling the data may be fairly complicated, reflection methods turn out to be quite practical if modern calculating methods are used. Intensities are measured in all the methods we shall consider, but we can discern two groups: (i) methods based on the formulae for the complex reflected amplitudes, and (ii) methods based on the formulae for reflected intensities.

(i) Methods involving determination of modulus and phase angle

(a) Observation of elliptically polarized light For the amplitudes of reflected light we have (33), (34) and (35). It is seen that the amplitudes have the general form $r = f(n, \kappa, \theta)$. As θ is known from experiment, and the amplitudes are complex, by splitting into real and imaginary components two equations will be obtained which can be solved for n and κ. Combining (33) and (34), replacing $|r_p/r_s|$ by ζ, and $(\Delta_p - \Delta_s)$ by Δ we have:

$$\frac{r_p}{r_s} = \zeta e^{i\Delta} = \frac{\sin\theta\ \mathrm{tg}\ \theta - (a - ib)}{\sin\theta\ \mathrm{tg}\ \theta + (a - ib)} \tag{50}$$

Applying a bilinear transformation and splitting into the components yields:

$$\frac{n^2 - n^2\kappa^2 - \sin^2\theta}{\sin^2\theta\ \mathrm{tg}^2\theta} = \frac{(1 - \zeta^2)^2 - 4\zeta^2\sin^2\Delta}{(1 + \zeta^2 + 2\zeta\cos\Delta)^2} \tag{51}$$

$$\frac{n^2\kappa}{\sin^2\theta\ \mathrm{tg}^2\theta} = \frac{2\sin\Delta(1 - \zeta^2)\zeta}{(1 + \zeta^2 + 2\zeta\cos\Delta)^2} \tag{52}$$

---

* It will be clear from our treatment in Section 3 that we have in mind application of specular reflection, which should not be confounded with spectroscopic methods using diffuse reflection from powdered samples. Spectra obtained by the latter method depend on grain size of the sample and are not simply related to the optical constants[13].

These two equations yield n and κ if the modulus ζ and the phase angle Δ are determined experimentally. To this end, the specimen is placed between two polarizers as shown in Fig. XI, 4.

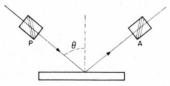

Fig. XI, 4. The optical system for the observation of elliptically polarized light.

Let the azimuth of the polarizer P be ψ_P, and ψ_A that of the analyser A. The amplitude of the s component after passing A will then be, according to (33)

$$|r_s|e^{i\Delta_s} \sin \psi_P \sin \psi_A$$

that of the p component according to (34)

$$|r_p|e^{i\Delta_p} \cos \psi_P \cos \psi_A$$

If we set A in the fixed position $\psi_A = 45°$, the transmitted energy will be

$$I = I_0 \frac{R_s}{2} (\sin^2 \psi_P + \zeta^2 \cos^2 \psi_P + \zeta \sin 2\psi_P \cos \Delta)$$

Setting ψ_P at different angles we then obtain:

$$\psi_P = 0° \qquad I_1 = I_0 \frac{R_s}{2} \zeta^2 \qquad\qquad (53a)$$

$$\psi_P = 90° \qquad I_2 = I_0 \frac{R_s}{2} \qquad\qquad (53b)$$

$$\psi_P = 45° \qquad I_3 = I_0 \frac{R_s}{2} \tfrac{1}{2}(1+\zeta^2+2\zeta \cos \Delta) \qquad\qquad (53c)$$

$$\psi_P = -45° \quad I_4 = I_0 \frac{R_s}{2} \tfrac{1}{2}(1+\zeta^2-2\zeta \cos \Delta) \qquad\qquad (53d)$$

There are several ways of constructing (51) and (52) from I_1, I_2, I_3 and I_4[14] but in order to minimize the interdependence of ζ and Δ, these are best obtained from the formulae

$$\zeta^2 = I_1/I_2$$

and

$$\cos \Delta = \frac{I_3-I_4}{I_3+I_4} \cdot \frac{1}{2}\left[\left(\frac{I_1}{I_2}\right)^{\frac{1}{2}}+\left(\frac{I_2}{I_1}\right)^{\frac{1}{2}}\right] \qquad\qquad (54)$$

The dependence of $\cos\Delta$ on I_1 and I_2 is only slight, as the factor in brackets is fairly constant over a wide range of ζ values[15].

(b) *Calculation of the phase angle*   As appears from (53a, b) the phase angle of reflection cannot be found experimentally for light polarized in the s or p directions. In these cases it remains linearly polarized and only its intensity can be measured. The phase angle can be calculated, however, if the intensity is known over the whole frequency spectrum. A good approximation is obtained if intensity is given over a complete band and into the wings as far as the points of zero slope.

The basis of such calculations is another type of Kramers–Kronig relation[2, 16], which gives the connection between the phase at frequency c and the modulus of the reflected amplitude. Its first application to reflection spectroscopy was given by ROBINSON and PRICE[17].

For computational purposes the required relation can be written in the form:

$$\Delta_{s_c} = \frac{1}{\pi} \int_0^\infty \frac{\mathrm{d}\ln|r_s|}{\mathrm{d}\nu} \ln\left|\frac{\nu+\nu_c}{\nu-\nu_c}\right| \mathrm{d}\nu \qquad (55)$$

$|r_s|$ being $\sqrt{R_s}$, which shows that the phase angle at frequency ν_c depends on the slope of the modulus over the whole spectrum, though the slope at ν_c makes the largest contribution owing to the weight function $\ln|(\nu+\nu_c)/(\nu-\nu_c)|$. The integration has the effect of smearing out an experimental error at one particular frequency over the whole spectrum. Once the complex amplitude is known completely, the optical constants follow from relations similar to (51) and (52), but derived from (33). The accuracy of the method is still uncertain. The value of $n\kappa$ reported by Robinson for the 2925 cm^{-1} band of polyethylene differs by something like an order of magnitude from the value one calculates from a transmission spectrum. BRODIN et al.[18] report a lack of validity of the Kramers–Kronig relation at low temperatures, and SPITZER and KLEINMAN[19] find poor accuracy in this type of calculation for $(n\kappa) < 0.1$.

(ii) *Methods based on the formulae for reflecting power*

The formulae (36) and (37) show that the reflected intensities at oblique incidence R_s and R_p are functions of n, κ and θ. As θ is known from experiment, we need for a determination of n and κ, two simultaneous equations which may be obtained by measuring any of the following combinations:

1. R_s at two angles θ_1 and θ_2
2. R_p at θ_1 and θ_2
3. R_s and R_p separately at one angle θ
4. R_p/R_s at θ_1 and θ_2
5. Reflected intensity of non-polarized light at θ_1 and θ_2.

In judging the relative merits of methods 1—5, we have to consider that in 1 and 2 the specimen must be replaced accurately by a standard mirror and that care must be taken to keep the effective aperture of sample and mirror equal. Method 3 requires in addition that the polarizer should be turned, which, if it occasions a lateral shift of the beam, may introduce an error. The same holds *a fortiori* for method 4 because there the common reference mirror is omitted, a feature which also necessitates corrections for instrument polarization. This polarization, which can occur in the mono-chromator, is also a serious drawback of method 5.

The difficulty of getting polarizers free from lateral shift, usually in-dicates application of method 1 or 2. Fore-optics suitable for the above-mentioned methods are described by SIMON[20] for vertical specimens and by FAHRENFORT[21] for horizontal ones.

For solution of the optical constants from the two reflectivity data obtained at one frequency, graphical procedures were given by SIMON[20] for methods 1, 2, 3 and 5 and by AVERY[22] for method 4. These procedures involve the use of precalculated families of curves, giving the reflecting power for a large number of n and κ values at a pair of fixed angles of incidence. For the experimental reflecting power at each of these angles, a series of possible (n, κ) combinations is read from the two graphs. These (n, κ) combinations determine two curves in the (n, κ) plane. The inter-section yields a pair of optical constants which holds for both experiments and hence is the unique combination.

Simon's curves for measurements with polarized light are given in Fig. XI, 5. They give a clear survey of the dependence of reflectivity on n and κ, and can therefore be used as a lead in choosing from the above methods the one best suited for a certain problem.

It will immediately be clear that methods 3 and 4 will give good results only at comparatively large θ, as there are only minor differences between R_s and R_p at small θ. Furthermore, method 1 will be more sensitive than method 2, *i.e.* small changes in n and κ give larger variations in R_s than in R_p in the range $1 < n < 4$ and $\kappa < 2$, but 2 will be superior to 1 if $\kappa > 2$ in the same n region.

For a systematic investigation of reflection spectra, the graphical procedure is both tiring and tiresome. Therefore a direct calculation of n and κ from experimental data with the help of calculating machines is more attractive if many data are to be handled.

A calculating procedure for method 3 has recently been published by HEILMAN[23] and for methods 1 and 4 by FAHRENFORT and VISSER[24].

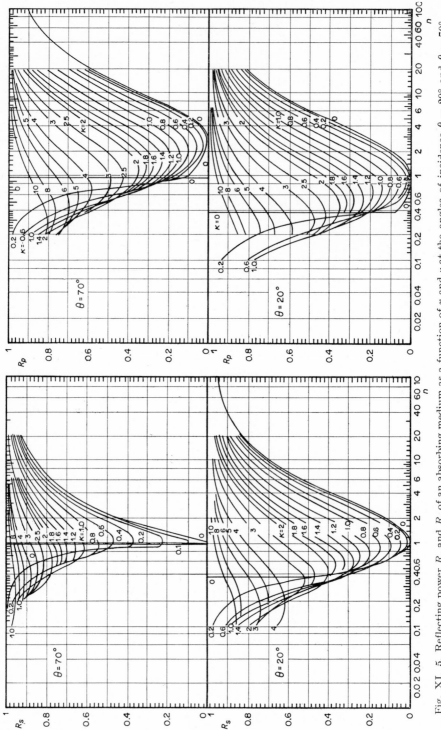

Fig. XI, 5. Reflecting power R_p and R_s of an absorbing medium as a function of n and κ at the angles of incidence $\theta = 20°$ and $\theta = 70°$.

(5) Accuracy of Reflection Methods. Attenuated Total Reflection

PRISHIVALKO[14] has recently compared the accuracies of the best variants of the methods discussed under (4B) above, *viz.* those of Beattie ((*i*)*a*, p. 390) and Simon ((*ii*)2, p. 392). He reports that according to extensive calculations based on variation in the reflecting power of 0.005 from the true value, Simon's method (2) gives results of substantially higher accuracy in the regions $0.4 < n < 2.4$ and $0.2 < \kappa < 3.0$, especially for low κ, but that for n and κ both exceeding a value 3 (as *e.g.* may happen in metals) Beattie's method is superior. Outside the regions indicated, the relative error in n or κ or both found for Simon's method rapidly grows larger than 10 per cent.

A κ value of 0.2, however, still corresponds to a very strong absorption. In organic chemistry, compounds having absorption bands in which κ reaches values as high as this are very scarce, which means that the reflection techniques discussed thus far will not give usable results for this important group of materials.

A considerable extension of the accessible field is reached if use is made of the special features of the phenomenon of total reflection[21]. It can easily be seen from Fig. XI, 5 that in the region where $n < 1$ and $\kappa < 0.3$, the

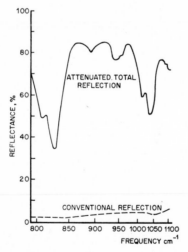

Fig. XI, 6. A comparison of the conventional, and the attenuated total reflection, spectrum of an epoxy resin.

sensitivity of the reflection (the *s* as well as the *p* component) to small changes in κ is much higher than in the region where $n > 1$. It is also seen that the relation between κ and R is reversed, as in the "total reflection" region intensity drops as κ increases. Thus, if we measure reflection at the interface between a transparent high-index material such as AgCl, KRS 5, AsS_3, Si or Ge, the relative refractive index at the interface will be smaller than unity, so that we can set θ larger than the critical angle for total reflection.

A spectrum of the reflected light will then show regions of attenuated reflection near the resonant frequencies, and hence will be similar to a transmission spectrum. The gain in spectral detail is adequately illustrated by Fig. XI, 6. The description of total reflection given in Section 3B, showing that the reflected light wave passes through the optically less dense medium over a distance of the order of a few wavelengths, accounts for the comparatively large magnitude of the attenuation effect.

Any of the methods described under (ii), p. 392, can be used to obtain the optical constants. Though method 2 gives a slightly better modulation of the spectra, 1 is the simpler with respect to data handling. The bare reflecting surface of the high-index material serves as the reference mirror.

Calculation[24] of the error in the optical constants introduced by an experimental error of ± 0.005 in R_s, showed that with attenuated total reflection for κ values down to $\kappa = 0.005$ it is less than 10 per cent, while the error in n remains well below 1 per cent.

(6) Results of Dispersion Studies

Systematic investigation of dispersion is still in its infancy. Even the work of the schools of Jaffe in Rehovoth and of Lecomte in Paris still consists largely of a search for the best methods of investigation. Reports on reflection measurements are scarce and are practically concerned only with those materials that resist absorption measurement. The methods using oblique incidence, which we consider to be the most promising, have been used only rarely. The trial and adjustment method at normal incidence, using assumed fundamental constants and the classical dispersion formula in order to fit a calculated reflection spectrum to the experimental one, is most commonly used. Increasing attention is being given to Kramers–Kronig calculations on normal-incidence spectra, even though strictly normal incidence is unattainable and the accuracy of the calculations is still unknown.

(6A) Gases

Though measurements by the prism method can often be carried through absorption bands, determination of band intensities is often restricted to the band wings, because there the influence of finite slit width on the shape of refraction lines vanishes[25]. In order to find the intensity S of a vibration–rotation line the approximations (48) and (49) are used:

$$n = n_0 + \frac{S/4\pi^2}{\nu_0(\nu_0 - \nu)}$$

from which S is easily determined. The integrated intensity A_i over the whole vibration–rotation band is then given by $A_i = \sum_m S_m$. Measurements with high resolution have yielded the data[26] in Table XI, 1.

TABLE XI, 1

ABSOLUTE INTENSITIES OF HCl BANDS FROM HIGH-RESOLUTION REFRACTION DATA

(Appropriate references are given in brackets)

Author	Gas	Band centre cm^{-1}	A_i from dispersion $cm^{-2}\ atm^{-1}$	A_i from absorption $cm^{-2}\ atm^{-1}$
Legay (27)	HCl	2886	149, 160	154(30), 158(31), 130(32)
Legay (28)	HCl	5723	3.58	3.64(31)
Jaffe, Hirschfeld and Kimel (29)	HCl	5723	3.95	2.87(33)
Kimel (26)	HCl	5723	3.46	

JAFFE[25] has given a survey of dispersion data on gases; Table XI, 2 is taken from this source.

TABLE XI, 2

BAND INTENSITIES DETERMINED FROM REFRACTION SPECTRA

(Appropriate references are given in brackets)

Gas	Band centre cm^{-1}	Intensity, $cm^{-2}\ atm^{-1}$	
		from dispersion	from absorption[a]
CO_2	670	161(34), 220(35)	168, 145, 153, 216, 217
	2350	2640(35), 2500(34)	2500, 2425, 2430
	3610+3716	40+40(35)	25+25, 26+28
CO	2170	265(35), 255(37)	394, 419, 237, 240
HCl	2886	171(36), 156(39)	154, 158, 130, 143
DCl	2090	90(39)	66
CH_4	3020	323(38)	270, 322
	1306	148(38)	135, 142
NO	1905	110(37)	133, 62, 75
N_2O	1285	240(39)	345, 220, 237
	590	32(39)	36, 19
	2224	1375(39)	1680, 1485, 1435
C_2H_4	995+950+810	365(39)	462, 326
	1890	24(39)	20
	3105+2990	171(39)	252, 154
	1444	46(39)	60, 39
C_2H_2	3285+3296	293(40)	250, 278, 590
	1328	91(40)	164
	733	723(40)	651, 720
CF_4	1267	4800(41)	4086, 3013
	632	56(41)	38
HBr	2560	41(42)	54

[a] For references on absorption measurements see ref. 25.

(6B) Dense media

(i) Inorganic materials

Because of the very strong absorption exhibited by dense inorganic materials their optical properties are studied largely by means of reflection spectroscopy.

Typical of the spectra are the very broad bands, which generally have secondary structure in the wings; a feature which is difficult to understand, especially for the alkali halides, which contain only one type of oscillator. The behaviour of such crystals having a large oscillator strength can easily be approximated with the aid of the dispersion formula of the type (48) in which the damping constant has been neglected.

It is seen that n has real values only for $\nu < \nu_0$ and for $\nu > \nu_l = (\nu_0^2 + \rho'/n_0^2)^{\frac{1}{2}}$, and that between these values n is imaginary. Hence, the reflecting power at normal incidence in the interval is given by:

$$R = \left| \frac{n-1}{n+1} \right|^2 = \left[\frac{(n^2+1)^{\frac{1}{2}}}{(n^2+1)^{\frac{1}{2}}} \right]^2 = 1$$

The reflection spectrum will have the shape of the full line in Fig. XI, 7. The dotted line shows the behaviour of reflection if a small damping term is introduced in the dispersion formula[43].

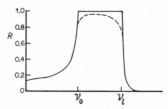

Fig. XI, 7. Reflection spectrum for large oscillator strength ——— without damping, - - - - - with a small damping term.

That in the harmonic approximation the width of the reflection band is determined by $(\nu_l - \nu_0)$ and that, with $(\nu_l^2 - \nu_0^2) = \rho'/n_0^2$, a broad band appears for substances with a large oscillator strength, has not always been understood even in recent literature[44].

The appearance of subsidiary maxima in the spectra of alkali halides has been the subject of many discussions.

If anharmonicity of the fundamental vibration is assumed, according to the theory of BORN and BLACKMAN[45], this structure may be explained[44, 46]. Another explanation which might be important for compounds having the diamond structure and for ZnO, was given by LAX and BURSTEIN[47]. These authors suggest that a deformation of the ionic charge distribution during vibration might lead to a second-order electric moment, which can also be used to explain the secondary maxima.

A third possibility has been given by GOTTLIEB[48], who suggests a coupling of the radiation field with the fundamental longitudinal mode in the crystal.

If, however, one assumes the harmonic approximation, it is possible to determine ρ'/n_0^2 by reading ν_0 and ν_l, the frequencies of the edges of the broad bands, directly from the reflection spectra. With

$$\rho' = \left(\frac{n_0^2+2}{3}\right)^2 \frac{N}{3\pi}\left(\frac{\partial\mu}{\partial Q}\right)^2 = \left(\frac{n_0^2+2}{3}\right)^2 \frac{Ne^2f}{\pi m},$$

values for the dipole derivative with respect to the normal mode[49] Q or the oscillator strength[50] can be obtained. Results are given in Table XI, 3.

TABLE XI, 3

DIPOLE DERIVATIVES AND OSCILLATOR STRENGTHS DETERMINED
FROM REFLECTION BAND EDGES

Crystal	ν_0 cm^{-1}	ν_l cm^{-1}	$\pm\partial\mu/\partial Q$ $cm^{3/2} sec^{-1}$
$NaNO_3$	1353	1450	217
$CaCO_3$	1410	1550	282
$CaCO_3$	871	890	80
ZnS	286	367	74

Crystal	$\omega_0 \cdot 10^{-13}$ c/sec	$\omega_l \cdot 10^{-13}$ c/sec	$\sqrt{f}$
AlSb	5.92	6.32	0.48
GaAs	5.04	5.35	0.43
GaSb	4.25	4.40	0.30
InP	5.74	6.38	0.60
InAs	3.95	4.38	0.56
InSb	3.28	3.46	0.34 (ref. 51)

A selection of work on strongly absorbing substances is given in Table XI, 4.

For quartz, extensive data are now available at room temperature and elevated temperatures up to 1270°C from the studies of SIMON[20], SIMON and McMAHON[65], REITZEL[66] and NEUROTH[67], who all used intensity measurements at oblique incidence.

In transparent regions, refractive index data were obtained by RAMADIER-DELBÈS[68].

SPITZER and KLEINMAN[19] made an extensive study of α-quartz between 2000 and 270 cm^{-1} at room temperature, and, using a high-speed computer, derived the optical constants by successive approximation of the fundamental constants ν_0, ρ' and g in (22) and (23) for a best fit to the reflection spectrum at normal incidence. The constants, giving an excellent reproduction of the experiments, are given in Table XI, 5.

TABLE XI, 4

A SURVEY OF DISPERSION STUDIES ON INORGANIC COMPOUNDS

Substance	Region, μ	Method	Calculated constants	References
NaCl	44–170	transm.; R_0, KK	optical	53
NaCl	33–77	successive approx.	γ, temp. depend.	52
NaCl	20–90	R_0+KK	optical+fundamental	54
KCl	20–90	—	—	54
LiF	7.5–77	—	γ, temp. depend.	48
LiF	15–36	R_s, $\theta = 70°$, 20°	optical+γ temp. depend.	55
CsBr	30–250	transm.+R_0	optical	56
CaF$_2$	15–40	R_s+R_p, $\theta = 70°$	optical	23
TlCl	20–300	R_0+KK	optical+fundamental	54
ZnS	15–65	—	—	54
PbNO$_3$	20–300	—	—	54
TiO$_2$	20–130	—	—	54
CaCO$_3$	20–150	—	—	54
CaCO$_3$	7.5–6.5	successive approx.	fundamental	57
NaNO$_3$	7.5–6.5	—	—	58
Ba oxyacetate	11–15.5	—	—	59
H$_2$O	1–15	transm.+R_0 (publ. data)	optical	60
H$_2$O	2–200	KK (on publ. data)	optical	61
SiC	1–25	successive approx.	optical+fundamental	62
ZnO	1–45	—	—	63
GaP	1–40	—	—	64
Quartz	see text			

TABLE XI, 5

DISPERSION PARAMETERS OF QUARTZ[19]

Ordinary ray			Extraordinary ray		
$\nu_0 (cm^{-1})$	ρ'/ν_0^2	g/ν_0	ν_0	ρ'/ν_0^2	g/ν_0
1227	0.009	0.11	1220	0.011	0.15
1163	0.010	0.006	1080	0.67	0.0069
1072	0.67	0.0071	778	0.10	0.010
797	0.11	0.009	593	0.006	0.04
697	0.018	0.012	509	0.05	0.014
450	0.82	0.009	495	0.66	0.009
394	0.33	0.007	364	0.68	0.014

(ii) Organic materials

Published work prior to 1957 on infra-red dispersion measurements on solvents has been reviewed by JAFFE and OPPENHEIM[9], who also report their own critical-angle measurements on n-C$_7$H$_{16}$, 1, 2,-C$_2$H$_4$Br$_2$, C$_6$H$_6$, C$_6$H$_{12}$, C$_2$Cl$_4$ and "Fluorolube".

JAFFE, GOLDRING and OPPENHEIM[10] measured refraction through the 3050 cm^{-1} band of CHCl$_3$ and the 2410 cm^{-1} band of CS$_2$.

LECOMTE[69] gives the reflection spectra of a number of organic liquids, while CAMEO and LECOMTE[70] show the refractive index spectra of a number of benzene derivatives. PITTMAN[71] reported refractive indices of $CHCl_3$ and $CHBr_3$ measured by the prism method and gave the oscillator strengths of the 3300 cm^{-1} and 1250 cm^{-1} bands.

VINCENT-GEISSE[72] measured dispersion of $CHBr_3$, $1,1,2,2\text{-}C_2H_2Br_4$ and $1,1,2,2\text{-}C_2H_2Cl_4$ by the interference method and compared the calculated intensities with those of GAPANOVA et al.[73] for $CHBr_3$ obtained from absorption. LISITSA and TSYASHCHENKO[74] give the optical constants of $CHCl_3$ in the $460-840$ cm^{-1} region.

Dispersion measurements by interference, resulting in data on CCl_4, CS_2, $CHCl_3$, C_6H_{12}, C_2Cl_4 and CH_2I_2, acetone and perfluoro-1,3,5-trimethyl cyclohexane are reported by KAGARISE[8]. On the basis of these data, FERGUSON and KAGARISE[75] calculate the effective field correction[76] $A_l/A_g = 1/n((n^2+2)/3)^2$ for the 1523 cm^{-1} band of CS_2 to be 1.40. Directly determined absorption coefficients for the gaseous and liquid (dissolved) states, however, were found to be essentially equal and in agreement with the A_g calculated from dispersion data for the liquid state. Thus A_l from dispersion was too large by a factor of 1.4.

In the case of the 1104 cm^{-1} band of CH_2I_2, KAGARISE[77] again finds equality in the directly measured values for A_l and A_g, but now corresponding to the A_l from dispersion, the A_g value being too small by a factor of 1.5.

It is not unusual for such comparisons using published data to be unsatisfactory, while direct comparison of absorption by solutions in several solvents can yield agreement within the experimental error, as was shown by JAFFE and KIMEL[78] for n-hexane.

Integrated intensities in C_6H_6, $CHCl_3$, $CHBr_3$, CCl_4 and CS_2 were derived by SCHATZ, MAEDA, HOLLENBERG and DOWS[79] from conventional reflection measurements by determining the ρ' values giving the best fit with

TABLE XI, 6

COMPARISON OF INTENSITIES OBTAINED FROM REFLECTION AND INTERFERENCE DATA

Liquid	ν cm^{-1}	$\tilde{n}$ refl.	$\tilde{n}$ interf.	A_i refl. 10^3 cm $mmole^{-1}$	A_i interf. 10^3 cm $mmole^{-1}$	Ref.
C_6H_6	760.2	1.468	1.488	$16.5 \pm 13\%$	$14.1 \pm 8.5\%$	12
CS_2	1497	1.587		$108 \pm 12\%$	$74.7 \pm 7.5\%$	80
$CHCl_3$	759	1.432		$34.2 \pm 13\%$	$28.1 \pm 8\%$	81
$CHBr_3$	656	1.576	1.564	$21.1 \pm 17\%$	18.1	72
CCl_4	784	1.276		$27.3 \pm 5\%$	} $46.0 \pm 5\%$	} 81
CCl_4	760	1.668		$20.4 \pm 15\%$		

experiment and applying (49). The A_i values are given in Table XI, 6 together with the results of interference studies on the same compounds.

The results for the majority of compounds are within the error ranges indicated, and the correspondence is not unsatisfactory except for the 1497 cm^{-1} band of CS$_2$.

This situation becomes worse, especially for the liquid state, if an additional comparison is made with absorption data, as is possible in the case of benzene[82] (Table XI, 7).

TABLE XI, 7

COMPARISON OF ABSOLUTE INTENSITIES[a] OF BENZENE, OBTAINED BY DIFFERENT METHODS

(Appropriate references are given in brackets)

Fundamental		687 cm^{-1}	1036 cm^{-1}	1480 cm^{-1}	3060 cm^{-1} triplet
Phase	Method				
Gas	absorption (83)	8.78	0.88	1.3	7.56
	absorption (84)	9.54	1.15	1.91	4.99
Liquid	interference (12)	14.1	1.8	2.8	8.4
	reflection	16.5[b]	1.23[c]		
	absorption (85)	3.5	0.67	1.2	1.15
Solid	absorption (86)	9.1	1.39	3.91	2.23
	reflection (82)	9.27[d]	1.63[d]	4.13[d]	

[a] Intensities in cm.mmole^{-1}.
[b] By conventional reflection (81).
[c] By attenuated total reflection (24).
[d] By Kramers-Kronig calculations on normal-incidence spectra.

For the solid state, the discrepancies are between absorption data rather than between absorption and reflection.

It cannot be denied that in general the scatter in the results is still fairly large. In this respect, however, we have to consider that a proper comparison of absorption data with those from conventional reflection is difficult because, depending on band intensity, either one or the other of the methods tends to become unreliable. Interference data also have a low accuracy in undiluted media, where absorption becomes appreciable.

The few available examples of more accurate measurements, such as those of Kimel and of Legay on gaseous HCl, show good agreement. The values for the 1036 cm^{-1} band of liquid benzene, obtained from absorption and from attenuated total reflection, also indicate a good correspondence.

Hence, it is confidently to be expected that in the future, dispersion studies will steadily become more reliable, and will prove to be a proper alternative to absorption studies. It will also become clear whether the tendency of dispersion results to give higher values of A_i than do absorption measurements, is confirmed.

REFERENCES

[1] M. BORN, *Optik*, Springer Verlag, Berlin, 1933.
[2] H. A. KRAMERS, *Atti Congr. Intern. Fis., Como*, 2 (1927) 545; *Physik. Z.*, 30 (1929) 522.
   R. DE L. KRONIG, *J. Opt. Soc. Am.*, 12 (1926) 547.
   T. S. MOSS, *Optical Properties of Semi-conductors*, Butterworths, London, 1959.
[3] J. S. TOLL, *Phys. Rev.*, 104 (1956) 1760.
   R. DE L. KRONIG, *Ned. Tijdschr. Natuurk.*, 9 (1942) 402.
[4] C. SCHAEFER AND G. GROOS, *Ann. Physik (N.F.)*, 32 (1910) 648.
[5] F. GOOS AND H. HÄNCHEN, *Ann. Physik*, 1 (1947) 333.
[6] S. P. F. HUMPHREYS OWEN, *Proc. Phys. Soc. (London)*, 77 (1961) 949.
[7] J. VINCENT-GEISSE AND J. LECOMTE, *Compt. Rend.*, 244 (1957) 577.
[8] R. E. KAGARISE, *J. Opt. Soc. Am.*, 50 (1960) 36.
[9] J. H. JAFFE AND U. OPPENHEIM, *J. Opt. Soc. Am.*, 47 (1957) 782.
[10] J. H. JAFFE, H. GOLDRING AND U. OPPENHEIM, *J. Opt. Soc. Am.*, 49 (1959) 1199.
[11] J. VINCENT-GEISSE, *J. Phys. Radium*, 9 (1947) 175; 20 (1959) 841.
[12] P. N. SCHATZ, *J. Chem. Phys.*, 32 (1961) 894.
[13] G. KORTÜM AND J. VOGEL, *Z. Physik. Chem. (Frankfurt)*, 18 (1958) 110; 230.
[14] A. P. PRISHIVALKO, *Opt. Spectry. (USSR) (English Transl.)*, 9 (1961) 131.
[15] J. R. BEATTIE, *Phil. Mag.*, 46 (1955) 235.
[16] H. W. BODE, *Network Analysis and Feedback Amplifier Design*, Van Nostrand, New York, 1945.
[17] T. S. ROBINSON AND W. C. PRICE, *Proc. Phys. Soc. (London)*, B65 (1952) 910; B66 (1953) 969.
[18] M. S. BRODIN, A. F. PRIKHOTKO AND M. S. SOSKIN, *Opt. Spectry. (USSR) (English Transl.)*, 6 (1959) 14.
[19] W. G. SPITZER AND D. A. KLEINMAN, *Phys. Rev.*, 121 (1961) 1324.
[20] I. SIMON, *J. Opt. Soc. Am.*, 41 (1951) 336.
[21] J. FAHRENFORT, *Spectrochim. Acta*, 17 (1961) 698.
[22] D. G. AVERY, *Proc. Phys. Soc. (London)*, B65 (1952) 425.
[23] G. HEILMAN, *Z. Naturforsch.*, 16a (1961) 714.
[24] J. FAHRENFORT AND W. M. VISSER, *Spectrochim. Acta*, 18 (1962) 1103.
[25] J. H. JAFFE, *Advan. Spectry.*, II, Interscience, New York, 1961, p. 263.
[26] S. KIMEL, *Diss.*, Amsterdam, 1960.
[27] F. LEGAY, *Diss.*, Paris, 1957.
[28] F. LEGAY, *Rev. d'Optique*, 37 (1958) 11.
[29] J. H. JAFFE, M. A. HIRSCHFELD AND S. KIMEL, *J. Chem. Phys.*, 29 (1958) 675.
[30] D. G. BOURGIN, *Phys. Rev.*, 32 (1928) 237.
[31] P. S. PENNET AND D. WEBER, *J. Chem. Phys.*, 21 (1953) 649.
[32] W. S. BENEDICT, R. HERMAN, G. E. MOORE AND S. SILVERMAN, *Can. J. Phys.*, 34 (1956) 830; 850.
[33] W. S. BENEDICT, R. HERMAN, G. E. MOORE AND S. SILVERMAN, *J. Chem. Phys.*, 26 (1957) 1671.
[34] J. STATESCU, *Phil. Mag.*, 30 (1915) 737.
[35] T. WETTERBLAD, *Diss.*, Uppsala, 1924.
[36] R. ROLLEFSON AND A. H. ROLLEFSON, *Phys. Rev.*, 48 (1935) 779.
[37] R. HAVENS, *Diss.*, Wisconsin, 1935.
[38] R. ROLLEFSON AND R. HAVENS, *Phys. Rev.*, 57 (1940) 710.
[39] C. F. HAMMER, *Diss.*, Wisconsin, 1948.
[40] R. L. KELLY, R. ROLLEFSON AND B. S. SCHURIN, *J. Chem. Phys.*, 19 (1951) 1595.
[41] B. S. SCHURIN, *J. Chem. Phys.*, 30 (1959) 1.
[42] B. S. SCHURIN AND R. ROLLEFSON, *J. Chem. Phys.*, 26 (1957) 1089.
[43] C. HAAS AND J. A. A. KETELAAR, *Phys. Rev.*, 103 (1956) 564.
[44] J. NEUBERGER AND R. D. HATCHER, *J. Chem. Phys.*, 34 (1961) 1733.
[45] M. BORN AND M. BLACKMAN, *Z. Physik*, 82 (1933) 551.
   M. BLACKMAN, *Z. Physik*, 86 (1933) 421.
   M. BORN AND K. HUANG, *Dynamical Theory of Crystal Lattices*, Clarendon Press, Oxford, 1954.

[46] H. BILZ, L. GENZEL AND H. HAPP, *Z. Physik*, 160 (1960) 535.
[47] M. LAX AND E. BURSTEIN, *Phys. Rev.*, 97 (1955) 39.
[48] M. GOTTLIEB, *J. Opt. Soc. Am.*, 50 (1960) 343.
[49] C. HAAS AND D. F. HORNIG, *J. Chem. Phys.*, 26 (1957) 707.
[50] G. PICUS, E. BURSTEIN, B. W. HENVIS AND M. HASS, *Phys. Chem. Solids*, 8 (1959) 282.
[51] W. G. SPITZER AND H. Y. FAN, *Phys. Rev.*, 99 (1955) 1893.
[52] M. HASS, *Phys. Rev.*, 117 (1960) 1497, ref. 1-3.
[53] R. GEICK, *Z. Physik*, 166 (1962) 122, ref. 1-14.
[54] F. ABELES AND J. P. MATHIEU, *Ann. Phys.*, 3 (1958) 5.
[55] G. HEILMAN, *Z. Physik*, 152 (1958) 368.
[56] R. GEICK, *Z. Physik*, 163 (1961) 499.
[57] C. HAAS, *Diss.*, Amsterdam, 1956.
[58] J. A. A. KETELAAR, C. HAAS AND J. FAHRENFORT, *Physica*, 20 (1954) 1259.
[59] C. DELOUPY, *Compt. Rend.*, 252 (1961) 3221.
[60] M. CENTENO, *J. Opt. Soc. Am.*, 31 (1941) 241.
[61] L. D. KISLOWSKII, *Opt. Spectry. (USSR) (English Transl.)*, 7 (1959) 201.
[62] W. G. SPITZER, D. KLEINMAN, D. WALSH AND C. J. FROSCH, *Phys. Rev.*, 113 (1959) 127; 133.
[63] J. COLLINS AND D. KLEINMAN, *Phys. Chem. Solids*, 11 (1959) 190.
[64] D. KLEINMAN AND W. G. SPITZER, *Phys. Rev.*, 118 (1960) 110.
[65] I. SIMON AND H. O. McMAHON, *J. Chem. Phys.*, 21 (1951) 23.
[66] J. REITZEL, *J. Chem. Phys.*, 23 (1955) 2407.
[67] N. NEUROTH, *Z. Physik*, 144 (1956) 85.
[68] J. RAMADIER-DELBÈS, *J. Phys. Radium*, 12 (1951) 954.
[69] J. LECOMTE, *Compt. Rend.*, 249 (1959) 2443.
[70] M. CAMEO AND J. LECOMTE, *Compt. Rend.*, 249 (1959) 2761.
     M. CAMEO, *Compt. Rend.*, 248 (1959) 1642.
[71] M. A. PITTMAN, *J. Opt. Soc. Am.*, 29 (1939) 358.
[72] J. VINCENT-GEISSE AND J. A. LADD, *Spectrochim. Acta*, 17 (1961) 627.
[73] N. E. GAPANOVA, M. P. LISITSA AND Y. P. TSYASHCHENKO, *Opt. Spectry. (USSR) (English Transl.)*, 8 (1960) 245.
[74] M. P. LISITSA AND Y. P. TSYASHCHENKO, *Opt. Spectry. (USSR) (English Transl.)*, 6 (1959) 396.
[75] E. E. FERGUSON AND R. E. KAGARISE, *J. Chem. Phys.*, 31 (1959) 236.
[76] S. R. POLO AND M. KENT WILSON, *J. Chem. Phys.*, 23 (1955) 2376.
[77] R. E. KAGARISE, *J. Chem. Phys.*, 31 (1959) 1258.
[78] J. H. JAFFE AND S. KIMEL, *J. Chem. Phys.*, 25 (1956) 374.
[79] P. N. SCHATZ, S. MAEDA, J. L. HOLLENBERG AND D. A. DOWS, *J. Chem. Phys.*, 34 (1961) 175.
[80] P. N. SCHATZ, *J. Chem. Phys.*, 29 (1958) 959.
[81] L. P. LINDSAY, S. MAEDA AND P. N. SCHATZ, *J. Chem. Phys.*, in the press.
[82] G. R. ANDERSON AND W. B. PERSON, *Symposium on Molecular Structure and Spectroscopy*, Columbus, Ohio, June 1960.
[83] H. SPEDDING AND D. H. WHIFFEN, *Proc. Roy. Soc. (London) Ser. A*, 238 (1956) 245.
[84] I. C. HISATSUNE AND E. S. JAYADEVAPPA, *J. Chem. Phys.*, 32 (1960) 565.
[85] W. B. PERSON AND C. A. SWENSON, *J. Chem. Phys.*, 33 (1960) 233.
[86] J. L. HOLLENBERG AND D. A. DOWS, *J. Chem. Phys.*, 34 (1961) 1061.

Chapter XII

Hydrogen Bonding and Solvent Effects

H. E. HALLAM

University College of Swansea, Swansea, Wales

In passing from the gas phase at low pressures, where the absorbing molecules are isolated from external influences, to a condensed phase, intermolecular forces will be expected to influence infra-red absorptions. The interactions may vary from the weak van der Waals attractive forces with energies of a few hundred calories, to the specific hydrogen-bonding interactions with energies of the order of a few kilocalories. Such molecular interactions modify the infra-red spectra in a number of ways — the frequencies of the normal vibrational modes of a molecule may be shifted to higher or lower values, intensities can be altered by factors of ten or more, and half-widths of bands may be greatly increased. These modifications arise partly from a shortened life for an excited vibrational state, and hence a "blurred" and slightly imprecise energy value, and partly as a result of the interactions of the electron-clouds of molecules which are in close proximity. Of the two effects, the latter is the more important and it is the aim of this chapter to discuss them and show how the measurement of the resultant spectral changes can lead to important information about intermolecular forces.

The most important of all interactions between molecules is that of hydrogen bonding. It has been a phenomenon of great interest to chemists for fifty years and is still the subject of much active study. An exhaustive and critical volume on this topic by PIMENTEL and McCLELLAN[1] was published in 1960 and provides in its Chapter 3 the most informative single account of the effects of H-bonding on infra-red and Raman spectra. The Proceedings[2] of an International Conference held in Ljubljana in 1957 contains many reviews on this interaction (see also refs. 3 and 4). The first section of this chapter deals with the effects of H-bonding interactions on infra-red spectra as an introduction to the weaker and less specific interactions which have yet to be fully reviewed.

(1) Nature and Occurrence of the H-Bond

A hydrogen bond is an interaction between a functional proton-donor group (X–H) and an electron-donor atom Y in the same or a different molecule, and is generally symbolized [X–H . . . Y]. Both X and Y are usually electronegative atoms; Y has either a lone pair of electrons or is a group with π-electrons. The energy of an H-bond is of the order of a few kilo-calories, weaker by a factor of ten than covalent bonds between atoms. The strongest hydrogen bonds are found in the bifluoride ion, [F–H . . . F]⁻ and in hydrogen fluoride. Less strong but amongst the commonest, are those in which the proton is donated by a carboxyl, hydroxyl, amine or amide group. Weaker hydrogen bonds are found with (C–H) and (S–H) groups, especially when the C or S atom is bound to a strongly electronegative group, for example, $CHCl_3$. The common electron donor atoms are O atoms in carbonyl and ether groups, N atoms in amines and N-heterocyclics, and halogen atoms.

*Inter*molecular H-bonds involving association of two or more molecules of the same or different compounds are those most commonly occurring. They can occur in the form of chains as in hydrogen fluoride, rings as in the case of carboxylic acids, or three-dimensional networks as in quinol (where the hydrogen bonds are shown joining hexagonal arrays of O-atoms at various levels):

Other H-bonds have the atoms X and Y as parts of the *same* molecule and are then *intra*molecular hydrogen bonds. Examples are found in ortho-substituted phenols, etc. (see *e.g.* Fig. XII, 4, p. 415).

(1A) Infra-red evidence for H-bonding

Clear evidence for a bond between (X–H) and Y which *specifically* involves the hydrogen atom (thus differentiating it from other types of associative interaction) came from infra-red spectroscopy[5] and the technique is still one of the most sensitive for establishing the presence of the H-bond.

It is clear that any attractive interaction on the H atom will affect all vibrational modes involving the (X–H) bond. The (X–H) stretching vibrations can be assumed to be localized, to a large extent, to the H-atom motion. The various (X–H . . . Y) vibrations are shown diagrammatically below, together with the approximate spectral region in which they are found:

Type of vibration	Description	Notation
←X—H→·············Y→	(X–H) stretch (3600–2500 cm^{-1})	ν(X–H)
	(X–H) in-plane bend (1650–1000 cm^{-1})	δ(X–H)
	(X–H) out-of-plane bend (900–250 cm^{-1})	γ(X–H)
←X←H·············Y→	H-bond stretch (200–30 cm^{-1})	ν(XH·····Y)

(2) X-H Absorption Bands

The most pronounced effect of H-bonding on the vibrational spectrum of a compound is the shift, $\Delta\nu$, of the (X–H) *stretching* mode and its overtones to *lower* frequencies. The shift is frequently considered to be the *primary* criterion of H-bonding. Furthermore, the magnitude of $\Delta\nu$ gives some measure of the energy of the interaction. The majority of infra-red investigations of H-bonding have been concerned with this mode.

(2A) Effect of concentration: determination of association constants

Most of the studies have been concerned with equilibria between various hydrogen-bonded species dissolved in an inert medium, a typical example of

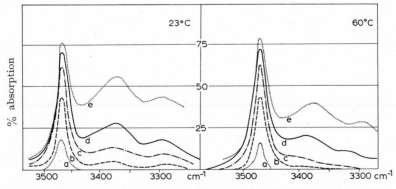

Fig. XII, 1. Concentration and temperature effects on the ν (N–H) frequencies of N-methyl urethane in carbon tetrachloride solutions: (a) 0.01 M; (b) 0.03 M; (c) 0.06 M; (d) 0.10 M; (e) 0.15 M. Cell length, 1.00 mm. *(From H. E. Hallam, Ph. D. Thesis, University of London (1954)).*

which is illustrated in Fig. XII, 1. The sharp absorption due to monomeric N-methyl urethane molecules at 3474 cm^{-1} is accompanied by a much broader absorption centred at about 3372 cm^{-1} when association occurs.

The decreased frequency, $\Delta v = 102$ cm^{-1}, clearly indicates that the amino group in the associated molecules participates in an interaction which reduces the restoring force in the (N–H) bond.

A similar change occurs on the progressive association of hydroxyl groups in phenols[6] and alcohols when the sharp peak near 3620 cm^{-1} is

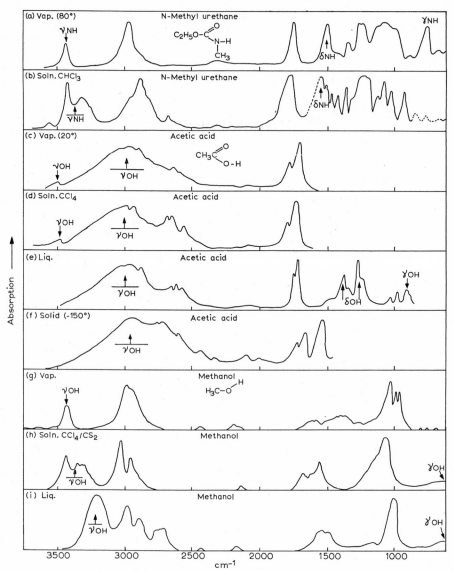

Fig. XII, 2. Infra-red spectra of some typical H-bonded compounds in various states. (a), (b) Unpublished spectra of H. E. Hallam; (c) to (f) from S. Bratož, D. Hadži and N. Sheppard, *Spectrochim. Acta*, 8 (1956) 249; (g) to (i) from V. Stuart and G. B. B. M. Sutherland, *J. Chem. Phys.*, 24 (1956) 561.

replaced by a broad absorption about 3330 cm^{-1}; for carboxyl groups the monomeric absorption at 3530 cm^{-1} is replaced by an exceedingly broad band extending from about 3330 to 2380 cm^{-1} (Fig. XII, 2).

Such absorptions are markedly concentration dependent and quantitative intensity measurements of the bands (cf. Chapter X) permit the determination of the association constant, $K = C_n/C_1^n$, for the monomer $\rightleftharpoons$ n-mer equilibrium, provided that the only important species over a wide concentration range are monomers and one type of cyclic n-mers. The determinations are usually based on measurements of the monomeric band and the concentration of monomer is related to the spectral absorbance (α) by the equation:

$$C_1 = \alpha/\varepsilon_1 l \tag{1}$$

where ε_1 is the molecular extinction coefficient of the monomer and l the cell length. An equation similar to (1) involving C_n and ε_n applies to the n-mer. It is, however, difficult to obtain ε_n and some workers have, with very little justification, assumed ε_n equal to ε_1 in order to calculate C_n. If it can be assumed that only one form of associated species (i.e. n-mer) is formed, then its concentration can be calculated from:

$$C = C_1 + nC_n \tag{2}$$

where C is the total concentration of the solute based on the monomer molecular weight. The dimerization of δ-valerolactam in carbon tetrachloride solution[7] illustrates such an association:

The restriction to a cyclic n-mer, mentioned above, is necessary because of the assumption that the concentration of monomer is proportional to the intensity of the absorption at some particular frequency. If an open or chain n-mer is formed, such as in N-methyl urethane or N-methyl acetamide:

the situation is complicated by the terminal (N–H) which is not involved in H-bonding and will absorb close to the monomeric ν(N–H).

If several different associates are formed, dimers, trimers, tetramers, etc., cyclic and/or chain, as is found for example with most phenols and alcohols, the problem of band overlap is generally too great to allow accurate equilibrium constants to be deduced. For details of such complications the reader is referred to original papers[6]. The methods of handling such data have been critically discussed by DAVIES and HALLAM[8].

(2B) Effect of temperature

A temperature rise of 10 to 20° C is sufficient to cause an appreciable shift in favour of monomers in most monomer $\rightleftharpoons$ n-mer equilibria. This results in a reduction in the association band intensity with a corresponding enhancement of the monomeric band intensity (Fig. XII, 1). Quantitative intensity–concentration measurements at several temperatures and, say, 20°C intervals, allow calculation of the thermodynamic parameters of H-bond formation, viz. ΔG, ΔH and ΔS.

Caution, however, is necessary here since the assumption is often made that ε does not vary with temperature. This has always been a questionable assumption[9] and recently[10, 11] evidence has accumulated that for solutions, ε is temperature-dependent. In non-associated solutions of alcohols the monomer band intensity is found to be temperature-sensitive; such behaviour indicates that the (O–H) group of the monomer interacts with the solvent in a way which influences the intensity of ν(O–H). In the light of recent work on the frequency shifts of ν(X–H) modes in various solvents, (see Section 10B), such an effect is not surprising. It is probably a general phenomenon for all (X–H) groups and more systematic work is required to assess the solvent effect on ν(X–H) extinction coefficients. Until this is established, quantitative association studies should, as far as possible, be made in non-polar hydrocarbon media. Further comparisons of association constants measured spectroscopically and by other techniques under identical conditions are also necessary.

(2C) Effect of solvent

The solvent influences the infra-red spectra of H-bonded molecules, apart from shifting the equilibria: however, this aspect is more conveniently dealt with in Section 10B, p. 425.

(2D) Intensity and band shape

The frequency lowering brought about by H-bond formation is accompanied by a marked increase in the integrated band area and in the breadth of the ν(X–H) absorption. The effect is often spectacular, band-widths of the order of several hundred wavenumbers being not uncommon, this independently of the phase (gas, liquid, solid) in which the H-bonding occurs (Fig. XII, 2). All such bands are broad: some have a smooth contour, whereas others consist of resolvable overlapping sub-bands. Together with the frequency lowering, this band broadening provides unequivocal evidence for the presence of H-bonding interaction.

Numerous explanations have been proposed to account for the band breadth and structure but the phenomena are still incompletely understood. A detailed discussion of them is outside the scope of this chapter and reference should be made to PIMENTEL and MCCLELLAN[1] and SHEPPARD'S paper in the Proceedings of the Ljubljana Conference[2]. The balance of evidence would seem to favour an interpretation based on interactions between anharmonic ν(X–H) and low frequency vibrations of the (X–H . . . Y) system. There is, however, considerable current activity in this field. CANNON[4] favours an alternative mechanism based on proton transfer across the barrier in the double-well potential curve in H-bonded systems. If the first excited state of the ν(X–H) vibration occurs above the level of the second minimum of this curve, the probability of proton transfer from one potential well to the other will be very much increased; this will lead to a shortening of the lifetime in the excited states, and so to a broadening of the absorption band.

Evidence which supports such an interpretation has recently been provided by BELLAMY[12] for systems in which cooperative proton transfer is feasible. In such H-bonded dimeric systems, e.g. 2-thiapyridone,

$$
\begin{array}{ccc}
\underset{\text{H}}{\text{N}} \cdots \underset{\text{H}}{\text{S}} & & \underset{\text{H}}{\text{N}} \cdots \underset{\text{H}}{\text{S}} \\
\text{S} \cdots \text{N} & \longleftrightarrow & \text{S} \cdots \text{N}
\end{array}
$$

proton transfer would be feasible since the simultaneous transfer of both protons would lead to uncharged structures. The spectra of these systems are quite remarkable in the very great breadth of the ν(X–H) band, the large number of resolved subsidiary peaks and the very low frequency of the band centre. For example, in 2-thiapyridone, there are 28 peaks between 3000 and 2000 cm^{-1}, the strongest one occurring at 2885 cm^{-1} which is approximately the band centre, and the overall band breadth is about 1000 cm^{-1}. Another striking feature is that at extreme dilution in carbon tetrachloride solution, very little free ν(N–H) absorption can be detected and the spectrum remains unchanged. This contrasts sharply with the normal pattern of behaviour for intermolecular H-bonds (cf. Section 4). The acid maleate ion[13] reproduces these features in an intramolecular H-bond.

(2E) Relationships between Δν and molecular parameters

In a variety of solid state systems possessing a well-defined H-bonded species (*cf.* Section 5), it has been found that $\Delta \nu$ is inversely related to the (X . . . Y) distance, R,

$$\overset{\overset{r}{\longleftrightarrow}}{\text{X–H}} \ldots \ldots \text{Y}$$
$$\longleftarrow \quad R \quad \longrightarrow$$

but directly related to the (X–H) distance, r.

It has long been inferred from the frequency lowering that the (X–H) bond length is increased on H-bonding[9], and this has been confirmed with the availability of precise (X–H) bond lengths from neutron diffraction and proton magnetic resonance spectroscopy. Although the data are still sparse and are mainly restricted to (O–H . . . O) and (N–H . . . O) systems, a simple relationship between $\Delta \nu$ and r is suggested.

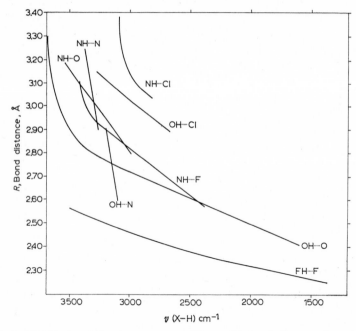

Fig. XII, 3. (X–H) stretching frequency *vs.* (X . . . . Y) bond distance in solids. (*From K. Nakamoto, M. Margoshes and R. E. Rundle, J. Am. Chem. Soc.,* 77 (1955) 6480).

There have been numerous direct relationships proposed between $\Delta \nu$ and R since RUNDLE and PARASOL[14] first showed one to exist between ν(O–H) in H-bonded solids and the (O . . . O) distance. At one time it was believed that a single relationship held for all (X–H . . . Y) bonds but it is now clear that a separate line is required for each type (Fig. XII, 3). Furthermore, it appears that at large values of R, $\Delta\nu$ makes an asymptotic approach towards zero. When R becomes appreciably shorter than the sum of the van der Waals' radii of (X–H) and Y, the frequency shift increases linearly with decrease in the (X ... Y) distance. The behaviour at very small values of R is not clearly defined, but the linear relation certainly fails before $\Delta\nu$ reaches the maximum value which has been observed in some cases. PIMENTEL and SEDERHOLM[15] give the following expressions, for example, as representing the best relations:

$$\text{(O–H ...... O)} \qquad \Delta\nu = 4.43 \cdot 10^3 \, (2.84 - R) \qquad (3)$$

$$\text{(N–H ...... O)} \qquad \Delta\nu = 0.548 \cdot 10^3 \, (3.21 - R) \qquad (4)$$

These relations are deduced for the solid phase but are of some value for estimating H-bond distances in the gas phase and in solution.

Whilst we cannot discuss the theoretical treatments of the H-bond, reference should be made here to the representation of LIPPINCOTT and SCHROEDER[16]. They have applied the highly successful Morse–Lippincott function for the internuclear potential energy of diatomic molecules (cf. Chapter IV) to the H-bond. Although they only consider a simplified linear (O–H ... O) system, they successfully predict the (O–H) distance, r, as a function of the (O ... O) distance R; the relation between $\Delta\nu$(O–H) and R; hydrogen bond energy and R; and the (O ... O) force constants and frequencies; all in excellent agreement with experimental data. From their analysis, the complete potential curve for the proton can be derived: this gives the potential barrier to proton transfer.

(2F) Relationships between $\Delta\nu$ and other molecular properties

A number of correlations have been suggested between $\Delta\nu$ and other physical properties of H-bonded systems. The first of these, between $\Delta\nu$ and ΔH, was proposed by BADGER and BAUER[17] for bonds involving the hydroxyl group. It was subsequently modified by BADGER[18] and by others but no completely satisfactory relation has been found. It has been pointed out[3] that a simple relationship cannot be anticipated since the frequency shift relates to the slope of the potential curve near the minimum (see Chapter IV) and does not directly determine a change in its depth. Nevertheless, the relative shift $[\Delta\nu/\nu(\text{X–H})]$ does provide a measure of ΔH as exemplified by the relationship between $\Delta\nu$(O–D) of methanol-d in a variety of solvent bases and ΔH(solution) of chloroform in the same bases[19, 20]. These $\Delta\nu$ values are thus related to the base strength, but as this topic and that of the acid strength of the proton donor serve as a convenient bridge between the two themes of this chapter, discussion of these data comes in Section 12.

(3) In-Plane and Out-of-Plane Bending Modes

The deformation modes $\delta(X–H)$ and $\gamma(X–H)$ have received far less attention than the $\nu(X–H)$ as they fall in the lower finger-print region of the spectrum and they frequently couple with other vibrational modes. Only in a few instances have the effects of H-bonding on their spectral properties been well substantiated. Several such bands are identified in Fig. XII, 2. Nevertheless, there are sufficient data to support the following generalizations:

(a) Frequency range: $\delta(X–H)$ 1000–1700 cm^{-1}

$\gamma(X–H)$ 300–900 cm^{-1}

(b) Frequency shift: *upwards* on H-bond formation, due to an increase in the restoring force tending to keep the (X–H) bond directed towards the Y atom. These relative upward shifts, $\Delta\nu/\nu$, are smaller than the relative downward shifts of the corresponding stretching modes.

(c) Intensity and band width: bending modes usually become broader and more intense on H-bonding but the effects are not so spectacular as those observed with the stretching modes. This is particularly so of the in-plane mode. The variation in the relative intensities of the three modes, ν, δ and γ, in different H-bonded species is as yet little understood.

(3A) The H-bond stretching and other very low frequencies

Perhaps the most significant of all the "H-bond frequencies" is the $\nu(X–H \ldots Y)$ mode, as it is the new *pseudo*-symmetric stretching frequency present only in the complex, and directly reflecting the strength of the H-bond. Whilst the corresponding frequency has often been assigned in Raman spectra, until recently comparatively few infra-red studies were available in the relevant low frequency region. However, in 1936 CARTWRIGHT[21] identified an absorption in ice at 160 cm^{-1} as the H-bond stretching frequency: in liquid formic acid it was given as 180 cm^{-1}, but PITZER et al.[22] have clearly identified it as an intense absorption at 237 cm^{-1} in gaseous formic acid.

Such low frequencies contribute significantly to the entropy and specific heat functions[23] and SLUTSKY and BAUER[24] have illustrated the importance in this respect of the bending and torsional modes of the (X–H) and Y components within the (X–H . . . Y) complex. These modes give H-bond systems extensive and often intense low frequency absorptions whose precise assignment is difficult, and they also apparently build up the unusually large atomic polarization term in many H-bonded species, e.g. in water $(\varepsilon'_\infty - n_D^2) = (4.5 - 1.8) = 2.7$.

(4) Intramolecular Hydrogen Bonds

Intramolecular H-bonds are formed only under specific spatial conditions, which give rise to appreciable differences in their spectral behaviour and make it necessary to discuss them separately from intermolecular H-bonds. In general, both types of H-bonding affect the vibrational bands in the same manner, but the intensity and band-width enhancement is usually much smaller for intramolecular bonds. The temperature effect is essentially the same and quantitative intensity measurements lead to the energy differences between the two species, *e.g.* the "free" and "H-bonded" isomers of *ortho*-substituted phenols (Fig. XII, 4).

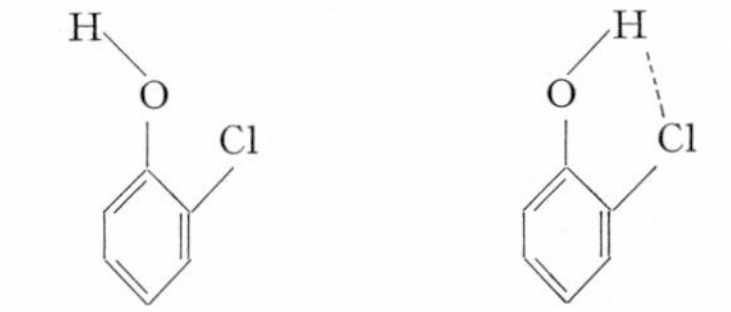

$$\text{"free" } \nu(\text{O–H}) \qquad\qquad \text{"bonded" } \nu(\text{O–H})$$
$$3600 \text{ cm}^{-1} \qquad\qquad\qquad 3542 \text{ cm}^{-1}$$

Fig. XII, 4. Isomeric *o*-chlorophenols, $\Delta H = 1.7$ kcal mole^{-1}.

The concentration effect in solutions, however, is significantly different. Since intramolecular H-bonding is an internal effect it persists even at the lowest concentrations and therefore retains its spectral behaviour. This is in marked contrast to the associated bands resulting from intermolecular association, which disappear at low concentrations, and it serves as the main guide in distinguishing between the two types of H-bond (see, however, Section 2D).

These intramolecular spectral effects provide a powerful technique for the elucidation of structural conformations in flexible molecular frameworks, the method being based on the evidence for a *cis* conformation between two functional groups which can form an H-bond. For example, β-diketones such as acetylacetone have been shown to exist mainly in the chelated mono-enolic form[25]:

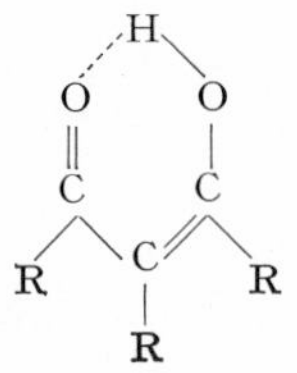

a broad band centred about 2800 cm^{-1} being assigned to the stretching mode of the bonded hydroxyl group. A weak band at 3570 cm^{-1} corresponds to the stretching of free hydroxyl groups and indicates the presence of a small proportion of *trans* molecules. In polyhydric alcohols[26] the presence of a single ν(O–H) about 3630 cm^{-1} provides conclusive evidence of a conformation in which the hydroxyl groups are so separated that intra-molecular H-bonds do not form:

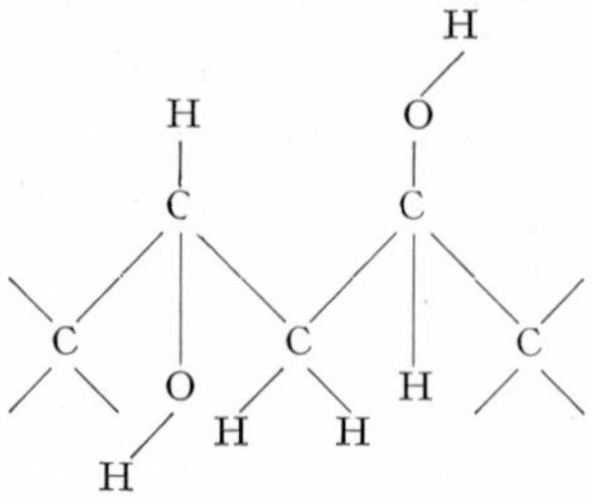

(*trans*)

If a second band appears at a lower frequency, usually about 3590 cm^{-1}, this arises from an H-bonded species and indicates the presence of a *cis* conformation:

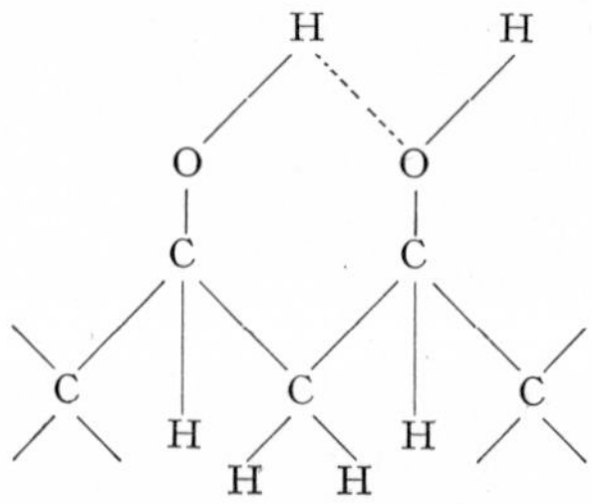

(*cis*)

(5) H-Bonding in Liquids and Solids

In the condensed phases the uncertainties in the number and nature of the polymeric species are frequently so great as to cause considerable difficulties in spectral interpretation. This is not always sufficiently appreciated since from the practical standpoint the liquid state is the most amenable to study and many investigations of H-bonding in pure liquids have been reported, some examples of which have been illustrated in Fig. XII, 2. The results can be summarized by saying that in the ν(X–H) region the absorptions of the many H-bonded species generally coalesce into a single broad band of considerable width. This effect is quite independent of the factors discussed in Section (2D) which also cause band broadening, but generally it cannot be separated from them in condensed phase spectra. Similar complications are also found in the regions of the deformation frequencies.

Apart from the qualitative indications of the presence of H-bonding, little further structural information can be obtained from liquid state spectra without a great deal of detailed systematic study. For structural detail each condensed phase is still best regarded as a problem of its own. Without careful comparison with the spectrum of the isolated molecule, or at least of the monomer at high dilution in an inert solvent, even qualitative deductions are doubtful.

(6) H-Bonding in Gases

Relatively few infra-red studies of H-bonding in the gaseous state have been reported. The main reason for this is that, for most substances, the temperature necessary to produce a pressure of vapour sufficient to record a spectrum with a simple 10 cm path-length cell disrupts all but the strongest H-bonds. Amides, for example, (Fig. XII, 2) show no indication of H-bonding in the vapour state. The early data were confined to carboxylic acids (Fig. XII, 2) and hydrogen fluoride. The same spectral effects of H-bonding are found in the gas phase as are observed in the condensed phases; the problem of their interpretation is, however, further complicated by the band envelope of the rotational fine structure of the monomer, (cf. Chapter IV), especially for low molecular weight gases, the ones most easily studied in the vapour state.

A significant paper by MILLEN et al.,[27] the aim of which is to investigate the origin of band broadening in the spectra of simple, gas phase complexes, deserves special mention. They observe strong bands for complexes formed in mixtures of hydrogen halides with various ethers, and they give a most plausible interpretation of the breadth and of the subsidiary peaks in terms of sum and difference bands of the (X–H) stretching frequency and the low-lying stretching frequency of the H-bond: i.e. v(X–H) and v(XH . . . Y) stretch.

Recent work in the author's laboratories suggests that the use of a multi-reflection long path cell at room temperature provides a simple means of studying the weaker H-bonds in the gas phase. The bonds must, of course, be strong enough for the associated frequency to be displaced sufficiently far from the rotational band envelope of the monomeric fundamental. Such an interaction is illustrated in a paper by DAGG and THOMPSON[28] on the vibrational–rotational spectrum of HCN, in which an unresolved band contour at 2093 cm^{-1} with a pair of maxima about 12 cm^{-1} apart is attributed to the (C$\equiv$N) stretching frequency in an (H–C$\equiv$N . . . H–C$\equiv$N) dimer. Such an assignment leads to an interpretation of the two maxima as P and R branches, the spacing of which measures the separation of the two HCN components and provides an estimate of the length of the H-bond in the gas phase[29]. JONES and SHEPPARD[29] have also shown the presence of a hydrogen bond of the type (H$_3$N. . . .H–C$\equiv$N) in gaseous mixtures of ammonia and hydrogen cyanide. From the contours of the vibrational bands attributed to this species an estimate has been made of the $(H_3N \ldots C)$ distance; the value obtained is similar to that estimated for the linear dimer of HCN but suggests that the H-bond formed is somewhat stronger than that in the latter species.

These investigations of H-bonding in the comparatively free environment of the gas phase are of particular importance. They should clarify many spectroscopic aspects still inadequately understood and they should provide much needed structural and other information for the better theoretical assessment of the H-bond.

(7) Vibrations of the Acceptor Group

In addition to the effects on the vibrations involving the H atom in the $(X-H \ldots Y)$ system, H-bond formation will also influence the vibrations within the acceptor group Y. The only vibration of this class which has received considerable attention is the stretching mode of the carbonyl group when involved in H-bonding $(C=O \ldots H-X)$ e.g. intermolecular H-bonding of carboxylic acids and amides, H-bonding between ketones and hydroxylic solvents (see Section (10C)).

In all cases H-bonding causes a downward shift of 5 to 25 cm^{-1} in $\nu(C=O)$ following the decrease in restoring force due to the proton inter-action. In non-polar solvents, a carbonyl doublet corresponding to "free" and "associated" molecular species can often be resolved.

(8) Deuteration Shift

Isotopic exchange of deuterium for the proton in the $(X-H)$ link normally lowers all the hydrogenic frequencies by a factor of approximately $\sqrt{2}$ due to the mass effect (cf. Chapter IV). The same effect is observed in $(X-H \ldots Y)$ hydrogen-bonded systems except that coupling interactions more frequently complicate the picture (especially for the deformation frequencies) producing anomalous $\nu(X-H)/\nu(X-D)$ ratios.

The lower frequency of deuterium bonds decreases the zero-point energy of the vibrational ground state which accordingly gives rise to (i) a slight contraction of the $(X-H)$ bond distance, (ii) a diminished dipole moment, and (iii) a potential barrier to transfer which is higher for D than for H atoms. All these factors must contribute to produce changes in the bond characteristics between the systems $(X-H \ldots Y)$ and $(X-D \ldots Y)$ which will be reflected in their respective spectral behaviour. These factors all imply a weakening of the 'hydrogen bond' and hence a lengthening of the $(X \ldots Y)$ distance, a feature which is well known in crystals from X-ray studies.

(9) **General Features of Solvent Effects**

It should now be abundantly clear that the ideal way to observe the infra-red spectrum of a compound is in the vapour state, since the molecules of a gas at low pressure are sufficiently far apart for molecular interactions to be neglected. However, this presents practical difficulties arising from the low volatility or ready decomposition in the vapour of most polyatomic molecules. As a result it is inevitable that many infra-red investigations involve the study of dilute solutions of the compound in a solvent. The solvent is advisedly non-polar, firstly, to ensure the minimum number and intensity of its own infra-red active frequencies and, secondly, to reduce complications from solvation interactions to a minimum. The main spectral range is reasonably covered using the combination of carbon tetrachloride (5000 to 1600 cm^{-1}) and carbon disulphide (1400 to 650 cm^{-1}) with double-beam solvent compensation. The gap between these can be covered by measurement in tetrachloroethylene.

The limitation of these solvents is solubility, so that more polar solvents such as chloroform and acetonitrile have often to be employed. The increased background problem due to the additional solvent frequencies can be overcome by choosing several solvents with appropriate "windows". The second difficulty, solute–solvent interaction, is, of course, magnified with increasing polarity of the solvent and it is with this topic that we will be concerned for the remainder of this chapter.

The passage from the gaseous state to the state of solution produces three characteristic effects in the vibrational spectrum of the solute:

(a) the rotational structure of the bands disappears or is replaced by a very simple contour;

(b) the band peaks do not correspond with the pure vibrational frequencies of the molecule in the gaseous state;

(c) the band half-widths are changed and their band intensities are enhanced.

The first effect has already been fully discussed in Chapter IV but band shape will receive some further mention here. The main interest, however, is in the band *position* and, to a lesser extent, the band intensity.

It is only in the last few years that extensive systematic studies of the effects of solvent environment on infra-red vibrational spectra have been made, and the phenomena are still far from being fully described, either experimentally or theoretically. There are two reviews of the subject[31, 32] which mainly cover the work of the respective authors' schools. Progress is also reported[33] in the Annual Reports of the Chemical Society.

Apart from the contribution which such studies make towards our fundamental knowledge of intermolecular forces, it is desirable that some relationship be found between the frequencies and intensities measured in solution and those obtained for the gas. In addition, since various solvents are used for solution studies, frequencies and intensities measured in different solvents should be inter-related. In order to facilitate individual

TABLE XII, 1

LITERATURE REFERENCES FOR SOLVENT EFFECTS ON GROUP FREQUENCIES

F, frequency shifts; I, intensity data; T, theory; C, correlations; S, steric factors; P, bond polar properties; A, frequency assignments

ν(B–H)	F : 46.
ν(C–H/D)	F : 31, 42, 46, 59, 63, 64, 75, 92.
	T : 41, 58, 63. I : 59, 63.
ν(N–H/D)	F : 31, 37, 46, 48, 49, 57, 68, 88, 89.
	T : 31, 37. I : 57, 88. C : 49, 68. S : 68.
ν(O–H/D)	F : 19, 20, 31, 46, 47, 48, 55, 63, 66, 70, 71, 72, 73, 74, 90, 91, 93, 94.
	T : 63, 93. I : 63. C : 19, 20, 47, 66, 70, 71, 73, 74, 94.
	S : 55, 90.
ν(Hal–H/D)	F : 31, 34, 77, 78, 79. I : 95.
	T : 31, 34, 77, 78, 79.
ν(P–H)	F : 95.
ν(S–H)	F : 31, 46, 95.
ν(Met–H)	F : 51, 52.
δ(C–H/D)	F : 42, 95. I : 42.
δ(N–H)	F : 68, 88, 95. I : 88.
δ(O–H)	F : 68.
ν(C=O)	F : 31, 38, 40, 45, 50, 62, 67, 69, 76, 82, 83.
	T : 31, 38, 40, 43, 45, 62, 76. I : 38, 62, 83.
	P : 62, 69. C : 84, 85. A : 67, 82.
ν(C=S)	F : 53. A : 53.
ν(N=O)	F : 69.
ν(P=O)	F : 69.
ν(S=O)	F : 69.
ν(C–Hal)	F : 44, 56, 60, 80, 86. T : 32, 43, 44, 56.
	I : 32, 56, 60, 80, 86. P : 56.
ν(C≡N)	F : 58, 61, 63, 87. T : 58, 61, 63, 87.
	I : 58, 61, 63.
ν(C≡O)	F : 51, 52, 95.
ν(C≡C)	F : 95.

discussion of the various chromophoric groups and to tabulate current work, Table XII, 1 lists publications in which the solvent effects on infra-red frequencies have been investigated.

(10) Solvent Shifts

When measured in solution the band peaks of all simple stretching vibrations are displaced to lower frequencies whereas those of the corresponding bending vibrations are shifted to higher frequencies. Before describing the individual solvent response of these frequencies and the anomalies from this general pattern of behaviour, it will be as well to survey the various theoretical treatments which have been proposed to account for these solvent-induced shifts.

(10A) Theories of solvent shifts

In order to compare frequency shifts in different regions of the spectrum, the observed displacements are discussed by reference to the vapour frequency:

$$\Delta \nu / \nu = (\nu_{vap} - \nu_{soln})/\nu_{vap}$$

Although experimental data were but fragmentary, a theoretical treatment of solvent shifts was given in 1937 by KIRKWOOD[34] and by BAUER and MAGAT[35]. The theory considers a simple model of a diatomic oscillator within a spherical cavity in a continuous solvent medium of macroscopic dielectric constant ε', and the shift is assumed to result from instantaneously induced polarization of the surrounding solvent molecules by the solute dipole. Using classical electrostatics and equating the energy of the vibrating dipole to that of an anharmonic oscillator in its reaction field, the expression

$$\Delta \nu / \nu = C(\varepsilon' - 1)/(2\varepsilon' + 1) \tag{5}$$

is derived, now commonly referred to as the KBM relationship. C is a constant which depends only upon the dimensions and electrical properties of the vibrating solute dipole.

This equation has been widely used and tested[36, 37], particularly by JOSIEN and her collaborators[31], and found to be inadequate in many instances (see Fig. XII, 5). In the electrostatic model leading to eqn. (5) it is clear that only the electronic contribution to the solvent polarization can follow the vibrational frequencies of the solute (ca. 10^{14} sec^{-1}). Molecular dipole relaxations are characterized by much lower frequencies (ca. 10^{11} sec^{-1}) so that dipole reorientation cannot be involved in the vibrational interaction. On this simplification it would appear appropriate[37, 38] to replace ε' by the refractive index factor n^2:

$$\Delta \nu / \nu = C(n^2 - 1)/(2n^2 + 1) \tag{6}$$

For non-polar solvents some slight improvement is found[31], but for polar solvents there are still considerable deviations from eqn (6). Such tests of the equation should employ refractive indices determined at infra-red frequencies, but because of the scarcity of these measurements, visible region values have to be used. However, the large deviations arise not from this assumption but from the over-simplified model, which considers only the bulk properties of the system and ignores nearest-neighbour interactions.

Two recent extensions[30, 39, 40] of the dielectric theory suggest that the effect of the solvent can be split up into three distinct components. PULLIN[40] treats the interaction as involving higher anharmonic terms in the expansions of the potential function for vibration, and of the electric dipole moment. His treatment gives a much clearer insight into solvent interactions

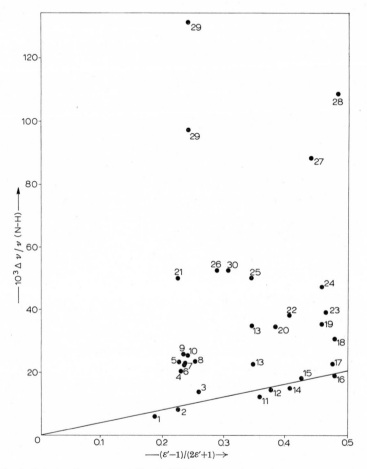

Fig. XII, 5. Relative frequency shift of ν(N–H) pyrrole in various solvents as a function of the dielectric constant of the solvent. Solvents: (1) *n*-hexane; (2) carbon tetrachloride; (3) carbon disulphide; (4) benzene; (5) *p*-xylene; (6) *m*-xylene; (7) toluene; (8) *o*-xylene; (9) mesitylene; (10) *pseudo*-cumene; (11) chloroform; (12) chlorobenzene; (13) anisole; (14) *sym*-tetrachloroethane; (15) 1,2-dichloroethane; (16) nitromethane; (17) nitrobenzene; (18) acetonitrile; (19) acetophenone; (20) ethyl acetate; (21) dioxan; (22) pyrrole; (23) acetone; (24) cyclohexanone; (25) diethyl ether; (26) di-*n*-butyl ether; (27) pyridine; (28) dimethyl sulphoxide; (29) triethylamine; (30) di-isopropyl ether. *(From ref. 43)*.

but, unfortunately, the resultant three-term relation contains several parameters difficult to evaluate and hence has found only limited use.

BUCKINGHAM[39] analyses the problem quantum mechanically in a more general manner, but still utilises the basic KBM model of a diatomic oscillator in a spherical solvent cavity. The interaction energy U of the solute–solvent system is expanded in a power series of $\xi = (r - r_e)/r_e$ the reduced inter-nuclear displacement from equilibrium (r_e).

$$U = U_e + U'\xi + \tfrac{1}{2}U''\xi^2 + \ldots \tag{7}$$

The terms in (7) depending upon ξ are introduced as perturbations of the Hamiltonian which describes the anharmonic oscillator. From the perturbed energy levels the frequency shift is found to be

$$\Delta\nu_{m,n}/\nu_{m,n} = \frac{B_e}{hc\omega_e^2}\left\{U'' - 3\frac{\alpha}{\omega_e}U'\right\} \tag{8}$$

where m and n identify the initial and final vibrational states, B_e is the rotational constant, ω_e the unperturbed vibrational frequency, h is Planck's constant, c the velocity of light and α the anharmonicity constant.

This equation makes two predictions which can readily be tested. Firstly, $\Delta\nu/\nu$ is independent of n, that is, the shift is twice as large for the first overtone, three times as large for the second, etc., as it is for the fundamental. Secondly, since the quantities B_e/ω_e^2 and α/ω_e are invariant with isotopic change, the theory predicts the value of $\Delta\nu/\nu$ to be the same for all isotopes.

For non-polar solvents, Buckingham expands (8) as a power series of the Onsager reaction-field factor, $g_\varepsilon = 2(\varepsilon'-1)/(2\varepsilon'+1)a^3$, (where a is the molecular radius) to obtain an extended form of (5)

$$\frac{\Delta\nu}{\nu} = C + C_1\left(\frac{\varepsilon'-1}{2\varepsilon'+1}\right) + C_2\left(\frac{\varepsilon'-1}{2\varepsilon'+1}\right)^2 + \ldots \tag{9}$$

For polar solvents he introduces two g factors, g_ε and $g_n = 2(n^2-1)/(2n^2+1)a^3$, because of the frequency dependence of ε', which leads to:

$$\frac{\Delta\nu}{\nu} = C_{00} + C_{10}\left(\frac{\varepsilon'-1}{2\varepsilon'+1}\right) + C_{20}\left(\frac{\varepsilon'-1}{2\varepsilon'+1}\right)^2 + C_{01}\left(\frac{n^2-1}{2n^2+1}\right) +$$

$$C_{11}\frac{(\varepsilon'-1)}{(2\varepsilon'+1)}\frac{(n^2-1)}{(2n^2+1)} + \ldots \tag{10}$$

where the C's are explicitly expressed in terms of the solute parameters, dipole moment, polarizability, and their derivatives. As a practical method of correlating small observed shifts, (10) is simplified:

in polar solvents to

$$\frac{\Delta\nu}{\nu} = C + C_\varepsilon\left(\frac{\varepsilon'-1}{2\varepsilon'+1}\right) + C_n\left(\frac{n^2-1}{2n^2+1}\right) \tag{11}$$

in non-polar solvents to

$$\frac{\Delta\nu}{\nu} = C + \tfrac{1}{2}(C_\varepsilon + C_n)\left(\frac{\varepsilon'-1}{2\varepsilon'+1}\right) \tag{12}$$

The three terms correspond closely to those elaborated by Pullin. Plotting the observed relative shifts in non-polar solvents against the dielectric function $(\varepsilon'-1)/(2\varepsilon'+1)$ (as with the KBM relationship but now ignoring the origin) yields values of C from the intercept and $(C_\varepsilon+C_n)$ from the slope. C_ε and C_n can then be evaluated from (11) using a shift in a polar solvent.

Although providing a more thorough treatment of the perturbing effect of the solvent medium this is still an over-simplified model, as Buckingham himself stresses, and it should only be expected to apply to those cases in which the equilibrium solute dipole moment greatly exceeds the induced moment. Moreover, it is confined to diatomic molecules, although it should apply reasonably well to essentially isolated bond vibrations in polyatomics. Practical applications of these relationships, which will be described in succeeding sections, confirm the improvement on the KBM approach but a number of cases, particularly $\nu(X–H)$ frequencies, still exhibit considerable deviations. These unquestionably arise from *specific* association interactions between solute and solvent molecules and it is evident that a comprehensive solvent theory must include a term to take these into account. A general expression for any $(\overset{\delta+}{X}–\overset{\delta-}{H}\ldots S)$ or $(\overset{\delta-}{X}–\overset{\delta+}{Y}\ldots S)$ localized interaction is probably not a practical proposition but an attempt to formulate a simple electrostatic interaction term has been made by LA LAU[41] for a (C–H) solute dipole in the solvent media acetone and acetonitrile. A more general empirical treatment has been given by CALDOW and THOMPSON[42] for solvents of the type R–H, which interact via their protons. They utilize a simple function of the Taft σ^* inductive factor of the residue R which is added as a fourth term $C_4\sigma^*$ to Buckingham's equations.

These four-term relations do not facilitate graphical testing but estimates of the four constants can be obtained by a least squares treatment of the observed shifts, and in a number of instances a sensible fit can be made of shifts in a wide range of solvents[42]. They can be considered to arise from three effects, (i) a bulk dielectric effect, the contribution of which is obtained by adding the C_ε and C_n terms; (ii) a specific interaction effect given by the C_4 term and (iii) a non-dipolar effect given by C. This last term involves contributions to the interaction energy which arise from dispersion, exchange and repulsive forces, and higher electrostatic moments. For groups which are not susceptible to strong dipole associations it may be possible[43, 44] to determine C directly from a Buckingham–KBM plot (Fig. XII, 9, p. 432). It has recently been suggested[45], however, that the C term may vary with each solvent.

The present theoretical situation can be summed up by saying that equations (11) and (12) suitably modified with a specific interaction term, whilst taking us closer to a rational explanation of solvent shifts, still fall short of a complete interpretation. Greater consideration must be given to other factors, particularly to dispersion forces, although their detailed calculation in these systems is at present impossible.

(10B) X–H stretching frequencies

The most solvent-sensitive frequencies are those of (X–H) bonds, due predominantly to the ability of the solute proton to form H-bonds with the solvent. Throughout the early infra-red literature there are numerous references to "anomalous" ν(X–H) frequencies measured in strongly basic solvents, *i.e.* proton acceptors. These quite rightly were accounted for by

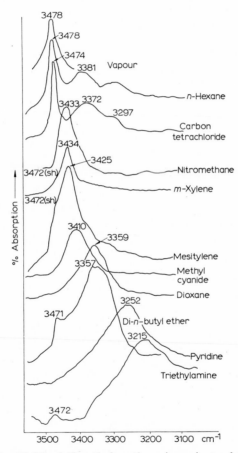

Fig. XII, 6. ν(N–H) of N-methyl urethane in various solvents (ref. 96).

solute–solvent (X–H . . . S) complex formation since they exhibit the same large $\Delta\nu$ and band width as found with H-bonds between like molecules. On the other hand, the literature equally abounds with values of the same ν(X–H) frequency measured in different non-polar solvents which, whilst

TABLE XII, 2

FREQUENCIES AND RELATIVE SHIFTS OF VARIOUS GROUPS IN DIFFERENT SOLVENTS

Solvent	Pyrrole[a]		N-Methyl urethane[b]						Fluoroform[c]	
	$v(N-H)$	$10^3\Delta v/v$	$v(N-H)$	$10^3\Delta v/v$	$v(C=O)$	$10^3\Delta v/v$	$\delta(N-H)$	$10^3\Delta v/v$	$v(C-F)$	$10^3\Delta v/v$
Vapour	3530	—	3478	—	1748	—	1495	—	1151	—
n-Hexane	3506	6.8	3478	0	1744	2.3	1512	11.4	1138.5	10.9
Carbon tetrachloride	3500	8.5	3474	1.2	1730	10.3	1502	4.7	1136.5	12.6
Chloroform	3486	12.5	3464	4.0	1706	24.0	1517	14.7	1132.5	16.1
Benzene	3458	20.4	3448	8.6	1733	8.6	1510	10.0	1128.5	19.1
Acetonitrile	3422	30.6	3410	19.6	1721	15.4	1507	8.0	1125	22.6
Acetone	3390	39.6	—	—	—	—	—	—	1120.5	26.5
Diethyl ether	3352	50.2	3357	34.8	1732	9.2	1530	23.4	—	—
Triethylamine	3187	97.2	3215	75.6	1728	11.4	1542	31.4	—	—
Aniline	—	—	—	—	1698	28.6	—	—	—	—

[a] ref. 46   [b] ref. 96   [c] ref. 44

not exhibiting such striking effects, nevertheless do display shifts to lower frequencies which vary according to the nature of the solvent. Until recently such small variations in group frequencies were often neglected as they were of the same order as the uncertainty of measurement. With the wider use of spectrometers with resolution of 1 to 2 cm^{-1}, such differences have been extensively observed and call for a rational explanation.

The first systematic experimental investigation of solvent shifts was made by JOSIEN and FUSON[37] in 1954, taking ν(N–H) of pyrrole as a convenient solute frequency. Since its solvent response is typical of ν(X–H) absorptions, a selection of these values is given in Table XII, 2 along with those of the corresponding vibration in N-methyl urethane. The latter are also depicted in Fig. XII, 6. They illustrate the very great influence which solvents have on hydrogenic frequencies, and stress the need for employing the same solvent medium when using infra-red frequencies for purposes of comparison.

The aim of JOSIEN and FUSON's work[37] was to test the KBM theory (Fig. XII, 5), and from this and later studies they concluded that the basic KBM relationship has only limited validity, and account for the large deviations exhibited by the polar solvents in terms of specific H-bonded complexes. The extensive work of Josien and her collaborators has recently been fully reviewed[31] and this reference will be used for their numerous contributions.

An alternative approach to solvent effects developed by BELLAMY, HALLAM and WILLIAMS[46] (BHW) following earlier work by GORDY[47], is by the direct comparison of the relative frequency shifts of different solutes in the same series of solvents. Some typical results are shown in Fig. XII, 7 in which the relative shifts of the (X–H) stretching frequencies of decaborane, N-methyl urethane, phenol and hydrogen chloride in a wide range of solvents, are each plotted against the corresponding shifts of ν(N–H) pyrrole in the same solvents. All hydrogenic stretching frequencies yield such linear BHW plots which have two significant features; (i) each has a characteristic slope, s, (ii) no discontinuity is found on progressing from non-polar to highly polar solvents.

These plots aim at eliminating properties of the solvents which operate to similar extents in the two cases, so that if $\Delta\nu$ is solely dependent upon some bulk property of the solvent such as ε', a simple linear relationship will generally result. The widely differing slopes illustrated in Fig. XII, 7 clearly indicate that the properties of the solute molecules are of paramount importance. This leads to the conclusion that the frequency shifts of (X–H) links are primarily due to specific group interactions in the various solute series. The proton of the solute (X–H) dipole seeks out a negatively-charged polar group of the solvent with which to associate. This might be a lone pair

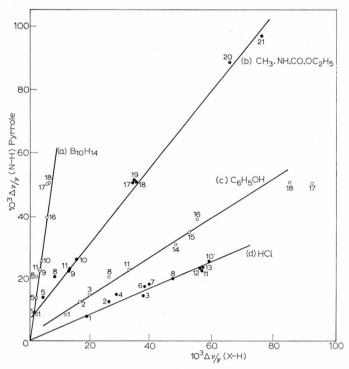

Fig. XII, 7. Relative shifts of (X–H) stretching frequencies of (a) decaborane, (b) N-methyl urethane, (c) phenol, (d) hydrogen chloride, in dilute solution in various solvents, plotted against the corresponding shifts of ν(N–H) pyrrole. Solvents: (1) carbon tetrachloride; (2) chloroform; (3) chlorobenzene; (4) *sym*-tetrachloroethane; (5) carbon disulphide; (6) *sym*-tetrabromoethane; (7) bromobenzene; (8) benzene; (9) nitrobenzene; (10) mesitylene; (11) anisole; (12) *pseudo*cumene; (13) *m*-xylene; (14) acetonitrile; (15) ethyl acetate; (16) acetone; (17) dioxan; (18) diethyl ether; (19) di-*n*-butyl ether; (20) pyridine; (21) triethylamine. (From refs. (46) and (96)).

orbital on a nitrogen or oxygen atom, a π-electron cloud or a chlorine atom:

$$\overset{\delta+}{X}-\overset{\delta-}{H}\ldots N\!\!<\qquad \overset{\delta+}{X}-\overset{\delta-}{H}\ldots O\!\!<\qquad \overset{\delta+}{X}-\overset{\delta-}{H}\ldots \pi \qquad \overset{\delta+}{X}-\overset{\delta-}{H}\ldots Cl-C\!\!<$$

The smooth transition, observed in all cases, in passing from polar solvents such as triethylamine, where the interaction is well-recognised as hydrogen bonding, to non-polar solvents such as carbon tetrachloride, in which it is envisaged as a weak electrostatic attraction directed towards the chlorine atom of a $\overset{\delta-}{(Cl}-\overset{\delta+}{C)}$ bond dipole, indicates that the type of interaction is fundamentally the same throughout, differing only in magnitude of the interaction energy. This is, perhaps, one of the most significant features of these studies. Early suggestions that a lower energy limit of about 1 kcal/mole could be accepted for an H-bond interaction no longer appear justifiable.

If H-bonding between solute and solvent were to cease at any given energy level a break might be expected in the individual BHW lines, below which the points would revert to a common line representing the macroscopic solvent factors. No such behaviour has been observed for any of the diverse (X–H) dipoles examined (Table XII, 1); even with the weakly interacting solutes such as decaborane, the behaviour in both polar and non-polar solvents parallels that of hydrogen chloride (Fig. XII, 7).

Further confirmation of the dominance of specific group interaction in these instances comes from mixed solvent studies[48] in which several absorption bands can be resolved, corresponding to the various solute–solvent interactions present. Fig. XII, 8 shows the results[48] of a study of ν(N–H)

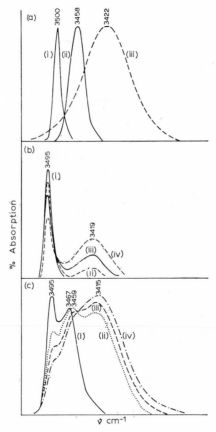

Fig. XII, 8. ν(N–H) pyrrole.

(a) In separate solvents: (i) carbon tetrachloride; (ii) benzene; (iii) acetonitrile.

(b) In mixtures of carbon tetrachloride and acetonitrile: (i) pure carbon tetrachloride; (ii) — (iv) increasing concentration of acetonitrile.

(c) In mixtures of carbon tetrachloride, benzene and acetonitrile: (i) 60 % CCl$_4$, 40 % C$_6$H$_6$; (ii) — (iv) increasing concentration of CH$_3$CN. (From ref. 48).

pyrrole in mixtures of carbon tetrachloride and acetonitrile. The two separate bands clearly correspond to individual solute–solvent complexes and they occur at essentially the same frequencies as in the separate solvents (Fig. XII, 8(b)). Moreover, their intensities depend upon the relative concentrations of the two solvents, just as the monomer/dimer bands of "normal" H-bonds depend upon the absolute concentration (*cf*. Fig. XII, 1). When a third component such as benzene is added, a new band appears which again corresponds to the frequency in the pure solvent (Fig. XII,8(c)). The interaction is competitive, so that when the concentration of acetonitrile, the strongest proton acceptor, exceeds $0.06\ M$, a negligible number of pyrrole molecules remain associated to the other solvents. In this way it is possible to observe each of the three main peaks at invariant frequencies in different mixtures covering a moderate range of dielectric constant. If general medium factors were determinative a *single* band would be expected, changing in position according to the composition of the mixture. Quantitative intensity measurements of such systems can lead to a direct determination of the proton-accepting powers of the solvents in terms of the formation constants for the (solute + solvent $\rightleftharpoons$ complex) equilibria in an analogous manner to the measurement of association constants discussed in Section (2A).

For (X–H) links which are already H-bonded, solvent shifts do not occur[48] until the solvent is a very strong proton acceptor which is capable of forming a stronger link with the (X–H) bond than that which already exists. These findings also would be difficult to explain on the basis of dielectric constant effects. They also offer a means of investigating inter- and intra-molecular H-bonds[48, 88].

To return to the slopes of the BHW plots. The major factors in solute–solvent group interactions are clearly the proton-donating powers of the various solutes in these media, relative to pyrrole as a standard. This is borne out by the slopes (s) for the hydrogen halides[46, 31]: HF, 0.39; HCl, 0.42; HBr, 0.44; HI, 0.63 which show a distinct trend with the electronegativity of the halogen. An examination[49] of the s-values of (N–H) bonds has shown a close relationship with the pK_a values of the bases. The relationship:

$$s = 0.375\ pK_a + 2.35 \qquad\qquad (13)$$

covers primary bases of all structural types with basicities from $pK_a - 3$ to $+12$. Another relationship:

$$s = 0.273\ pK_a + 1.35 \qquad\qquad (14)$$

is found for all secondary bases.

(10C) X=O stretching frequencies

Turning to a dipole whose free end is of opposite sign to that in (X–H),

(X=O) bonds where X is C, N, P or S have received most attention. All are solvent-sensitive, the frequency displacement again being to lower values but far smaller (Table XII, 2) than in (X–H). Furthermore, and of greater consequence, the solvent pattern is altogether different. For example, ethers which have a marked effect on (X–H) have relatively little on (X=O), whereas the greatest (X=O) shifts occur in solvents such as chloroform in which (X-H) bonds are only slightly affected.

KBM plots of such data[31, 38] show fewer deviations from linearity[43] than those obtained from (X–H) shifts, due presumably to a decrease in specific interaction terms. The number and strength of (X–H) interactions is certainly reduced since the use of strong proton donor solvents, giving $(X\overset{\delta-}{=}O\ldots\overset{\delta+}{H}-X)$ interactions, is very restricted (due to absorptions from H-bonding in the liquid state).

The extent of the role played by dielectric factors in these cases is still a matter of debate. When plotted against a chosen standard frequency, usually ν(C=O) acetophenone[50], the relative shifts give good straight lines with characteristic slopes. As before, no break or change of slope of any of these lines is found on passing from a proton-donating solvent such as trifluoroethanol to a non-donor such as ether. Although this would again appear to indicate that localized association is the controlling factor in determining the frequency shifts, the slopes have generally been found not to parallel other physical measures of bond polarity[50]. The accumulated experimental data indicate that the solvent sensitivities of (X=O) links are complex functions of several factors including contributions from bulk dielectric effects, specific interactions and non-specific dispersion forces. Some assessment of these can be obtained by applying equations (11) and (12). For example, in the case of carbonyl frequencies CALDOW and THOMPSON[42] assess the dielectric factor to account for about a quarter of the total effect, a value which is probably sufficient to obscure any relationships involving bond polar properties which might be expected as a result of specific dipole–dipole $(\overset{\delta+}{C}\overset{\delta-}{=}O\ldots\overset{\delta+}{H}-\overset{\delta-}{X})$ regularities. This picture is confirmed by numerous mixed solvent studies[45] in which resolvable components due to competing interactions are rarely reported.

(10D) C–Halogen stretching frequencies

(C–F) and (C–Cl) bonds, being singlet linkages of high polarity, are also solvent-sensitive[44], their behaviour (Table XII, 2) being very similar to that of (X=O) links. Strong proton-donating solvents, when solvent background allows their use, cause appreciable frequency shifts accountable in terms of $(\text{C}-\overset{\delta-}{\text{Hal}}\ldots\overset{\delta+}{\text{H}}-X)$ interactions. Significant shifts are also exhibited in solvents such as dimethyl formamide and dimethyl sulphoxide, which normally function as electron donors. Since these solvents have high dielectric constants, it is of interest to examine the data by means of the KBM plot (Fig. XII, 9): this provides the best fit yet obtained[43, 44] for the simple function, especially when applied, following Buckingham, to yield an intercept C.

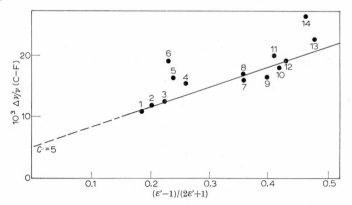

Fig. XII, 9. Relative frequency shift of ν(C–F) of fluoroform at 1151 cm^{-1} in dilute solution as a function of the dielectric constant of the solvent.

Solvents: (1) n-hexane; (2) cyclohexane; (3) carbon tetrachloride; (4) carbon disulphide; (5) toluene; (6) benzene; (7) chloroform; (8) 1,2-dibromoethane; (9) methyl iodide; (10) methylene chloride; (11) methylene bromide; (12) 1,2-dichloroethane; (13) acetonitrile; (14) acetone. (From ref. 44).

Taking C values thus obtained and using a least squares fit of the observed shifts in equations (11) and (12) yields C_ε, C_n and C_4. The indications are that the dielectric shift now contributes about 40 to 50 per cent of the overall solvent shift.

(C–Hal) shifts yield linear BHW plots but, as might be anticipated, the s-values provide no measure of bond polarity, although within the closely related methyl halides there is a distinct trend, as with the hydrogen halides.

A number of mixed solvents can be found to cover a wide range of ε' and in no instance can two absorption peaks be resolved: the ν(C–Hal) band moves progressively to lower frequency with increasing proportions of polar solvent.

(10E) C≡X stretching frequencies

Apart from ν(C≡N) these bonds have not received as much attention as (X=O) but there are sufficient data to show that they exhibit only small frequency shifts. For example, the greatest shift recorded[42] for ν(C≡N) is 12 cm^{-1} for vapour → acetone. ν(C≡C) is practically unaffected by solvents.

The $\nu(C\equiv O)$ in a number of metal and substituted metal carbonyls has been briefly examined[51, 52] but the results are too few and too complex to provide generalizations. Some move to lower frequencies, whilst others are raised, and tentative interpretations (cf. Section 13) have been proposed in terms of the nature of the metal–carbon bonding.

(10F) C=S stretching frequencies

$\nu(C=S)$ modes follow the same behaviour[53] as their carbonyl analogues, although, due to the lower electronegativity of S compared with O, the relative shifts are considerably smaller.

(10G) X–H deformation frequencies

No systematic study of $\delta(X-H)$ modes has been reported but there exist scattered data for cases where X is C, O and N. They all exhibit an *upward* frequency shift (Table XII, 2), a behaviour completely analogous to that of hydrogen bonded δ-modes (Section 3). This also adds weight to the conclusion that (X–H) solvent shifts are predominantly controlled by specific H-bond interactions.

(10H) Anomalous behaviour

(i) Steric factors

The discussion of solvent effects thus far has been confined to pure vibrational modes which were considered to be free from such influences as coupling interactions, steric interactions, etc.

It has long been apparent that such factors cause an anomalous solvent response. For example HCl shows a doublet structure in a number of solvents[34] which persists even at extreme dilution and cannot, therefore, be ascribed to self-association: likewise benzyl alcohol in benzene[54]. For HCl in anisole[46] the lower of the two frequencies arises from the association between HCl and the ether oxygen atom, as the shift is similar to that found in diethyl ether: the higher HCl frequency is close to that of HCl in benzene solution and is ascribed to the presence of (HCl...π–bond) complexes.

Many of these multiple interactions are known; one simple example is clearly illustrated in Fig. XII, 6 for N-methyl urethane in *m*-xylene, mesitylene, di-*n*-butyl ether and triethylamine, where the peak or shoulder at 3472 cm^{-1} corresponds to a virtually non-interacting $\nu(N-H)$ in addition to the main (N–H ... π–bond), (N–H ... O) and (N–H ... N) interactions. In this instance, there is little uncertainty in interpretation but occasionally the interaction anticipated as the minor one provides the main absorption. Di-*n*-butyl ether is one such example, the ether-oxygen interaction (with X–H) frequently being absent because steric hindrance restricts solvation by the lone-pair electrons of the O-atom (see following page).

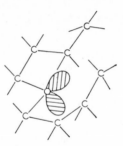

Di–*n*–butyl ether.

The inverse effect is observed in instances where the solute dipoles are "buried" in the molecule. The most interesting example of this is in the series of *ortho*-substituted phenols[55]. With increasing size of hydrocarbon groups in the *ortho* positions little change in the solvent sensitivity of ν(O–H) is observed before the 2,6 di-*tert*-butyl compound. The behaviour of this phenol on passing from one solvent to another is very different from the others. In diethyl ether there appears to be no solvent interaction as ν(O–H) is the same as in *n*-hexane, but in dioxan in which the steric hindrance is reduced by bending back the (CH$_2$) groups, there is a marked frequency shift.

(ii) Coupling interactions

If a vibrational mode is strongly coupled, then it is clearly a non-localized group frequency and its behaviour will differ from an essentially localized mode. The response to solvents will be a resultant of the coupled components and will not, therefore, be simple.

Several examples have been observed[50, 56, 81] and it appears, though this is by no means certain, that BHW plots of such frequencies are smooth curves. In at least one instance[81], the well-known Fermi-resonance doublet of carbon tetrachloride at 780 cm^{-1}, there is a discontinuity in the BHW plot which may represent a breakdown in the coupling, the vibrations reverting to the uncoupled frequencies. Early hopes that this technique would provide a method for decoupling vibrations have not, however, been realized.

(10I) Overtone and isotopic frequencies

Solvent data on overtone and isotope frequencies are fragmentary and entirely confined to (X–H) modes (Table XII, 1). Most of it is fairly old and insufficiently precise for present comparisons but insofar as it can be used, the prediction of Buckingham (Section 10A), that $(\Delta\nu)_{m,n}$ is independent of the nuclear masses and n, appears to be substantiated[95].

(11) Band Shapes and Intensities

If only in view of the experimental difficulties attached to accurate intensity measurements even under ideal conditions of negligible solvent background (*cf.* Chapter X), it is not surprising that solvent influences on integrated band intensities (A) are little understood. Systematic investigation of A in a variety of solvents is further restricted, as in many instances accurate band area measurement is impossible even if peak frequencies are adequately defined. Data exist for numerous chromophores in one or two solvents, mainly due to THOMPSON *et al.*[57], some of which have recently been extended[58] to provide a test for Buckingham's theories[39] of solvent influences. Other systematic studies reported are on ν(C–D) of $CDCl_3$ by PIMENTEL[59]; ν(C–Cl) of $CHCl_3$ by WHIFFEN[60]; ν(C≡N) by BAYLISS *et al.*[61]; and ν(C=O) by ITO *et al.*[62] and by KAGARISE and WHETSEL[45]. BROWN[63] has also studied (C≡N), (O–H) and (C–H) in the limited range of four solvents. These are not sufficiently comprehensive to make any firm generalizations but several trends are apparent:

(i) There is an increase in A in passing from vapour to solution in a non-polar solvent.

(ii) The changes in A thereafter, in passing to more polar solvents are in some cases slight (ν(C–D) of $CDCl_3$)[59], but in others quite dramatic (ν(N–H) in anilines)[57]; sometimes as much as a ten-fold intensification occurring.

(iii) The solvent order for increasing A follows no regular trend with ε'.

(iv) There is a fair parallel between the solvent influence on A and $\Delta\nu$; and between the band-width at half-absorbance and $\Delta\nu$.

These are but tentative indications and there are already some significant deviations, particularly with aromatic solvents. There are some instances where A varies appreciably but where the frequency remains almost unaltered (ν(C≡N)).

Very little study has been made of band shape except for sterically-hindered interactions, which were discussed in Section (10H). It is, however, apparent that the shape is appreciably solvent-dependent and it has been pointed out[58] that the resultant band contours are not in general described satisfactorily by either the Lorentz or Gauss function.

(11A) Theories of solvent influences on intensities

Various theories proposed to account for the solvent variation of A have recently been summarized with a full bibliography in reference (32).

It is apparent that neither the simple Debye nor the Onsager cavity field factor, upon which they are all founded, is satisfactory, derived as they are for pure liquids. All the theories predict a positive solvent effect but none is able to yield the precise magnitude of the effect.

Buckingham[39] has extended the Onsager model in a way previously indicated (Section 10A) and derives for the solution/gas phase intensity ratio the equation:

$$\frac{A_s}{A_g} = \left[\frac{9n^2}{(n^2+2)(2n^2+1)}\right]^2 \left[1 + C_\varepsilon \frac{\varepsilon'-1}{2\varepsilon'+1} + C_n \frac{n^2-1}{2n^2+1}\right] \tag{15}$$

where C_ε and C_n are constants for a particular solute, and n and ε' are the refractive index and dielectric constant of the solvent.

This does give the correct order of magnitude when applied[32] to the ν(C–Cl) values of WHIFFEN[60] but there are some anomalies in the predicted solvent order.

BUCKINGHAM[39] has also provided a second treatment which yields the equation (where μ = bond moment and α = bond polarizability):

$$\left(\frac{2n^2+1}{3n\sqrt{n}}\right)\left(\frac{A_s}{A_g}\right)^{\frac{1}{2}} = 1 + 0.6\left(\frac{n^2-1}{2n^2+1}\right) + \frac{2\mu_e\alpha'}{\mu'a^3}\left(\frac{\varepsilon'-1}{2\varepsilon'+1}\right) + \cdots \tag{16}$$

This offers a more direct test, in that if the expression:

$$F = \left[\left(\frac{2n^2+1}{3n\sqrt{n}}\right)\left(\frac{A_s}{A_g}\right)^{\frac{1}{2}} - 1 - 0.6\left(\frac{n^2-1}{2n^2+1}\right)\right] \tag{17}$$

is plotted against $(\varepsilon'-1)/(2\varepsilon'+1)$, a straight line of slope $2\mu_e\alpha'/\mu'a^3$ would be expected. $(\mu' = d\mu/dr; \alpha' = d\alpha/dr)$. The first tests of this function[58] indicate that it fails for ν(C–H) and ν(C≡N) of HCN in a variety of solvents but is moderately successful for ν(C≡N) in CH_3CN and CCl_3CN and[32] for ν(C–Cl) in $CHCl_3$.

Although it is too early to say how far these treatments may require modification it would appear[25], in the light of the $\Delta\nu$ studies, that a dipolar interaction term is also necessary.

(12) Correlations of $\Delta\nu$ with other Molecular Properties

The first correlation in this field, found by GORDY[19], was between $\Delta\nu$(O–D) of CH_3OD in a variety of basic solvents and (i), pK_a values of the bases; (ii), ΔH of solution of $CHCl_3$ in the same bases. These early studies were concerned only with H-bonding in strong proton-accepting solvents but precise $\Delta\nu$ data are now available for extremely weak acceptors. The $\Delta\nu/\Delta H$ correlation, however, is only slightly supported, as most thermodynamic data are too imprecise to detect the small changes that may arise from the weaker interactions. Such correlations thus offer a possible empirical method for estimating small heats of solution.

Gordy's $\Delta\nu/pK_a$ relation has been extended for various classes of proton donors. A more satisfactory correlation[49], however, is that between s (the BHW slope) and pK_a (equations (13), (14)) since whereas $\Delta\nu$ values reflect the acid character of the solute in a given solvent, s values are independent of solvent and reflect the absolute acidity of the solute.

Chemical shifts in n.m.r. spectra are strongly influenced by H-bonding and solvent interactions, and several relationships between these effects and infra-red solvent shifts have been reported[64]. Such studies[65] provide conclusive evidence for the existence of (X–H . . . π) associations.

RICHARDS and WALKER[66] have reported significant correlations between solvent influences on dipole moments and on ν(O–H) for variously substituted phenols. Their results show in a number of these cases the determining rôle of dipole–dipole interactions.

BELLAMY and WILLIAMS[30] have pointed out a significant correlation between the frequency shifts which take place in solution and those that occur when solvent molecules are adsorbed on an active surface. Adsorption on to microporous glass is known to take place through direct association with the hydroxyl groups on the glass surface and ν(O–H) is dependent upon the strength of the local association and, therefore, upon the nature of the adsorbed molecules. The exact correlation between these ν(O–H) shifts and ν(N–H) pyrrole dissolved in the same solvents, reinforce the conclusion that dielectric factors play an insignificant role in ν(X–H) solvent shifts.

(13) Applications of Solvent Studies

Even though quantitative interpretation of solvent effects is not yet possible, the experimental data can be put to considerable use.

The "solvent variation technique" offers a means of displacing the frequencies of characteristic vibrational modes within a molecule, without resort to isotopic exchange. Bonds of different type show different solvent shifts and sequence; and it is possible to verify questionable frequency assignments by observing whether the band in question shifts in solution in the expected fashion. BELLAMY and ROGASCH[67], for example, were able to show that the carbonyl absorption in 4-pyridones occurs near 1590 cm^{-1} and that the 1650 cm^{-1} band is due to some less polar group such as (C=C). The general applicability of this method is illustrated by the way in which BELLAMY and ROGASCH[53] resolved the many anomalies in (C=S) group correlations and reassigned the ν(C=S) frequency.

Bonds of similar type will exhibit the same solvent pattern but can be characterized by the *solvent slope* provided sufficient data are available. For example, ketonic carbonyls[50] have s-values of about unity whereas amide and urethane carbonyls[68, 96] which have similar frequencies, fall in the range 0.4 to 0.6. The ability of the "solvent technique" to solve an assignment problem depends upon (i) how well the particular band can be followed in various solvents and (ii) how well-localized is the vibration in question.

In many instances solvent variation provides additional information on the polarity of the bonds under study[56]. Variations in band intensities are also observed[69] for conformational isomers resulting from changes in the isomeric ratio. Attention should also be drawn to recent examples[51, 52] in the inorganic field which promise to yield interesting information on the polarity of ligand bonds in metal complexes.

It would seem appropriate to give here some advice on the choice of solvents for recording solution spectra. Whenever solubility permits, a saturated aliphatic hydrocarbon should be used; failing this, a solvent should be selected with attention to its solvation properties. Solvents such as $CHCl_3$, often used to observe carbonyl frequencies because of adjacent CCl_4 and CS_2 absorptions, effect a lowering of about 20 cm^{-1} — sufficient to invalidate inferences made from group correlation tables unless these have been compiled from $CHCl_3$ solution data. The stage has now been reached, perhaps, when correlation tables should be restricted to data in comparable solvents. This could well lead to closer and more subtle correlations than exist at present.

(14) Conclusions

From the discussion in this chapter the following aspects of solvent interactions can be listed:

(i) There are no truly inert solvents: all vibrational frequencies other than those of non-polar links and skeletal modes are solvent sensitive.

(ii) They cause frequency shifts and intensity changes analogous to, and inseparable from, those produced by H-bonding.

(iii) The pattern of similarity between dipole association and H-bonding suggests that a unified theory for both will suffice.

(iv) The spectral effects provide a criterion of intermolecular association which frequently specifically indicate the mode of interaction.

(v) They offer a direct test to distinguish between many group frequencies.

(vi) They provide a means of investigating bond polar properties.

REFERENCES

[1] G. C. PIMENTEL AND A. L. McCLELLAN, *The Hydrogen Bond*, W. H. Freeman & Co., San Francisco and London, 1960.

[2] D. HADŽI, *Hydrogen Bonding*, Pergamon Press, London, 1959.

[3] M. DAVIES, *Ann. Rept. Progr. Chem. (Chem. Soc. London)*, 43 (1946) 5.

[4] C. G. CANNON, *Spectrochim. Acta*, 10 (1958) 341.

[5] R. FREYMANN, *Compt. Rend.*, 195 (1932) 39.

[6] J. J. FOX AND A. E. MARTIN, *Proc. Roy. Soc. (London)*, Ser. A, 162 (1937) 419.

[7] M. TSUBOI, *Bull. Chem. Soc. Japan*, 24 (1951) 75.

[8] M. DAVIES AND H. E. HALLAM, *J. Chem. Educ.*, 33 (1956) 322.

[9] M. DAVIES AND G. B. B. M. SUTHERLAND, *J. Chem. Phys.*, 6 (1938) 767.

[10] J. N. FINCH AND E. R. LIPPINCOTT, *J. Chem. Phys.*, 24 (1956) 908.

[11] U. LIDDEL AND E. D. BECKER, *J. Chem. Phys.*, 25 (1956) 173.

[12] L. J. BELLAMY AND P. E. ROGASCH, *Proc. Roy. Soc. (London)*, Ser. *A*, 257 (1960) 98

[13] H. M. E. CARDWELL, J. D. DUNITZ AND L. E. ORGEL, *J. Chem. Soc.*, (1953) 3740.

[14] R. E. RUNDLE AND M. PARASOL, *J. Chem. Phys.*, 20 (1952) 1487.

[15] G. C. PIMENTEL AND C. H. SEDERHOLM, *J. Chem. Phys.*, 24 (1956) 639.

[16] E. R. LIPPINCOTT AND R. SCHROEDER, *J. Chem. Phys.*, 23 (1955) 1099.

[17] R. M. BADGER AND S. H. BAUER, *J. Chem. Phys.*, 5 (1937) 839.

[18] R. M. BADGER, *J. Chem. Phys.*, 8 (1940) 288.

[19] W. GORDY AND S. C. STANFORD, *J. Chem. Phys.*, 9 (1941) 204.

[20] M. TAMRES, *J. Am. Chem. Soc.*, 74 (1952) 3375.

[21] E. CARTWRIGHT, *Phys. Rev.*, 49 (1936) 470.

[22] T. MIYAZAWA AND R. S. PITZER, *J. Am. Chem. Soc.*, 81 (1959) 174.

[23] J. O. HALFORD, *J. Chem. Phys.*, 14 (1946) 395.

[24] L. SLUTSKY AND S. H. BAUER, *J. Am. Chem. Soc.*, 76 (1954) 270.

[25] S. BRATOŽ, D. HADŽI AND G. ROSSMY, *Trans. Faraday Soc.*, 52 (1956) 464.

[26] L. P. KUHN, *J. Am. Chem. Soc.*, 76 (1954) 4323.

[27] J. ARNOLD, J. E. BERTIE AND D. J. MILLEN, *Proc. Chem. Soc.*, (1961) 121.

[28] I. R. DAGG AND H. W. THOMPSON, *Trans. Faraday Soc.*, 52 (1956) 455.

[29] W. J. JONES AND N. SHEPPARD, Personal Communication.

[30] Discussion on The Effect of Environment upon Molecular Energy Levels, *Proc. Roy. Soc. (London)*, Ser. *A*, 255 (1960) 1-81.

[31] M. L. JOSIEN, *Molecular Spectroscopy, Proceedings of the Fifth European Congress, Amsterdam 1961*, Butterworth Sci. Publ., London, 1962.

[32] H. E. HALLAM, *Spectroscopy, Proceedings of the Institute of Petroleum Hydrocarbon Research Group Third Conference, London, 1962*, The Institute of Petroleum, London, 1962, p. 245.

[33] R. L. WILLIAMS, *Ann. Rept. Progr. Chem. (Chem. Soc. London)*, (1962) 34.

[34] J. G. KIRKWOOD, in W. WEST AND R. T. EDWARDS, *J. Chem. Phys.*, 5 (1937) 14.

[35] E. BAUER AND M. MAGAT, *J. Phys. Radium*, 9 (1938) 319.

[36] L. H. JONES AND R. M. BADGER, *J. Am. Chem. Soc.*, 73 (1951) 3132.

[37] M. L. JOSIEN AND N. FUSON, *J. Chem. Phys.*, 22 (1954) 1169, 1264.

[38] N. S. BAYLISS, A. R. H. COLE AND L. H. LITTLE, *Australian J. Chem.*, 8 (1955) 26.

[39] A. D. BUCKINGHAM, *Proc. Roy. Soc. (London)*, Ser. *A*, 248 (1958) 169; *Trans. Faraday Soc.*, 56 (1960) 753.

[40] A. D. E. PULLIN, *Spectrochim. Acta*, 13 (1958) 125; 16 (1960) 12.

[41] C. LA LAU, *Molecular Spectroscopy, Proceedings of the Institute of Petroleum Hydrocarbon Research Group Second Conference, London, 1958*, Pergamon Press, London, 1959, p. 205.

[42] G. L. CALDOW AND H. W. THOMPSON, *Proc. Roy. Soc. (London)*, Ser. *A*, 254 (1960) 1.

[43] H. E. HALLAM AND T. C. RAY, *Nature*, 189 (1961) 915.

[44] H. E. HALLAM AND T. C. RAY, *Trans. Faraday Soc.*, 58 (1962) 1299.

[45] K. B. WHETSEL AND R. E. KAGARISE, *Spectrochim. Acta*, 18 (1962) 315, 329, 341.

[46] L. J. BELLAMY, H. E. HALLAM AND R. L. WILLIAMS, *Trans. Faraday Soc.*, 54 (1958) 1120.

[47] W. GORDY, *J. Chem. Phys.*, 9 (1941) 215.

[48] L. J. BELLAMY AND H. E. HALLAM, *Trans. Faraday Soc.*, 55 (1959) 220.

[49] E. A. CUTMORE AND H. E. HALLAM, *Trans. Faraday Soc.*, 58 (1962) 40.

[50] L. J. BELLAMY AND R. L. WILLIAMS, *Trans. Faraday Soc.*, 55 (1959) 14.

[51] C. C. BARRACLOUGH, J. LEWIS AND R. S. NYHOLM, *J. Chem. Soc.*, (1961) 2582.

[52] D. M. ADAMS, *Proc. Chem. Soc.*, (1961) 431; *Spectroscopy, Proceedings of the Institute of Petroleum Hydrocarbon Research Group Third Conference, London, 1962*, The Institute of Petroleum, London, 1962, p. 265.

[53] L. J. BELLAMY AND P. E. ROGASCH, *J. Chem. Soc.*, (1960) 2218.

[54] M. DAVIES, *J. Chem. Phys.*, 8 (1940) 586.

[55] L. J. BELLAMY AND R. L. WILLIAMS, *Proc. Roy. Soc. (London)*, Ser. *A*, 254 (1960) 119.

[56] H. E. HALLAM AND T. C. RAY (to be published).

[57] P. J. KRUEGER AND H. W. THOMPSON, *Proc. Roy. Soc. (London)*, Ser. *A*, 243 (1957) 143.

[58] G. L. CALDOW, D. CUNLIFFE-JONES AND H. W. THOMPSON, *Proc. Roy. Soc. (London), Ser. A,* 254 (1960) 17.

[59] C. M. HUGGINS AND G. C. PIMENTEL, *J. Chem. Phys.,* 23 (1955) 896.

[60] D. H. WHIFFEN, *Trans. Faraday Soc.,* 49 (1953) 878.

[61] N. S. BAYLISS, A. R. H. COLE AND L. H. LITTLE, *Spectrochim. Acta,* 15 (1959) 12.

[62] M. ITO, K. INUZUKA AND S. IMANISHI, *Bull. Chem. Soc. Japan,* 34 (1961) 467.

[63] T. L. BROWN, *Spectrochim. Acta,* 10 (1957) 149.

[64] E. B. WHIPPLE, J. H. GOLDSTEIN, L. MANDELL, G. S. REDDY AND G. R. McCLURE, *J. Am. Chem. Soc.,* 81 (1959) 1321.

[65] L. W. REEVES AND W. G. SCHNEIDER, *Canad. J. Chem.,* 35 (1957) 251.

[66] J. H. RICHARDS AND S. WALKER, *Trans. Faraday Soc.,* 57 (1961) 399, 406, 412.

[67] L. J. BELLAMY AND P. E. ROGASCH, *Spectrochim. Acta,* 16 (1960) 30.

[68] E. A. CUTMORE AND H. E. HALLAM, *Proceedings of Fourth Conference of European Molecular Spectroscopy, Bologna,* 1959, Pergamon Press, London, 1961.

[69] L. J. BELLAMY, C. P. CONDUIT, R. J. PACE AND R. L. WILLIAMS, *Trans. Faraday Soc.,* 55 (1959) 1677.

[70] W. GORDY, *J. Chem. Phys.,* 7 (1937) 93.

[71] W. GORDY AND S. C. STANFORD, *J. Chem. Phys.,* 8 (1940) 170.

[72] W. LUTTKE AND R. MECKE, *Z. Electrochem.,* 53 (1949) 241.

[73] S. SEARLES AND M. TAMRES, *J. Am. Chem. Soc.,* 73 (1951) 3704.

[74] S. SEARLES, M. TAMRES AND G. M. BARROW, *J. Am. Chem. Soc.,* 75 (1953) 71.

[75] R. C. LORD, B. NOLIN AND H. D. STIDHAM, *J. Am. Chem. Soc.,* 77 (1955) 1365.

[76] R. J. W. LE FEVRE, *Australian J. Chem.,* 14 (1961) 312.

[77] L. GALATRY, *Compt. Rend.,* 246 (1958) 3442.

[78] F. SCHULLER, L. GALATRY AND B. VODAR, *Spectrochim. Acta,* 16 (1960) 789.

[79] L. GALATRY AND F. G. SCHULLER, *Proceedings of C.N.R.S. Research Colloquium,* Belle Vue, Paris, 1957, p. 155.

[80] P. TUOMIKOSKI, *J. Chem. Phys.,* 20 (1952) 1054.

[81] T. C. RAY, *Ph. D. Thesis,* University of Wales, 1962.

[82] L. J. BELLAMY, B. R. CORNELLY, A. R. PHILPOTTS AND R. L. WILLIAMS, *Z. Elecktrochem.,* 64 (1960) 563.

[83] D. J. JEWELL AND H. W. THOMPSON, *Spectrochim. Acta,* 13 (1958) 254.

[84] M. ITO, K. INUZUKA AND S. IMANISHI, *J. Chem. Phys.,* 31 (1959) 1694.

[85] M. HORAK, J. JONAS AND J. PLIVA, *Tetrahedron Letters,* (1959), 19.

[86] T. YOSHINO, *Bull. Chem. Soc. Japan,* 27 (1954) 592; *J. Chem. Phys.,* 24 (1956) 76.

[87] L. B. ARCHIBALD AND A. D. E. PULLIN, *Spectrochim. Acta,* 12 (1958) 34.

[88] L. K. DYALL, *Australian J. Chem.,* 13 (1960) 230; *Spectrochim. Acta,* 17 (1961) 291.

[89] K. B. WHETSEL, W. E. ROBERTSON AND M. W. KRELL, *Anal. Chem.,* 32 (1960) 1281.

[90] L. J. BELLAMY, G. EGLINTON AND J. F. MORMAN, *J. Chem. Soc.,* (1961) 4762.

[91] H. TSUBOMURA, *J. Chem. Phys.,* 23 (1955) 2130.

[92] B. WOJTKOWIAK AND R. ROMANET, *Compt. Rend.,* 250 (1960) 3980.

[93] C. G. CANNON AND B. C. STACE, *Spectrochim. Acta,* 13 (1958) 253.

[94] M. R. BASILA, *J. Chem. Phys.,* 35 (1961) 1151.

[95] Unpublished work. Author's laboratories.

[96] E. A. CUTMORE, *M. Sc. Thesis,* University of Wales, 1961.

Chapter XIII

Infra-red Emission Spectra

W. C. PRICE

King's College, London

The emission of infra-red radiation from excited systems is a subject of widespread interest. In the case of gases its study provides three main types of information:

(i) Measurements on the vibration–rotation bands of high quantum numbers, which can be observed in emission and not conveniently obtained in absorption, enable the molecular parameters for high energy states to be determined.

(ii) From the relative intensities of the bands the populations of the upper levels can be found and values for the "vibrational" and "rotational" temperatures calculated.

(iii) Information concerning the excitation processes (thermal, chemical, electrical, etc) by which the upper levels are populated can also be derived from the distribution of intensity amongst the various possible bands.

It is thus of considerable importance in the study of combustion processes, electrical discharges, shock tube phenomena, as well as topics such as the re-entry of satellites into the atmosphere. The calculation of the radiation equilibrium in systems of hot gases is also important in meteorology in connection with the thermal balance in the atmosphere, in astrophysics and in many other fields. For these reasons a growing amount of attention is being given to the study of the infra-red emission spectra of the gases concerned in these processes. It is however a very complicated subject and involves the estimation of the emissivities and populations of all the rotational, vibrational and electronic energy levels concerned. Account must also be taken of the variation of their width with pressure, temperature etc. Specialized texts such as those of PENNER[1] and GAYDON[2] deal in detail with some of these applications. It will only be possible here to give an elementary discussion of the fundamental theoretical basis of infra-red emission. This will be followed by a description of the emission spectra of some simple molecules which illustrate how these spectra can be used to give more accurate values of the constants which determine the higher rotational and vibrational levels. Some discussion of the nature of the excitation which gives rise to the observed populations will be included.

The study of the infra-red radiation from solids has engaged the attention of physicists since the time of Kirchhoff, and with Planck's interpretation of the frequency dependence of black body radiation, it helped to lay the foundations of quantum theory. In recent years our increased knowledge of the solid state has revived interest in this field and topics such as the infra-red photoluminescence of semiconductors and the development of narrow band sources such as infra-red lasers are now bringing this subject once again to the forefront. It will therefore be appropriate to include in this chapter a brief account of the main aspects of the infra-red emission from solids.

(1) Black Body Radiation

Planck derived his celebrated formula for the "black body" radiation in a uniform temperature enclosure (*i.e.* one in which there is an equilibrium exchange between the radiation and other forms of energy) by assuming that energies 0, $h\nu$, $2h\nu$ ... $nh\nu$ could be associated with each of the stationary modes $0, 1, \ldots n$ of the radiation. It can readily be shown that for unpolarized radiation the number of modes of oscillation per unit volume with frequencies between ν and $(\nu+d\nu)$ is given by $8\pi^2\nu^2 d\nu/c^3$. Using the quantum statistical distribution (N_n proportional to exp $(-nh\nu/kT)$) the mean energy per mode is given by $h\nu/(e^{h\nu/kT}-1)$, from which the energy per unit volume of the radiation in the frequency range ν to $(\nu+d\nu)$ is given by

$$\rho_\nu d\nu = 8\pi \frac{\nu^2}{c^3} \frac{h\nu d\nu}{(e^{h\nu/kT}-1)} \tag{1}$$

ρ_ν being the spectral density of the energy of the radiation. The quantity which can be most readily compared with experiment is the radiant energy emitted per second from a unit area of surface within the frequency range ν to $(\nu+d\nu)$. For unit frequency range this is the emissive power, E_ν, which by arguments similar to those employed in the kinetic theory of gases is equal to $c\rho_\nu/4$; thus for a black body

$$E_\nu d\nu = \frac{2\pi h}{c^2} \frac{\nu^3 d\nu}{e^{h\nu/kT}-1}$$

The total radiation emitted at all frequencies is $\int_0^\infty E_\nu d\nu$ from which on integration we obtain Stefan's Law.

$$E_{\text{total}} = \frac{2\pi^5 k^4 T^4}{15h^3c^3} = \sigma T^4 \qquad (\sigma = 5.714 \cdot 10^{-5} \text{erg cm}^{-2} \text{ }^\circ\text{K}^{-4})$$

For a non-black opaque surface with spectral reflectivity r_ν, the fraction of the incident energy absorbed in the range ν to $(\nu+d\nu)$ is $(c/4)\,\rho_\nu(1-r_\nu)d\nu$. At equilibrium this must be equal to the energy emitted from unit area in unit time. The latter is thus equal to $(c/4)\,\rho_\nu\varepsilon_\nu d\nu$ where $\varepsilon_\nu = (1-r_\nu)$ and is called the spectral emissivity. For a black body it is unity $(r_\nu = 0)$ and for a non-black body it measures the ratio of the energy radiated from unit area in unit time in the range ν to $(\nu+d\nu)$ to that radiated by a black body. The fraction of the radiation not reflected by an opaque non-black surface must be absorbed and it is clear that $(1-r_\nu) = \alpha_\nu = \varepsilon_\nu$. Thus the spectral absorptivity (α_ν) of such a surface equals its spectral emissivity.

If we take Planck's expression for the energy of the radiation in its wavelength form, differentiate with respect to λ holding T constant and put the result equal to zero, we find the condition which determines the wavelength for which the energy density is a maximum. This is given by

$$\lambda_{\max} T = \frac{hc}{4.965k} = 0.2884 \text{ cm } °\text{K}$$

which is Wien's Displacement Law.

(2) Transition Probabilities

Consider a system of particles, which we shall take for simplicity to be atoms, existing only in discrete energy states. Let us confine our attention to two of these states, 'u' designating the upper and 'l' the lower energy state. Let $A_{u-l}dt$ be the probability that in the time dt an excited atom passes from the upper to the lower state with the emission of radiation, then A_{u-l} is the Einstein coefficient of spontaneous emission. It is clear that such emission will be random both in phase and direction.

In the presence of radiation of frequency ν corresponding to the difference in energy between the upper and lower states, atoms in the lower state will pass to the upper state by absorption of radiation with a probability $B_{l-u} \cdot \rho_\nu \cdot dt$ where ρ_ν is the spectral density of the radiation field; this defines B_{l-u}, the Einstein coefficient for induced absorption. There is also a probability that an excited atom will be induced by the presence of the radiation field to pass to the lower energy state emitting a photon of frequency ν, coinciding in phase and direction with that of the disturbing radiation. The probability of such a process happening in time dt is given by $B_{u-l} \cdot \rho_\nu \cdot dt$ where B_{u-l} is the Einstein coefficient of induced emission.

Under equilibrium conditions the number of atoms in the upper state which change to the lower state by the emission of radiation must be equal to the number of atoms which transfer from the lower to the upper state by absorbing a quantum $h\nu$. Thus if N_l and N_u are the numbers of atoms in the lower and upper states respectively we have

$$N_l B_{l-u} \rho_\nu = N_u (A_{u-l} + B_{u-l} \rho_\nu)$$

and since $N_l/N_u = g_l/g_u \exp (h\nu/kT)$, where g is the degeneracy of the level, we have by substitution

$$\rho_\nu = \frac{A_{u-l}/B_{u-l}}{[(g_l/g_u)(B_{l-u}/B_{u-l})\exp (h\nu/kT) - 1]}$$

from which by comparison with (1) we obtain

$$A_{u-l} = \frac{8\pi h \nu^3}{c^3} B_{u-l}$$

and

$$g_l B_{l-u} = g_u B_{u-l}$$

The interaction of electromagnetic radiation with an atomic system is in first approximation its interaction with the electric dipole moment M of the system whose components in the direction of a coordinate Q are $M_Q = \sum_j e Q_j$.

In the quantum mechanical treatment of this problem it is found that the probability of a transition between the two states l and u is proportional to the square of the magnitude of the vector quantities, known as the matrix elements of the dipole moment, whose components depend in the following manner on the wave functions of the two states

$$|R_{l-u}|^2 = |X_{l-u}|^2 + |Y_{l-u}|^2 + |Z_{l-u}|^2 = \left(\int \psi_l \left| \sum_j e Q_j \right| \psi_u \, d\tau \right)^2$$

where Q_j represents the vectorial distance of the jth electron from the centre of the coordinate system. X, Y and Z are the matrix elements of the x, y and z components of the electric dipole moment. It can be shown theoretically[3] that they are related to the Einstein coefficients as follows

$$B_{u-l} = \frac{2\pi}{3h^3} |R_{l-u}|^2, \quad B_{l-u} = \frac{g_u}{g_l} \frac{2\pi}{3h^3} |R_{l-u}|^2$$

and

$$A_{u-l} = \frac{64\pi^4}{3hc^3} \frac{g_u}{g_l} \nu_{ul}^3 |R_{u-l}|^2$$

The absorption in a gas is usually expressed by the relation $I_\nu = I_\nu^0 e^{-k_\nu x}$ where I_ν^0 and I_ν are the intensities before and after transmission through a column of length x cm of the gas at 0°C and 1 atmosphere pressure. For a small thickness Δx the radiation absorbed by the transition $l \to u$ is given by

$$I_{l-u}(\text{abs.}) = \int (I_\nu^0 - I_\nu) \, d\nu = I_\nu^0 \Delta x \int k_\nu d\nu$$

where the incident intensity I_ν^0 is assumed to be constant over the width of the line or band. Now by the definition of B_{l-u} this is also equal to $I_\nu^0 N_l B_{l-u} \boldsymbol{h} \nu_{lu} \Delta x$ and consequently

$$\int k_\nu \, d\nu = N_l B_{l-u} \boldsymbol{h} \nu_{lu} = \frac{8\pi^3 \nu_{lu}}{3hc} N_l |\boldsymbol{R}_{u-l}|^2$$

Thus the integrated absorption, an experimental quantity, can be compared with the theoretical quantity $\boldsymbol{R}_{u-l}$. It is frequently convenient to express the integrated absorption in terms of oscillator strengths f_{l-u} (or f-value). This represents the ratio of the number of classical oscillators (e, x), which would give the same absorption strength, to the number N_l of absorbers in the lower state. It can be shown[3] that

$$f_{l-u} = \frac{\boldsymbol{m}\boldsymbol{h}c^2}{\pi e^2} \nu_{ul} B_{l-u}$$

or

$$\int k_\nu d\nu = \frac{\pi e^2}{mc^2} N_l f_{l-u}$$

When nearly all the molecules are in the lower state this quantity is equal to $2.38 \cdot 10^7 f_{l-u}$. The emission oscillator strength f_{u-l} is related to f_{l-u} by the relation $f_{u-l} = -(g_l/g_u) f_{l-u}$ and can thus be calculated from the absorption measurements.

(3) Lifetimes of Excited States

From the definitions of the Einstein coefficients it is readily seen that the mean lifetime τ_u in an excited state E_u (*i.e.* the time in which the population diminishes to $1/e$ of its initial value) is given by

$$\frac{1}{\tau_u} = \sum_l A_{u-l} + \sum_l B_{u-l} \rho \nu_{lu} + \sum_{u'} B_{u-u'} \rho \nu_{uu'}$$

| (spontaneous emission) | (induced emission) | (induced absorption) |

where u' refers to energy states lying above E_u.

Thus for equilibrium conditions

$$\frac{1}{\tau_u} = \sum_l A_{u-l} \left\{ 1 + \frac{1}{\exp{(\boldsymbol{h}\nu_{lu}/\boldsymbol{k}T)} - 1} \right\} + \sum_{u'} A_{u-u'} \frac{g_{u'}}{g_u} \frac{1}{\exp{(\boldsymbol{h}\nu_{uu'}/\boldsymbol{k}T)} - 1}$$

The contributions to τ_u^{-1} made by the radiation field are evidently important only if $\boldsymbol{h}\nu_{lu}/\boldsymbol{k}T \leq 1$ or $\boldsymbol{h}\nu_{uu'}/\boldsymbol{k}T \approx 1$ *i.e.* at high temperatures or for transitions lying in the far infra-red.

Comparison with experimental observations shows that the lifetimes of excited states in vibrational transitions are of the order 10^{-3} to 10^{-1} sec, whereas the corresponding electronic lifetimes are generally much shorter *e.g.* from 10^{-6} to 10^{-8} sec.

References p. 458

(4) **Infra-red Emission from Gases**

The infra-red emission to be expected from a gas is illustrated diagrammatically in Fig. XIII, 1a. Only the lowest electronic state need normally be
considered since, except at very high temperatures, the fraction of the
molecules in upper electronic states is so small that the emission due to transitions between the rotational–vibrational levels of the excited state will be

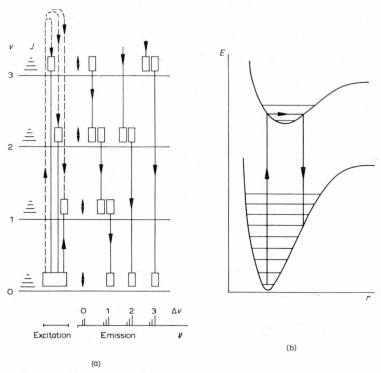

(a)

(b)

Fig. XIII, 1. (a) Excitation and emission of rotational–vibrational transitions of lowest
electronic state.
(b) Excitation of high vibrational ground state levels *via* an upper electronic state.

of negligible intensity. The departure from equilibrium conditions accompanying the excitation leads to difficulties in the definition of temperature, and it
is customary, for purposes of discussion, to refer separately to electronic,
vibrational, rotational and translational temperatures. These quantities are
defined for equilibrium conditions. Thus, for simple diatomic molecules, if it
is assumed that there is thermal equilibrium then the fraction of molecules
with rotational and vibrational quantum numbers J and v is given by

$$N_{vJ} = \frac{(2J+1)}{Q_J Q_v} \exp\left[\frac{-B_v J(J+1)hc - (v+\tfrac{1}{2})hc\omega_e}{kT}\right]$$

where Q_J and Q_v are the partition functions of the rotational and vibrational energy respectively. Assuming that the transition moment $|\mathbf{R}|$ is constant for all the lines of a particular rotation–vibration band, we have

$$I_{em} = \text{constant} \cdot \nu^4 \cdot (2J'+1) \exp[-B'J'(J'+1)\mathbf{hc}/\mathbf{kT}]$$

Actually there is a slight dependence of $|\mathbf{R}|$ upon J which can be taken into account by using $(J'+J''+1)$ for $(2J'+1)$. Thus if $\log(I_{em}) - \log[(J'+J''+1)\nu^4]$ is plotted against $J'(J'+1)$, a straight line is obtained whose slope is $B_v\mathbf{hc}/\mathbf{kT}$. If the relative line intensities have been measured and the rotational constant is known, a "rotational" temperature of the source may be determined. The measured emission intensities should be corrected for self-absorption. An effective "vibrational" temperature can similarly be obtained by plotting the sums of the band strengths (I_{em}/ν^4) of all the bands with the same upper state (*i.e.* the same v' progression) against the vibrational term values $G(v')$, when a straight line of slope $\mathbf{hc}/\mathbf{kT} = 1.44/T$ should be obtained.

(4A) Thermal emission

Simple cases of emission due to the population of the upper states by purely

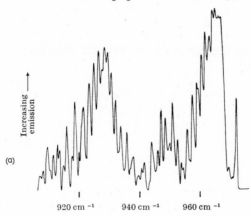

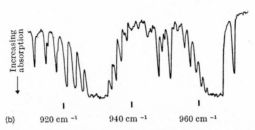

Fig. XIII, 2. (a) Spectrum of part of the ν_2 band of ammonia in emission; gas temperature 70°C, pressure 11 mm Hg, path 10 cm. (b) The absorption spectrum. (Gebbie, Roland and Delbouille, National Physical Laboratory, ref. 4).

thermal equilibrium processes are difficult to observe with good resolving power. This is because of the relatively small fraction of the molecules present in excited vibrational states under equilibrium conditions at normally accessible temperatures, coupled with the low oscillator strengths (low effective emissivity) and the relatively small ν^4 factor common to all infra-red molecular emission. The emission of ammonia from a cell containing the gas at $350°$K has been observed in the regions $900-1000$ cm^{-1} and $3300-3500$ cm^{-1} and is given as an example of purely thermal emission[4], see Fig. XIII, 2. Advantage was taken of the high light gathering power of an interferometer to observe this emission with good resolution. It was possible to resolve the main rotational features of the bands. Because of the relatively low temperatures involved, these exhibit an intensity distribution not differing greatly from the absorption spectrum. The high instantaneous temperatures achieved in a shock tube can be used to obtain thermal emission and the $\Delta v = 1 \to 0$ band of nitric oxide has been obtained in a glass shock tube fitted with a sapphire window using an indium antimonide photoconductive detector with filters to isolate the band[5]. Vibrational relaxation times of $5-10$ μsec. were observed at densities of 0.07 atmos. and the probability of de-excitation from the first vibrational level was found to be $8 \cdot 10^{-4}$ at $500°$K.

(4B) Flame emission

In order to obtain sufficiently strong emission to enable well resolved spectra to be obtained with grating spectrometers and high sensitivity detectors, it is necessary to populate the high energy molecular states by more specific non-equilibrium processes. The most common of these is the combustion process. In such processes the rearrangement of the electrons with respect to the nuclei of the reacting molecules, which is implied in the chemical reaction, produces new potential surfaces in which the atoms will not in general be located near the minima. The products will thus initially have considerable vibrational energy which ultimately they lose either by radiation or by conversion into translational and rotational energy by collisions. Occasionally the species formed will be in a higher electronic state than its ground state, and it will lose its electronic energy either by radiation as chemiluminescence or by deactivation in collisions in which a complex is formed, enabling this energy to be converted into vibrational and translational energy. As a result of the above considerations it might be anticipated that the main emission will arise from the stable products of combustion such as water, carbon dioxide, carbon monoxide etc., and that little emission is to be expected from the initial reactants. This is what is found in practice.

The early studies of the emission from flames were limited by the inadequate resolving power and sensitivity of the instruments. However, in recent years a great deal of high resolution work has been carried out on flames, notably by PLYLER[6] and his coworkers. Some early work of STRONG[7] who observed the far infra-red emission of HCl from a chlorine–hydrogen flame in 1934 should be mentioned. He obtained a considerable number of lines with high J values of from 17 to 33.

We shall describe, as a typical example of a high resolution ($ca.$ 0.1 cm^{-1}) study of infra-red flame emission, the bands of carbon monoxide in the range 4200—4400 cm^{-1} as obtained by Plyler and Tidwell from an oxy-acetylene flame. They used a 4,000 line/cm grating in the second order with a sensitive lead sulphide photoconductive detector. A part of the spectrum is shown in Fig. XIII, 3. It can be seen that because of the excitation to high

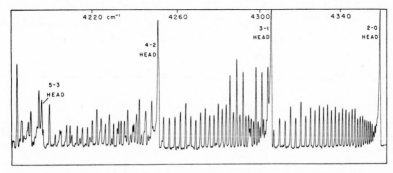

Fig. XIII, 3. Emission spectrum of carbon monoxide from an oxyacetylene flame in range 4200—4400 cm^{-1}. (Plyler and Tidwell, National Bureau of Standards, ref. 5).

rotational levels the lines of the R branches go to sharp heads and then fold back on themselves. In absorption, lines of sufficiently high J to form a head are not observed. Band heads are of course a familiar phenomenon in electronic spectra where the moments of inertia of the upper and lower states are often considerably different from one another. This difference, which causes band head formation, is much smaller when it arises only from the anharmonic nature of the ground state potential energy curve as in infra-red spectra, and higher J values are then required to reach the band head. In the case of the $\Delta v = 3—1$ band of CO the head occurs over the range $R48$ to $R53$ and the lines $R53$ to $R67$ are folded back over the region extending from $R33$ to $R48$. Under the burning conditions when this spectrum was observed, the line $R26$ was the most intense. Because of the elevated temperature, the intensity of the lines near the centre of the $2—0$ band is low and the first line to stand out above the noise level is $R3$. From the measurements of the lines, it is possible to obtain very accurate values of the molecular parameters involved in the expressions for the vibrational and the rotational terms $G(v)$ and $F_v(J)$ respectively.

The 'rotational' temperatures obtained from the intensity distribution of the rotational lines are in the neighbourhood of 2600° K, depending upon conditions in the flame. This is in agreement with the flame temperature measured by other means and indicates the rapid establishment of equipartition between rotational and translational energy. Relaxation times for this process are probably of the order 10^{-8} sec., so that not many collisions are necessary before equilibrium is attained. In the case of the excitation of these bands in a discharge, somewhat higher rotational temperatures of about 3000 °K were obtained and the lines out to $J = 100$ observed.

The transfer between vibrational and translational energy has long been known to be inefficient compared with the rotational–translational interchange and thus 'vibrational' temperatures do not agree very well with 'equilibrium' temperatures deduced by other means. They are much more characteristic of the mechanisms by which the excited states are populated. In the case of carbon monoxide there is an exceptionally high excitation of the higher vibrational levels. Transitions from $v' = 8$ (and $v' = 12$ in a discharge) are observed both in the $\Delta v = 1$ and the $\Delta v = 2$ sequences. Fig. XIII, 4 shows a low dispersion recording of the emission of the $\Delta v = 2$

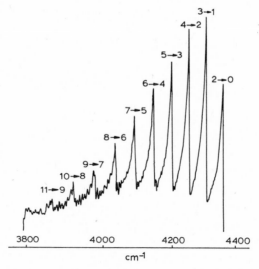

Fig. XIII, 4. Emission from carbon monoxide in the range 3800—4400 cm^{-1}.

transitions from an electrical discharge in CO. The $\Delta v = 3$, 4 and 5 systems are similar except that, because of the rapidly decreasing transition moment, they are progressively weaker and have correspondingly lower emissivities. The 'vibrational' temperatures calculated from the intensity distribution are in the neighbourhood of 4000 °K, which is much higher than those associated with the rotational structure. The similarity of the intensity distribution of the vibrational emission spectra from flames and discharges in CO indicates a similar selective excitation for the two processes. This is probably along the lines suggested by Fig. XIII, 1b and will be discussed later.

(4C) Spectra from electrical discharges

The population of the higher energy levels of a molecular system can also be brought about by an electrical discharge. This has certain advantages over the flame since oxygen is excluded and the excitation of the substances directly introduced into the discharge can be expected, rather than merely their products of combustion. In favourable cases the spectrum of only one substance can be observed instead of the overlapping spectra of many products of combustion. The emission spectra of radicals might also have been expected to occur but in practice it turns out that, with the notable exception of (OH) and one or two others, the lifetimes of radicals are not long enough for concentrations to be built up which are sufficiently large to give rise to observable spectra. It should also be mentioned that only molecules with stable excited electronic states or ones which dissociate into radicals which recombine to give the original molecule, show strong emission in the discharge; e.g. emission from CO_2 is strong but from N_2O it is weak, although their oscillator strengths are comparable.

The excitation is usually carried out by a radio frequency field applied externally to a quartz tube about 1″ diameter with sapphire windows[8]. The highest pressures under which the tube will operate, usually about $10-12$ cm Hg, give the strongest infra-red emission, the intensity of which is roughly proportional to the pressure. Under these conditions the discharge is confined to a narrow region about 1 cm in diameter along the axis of the tube. In the case of gases which decompose in the discharge, such as hydrocarbons, ammonia and most polyatomic gases, it is necessary to maintain a fast flow rate through the tube. With other gases e.g. CO, CO_2, HCl, DCl, etc. only a slow flow is necessary.

Excitation in the discharge arises from the impact of fast electrons. Because of the relatively small mass of the electrons, little kinetic energy can be transferred directly to the molecules, and electronic excitation must in general be the first step. If the minima of the potential surfaces of the excited electronic state do not correspond to the same internuclear separations as in the ground state, then vibration will occur about these minima. Since in such vibrations most time is spent at the turning points, then, as can be seen from Fig. XIII, 1b, there will be a definite probability of the system returning to the lower state when the interatomic distances are larger than their equilibrium values; thus a vibrationally excited molecule is produced. On account of the anharmonicity of the potential curves, the probability of this happening is greater than the probability of return by the original excitation path because of the greater time spent at large inter-nuclear distances. Further, the photon emitted in the latter case can excite an adjacent molecule but the photon emitted in the former case cannot re-excite a non-vibrating molecule. Thus the radiation is imprisoned until it does produce vibrationally excited molecules, after which it can escape. An appreciable number of electron impacts will give rise to vibrationally excited molecules in this way, though this is only one of several mechanisms that can be suggested. It is probably operative in producing the emission of the carbon monoxide bands already described. This is, in fact, confirmed by the intensity of the ultra-violet and visible positive bands in which there is a preferential change of the vibrational quantum number by about 11, corresponding to the largest vibrational quantum observed in the infra-red emission spectrum.

Some of the other important mechanisms which may cause the pro-duction of vibrationally excited species involve the recombination of two

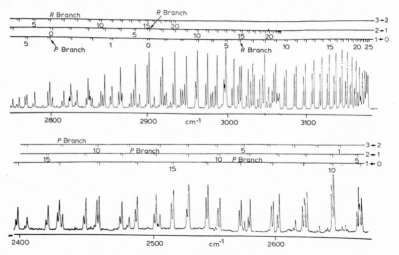

Fig. XIII, 5. Emission from HCl in the range 2400—3200 cm^{-1} excited by electrical discharge.

radicals or atoms, possibly in the presence of a third body or with the emission of ultra-violet or visible radiation. It is possible that one of these processes is involved in the production of vibrationally excited HCl, for which the emission spectrum is rather similar to that observed for the chemiluminescence from atomic hydrogen and chlorine (see p. 453). Fig. XIII, 5 shows the emission[8] of the $\Delta v = 1$ transitions in HCl (pressure 10 cm, current 0.7 amp, spectral resolution *ca.* 0.10 cm^{-1}). The emission extends over nearly 1000 cm^{-1} and the $\Delta v = 1 \to 0$, $2 \to 1$, and $3 \to 2$ transitions are clearly evident. The lines due to the two isotopes of chlorine are well resolved. A well-developed R band head occurs in the $1 \rightarrow 0$ transition for $J = 25$ and the P branch can be followed out to $P(30)$ for the $1 \rightarrow 0$ transition. Because these different transitions can be measured in the same spectral region, the constants derived from them are not so subject to errors of standardization as when they are obtained from measurements in widely different regions, *e.g.* from the fundamental and overtones.

The emission of polyatomic molecules such as CH_4 and NH_3 is weak and the rotational envelopes of the spectra obtained suggest relatively low excitation. The mechanism cannot in these cases involve excited electronic states as suggested for CO, but is more closely a thermal one, due probably to collisions with other excited species.

Relaxation phenomena in molecular discharges are in sharp contrast to those in atomic discharges such as discharges in the noble gases. This is because the processes whereby electronic energy can be converted into translational energy *via* vibrational and rotational energy as discussed for carbon monoxide and illustrated in Fig. XIII, 1b, are not available for atoms. There is therefore very much less degradation of the electronic energy into thermal energy and atomic discharges have a much higher luminous efficiency. Atomic transitions which occur in the infra-red are usually either between states of high principal quantum number or between low lying states corresponding to forbidden transitions. Their f-numbers are not usually very high and the lines are relatively weak. However, some lines such as the near infra-red lines of mercury are quite strong.

(4D) Chemiluminescence

Infra-red emission by chemiluminescence has been observed in the reaction of atomic hydrogen with chlorine: $H + Cl_2 = HCl^* + Cl$, the star indicating vibrational excitation in the ground electronic state[9]. Although the emission was weak, it was possible to resolve the fundamental emission into rotational lines and to obtain a fairly detailed analysis of the vibrational and rotational energy distribution in the HCl^* product under steady state conditions. Further systems giving infra-red chemiluminescence in which the vibrationally excited product is formed by an association reaction were $H + HCl$, $H + DCl$, and $D + HCl$. The reactions $H + O_3 \rightarrow OH^* + O_2$ and several others have also been studied. From the stationary-state population-distribution among vibrational levels it is possible to calculate the relative rates of reaction into the various accessible vibrational levels of the vibrationally excited product ($v = 1$ to 6 for HCl^* formed in the reaction ($H + Cl_2$) and $v = 1$ to 9 for (OH^*) formed in the reaction ($H + O_3$)). For ($H + Cl_2$) this calculation showed the rates of reaction to be progressively less into successively higher vibrational levels of HCl. For ($H + O_3$) the rate of reaction is found to be similar into all the observed vibrational levels of

(OH). It is clear that infra-red observations of chemiluminescence are going to give considerable information on these simple reactions.

(5) Infra-red Emission from Solids

(5A) Emission from crystalline, amorphous and non-metallic solids

In discussing the infra-red emission from non-black solids it is desirable to proceed from Kirchhoff's Law which, for a plate of material in a uniform temperature enclosure, can be stated in terms of the following equations

$$\varepsilon_\nu = 1 - \tau_\nu - r_\nu = \alpha_\nu$$

where ε_ν, τ_ν, r_ν and α_ν are the spectral emissivity, transmissivity, reflectivity and absorptivity respectively of the material at the temperature T. The equations simply express the fact that the surface must return to the radiation stream any radiation which the substance removes from it. For non-opaque materials, where the absorption will depend upon the thickness, it is necessary that the quantities concerned be taken for the same thicknesses of sample. In the case of anisotropic materials it must be remembered that for Kirchhoff's Law to hold it is also necessary that the measurements should all refer to the same state of polarization and direction of propagation relative to the crystal axes. Experimental confirmation of the relation has been obtained for the crystal calcite by KETELAAR and HAAS[10]. They measured the emissivities and reflectivities in the region $1600-800$ cm^{-1} for plates of calcite at temperatures of 300°C, for radiation polarized at different orientations with respect to the crystal axis. For the thicknesses of the plates used (≈ 1 mm), the transmissivity was virtually zero in this range, so that $\varepsilon_\nu = 1 - r_\nu$. The two strong bands occurring in the region are due to the carbonate ion and correspond respectively to the antisymmetrical $(CO_3)^{2-}$ stretching vibration, which is polarized perpendicular to the optic axis (1475 cm^{-1}), and to the out-of-plane bending vibration which is polarized parallel to the optic axis (880 cm^{-1}). Very good agreement was found between the emissivity curves obtained directly and the values of $(1 - r_\nu)$ from the reflectivity measurements which were made over a variety of angles of propagation and orientations of the plane of polarization. Thus Kirchhoff's Law was shown to be valid for anisotropic media where orientation and polarization effects exist which strongly influence both the emission and the reflection spectra.

From the relation between emissivity and absorptivity contained in Kirchhoff's Law, it is clearly indicated that in order to obtain strong selective infra-red emission it is necessary to use materials which have strong absorption bands in the required region. It must, of course, be understood that in no case can this exceed the "full" radiation corresponding to the temperature employed. Ionic crystals in their reststrahlen regions have extremely strong absorption bands, but unfortunately, few of these substances remain crystalline at high enough temperatures for them to be used effectively as strong selective sources. However, magnesium oxide and thorium oxide are very refractory materials with strong absorption in the far infra-red. A coating of these oxides on the fused quartz envelope of a mercury discharge lamp, which is commonly used as a source in the far infra-red, greatly improves its selective emission.

The Nernst filament has strong selective emission in the region 2000–600 cm^{-1}. It is mainly composed of the oxide of the rare earth zirconium and its emissive properties arise from the strong interband transitions of this semiconducting material which lie in this region. The 'Globar' rod of silicon carbide, which has superior emissivity to the Nernst at frequencies lower than 600 cm^{-1}, is possibly a black body emitter on account of the porous nature of its surface. Its use is limited by the maximum temperature at which it can be run and by its high power consumption. Conversely to the above examples, when a low emission is required in, say, the near infra-red, coupled with a high emission in the visible, as is desirable in the case of a gas mantle, it is necessary to choose a substance with relatively weak absorption in the near infra-red but strong (electronic) absorption in the visible region. Thorium oxide mixed with small quantities of cerium oxide has this property and its use in gas mantles gives them their high luminous efficiency. The emissivity of such mantles drops from about 0.8 in the visible to 0.1 in the near infra-red. However, from about 1000 cm^{-1} to lower frequencies, where strong absorption bands of the material occur, the emissivity again rises to 0.8–0.9 and the gas mantle has been used as a selective source in this region.

(5B) Emission from metals

Because of their high reflectivities, the emissivities of metals in the infra-red are not very great, as is to be expected from the relation $\varepsilon_\nu = 1-r_\nu$. Drude showed from classical electromagnetic theory that the emissivity (and reflectivity) of a metal at a given temperature depends upon the frequency of the radiation in first approximation according to the relation $\varepsilon_\nu \approx 0.365$ $(\rho\nu)^{\frac{1}{2}}$ where ρ is the electrical resistivity. This relation has been shown experimentally to hold for frequencies up to about 5000 cm^{-1}. Values of ε_ν for tungsten at 2450° K, range from 0.2 at 5000 cm^{-1}, to 0.4 in the visible. The fact that the resistivity varies inversely as the absolute temperature helps to push up the emissivity at higher temperatures. It is partly because of this increase in emissivity and also because it is capable of being run at very high temperatures, that the tungsten filament lamp is the one with the highest luminous efficiency.

(5C) Photoluminescence

The "non-thermal" methods of populating the higher energy states of solids are those involving electroluminescence and photoluminescence (phosphorescence and fluorescence). Little infra-red work has as yet been done on the first of these which is concerned with the direct conversion of electrical energy into radiation in a semiconductor. This may arise from electron–hole recombination or photon emission following the electron impact excitation of an activator atom. The infra-red photoluminescence of many semiconductors such as cuprous oxide and the sulphides and tellurides of zinc, cadmium, mercury and lead have been investigated down to frequencies of 2000 cm^{-1} by taking advantage of the ability of high sensitivity modern photoconductive cells to detect this weak emission. It has been found that by illumination of a material with radiation in a fairly narrow specific "excitation" band, an "emission" band at a specific lower frequency is obtained. The actual "emission" and "excitation" ranges are slightly dependent on the sample temperature. In the case of lead sulphide, excitation in the region of 3700 cm^{-1} is associated with emission near 2800 cm^{-1} for temperatures of 90° K. It is thought that in this material emission arises from electron transitions between a level very close to the bottom of the conduction band and another near the top of the valence band, the charge carriers being trapped before the transitions occur. There are many similar examples and it is clear that infra-red emission studies are going to be of considerable value in elucidating the nature of the energy level systems of semiconductors[11].

(5D) Solid state lasers

We conclude this chapter with a brief discussion of infra-red lasers. In these devices, monochromatic emission is obtained by the selective population of certain upper levels which are stimulated to emit in phase, giving rise to an intense beam of coherent radiation of sharply defined frequency. The intensity of the induced emission is proportional to $N_u B_{u-l} \rho(\nu_{l-u})$, the quantities being as previously defined. In order to make the system "lase" it is therefore necessary (i) to populate the upper state as highly as possible, (ii) to maintain a high density of coherent radiation and (iii) to depopulate the lower state in order to prevent reduction of the radiation field by self absorption. Although the stimulated radiation may initially be of small intensity, it can be imprisoned by multiple internal reflection between the end faces of the crystal, if these are plane parallel and of high reflectivity, as in the Fabry Perot interferometer. As the radiation density grows by the coherent addition of radiation from n excited atoms, its intensity increases as n^2, and the electric field, which stimulates further atoms to emit, increases the factor to n^4. This is in contrast to increases of only n and n^2

respectively for incoherent radiation. The fields are so strong that virtually all the excited atoms over a large volume of the crystal are stimulated and contribute to produce an intense pulse of coherent radiation which emerges through one of the end faces, which, though highly reflecting, is made slightly transparent for this purpose.

The first laser to operate was the ruby laser[12]. This employs the levels of the Cr^{3+} ions dispersed in alumina. The mechanism is as follows. Pump power from a flash tube is used to raise the chromium ions to a band of excited states (see Fig. XIII, 6A) which are broadened because of their

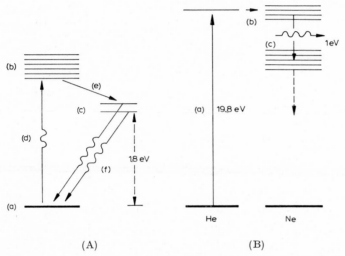

(A)   (B)

Fig. XIII, 6. (A) Level scheme for ruby laser. (a) Ground state, (b) broad band of excited states, (c) metastable state (doublet), (d) pumping transitions, (e) drop to metastable states, (f) fluorescent and stimulated emission.

(B) Level scheme for helium and neon as used in the gas laser. (a) excitation of helium atoms by the discharge to a metastable state, (b) transfer of energy to neon atoms by collisions of the second kind, (c) stimulated emission to lower states of neon.

interaction with the atoms of the host lattice. Because of the breadth of these bands a great deal of pump power can be absorbed by the crystal. The ions fall from this band to a metastable level, in fact a doublet, from which they return to the ground state by emitting the characteristic red fluorescence of ruby. If the conditions are right, an intense coherent beam of very narrow frequency width is emitted by the crystal, corresponding to this transition.

A disadvantage of the pulsed ruby laser is the large amount of optical pumping which is required to depopulate the ground state, which is the lower state of the emissive transition. If this is not done, the radiation field will be weakened by self absorption. If an ion could be found for which a strong narrow line exists with a final state lying somewhat above the ground state, then, because of the low population of such a state, absorption from it would not seriously weaken the radiation field. An example of such a material is the Sm^{2+} ion in a calcium fluoride crystal which, when operated at liquid helium temperatures, has its lower level virtually empty. This crystal will operate on much smaller pump power and is capable of operating with continuous rather than pulsed illumination. Many similar materials, *eg.* rare earth ions in host lattices such as CaF_2, SrF_2, BaF_2, $CaWO_4$ and glass, can be used to obtain laser emission in the infra-red. Laser emission can also be obtained at the junction of suitably doped gallium arsenide, the energy being provided by the current flowing across it.

(5E) Gas lasers

Continuous operation can easily be obtained with a gas laser. Of these the most successful one at present consists of a mixture of helium and neon excited by an R.F. discharge between suitable multiple reflecting plates. The helium gas is excited to metastable states from which the energy is transferred by collisions of the second kind to closely adjacent levels of the neon atom (Fig. XIII, 6B). A further set of levels about 1 eV below these provide suitable lower levels to which laser action may take place. The strongest transitions of this stimulated emission are in the near infra-red, at about 8700 cm^{-1}. Lasers using diatomic gases have been made which operate by the production of excited states by dissociation in the discharge.

REFERENCES

[1] S. S. PENNER, *Quantitative Molecular Spectroscopy and Gas Emissivities*, Addison-Wesley, Cambridge, Mass., 1959.
[2] A. G. GAYDON, *The Spectroscopy of Flames*, Chapman & Hall, London, 1957.
[3] E. U. CONDON AND G. H. SHORTLEY, *The Theory of Atomic Spectra*, Cambridge University Press, Cambridge, 1957.
[4] H. A. GEBBIE, G. ROLAND AND L. DELBOUILLE, *Nature*, 191 (1961) 264.
[5] F. ROBBEN, *J. Chem. Phys.*, 31 (1959) 420.
[6] E. K. PLYLER AND E. D. TIDWELL, *J. Res. Natl. Bur. Std. A*, 61 (1958) 263.
[7] J. STRONG, *Phys. Rev.*, 45 (1934) 877.
[8] H. M. MOULD, W. C. PRICE AND G. R. WILKINSON, *Spectrochim. Acta*, 16 (1960) 479.
[9] J. K. CASHION AND J. C. POLANYI, *Proc. Roy. Soc. (London) Ser. A*, 258 (1960) 529.
[10] J. A. A. KETELAAR AND C. HAAS, *Physica*, 22 (1956) 1283.
[11] G. F. J. GARLICK, *Phys. Chem. Solids*, 8 (1959) 449.
[12] A. L. SHAWLOW, *Sci. Am.*, 204 (1961) 52.

Index

The discussion of the item indexed may extend over some pages after that numbered. Authors' names are restricted to those appearing in the text: those in the reference lists are not necessarily included.

INDEX

PRINTED IN THE NETHERLANDS BY N.V. DIJKSTRA'S DRUKKERIJ
V.H. BOEKDRUKKERIJ GEBROEDERS HOITSEMA, GRONINGEN